A2-Level Chemistry for AQA

The Complete Course for AQA

Contents

Introduction

How Science Works

Unit 4

Unit 5

Section 1: Thermodynamics

Section 2: Period 3 and Redox Equilibria

Section 3: Transition Metals

Section 4: Inorganic Reactions

Investigative and Practical Skills

HOW SCIENCE WORKS

Exam Help

EXAM HELP

Reference

How to use this book

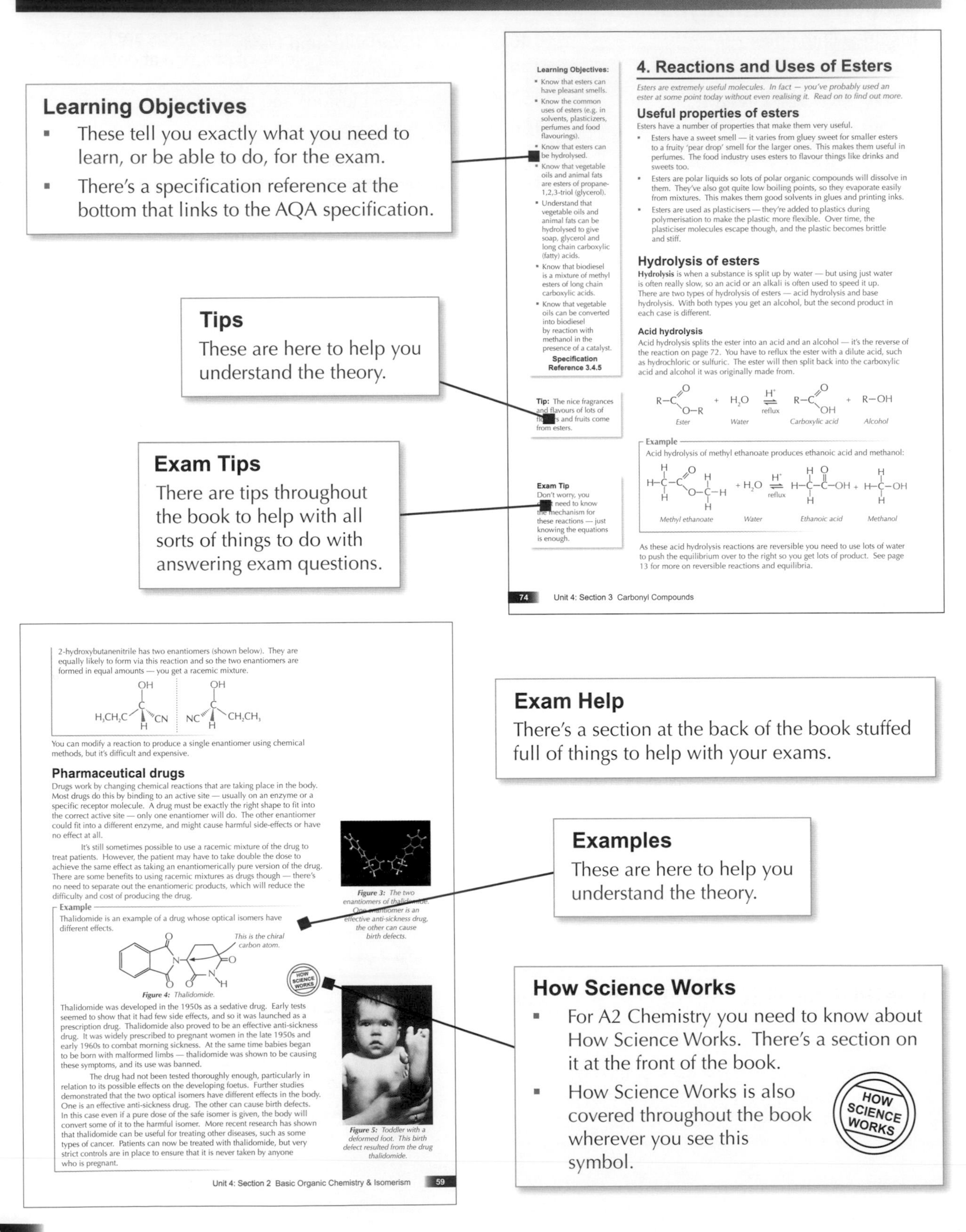

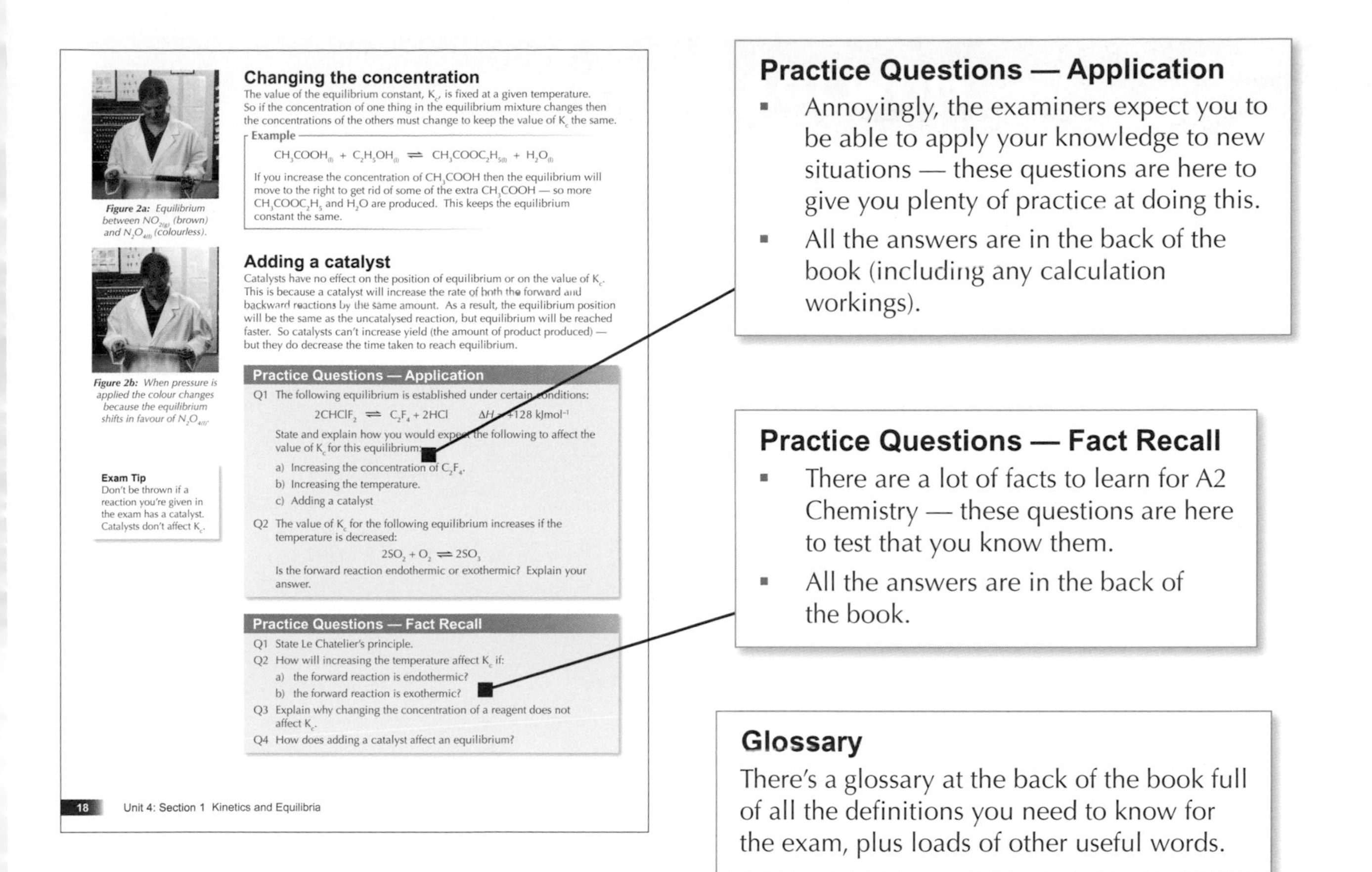

Changing the concentration

The value of the equilibrium constant, K_c, is fixed at a given temperature. So if the concentration of one thing in the equilibrium mixture changes then the concentrations of the others must change to keep the value of K_c the same.

Example

$CH_3COOH_{(l)} + C_2H_5OH_{(l)} \rightleftharpoons CH_3COOC_2H_{5(l)} + H_2O_{(l)}$

If you increase the concentration of CH_3COOH then the equilibrium will move to the right to get rid of some of the extra CH_3COOH — so more $CH_3COOC_2H_5$ and H_2O are produced. This keeps the equilibrium constant the same.

Figure 2a: Equilibrium between $NO_{2(g)}$ (brown) and $N_2O_{4(g)}$ (colourless).

Adding a catalyst

Catalysts have no effect on the position of equilibrium or on the value of K_c. This is because a catalyst will increase the rate of both the forward and backward reactions by the same amount. As a result, the equilibrium position will be the same as the uncatalysed reaction, but equilibrium will be reached faster. So catalysts can't increase yield (the amount of product produced) — but they do decrease the time taken to reach equilibrium.

Figure 2b: When pressure is applied the colour changes because the equilibrium shifts in favour of $N_2O_{4(g)}$.

Practice Questions — Application

Q1 The following equilibrium is established under certain conditions:

$2CHClF_2 \rightleftharpoons C_2F_4 + 2HCl \quad \Delta H = +128\ kJmol^{-1}$

State and explain how you would expect the following to affect the value of K_c for this equilibrium:

a) Increasing the concentration of C_2F_4.

b) Increasing the temperature.

c) Adding a catalyst

Q2 The value of K_c for the following equilibrium increases if the temperature is decreased:

$2SO_2 + O_2 \rightleftharpoons 2SO_3$

Is the forward reaction endothermic or exothermic? Explain your answer.

Exam Tip

Don't be thrown if a reaction you're given in the exam has a catalyst. Catalysts don't affect K_c.

Practice Questions — Fact Recall

Q1 State Le Chatelier's principle.

Q2 How will increasing the temperature affect K_c if:

a) the forward reaction is endothermic?

b) the forward reaction is exothermic?

Q3 Explain why changing the concentration of a reagent does not affect K_c.

Q4 How does adding a catalyst affect an equilibrium?

18 Unit 4: Section 1 Kinetics and Equilibria

Practice Questions — Application

- Annoyingly, the examiners expect you to be able to apply your knowledge to new situations — these questions are here to give you plenty of practice at doing this.
- All the answers are in the back of the book (including any calculation workings).

Practice Questions — Fact Recall

- There are a lot of facts to learn for A2 Chemistry — these questions are here to test that you know them.
- All the answers are in the back of the book.

Glossary

There's a glossary at the back of the book full of all the definitions you need to know for the exam, plus loads of other useful words.

Exam-style Questions

- Practising exam-style questions is really important — you'll find some at the end of each section.
- They're the same style as the ones you'll get in the real exams — some will test your knowledge and understanding and some will test that you can apply your knowledge.
- All the answers are in the back of the book, along with a mark scheme to show you how you get the marks.

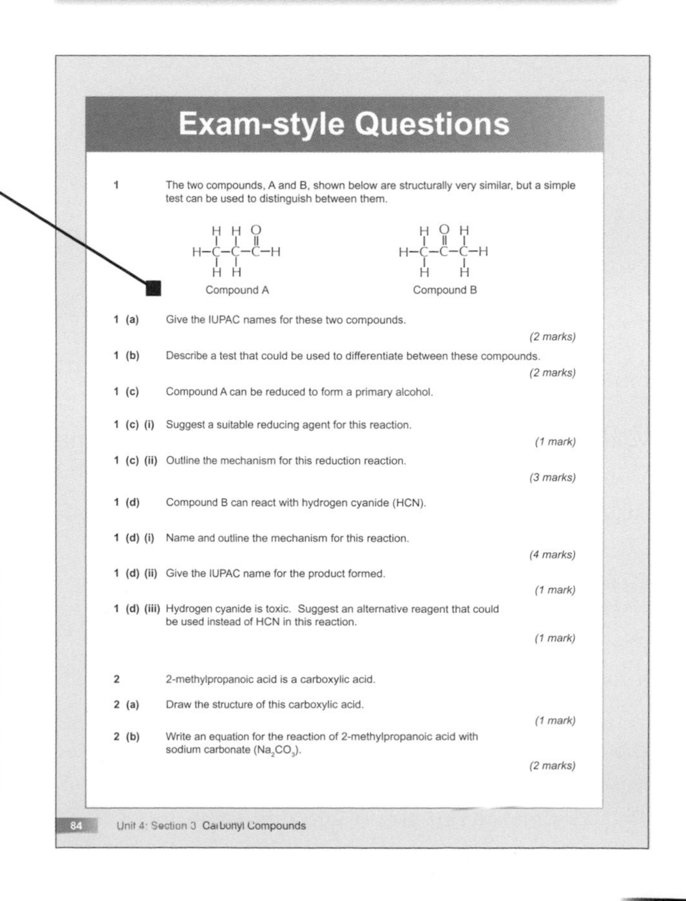

Exam-style Questions

1 The two compounds, A and B, shown below are structurally very similar, but a simple test can be used to distinguish between them.

1 (a) Give the IUPAC names for these two compounds. *(2 marks)*

1 (b) Describe a test that could be used to differentiate between these compounds. *(2 marks)*

1 (c) Compound A can be reduced to form a primary alcohol.

1 (c) (i) Suggest a suitable reducing agent for this reaction. *(1 mark)*

1 (c) (ii) Outline the mechanism for this reduction reaction. *(3 marks)*

1 (d) Compound B can react with hydrogen cyanide (HCN).

1 (d) (i) Name and outline the mechanism for this reaction. *(4 marks)*

1 (d) (ii) Give the IUPAC name for the product formed. *(1 mark)*

1 (d) (iii) Hydrogen cyanide is toxic. Suggest an alternative reagent that could be used instead of HCN in this reaction. *(1 mark)*

2 2-methylpropanoic acid is a carboxylic acid.

2 (a) Draw the structure of this carboxylic acid. *(1 mark)*

2 (b) Write an equation for the reaction of 2-methylpropanoic acid with sodium carbonate (Na_2CO_3). *(2 marks)*

84 Unit 4: Section 3 Carbonyl Compounds

Investigative and Practical Skills

- For A2-Chemistry you'll have to complete Unit 6 — Investigative and Practical Skills.
- There's a section at the back of the book with loads of stuff to help you plan, analyse and evaluate experiments.

Published by CGP

Editors:
Katie Braid, Mary Falkner, Helen Ronan, Megan Tyler, Karen Wells.

Contributors:
Mike Bossart, Robert Clarke, Ian H. Davis, John Duffy, Lucy Muncaster, Paul Warren.

ISBN: 978 1 84762 792 6

With thanks to Chris Elliss and Glenn Rogers for the proofreading.
With thanks to Laura Jakubowski and Anna Lupton for the copyright research.
AQA Specification reference points are reproduced by permission of Assessment and Qualifications Alliance.

Groovy website: www.cgpbooks.co.uk

Printed by Elanders Ltd, Newcastle upon Tyne.
Jolly bits of clipart from CorelDRAW®

The Scientific Process

Science tries to explain how and why things happen. It's all about seeking and gaining knowledge about the world around us. Scientists do this by asking questions, suggesting answers and then testing them to see if they're correct — this is the scientific process.

Developing and testing theories

A **theory** is a possible explanation for something. Theories usually come about when scientists observe something and wonder why or how it happens. (Scientists also sometimes form a **model** too — a simplified picture or representation of a real physical situation.) Scientific theories and models are developed and tested in the following way:

- Ask a question — make an observation and ask why or how whatever you've observed happens.
- Suggest an answer, or part of an answer, by forming a theory or a model (a possible explanation of the observations or a description of what you think is actually happening).
- Make a prediction or **hypothesis** — a specific testable statement, based on the theory, about what will happen in a test situation.
- Carry out tests — to provide evidence that will support the prediction or refute it.

Tip: A theory is only scientific if it can be tested.

Examples

Question: Why does sodium chloride dissolve in water?

Theory: Sodium chloride is made up of charged particles which are pulled apart by the polar water molecules (see page 153).

Hypothesis: Sodium chloride will dissolve in polar solvents but not in non-polar solvents.

Test: Add sodium chloride to polar solvents such as water and to non-polar solvents such as toluene. If it dissolves in the polar solvents but not in the non-polar solvents then the evidence would support the hypothesis.

Question: How do substances change during a redox reaction?

Theory: During a redox reaction electrons move from one substance to the other.

Hypothesis: When electrons move, a current flows. So a current will flow between the electrodes of an electrochemical cell when an oxidation reaction takes place at one electrode and a reduction reaction at the other.

Test: Set up an electrochemical cell using substances with different electrode potentials. Put an ammeter in the circuit and observe whether a current is flowing. If a current is flowing then this evidence supports the hypothesis.

***Figure 1:** Sodium chloride dissolving in water.*

Tip: The results of one test can't prove that a theory is true — they can only provide a piece of evidence to back it up. There's more about this on page 3.

PHILOSOPHICAL
TRANSACTIONS:
GIVING SOME
ACCOMPT
OF THE PRESENT
Undertakings, Studies, and Labours
OF THE
INGENIOUS
IN MANY
CONSIDERABLE PARTS
OF THE
WORLD.

Vol I.
For Anno 1665, and 1666.

In the SAVOY,
Printed by T. N. for John Martyn at the Bell, a little without Temple-Bar, and James Allestry in Duck-Lane, Printers to the Royal Society.

Figure 2: *The first scientific journal, 'Philosophical Transactions of the Royal Society', published in 1665.*

Communicating results

The results of testing a scientific theory are published — scientists need to let others know about their work. Scientists publish their results in scientific journals. These are just like normal magazines, only they contain scientific reports (called papers) instead of the latest celebrity gossip.

Scientists use standard terminology when writing their reports. This way they know that other scientists will understand them. For instance, there are internationally agreed rules for naming organic compounds, so that scientists across the world will know exactly what substance is being referred to (see page 46).

Scientific reports are similar to the lab write-ups you do in school. And just as a lab write-up is reviewed (marked) by your teacher, reports in scientific journals undergo **peer review** before they're published. The report is sent out to peers — other scientists who are experts in the same area. They go through it bit by bit, examining the methods and data, and checking it's all clear and logical. Thorough evaluation allows decisions to be made about what makes a good methodology or experimental technique. Individual scientists may have their own ethical codes (based on their humanistic, moral and religious beliefs), but having their work scrutinised by other scientists helps to reduce the effect of personal bias on the conclusions drawn from the results.

When the report is approved, it's published. This makes sure that work published in scientific journals is of a good standard. But peer review can't guarantee the science is correct — other scientists still need to reproduce it. Sometimes mistakes are made and bad work is published. Peer review isn't perfect but it's probably the best way for scientists to self-regulate their work and to publish quality reports.

Tip: Scientific research is often funded by companies who have a vested interest in its outcomes. Scientists are ethically obliged to make sure that this does not bias their results.

Validating theories

Other scientists read the published theories and results, and try to test the theory themselves. This involves repeating the exact same experiments, using the theory to make new predictions, and then testing them with new experiments. This is known as **validation**. If all the experiments in the world provide evidence to back it up, the theory is thought of as scientific 'fact' (for now). If new evidence comes to light that conflicts with the current evidence the theory is questioned all over again. More rounds of testing will be carried out to try to find out where the theory falls down. This is how the scientific process works — evidence supports a theory, loads of other scientists read it and test it for themselves, eventually all the scientists in the world agree with it and then bingo, you get to learn it.

Tip: Once an experimental method is found to give good evidence it becomes a <u>protocol</u> — an accepted method to test that particular thing that all scientists can use.

Example

The structure of benzene

Benzene is an organic molecule with the formula C_6H_6. It was first purified in 1825, but nobody knew back then what its structure was like.

In 1865 Kekulé suggested a possible structure for the benzene molecule. His idea was a ring of six carbon atoms with alternate double and single bonds between them, with one hydrogen atom bonded to each carbon.

But in the 20th century, data from X-ray diffraction studies and enthalpy experiments suggested that the Kekulé model was wrong. So scientists came up with a new model (the delocalised electron model) that fitted the new data better. (There's lots more about this on pages 87 and 88). This is the model of the benzene molecule that we use today.

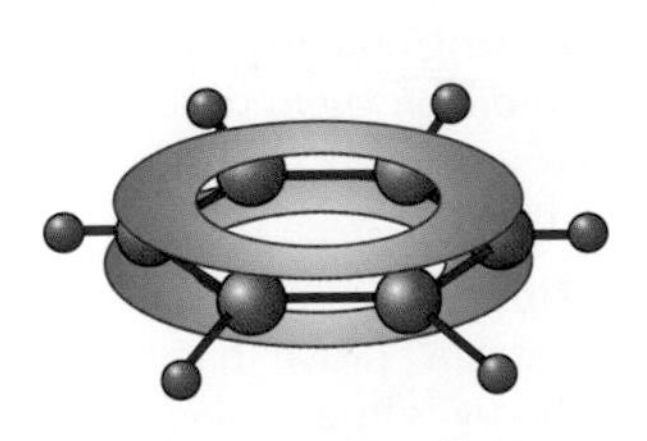

Figure 3: *A representation of the delocalised electron model of benzene.*

How do theories evolve?

Our currently accepted theories have survived this 'trial by evidence'. They've been tested over and over again and each time the results have backed them up. But they never become totally indisputable fact. Scientific breakthroughs or advances could provide new ways to question and test the theory, which could lead to changes and challenges to it. Then the testing starts all over again. This is the tentative nature of scientific knowledge — it's always changing and evolving.

Tip: Sometimes data from one experiment can be the starting point for developing a new theory.

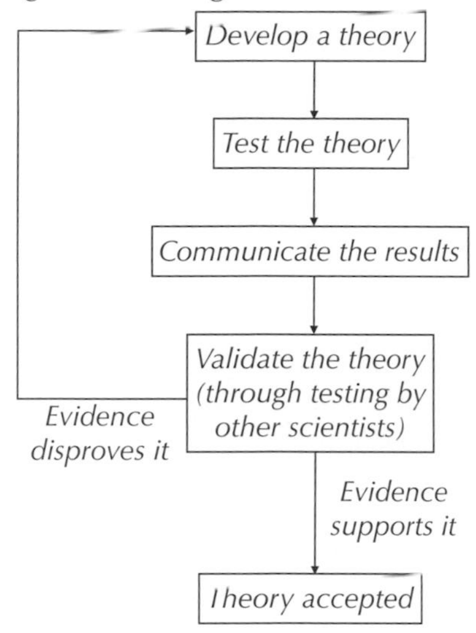

Figure 4: *Flow diagram summarising the scientific process.*

Example

CFCs and the ozone layer

When CFCs were first used in fridges in the 1930s, scientists thought they were problem-free — well, why not? There was no evidence to say otherwise. It was decades before anyone found out that CFCs were actually making a whopping great hole in the ozone layer.

A couple of scientists developed a theory that CFCs were destroying ozone in the stratosphere, and this was tested, shared and validated by other scientists worldwide. The rigour of the scientific process meant that there was strong enough evidence against CFCs that governments could impose bans and restrictions in order to protect the ozone layer.

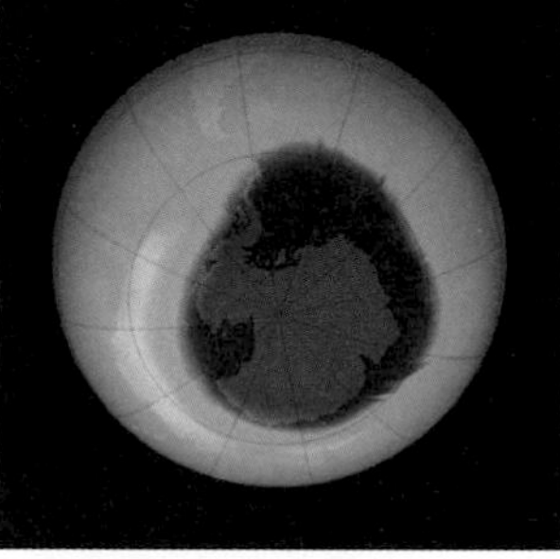

Figure 5: *The Antarctic ozone hole.*

Collecting evidence

1. Evidence from lab experiments

Results from controlled experiments in laboratories are great. A lab is the easiest place to control **variables** so that they're all kept constant (except for the one you're investigating). This means you can draw meaningful conclusions.

Tip: There's more on controlling variables and drawing conclusions from lab experiments on pages 232 and 235 in the Investigative and Practical Skills section.

Example

Reaction rates

If you're investigating how temperature affects the rate of a reaction you need to keep everything but the temperature constant. This means controlling things like the pH of the solution, the concentration of the solution, etc. Otherwise there's no way of knowing if it's the change in temperature that's affecting the rate, or some other changing variable.

Figure 6: *Tap water can be chlorinated, but it's hard to design a fair and ethical test to measure its true effects.*

2. Investigations outside the lab

There are things you can't study in a lab. And outside the lab controlling the variables is tricky, if not impossible.

Examples

Are increasing CO_2 emissions causing climate change?

There are other variables which may have an effect, such as changes in solar activity. You can't easily rule out every possibility. Also, climate change is a very gradual process. Scientists won't be able to tell if their predictions are correct for donkey's years.

Does drinking chlorinated tap water increase the risk of developing certain cancers?

There are always differences between groups of people. The best you can do is to have a well-designed study using matched groups — choose two groups of people (those who drink tap water and those who don't) which are as similar as possible (same mix of ages, same mix of diets etc.).
But you still can't rule out every possibility. Taking newborn identical twins and treating them identically, except for making one drink gallons of tap water and the other only pure water, might be a fairer test, but it would present huge ethical problems.

Science and decision-making

Lots of scientific work eventually leads to important discoveries that could benefit humankind and improve everyone's quality of life. But there are often risks attached (and almost always financial costs). Society (that's you, me and everyone else) must weigh up the information in order to make decisions — about the way we live, what we eat, what we drive, and so on. Information can also be used by politicians to devise policies and laws. However, there is not always enough information available for society and politicians to be certain about the decisions made. The scientific evidence we do have can also be overshadowed by other influences such as personal bias and beliefs, public opinion, and the media. Decisions are also affected by social, ethical and economic factors.

Tip: Don't get mixed up — it's not the scientists who make the decisions, it's society. Scientists just produce evidence to help society make the decisions.

Examples

Fuel cells

Hydrogen-oxygen fuel cells can now be made (see page 184).
They're better for the environment than batteries, because their only waste product is water. But energy is used to produce the hydrogen and oxygen. And hydrogen is flammable, so it's tricky to store safely.

Developing drugs

Pharmaceutical drugs are expensive to develop and drug companies want to make money. So they put lots of effort into developing drugs that they can sell for a good price. Society has to consider the cost of buying drugs — the NHS can't afford the most expensive drugs without sacrificing other things.

Disposal of plastics

Synthetic polymers are very useful — they're cheap to produce and very durable. But they're hard to dispose of (they don't break down easily).
So we need to make choices about how we can best dispose of plastics (see pages 108-110) and whether we should try to reduce the amount that we use, or work to develop more biodegradable plastics.

Figure 7: *Waste plastic on a landfill site.*

1. Rate Equations

Being able to work out the rate of a chemical reaction is a really important part of A2 Chemistry. You've already learnt a bit about reaction rates in AS but now it's time to cover things in a bit more detail.

Learning Objectives:
- Understand and be able to use rate equations of the form Rate = $k[A]^m[B]^n$.
- Be able to explain the qualitative effect of changes in temperature on the rate constant, k.

Specification Reference 3.4.1

Reaction rates

The reaction rate is the change in the amount of reactants or products per unit time (normally per second). If the reactants are in solution, the rate will be change in concentration per second and the units will be $moldm^{-3}s^{-1}$.

If you draw a graph of the amount of reactant or product against time for a reaction, the rate at any point is given by the gradient at that point on the graph. If the graph's a curve, you have to draw a tangent to the curve and find the gradient of that. A tangent is a line that just touches a curve and has the same gradient as the curve does at that point. Figure 1 shows how a graph of the concentration of a reactant against time might look.

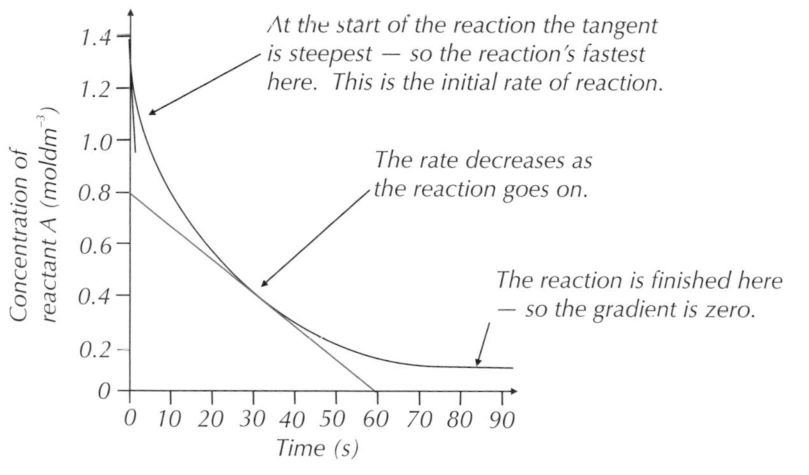

Figure 1: *Graph showing the concentration of a reactant against time.*

The rate equation

Rate equations look ghastly, but all they're really telling you is how the rate is affected by the concentrations of reactants. For a general reaction: **A + B → C + D**, the rate equation is:

$$\text{Rate} = k[A]^m[B]^n$$

The square brackets mean the concentration of whatever's inside them. So [A] means the concentration of A and [B] means the concentration of B. The units of rate are $moldm^{-3}s^{-1}$. m and n are the **orders of reaction** (more on this below) and k is the **rate constant** (see next page).

Tip: In this example there are only two reactants but rate equations can be written for equations with any number of reactants. E.g. if there were three reactants the equation would be:

Rate = $k[A]^m[B]^n[C]^x$

Reaction orders

m and n are the orders of the reaction with respect to reactant A and reactant B. m tells you how the concentration of reactant A affects the rate and n tells you the same for reactant B.

Exam Tip
m and n could take any value but in the exam you'll only have to deal with rate equations where m and n are 0, 1 or 2.

Tip: If the overall order of reaction is one it's called a first order reaction, if it's two it's called a second order reaction, and so on.

- If [A] changes and the rate stays the same, the order of reaction with respect to A is 0. So if [A] doubles, the rate will stay the same. If [A] triples, the rate will stay the same.
- If the rate is proportional to [A], then the order of reaction with respect to A is 1. So if [A] doubles, the rate will double. If [A] triples, the rate will triple.
- If the rate is proportional to $[A]^2$, then the order of reaction with respect to A is 2. So if [A] doubles, the rate will be $2^2 = 4$ times faster. If [A] triples, the rate will be $3^2 = 9$ times faster.

The overall order of the reaction is m + n. So, if m was 2 and n was 1 the overall order of the reaction would be 2 + 1 = 3.

The rate constant

k is the rate constant — the bigger it is, the faster the reaction. The rate constant is always the same for a certain reaction at a particular temperature — but if you increase the temperature, the rate constant rises too.

When you increase the temperature of a reaction, the rate of reaction increases. The concentrations of the reactants and the orders of reaction haven't changed though. So it must be an increase in the value of k which has increased the rate of reaction.

Writing rate equations

You need to know how to write rate equations for reactions. This example shows you how:

Figure 2: Students measuring the rate of a reaction which produces a gas as a product.

Example

The chemical equation below shows the acid–catalysed reaction between propanone and iodine.

$$CH_3COCH_{3(aq)} + I_{2(aq)} \xrightarrow{H^+_{(aq)}} CH_3COCH_2I_{(aq)} + H^+_{(aq)} + I^-_{(aq)}$$

This reaction is first order with respect to propanone, first order with respect to $H^+_{(aq)}$ and zero order with respect to iodine. Write the rate equation for this reaction.

In this example there are three things that you need to think about — the orders of reaction of propanone (CH_3COCH_3), iodine (I_2) and hydrogen ions (H^+). (Even though H^+ is a catalyst, rather than a reactant, it can still be in the rate equation because it affects the rate of reaction.) So the rate equation will be in the form Rate = $k[A]^m[B]^n[C]^x$.

You're told the reaction orders with respect to each reactant in the question so just use that information to construct the rate equation:

$$\text{Rate} = k[CH_3COCH_3]^1[H^+]^1[I_2]^0$$

But $[X]^1$ is usually written as [X], and $[X]^0$ equals 1 so is usually left out of the rate equation. So you can simplify the rate equation to:

$$\text{Rate} = k[CH_3COCH_3][H^+]$$

This rate equation shows that the rate of reaction is proportional to the concentrations of propanone and H^+. So doubling the concentration of either propanone or H^+ will double the rate of the reaction.
The overall order of this reaction is 2 — it's a second order reaction.

Tip: When simplifying rate equations think about the indices laws from maths — the same rules apply here. Anything to the power of zero is one (e.g. $[X]^0 = 1$) and anything to the power of one doesn't change (e.g. $[X]^1 = [X]$).

Calculating the rate constant

If you know the orders of a reaction, you can use the rate equation and experimental data to work out the rate constant, k. The units of k vary, so you'll need to work them out too.

Example

The reaction below is second order with respect to NO and zero order with respect to CO and O_2.

$$NO_{(g)} + CO_{(g)} + O_{2(g)} \rightarrow NO_{2(g)} + CO_{2(g)}$$

At a certain temperature, the rate is 1.76×10^{-3} $moldm^{-3}s^{-1}$, when $[NO_{(g)}] = [CO_{(g)}] = [O_{2(g)}] = 2.00 \times 10^{-3}$ $moldm^{-3}$. Find the value of the rate constant, *k*, at this temperature.

- To answer this question you first need to write out the rate equation:

$$\text{Rate} = k[NO]^2[CO]^0[O_2]^0 = k[NO]^2$$

- Next insert the concentration and the rate, which were given to you in the question:

$$\text{Rate} = k[NO]^2$$
$$1.76 \times 10^{-3} = k \times (2.00 \times 10^{-3})^2$$

- Rearrange the equation and calculate the value of k:

$$k = \frac{1.76 \times 10^{-3}}{(2.00 \times 10^{-3})^2} = 440$$

- Find the units of k by putting the other units in the rate equation:

$$\text{Rate} = k[NO]^2 \quad \text{so} \quad moldm^{-3}s^{-1} = k \times (moldm^{-3})^2$$

- Rearrange the equation to get k:

$$k = \frac{moldm^{-3}s^{-1}}{(moldm^{-3})^2}$$

- Cancel out units wherever possible. In this example you can cancel out a $moldm^{-3}$ from the top and bottom lines of the fraction:

$$k = \frac{\cancel{moldm^{-3}}s^{-1}}{\cancel{(moldm^{-3})}(moldm^{-3})} = \frac{s^{-1}}{moldm^{-3}}$$

- Get rid of the fraction by inversing the powers of whatever's on the bottom line:

$$k = \frac{s^{-1}}{moldm^{-3}} = mol^{-1}dm^3s^{-1}$$

- So the answer is:

$$k = 440\ mol^{-1}dm^3s^{-1}$$

Exam Tip
If you're asked to calculate the rate constant in an exam, make sure you show your working out. That way you might get some marks even if your final answer is wrong.

Exam Tip
If you get stuck in a calculation, re-read the question to check that you've not missed any information — it's dead easy to miss stuff the first time round.

Tip: You need to know how to work out what units your answer is in — it crops up a lot in this section so it's important that you understand how to do it. Have a look at page 244 for more on units.

Tip: 'Inversing the powers' just means switching the sign. So if you've got a mol^2dm^{-6} on the bottom of the fraction it becomes $mol^{-2}dm^6$, if you've got $mol^{-3}dm^9$ it becomes mol^3dm^{-9}, and so on.

Practice Questions — Application

Q1 The following reaction occurs under certain conditions:

$$2H_{2(g)} + 2NO_{(g)} \rightarrow 2H_2O_{(g)} + N_{2(g)}$$

This reaction is first order with respect to H_2 and second order with respect to NO.

a) Construct the rate equation for this reaction.

b) What is the overall order of this reaction?

c) How would you expect the rate of reaction to change if the concentration of NO were doubled?

Q2 The reaction below is second order with respect to NO and first order with respect to Cl_2:

$$2NO_{(g)} + Cl_{2(g)} \rightarrow 2NOCl_{(g)}$$

The rate of reaction is 5.85×10^{-6} moldm^{-3}s^{-1} at 50 °C, when the concentration of both NO and Cl_2 is 0.400 moldm^{-3}.

a) Write the rate equation for this reaction.

b) Calculate the value of the rate constant (k) for this reaction at 50 °C.

c) How would you expect the value of k to change if the temperature were increased?

d) Calculate the expected rate of reaction if 0.500 moldm^{-3} NO were mixed with 0.200 moldm^{-3} Cl_2 at 50 °C.

Exam Tip
When answering calculation questions like these always remember to give the units for your answer.

Exam Tip
In the exam, you should give your answers to the same number of significant figures as used in the question. Here, the values in the question are given to 3 sig.fig. so you should give your answer to 3 sig.fig. as well.

Practice Questions — Fact Recall

Q1 What is a reaction rate?

Q2 What does the rate equation tell you?

Q3 In the rate equation Rate = $k[A]^m[B]^n$, what do the following represent:

a) k? b) [A]? c) m?

Q4 What are the units of reaction rate?

2. The Initial Rates Method

Rate equations are really useful, but to work out the rate equation you need to know the orders of a reaction. These can be determined experimentally using the initial rates method.

Learning Objective:

- Be able to derive the rate equation for a reaction from data relating initial rate to the concentrations of different reactants.

Specification Reference 3.4.1

Finding the initial rate

The initial rate of a reaction is the rate right at the start of the reaction. You can find this from a concentration–time graph. You can collect data for a concentration–time graph by setting up a reaction and then monitoring the amount of a reactant over time. The amount of reactant decreases with time because it gets used up in the reaction. Once the reaction is complete, plotting the concentration of reactant against time gives a concentration–time graph.

Once you have a concentration–time graph, you can find the initial rate of reaction by calculating the gradient of the curve at time = 0. Just draw a **tangent** to the curve at time = 0 and draw in horizontal and vertical lines to make a triangle with the tangent as its longest side. Label the horizontal line x and the vertical line y. The gradient of the line is the change in y divided by the change in x and this represents the initial rate of reaction — see Figure 1.

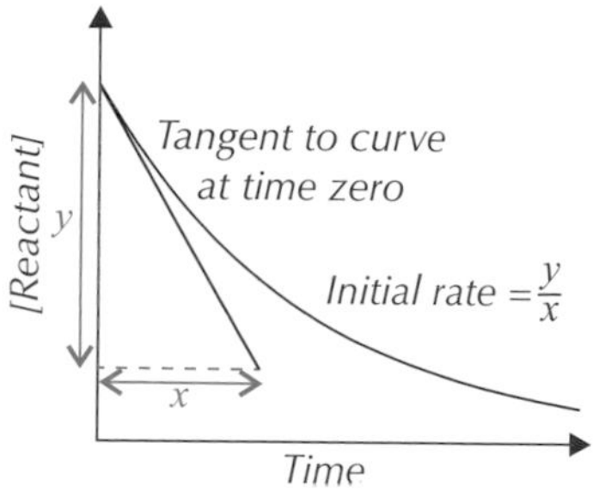

Figure 1: Graph showing how to calculate the initial rate of reaction.

Tip: A tangent is a line that just touches a curve and has the same gradient as the curve does at that point.

Using the initial rates method

Here's a quick explanation of how to use the initial rates method to work out the order of reaction for each reactant:

Step 1: Set up a reaction and monitor the amount of reactant/product over time.

Step 2: Repeat the experiment several times using different initial concentrations of reactants. You should usually only change one of the concentrations at a time, keeping the rest constant.

Step 3: Calculate the initial rate for each experiment using the method above.

Step 4: Finally, see how the initial concentrations affect the initial rates and figure out the order for each reactant.

The examples below and on the next page show you how to do this. Once you know the orders, you can work out the rate equation.

Figure 2: Measuring the rate of a reaction that involves a colour change.

Examples

The table below shows the results of a series of initial rate experiments for the reaction $2NO_{(g)} + Cl_{2(g)} \rightarrow 2NOCl_{(g)}$. Write down the rate equation for the reaction. The temperature remained constant throughout.

Experiment no.	[NO] (moldm^{-3})	[Cl_2] (moldm^{-3})	Initial rate (moldm^{-3}s^{-1})
1	0.125	0.125	1.79×10^{-7}
2	0.250	0.125	7.16×10^{-7}
3	0.250	0.250	1.43×10^{-6}

- Look at experiments 1 and 2 — when [NO] doubles (and the concentration of Cl_2 stays constant) the rate is four times faster, and $4 = 2^2$. So the reaction is second order with respect to NO.

Exam Tip
You need to be able to work out orders of reactions from initial rates data in the exam, so make sure you learn these steps.

- Look at experiments 2 and 3 — when $[Cl_2]$ doubles (but the concentration of NO stays constant), the rate is two times faster, and $2 = 2^1$. So the reaction is first order with respect to Cl_2.

So the rate equation is: $\text{Rate} = k[NO]^2[Cl]$

The table below shows the results of a series of initial rate experiments for the reaction $NO_{(g)} + CO_{(g)} + O_{2(g)} \rightarrow NO_{2(g)} + CO_{2(g)}$.
The experiments were carried out at a constant temperature.
Write down the rate equation for the reaction.

Experiment number	[NO] ($moldm^{-3}$)	[CO] ($moldm^{-3}$)	$[O_2]$ ($moldm^{-3}$)	Initial rate ($moldm^{-3}s^{-1}$)
1	2.0×10^{-2}	1.0×10^{-2}	1.0×10^{-2}	0.17
2	6.0×10^{-2}	1.0×10^{-2}	1.0×10^{-2}	1.53
3	2.0×10^{-2}	2.0×10^{-2}	1.0×10^{-2}	0.17
4	4.0×10^{-2}	1.0×10^{-2}	2.0×10^{-2}	0.68

- Look at experiments 1 and 2 — when [NO] triples (and all the other concentrations stay constant) the rate is nine times faster, and $9 = 3^2$. So the reaction is second order with respect to NO.
- Look at experiments 1 and 3 — when [CO] doubles (but all the other concentrations stay constant), the rate stays the same. So the reaction is zero order with respect to CO.
- Look at experiments 1 and 4 — the rate of experiment 4 is four times faster than experiment 1. The reaction is second order with respect to [NO], so the rate will quadruple when you double [NO]. But in experiment 4, $[O_2]$ has also been doubled. As doubling $[O_2]$ hasn't had any additional effect on the rate, the reaction must be zero order with respect to O_2.

Now that you know the order with respect to each reactant you can write the rate equation, $\text{Rate} = k[NO]^2$.

You can then calculate k at this temperature by putting the concentrations and the initial rate from one of the experiments into the rate equation.

Exam Tip
You would usually only change one concentration at a time but you could get a question where more than one concentration changes — don't get confused, the principle is the same.

Tip: It doesn't matter which experiment you use to calculate k. The value of k should be the same for all of them because they have all been done at the same temperature.

Practice Question — Application

Q1 The table below shows the results of a series of initial rate experiments for the reaction:

$$2A + B + C \rightarrow AB + AC$$

Experiment number	[A] ($moldm^{-3}$)	[B] ($moldm^{-3}$)	[C] ($moldm^{-3}$)	Initial rate ($moldm^{-3}s^{-1}$)
1	1.2	1.2	1.2	0.25
2	1.2	2.4	1.2	1.00
3	1.2	2.4	3.6	3.00
4	0.6	2.4	1.2	0.50

a) Write down the rate equation for this reaction.

b) Calculate the rate constant (k).

3. The Rate-Determining Step

Reaction mechanisms show step by step how a chemical reaction takes place. The most important step is the rate-determining step — that's what these pages are all about.

What is the rate-determining step?

Mechanisms can have one step or a series of steps. In a series of steps, each step can have a different rate. The overall rate is decided by the step with the slowest rate — the **rate-determining step**.

The rate equation is handy for working out the mechanism of a chemical reaction. You need to be able to pick out which reactants from the chemical equation are involved in the rate-determining step. This isn't too hard — if a reactant appears in the rate equation, it must affect the rate. So this reactant, or something derived from it, must be in the rate-determining step. If a reactant doesn't appear in the rate equation, then it won't be involved in the rate-determining step and neither will anything derived from it.

An important point to remember about rate-determining steps and mechanisms is that the rate-determining step doesn't have to be the first step in a mechanism. Also, the reaction mechanism can't usually be predicted from just the chemical equation.

Orders of reaction and the rate-determining step

The order of a reaction with respect to a reactant shows the number of molecules of that reactant that are involved in the rate-determining step. So, if a reaction's second order with respect to X, there'll be two molecules of X in the rate-determining step.

Example

The mechanism for the reaction between chlorine free radicals ($Cl\cdot$) and ozone (O_3) consists of two steps:

$Cl\cdot_{(g)} + O_{3(g)} \rightarrow ClO\cdot_{(g)} + O_{2(g)}$ *This step is slow — it's the rate determining step.*

$ClO\cdot_{(g)} + O\cdot_{(g)} \rightarrow Cl\cdot_{(g)} + O_{2(g)}$ *This step is fast.*

$Cl\cdot$ and O_3 are both in the rate determining step so must both be in the rate equation. So, the rate equation will be:

$$\text{Rate} = k[Cl\cdot]^m[O_3]^n$$

There's only one $Cl\cdot$ and one O_3 molecule in the rate-determining step, so the orders, m and n, are both 1. So the rate equation is:

$$\text{Rate} = k[Cl\cdot][O_3]$$

Reaction mechanisms

If you know which reactants are in the rate-determining step, you can work out the reaction mechanism.

Examples

2–bromo–2–methylpropane can react with the nucleophile OH^- to give 2–methyl propan–2–ol and bromide ions (Br^-).

There are two possible mechanisms for this reaction. Here's one...

$$(CH_3)_3C{-}Br + OH^- \longrightarrow (CH_3)_3C{-}OH + Br^-$$

Learning Objective:

- Understand that the orders of reactions with respect to reactants can be used to provide information about the rate determining/limiting step of a reaction.

Specification Reference 3.4.1

Tip: The rate-determining step is also known as the rate-limiting step

Tip: Catalysts can appear in rate equations, so they can be in rate-determining steps too.

Tip: See pages 5-7 for more on rate equations.

... and here's the other one:

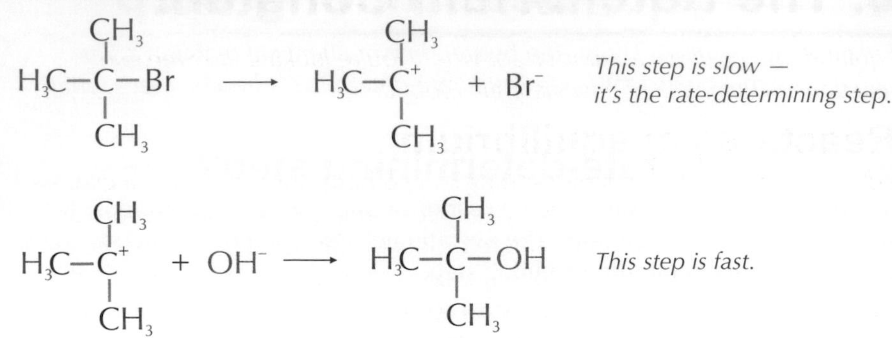

Exam Tip
In the exam, you could be given reactions with three or even four steps, but don't be put off — you work it out in exactly the same way.

The actual rate equation was worked out using rate experiments. It is:

$$\text{Rate} = k[(CH_3)_3CBr]$$

OH^- isn't in the rate equation, so it can't be involved in the rate-determining step. The second mechanism is correct because OH^- isn't in the rate-determining step.

Nitrogen monoxide can react with oxygen to produce nitrogen dioxide:

$$2NO + O_2 \rightarrow 2NO_2$$

The reaction mechanism for this reaction is made up of two steps:

Step 1 — $NO + NO \rightarrow N_2O_2$
Step 2 — $N_2O_2 + O_2 \rightarrow 2NO_2$

The rate equation for this reaction is:

$$\text{Rate} = k[NO]^2[O_2]$$

So you know that the rate-determining step must involve 2 molecules of NO and 1 molecule of O_2. Neither step 1 nor step 2 contains all the molecules you'd expect from the rate equation. But in step 2 there's an intermediate molecule, N_2O_2, that's derived from 2 molecules of NO. So step 2 is the rate-determining step.

Practice Questions — Application

Q1 The reaction $NO_2 + CO \rightarrow NO + CO_2$ has a two-step mechanism:

Step 1: $2NO_2 \rightarrow NO + NO_3$
Step 2: $NO_3 + CO \rightarrow NO_2 + CO_2$

The rate equation for this reaction is rate = $k[NO_2]^2$.

a) What is the rate-determining step of this reaction? Explain your answer.

b) A one-step mechanism was also proposed for this reaction. How can you tell that this reaction isn't a one-step mechanism?

Q2 The rate-determining step for a reaction between three reactants (A, B and C) is $2A + B + C \rightarrow X + Y$. Predict the rate equation for this reaction.

Practice Questions — Fact Recall

Q1 What is the rate-determining step of a chemical reaction?

Q2 A reaction is second order with respect to oxygen. How many molecules of oxygen are involved in the rate-determining step?

4. The Equilibrium Constant

Equilibrium constants are important when you're looking at reversible reactions. The next few pages are all about them.

Learning Objectives:

- Know that K_c is the equilibrium constant calculated from equilibrium concentrations for a system at constant temperature.
- Be able to construct an expression for K_c for a homogenous system in equilibrium and perform calculations involving such expressions.

Specification Reference 3.4.2

Reactions at equilibrium

Lots of changes are reversible — they can go both ways. To show a change is reversible, you stick in a $\rightleftharpoons$. As the reactants get used up, the forward reaction slows down — and as more product is formed, the reverse reaction speeds up. After a while, the forward reaction will be going at exactly the same rate as the backward reaction. The amounts of reactants and products won't be changing any more, so it'll seem like nothing's happening. It's a bit like you're digging a hole while someone else is filling it in at exactly the same speed. This is called a **dynamic equilibrium**. Equilibria can be set up in physical systems and chemical systems:

Examples

Physical Systems

When liquid bromine is shaken in a closed flask, some of it changes to orange bromine gas. After a while, equilibrium is reached — bromine liquid is still changing to bromine gas and bromine gas is still changing to bromine liquid, but they are changing at the same rate.

$$Br_{2(l)} \rightleftharpoons Br_{2(g)}$$

Chemical Systems

If hydrogen gas and iodine gas are mixed together in a closed flask, hydrogen iodide is formed.

$$H_{2(g)} + I_{2(g)} \rightleftharpoons 2HI_{(g)}$$

Imagine that 1.0 mole of hydrogen gas is mixed with 1.0 mole of iodine gas at a constant temperature of 640 K. When this mixture reaches equilibrium, there will be 1.6 moles of hydrogen iodide and 0.2 moles of both hydrogen gas and iodine gas. No matter how long you leave them at this temperature, the equilibrium amounts never change. As with the physical system, it's all a matter of the forward and backward rates being equal.

Figure 1: A flask containing bromine at equilibrium.

A dynamic equilibrium can only happen in a closed system (a system where nothing can get in or out) at a constant temperature.

Tip: Most organic reactions are reversible but sometimes the reverse reaction is so slow that the reaction is thought of as going one way.

The equilibrium constant, K_c

If you know the molar concentration of each substance at equilibrium, you can work out the **equilibrium constant, K_c**. This is a ratio worked out from the concentrations of the products and reactants after equilibrium is reached. Your value of K_c will only be true for that particular temperature. Before you can calculate K_c, you have to write an expression for it. Here's how:

The lower-case letters a, b, d and e are the number of moles of each substance in the equation.

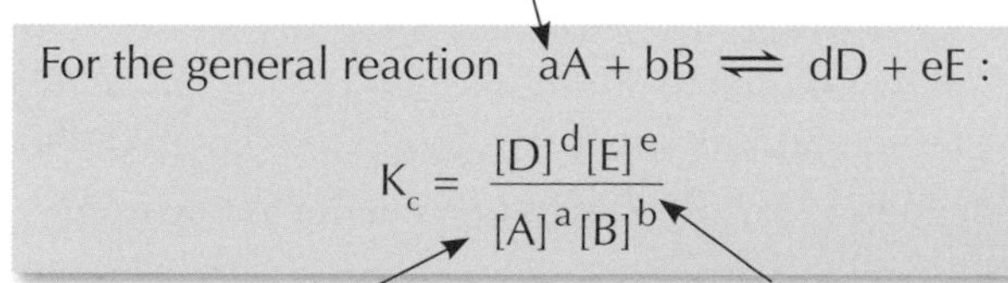

The square brackets, [ ], mean concentration in $moldm^{-3}$.

The products go on the top line and the reactants go on the bottom line.

Tip: The superscript numbers look like the orders of reaction that you saw in rate equations. But they're not — they're the numbers of moles in the equation.

Tip: If K_c is large, at equilibrium there will be lots of product and not much reactant. If K_c is small, it's the other way around — at equilibrium there'll be loads of reactant but not much product.

Example

For the reaction $H_{2(g)} + I_{2(g)} \rightleftharpoons 2HI_{(g)}$ there are two reactants (H_2 and I_2) and one product (HI). There's one mole of each of the reactants and two moles of the product so the expression for K_c is:

$$K_c = \frac{[HI]^2}{[H_2]^1[I_2]^1} = \frac{[HI]^2}{[H_2][I_2]}$$

Calculating K_c

If you know the equilibrium concentrations, just bung them in your expression. Then with a bit of help from the old calculator, you can work out the value for K_c. The units are a bit trickier though — they vary, so you have to work them out after each calculation.

Exam Tip
In exam questions on K_c you'll often be told the temperature. You don't need this value for your calculation — it's just so you know the temperature is constant.

Example

For the hydrogen iodide example above, the equilibrium concentrations are: [HI] = 0.80 moldm^{-3}, [H_2] = 0.10 moldm^{-3} and [I_2] = 0.10 moldm^{-3} at 640 K. What is the equilibrium constant for this reaction at 640 K?

Just stick the concentrations into the expression for K_c:

$$K_c = \frac{[HI]^2}{[H_2][I_2]} = \frac{0.8^2}{0.1 \times 0.1} = 64$$

To work out the units of K_c put the units in the expression instead of the numbers:

$$K_c = \frac{(moldm^{-3})^2}{(moldm^{-3})(moldm^{-3})} = \frac{\cancel{(moldm^{-3})(moldm^{-3})}}{\cancel{(moldm^{-3})(moldm^{-3})}}$$

The concentration units cancel, so there are no units and K_c is just 64.

Tip: Don't forget — when you're calculating K_c the products go on the top line and the reactants go on the bottom line.

Tip: K_c has no units in this example but this won't always be the case, so always work the units out — there's often a mark for giving the correct units in the exam.

You might have to figure out some of the equilibrium concentrations before you can find K_c. To do this follow these steps:

Step 1: Find out how many moles of each reactant and product there are at equilibrium. You'll usually be given the number of moles at equilibrium for one of the reactants. You can then use the balanced reaction equation to work out the number of moles of all the others.

Step 2: Calculate the molar concentrations of each reactant and product by dividing each number of moles by the volume of the reaction. You'll be told the volume in the question but you may have to convert it into different units. To work out molar concentrations you need the volume to be in dm^3.

Tip: The molar concentration is just the concentration in moldm^{-3}.

Once you've done this you're ready to substitute your values into the expression for K_c and calculate it.

Exam Tip
With long wordy questions like this it can help to highlight the important bits of information before you start — e.g. any concentrations or volumes you're likely to need for the calculation.

Example

0.20 moles of phosphorus(V) chloride decomposes at 600 K in a vessel of 5.00 dm^3. The equilibrium mixture is found to contain 0.080 moles of chlorine. Write the expression for K_c and calculate its value, including units.

$$PCl_{5(g)} \rightleftharpoons PCl_{3(g)} + Cl_{2(g)}$$

1. Find out how many moles of PCl_5 and PCl_3 there are at equilibrium:
   - The equation tells you that when 1 mole of PCl_5 decomposes, 1 mole of PCl_3 and 1 mole of Cl_2 are formed.
   - So if 0.080 moles of chlorine are produced at equilibrium, then there will be 0.080 moles of PCl_3 as well.
   - 0.080 mol of PCl_5 must have decomposed, so there will be 0.12 moles left (0.20 – 0.080 = 0.12).
2. Divide each number of moles by the volume of the flask to give the molar concentrations:

$$[PCl_3] = [Cl_2] = \frac{0.080}{5.00} = 0.016 \text{ moldm}^{-3}$$

$$[PCl_5] = \frac{0.12}{5.00} = 0.024 \text{ moldm}^{-3}$$

Put the concentrations in the expression for K_c and calculate it:

$$K_c = \frac{[PCl_3][Cl_2]}{[PCl_5]} = \frac{[0.016][0.016]}{[0.024]} = 0.011$$

Now find the units of K_c:

$$K_c = \frac{(\text{moldm}^{-3})(\text{moldm}^{-3})}{\text{moldm}^{-3}} = \text{moldm}^{-3}$$

So K_c = 0.011 moldm^{-3}

Exam Tip
You may be asked to calculate the molar amounts of some substances in an earlier part of the question — if this happens you can reuse your answers to find K_c. Handy.

Exam Tip
When you're writing expressions for K_c make sure you use [square brackets]. If you use (rounded brackets) you won't get the marks.

Using K_c

If you know the value of K_c you can use it to find unknown equilibrium concentrations. Here's how you do it:

Step 1: Put all the values you know into the expression for K_c.

Step 2: Rearrange the equation and solve it to find the unknown values.

Example

When ethanoic acid was allowed to reach equilibrium with ethanol at 25 °C, it was found that the equilibrium mixture contained 2.0 moldm^{-3} ethanoic acid and 3.5 moldm^{-3} ethanol. The K_c of the equilibrium is 4.0 at 25 °C. What are the concentrations of the other components?

$$CH_3COOH_{(l)} + C_2H_5OH_{(l)} \rightleftharpoons CH_3COOC_2H_{5(l)} + H_2O_{(l)}$$

1. Put all the values you know in the K_c expression:

$$K_c = \frac{[CH_3COOC_2H_5][H_2O]}{[CH_3COOH][C_2H_5OH]} \quad \text{so} \quad 4.0 = \frac{[CH_3COOC_2H_5][H_2O]}{2.0 \times 3.5}$$

2. Rearranging this gives:

$$[CH_3COOC_2H_5][H_2O] = 4.0 \times 2.0 \times 3.5 = 28.0$$

From the equation, you know that $[CH_3COOC_2H_5] = [H_2O]$, so:

$$[CH_3COOC_2H_5] = [H_2O] = \sqrt{28} = 5.3 \text{ moldm}^{-3}$$

The concentration of $CH_3COOC_2H_5$ and H_2O is 5.3 moldm^{-3}

Tip: The units of concentration should always be moldm^{-3}. If your answer doesn't give you this then go back and check your calculation to see where you've gone wrong.

Practice Questions — Application

Q1 The following equilibrium exists under certain conditions:

$$C_2H_4 + H_2O \rightleftharpoons C_2H_5OH$$

a) Write out the expression for the equilibrium constant, K_c, for this reaction.

5.00 moles of C_2H_5OH was placed in a container and allowed to reach equilibrium. At a certain temperature and pressure the equilibrium mixture was found to contain 1.85 moles of C_2H_4, and have a total volume of 15.0 dm^3.

b) Determine the number of moles of each substance at equilibrium.

c) Calculate the molar concentrations (in $moldm^{-3}$) of all the reagents at equilibrium.

d) Calculate K_c for this equilibrium.

At a different temperature and pressure the equilibrium constant (K_c) for this reaction is 3.8 and the equilibrium mixture contained 0.80 $moldm^{-3}$ C_2H_5OH.

e) Determine the equilibrium concentrations of C_2H_4 and H_2O under these conditions.

Tip: Don't forget — you need to work out the units of K_c too.

Q2 Under certain conditions the following equilibrium is established:

$$2SO_2 + O_2 \rightleftharpoons 2SO_3$$

a) Write out an expression for K_c for this reaction.

At a certain temperature the equilibrium concentrations for the three reagents were found to be:

SO_2 = 0.250 $moldm^{-3}$, O_2 = 0.180 $moldm^{-3}$, SO_3 = 0.360 $moldm^{-3}$

b) Calculate K_c for this equilibrium.

c) If all other conditions (including the concentrations of O_2 and SO_3) were to stay the same, what would the equilibrium concentration of SO_2 have to be for K_c to be 15?

Practice Questions — Fact Recall

Q1 Explain what is meant by the term "dynamic equilibrium".

Q2 What conditions are needed for a dynamic equilibrium to be established?

Q3 Write out an expression for K_c for the general reaction:

$$aA + bB \rightleftharpoons dD + eE$$

Q4 What are the units of K_c?

5. Changing the Equilibrium

The position of equilibrium for a reaction can change if conditions change, but not all changes in conditions result in a change in the value of K_c.

Learning Objectives:

- Be able to predict the effects of changes of temperature on the value of the equilibrium constant.
- Understand that the value of the equilibrium constant is not affected by changes either in concentration or the addition of a catalyst.

Specification Reference 3.4.2

Changing the position of equilibrium

If you change the concentration, pressure or temperature of a reversible reaction, you're going to alter the position of equilibrium. This just means you'll end up with different amounts of reactants and products at equilibrium.

- If the position of equilibrium moves to the left, you'll get more reactants.

$$H_{2(g)} + I_{2(g)} \rightleftharpoons 2HI_{(g)}$$

- If the position of equilibrium moves to the right, you'll get more products.

$$H_{2(g)} + I_{2(g)} \rightleftharpoons 2HI_{(g)}$$

There's a rule that lets you predict how the position of equilibrium will change if a condition changes. This rule is known as **Le Chatelier's Principle**:

> Le Chatelier's Principle: If there's a change in concentration, pressure or temperature, the equilibrium will move to help counteract the change.

Tip: You've come across Le Chatelier's Principle before — in Unit 2 of AS Chemistry.

So, basically, if you raise the temperature, the position of equilibrium will shift to try to cool things down. And if you raise the pressure or concentration, the position of equilibrium will shift to try to reduce it.

Although changes in temperature and changes in concentration both affect the position of the equilibrium, only changing the temperature affects the value of K_c.

Figure 1: *Henri Le Chatelier.*

Changing the temperature

If you increase the temperature, you add heat. The equilibrium shifts in the **endothermic** (positive ΔH) direction to absorb the heat. Decreasing the temperature removes heat energy. The equilibrium shifts in the **exothermic** (negative ΔH) direction to try to replace the heat. If the forward reaction's endothermic, the reverse reaction will be exothermic, and vice versa. If the change means more product is formed, K_c will rise. If it means less product is formed, then K_c will decrease.

Examples

The reaction below is exothermic in the forward direction:

Exothermic →

$$2SO_{2(g)} + O_{2(g)} \rightleftharpoons 2SO_{3(g)} \qquad \Delta H = -197 \text{ kJmol}^{-1}$$

← *Endothermic*

If you increase the temperature, the equilibrium shifts to the left (in the endothermic direction) to absorb some of the extra heat energy. This means that less product's formed so the concentration of product ($[SO_3]$) will be less.

$$K_c = \frac{[SO_3]^2}{[SO_2]^2[O_2]}$$

As $[SO_3]$ will be a smaller value, K_c will also be lower.

The reaction below is endothermic in the forward direction:

Endothermic →

$$2CH_4 \rightleftharpoons 3H_2 + C_2H_2 \qquad \Delta H = +377 \text{ kJmol}^{-1}$$

← *Exothermic*

This time increasing the temperature shifts the equilibrium to the right. This means more product's formed, so K_c increases.

Tip: The ΔH values given for reversible reactions show the ΔH of the forward reaction.

Tip: If the temperature decreases the opposite will happen — for reactions that are exothermic in the forward direction K_c will increase and for reactions that are endothermic in the forward direction K_c will decrease.

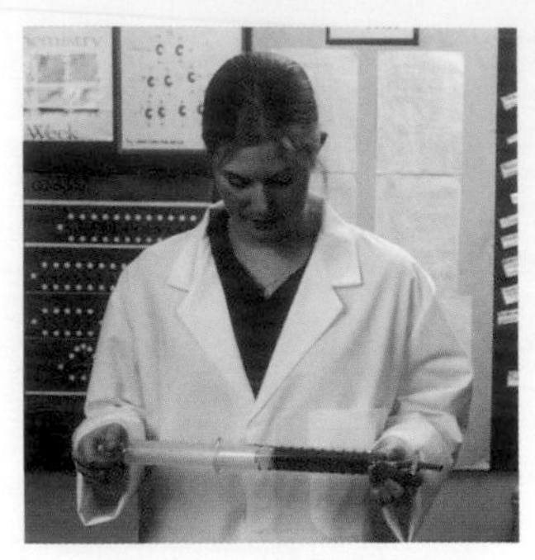

Figure 2a: Equilibrium between $NO_{2(g)}$ (brown) and $N_2O_{4(l)}$ (colourless).

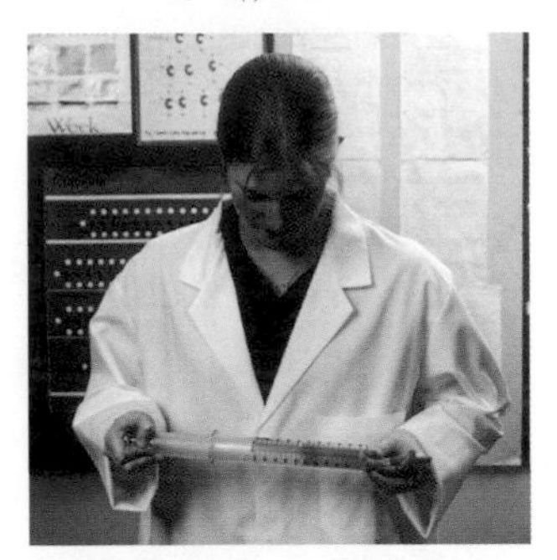

Figure 2b: When pressure is applied the colour changes because the equilibrium shifts in favour of $N_2O_{4(l)}$.

Changing the concentration

The value of the equilibrium constant, K_c, is fixed at a given temperature. So if the concentration of one thing in the equilibrium mixture changes then the concentrations of the others must change to keep the value of K_c the same.

Example

$$CH_3COOH_{(l)} + C_2H_5OH_{(l)} \rightleftharpoons CH_3COOC_2H_{5(l)} + H_2O_{(l)}$$

If you increase the concentration of CH_3COOH then the equilibrium will move to the right to get rid of some of the extra CH_3COOH — so more $CH_3COOC_2H_5$ and H_2O are produced. This keeps the equilibrium constant the same.

Adding a catalyst

Catalysts have no effect on the position of equilibrium or on the value of K_c. This is because a catalyst will increase the rate of both the forward and backward reactions by the same amount. As a result, the equilibrium position will be the same as the uncatalysed reaction, but equilibrium will be reached faster. So catalysts can't increase yield (the amount of product produced) — but they do decrease the time taken to reach equilibrium.

Exam Tip
Don't be thrown if a reaction you're given in the exam has a catalyst. Catalysts don't affect K_c.

Practice Questions — Application

Q1 The following equilibrium is established under certain conditions:

$$2CHClF_2 \rightleftharpoons C_2F_4 + 2HCl \qquad \Delta H = +128 \text{ kJmol}^{-1}$$

State and explain how you would expect the following to affect the value of K_c for this equilibrium:

a) Increasing the concentration of C_2F_4.

b) Increasing the temperature.

c) Adding a catalyst

Q2 The value of K_c for the following equilibrium increases if the temperature is decreased:

$$2SO_2 + O_2 \rightleftharpoons 2SO_3$$

Is the forward reaction endothermic or exothermic? Explain your answer.

Practice Questions — Fact Recall

Q1 State Le Chatelier's principle.

Q2 How will increasing the temperature affect K_c if:

a) the forward reaction is endothermic?

b) the forward reaction is exothermic?

Q3 Explain why changing the concentration of a reagent does not affect K_c.

Q4 How does adding a catalyst affect an equilibrium?

6. Acids and Bases

There are a few different theories about what makes an acid and what makes a base. One of those theories is the Brønsted–Lowry theory. Here it is...

Learning Objectives:
- Know that an acid is a proton donor.
- Know that a base is a proton acceptor.
- Know that acid–base equilibria involve the transfer of protons.
- Know that weak acids and weak bases dissociate only slightly in aqueous solution.
- Know that water is weakly dissociated.
- Know that $K_w = [H^+][OH^-]$.

Specification Reference 3.4.3

Brønsted–Lowry acids and bases

Brønsted–Lowry acids are proton donors — they release hydrogen ions (H^+) when they're mixed with water. For example, for the general acid HA:

$$HA_{(aq)} \rightleftharpoons H^+_{(aq)} + A^-_{(aq)}$$

Brønsted–Lowry bases do the opposite — they're proton acceptors. When they're in solution, they grab hydrogen ions from water molecules. For example, for the general base B:

$$B_{(aq)} + H_2O_{(l)} \rightleftharpoons BH^+_{(aq)} + OH^-_{(aq)}$$

Dissociation in water

Acids and bases dissociate in water. This just means they break up into positively and negatively charged ions. The amount of dissociation depends on how weak or strong the acid or base is. **Strong acids** dissociate (or ionise) almost completely in water — nearly all the H^+ ions will be released. **Strong bases** (like sodium hydroxide) ionise almost completely in water too.

Examples

Hydrochloric acid is a strong acid: $HCl_{(g)} \rightarrow H^+_{(aq)} + Cl^-_{(aq)}$

Sodium hydroxide is a strong base: $NaOH_{(s)} \rightarrow Na^+_{(aq)} + OH^-_{(aq)}$

These reactions are really reversible reactions but the equilibrium lies extremely far to the right, so only the forward reaction is shown in the equation.

Figure 1: J.N. Brønsted — co–writer of the Brønsted–Lowry theory.

Weak acids (e.g. ethanoic or citric) dissociate only very slightly in water — so only small numbers of H^+ ions are formed. An equilibrium is set up which lies well over to the left. **Weak bases** (such as ammonia) only slightly dissociate in water too. Just like with weak acids, the equilibrium lies well over to the left.

Examples

Ethanoic acid is a weak acid: $CH_3COOH_{(aq)} \rightleftharpoons CH_3COO^-_{(aq)} + H^+_{(aq)}$

Ammonia is a weak base: $NH_{3(aq)} + H_2O_{(l)} \rightleftharpoons NH_4^+{}_{(aq)} + OH^-_{(aq)}$

Tip: You never really get H^+ ions by themselves in water — they're always combined with H_2O to form hydroxonium ions, H_3O^+. But don't worry too much about this — you can just use H^+ when writing dissociation equations.

Acid and base reactions

Acids can't just throw away their protons — they can only get rid of them if there's a base to accept them. In this reaction the acid, HA, transfers a proton to the base, B:

$$HA_{(aq)} + B_{(aq)} \rightleftharpoons BH^+_{(aq)} + A^-_{(aq)}$$

It's an equilibrium, so if you add more HA or B, the position of equilibrium moves to the right. But if you add more BH^+ or A^-, the equilibrium will move to the left. See page 17 for the rule about this. When an acid is added to water, water acts as the base and accepts the proton:

$$HA_{(aq)} + H_2O_{(l)} \rightleftharpoons H_3O^+_{(aq)} + A^-_{(aq)}$$

Tip: Remember — for $HA_{(aq)} \rightleftharpoons H^+_{(aq)} + A^-_{(aq)}$ the equilibrium's far to the left for weak acids, and far to the right for strong acids.

The ionic product of water, K_w

Water dissociates into hydroxonium ions and hydroxide ions. So this equilibrium exists in water:

$$H_2O_{(l)} + H_2O_{(l)} \rightleftharpoons H_3O^+_{(aq)} + OH^-_{(aq)}$$

If you remove an H_2O from both sides, this simplifies to:

$$H_2O_{(l)} \rightleftharpoons H^+_{(aq)} + OH^-_{(aq)}$$

And, just like for any other equilibrium reaction, you can apply the equilibrium law and write an expression for the equilibrium constant:

$$K_c = \frac{[H^+][OH^-]}{[H_2O]}$$

Water only dissociates a tiny amount, so the equilibrium lies well over to the left. There's so much water compared to the amounts of H^+ and OH^- ions that the concentration of water is considered to have a constant value. So if you multiply the expression you wrote for K_c (which is a constant) by $[H_2O]$ (another constant), you get a constant. This new constant is called the ionic product of water and it is given the symbol K_w.

Tip: You'll be using K_w to calculate pHs later in this section, so make sure you understand what it means.

$$K_w = K_c \times [H_2O] = \frac{[H^+][OH^-]}{\cancel{[H_2O]}} \times \cancel{[H_2O]}$$

So... $K_w = [H^+][OH^-]$

K_w always has the same value for an aqueous solution at a given temperature. For example, at 298 K (25 °C), K_w has a value of 1.00×10^{-14} mol^2dm^{-6}. In pure water, there is always one H^+ ion for each OH^- ion. So $[H^+] = [OH^-]$. That means if you are dealing with pure water, then you can say that:

Tip: The units of K_w are always mol^2dm^{-6} because $moldm^{-3} \times moldm^{-3} = mol^2dm^{-6}$.

$$K_w = [H^+]^2$$

Exam Tip
Remember — K_w only equals $[H^+]^2$ in pure water. If you're asked to write an expression for K_w, always give $K_w = [H^+][OH^-]$.

Practice Questions — Fact Recall

Q1 What is the definition of:
- a) A Brønsted–Lowry acid?
- b) A Brønsted–Lowry base?

Q2 Write out the equations for:
- a) A general acid (HA) dissociating in water.
- b) A general base (B) dissociating in water.
- c) A general acid (HA) reacting with a general base (B)

Q3 a) What type of acid dissociates almost completely in water?
- b) What type of base dissociates only slightly in water?

Q4 Write out the equation for the dissociation of water.

Q5 a) What is K_w?
- b) Write out the equation for K_w.
- c) What are the units of K_w?

Q6 Explain why, in pure water, the expression for K_w can be simplified to $K_w = [H^+]^2$.

7. pH Calculations

There are lots of pH calculations that you'll need to be able to do in your exam. The next few pages tell you everything you need to know to do them.

Learning Objectives:

- Know that $pH = -\log_{10}[H^+]$, where [ ] represents the concentration in $moldm^{-3}$.
- Be able to convert concentration into pH and vice versa.
- Be able to calculate the pH of a strong acid from its concentration.
- Be able to calculate the pH of a strong base from its concentration.

Specification Reference 3.4.3

The pH scale

The pH scale is a measure of the hydrogen ion concentration in a solution. The concentration of hydrogen ions in a solution can vary enormously, so those wise chemists of old decided to express the concentration on a logarithmic scale. pH can be calculated using the following equation:

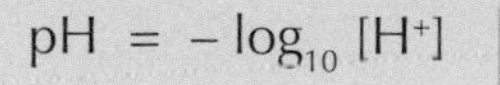

$$pH = -\log_{10}[H^+]$$

$[H^+]$ is the concentration of hydrogen ions in a solution, measured in $moldm^{-3}$. So, if you know the hydrogen ion concentration of a solution, you can calculate its pH by sticking the numbers into the formula.

Example

A solution of hydrochloric acid has a hydrogen ion concentration of 0.01 $moldm^{-3}$. What is the pH of the solution?

$$pH = -\log_{10}[H^+]$$
$$= -\log_{10} 0.01$$
$$= 2.00$$

Just substitute the $[H^+]$ value into the pH formula and solve.

Exam Tip

In the exam, you'll always be asked to give your pH values to 2 decimal places.

The pH scale normally goes from 0 (very acidic) to 14 (very alkaline). pH 7 is regarded as being neutral. Solutions that have a very low pH include strong acids such as HCl and H_2SO_4. Strong bases such as NaOH and KOH have a very high pH. Pure water has a pH of 7 and is neutral.

Tip: To calculate logarithms you need to use the 'log' button on your calculator. Different calculators work differently so make sure you know how to calculate logs on yours.

Calculating $[H^+]$ from pH

If you've got the pH of a solution, and you want to know its hydrogen ion concentration, then you need the inverse of the pH formula:

$$[H^+] = 10^{-pH}$$

Now you can use this formula to find $[H^+]$.

Example

A solution of sulfuric acid has a pH of 1.52. What is the hydrogen ion concentration of this solution?

$$[H^+] = 10^{-pH}$$
$$= 10^{-1.52}$$
$$= 0.030\ moldm^{-3}$$
$$= 3.0 \times 10^{-2}\ moldm^{-3}$$

Just substitute the pH value into the inverse pH formula and solve.

Figure 1: *pH can be measured using a pH meter like this one.*

Tip: The strength of an acid has nothing to do with its concentration. How strong an acid is depends on how much it dissociates in water. The concentration is just how diluted the acid is.

Practice Questions — Application

Q1 A solution of sulfuric acid (H_2SO_4) has a hydrogen ion concentration of 0.05 $moldm^{-3}$. Calculate the pH of this solution.

Q2 A solution of nitric acid (HNO_3) has a pH of 2.86. Calculate the concentration of hydrogen ions in this solution.

Q3 Calculate the pH of a solution of hydrochloric acid (HCl) with a hydrogen ion concentration of 0.02 $moldm^{-3}$.

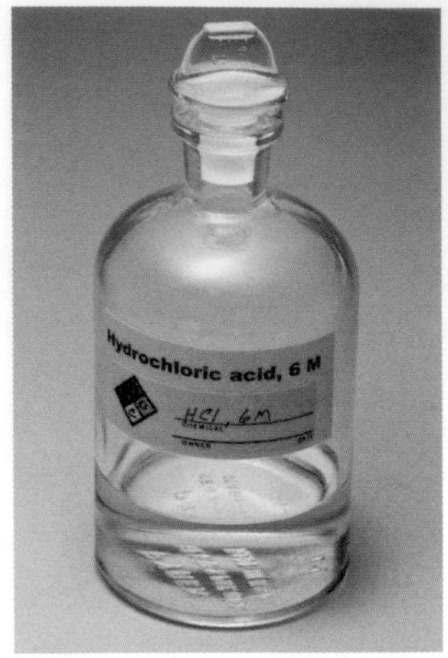

Figure 2: Hydrochloric acid is a strong acid.

Exam Tip
Calculating the pH of acids from their concentrations comes up in loads of calculations so you need to be really confident that you know how to do it.

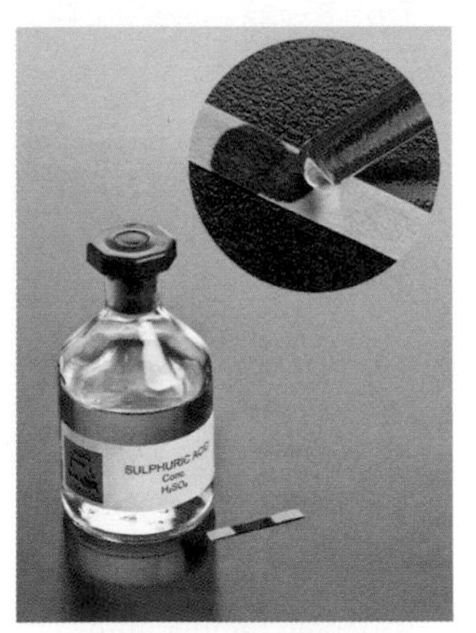

Figure 3: Concentrated H_2SO_4 is a strong acid. It turns this universal indicator paper purple, which shows it has a pH between 0 and 1.

Tip: The rule that $[H^+] = 2 \times [HA]$ is only true for strong diprotic acids — you can't apply the same rule to weak diprotic acids because they don't fully ionise.

pH of strong monoprotic acids

Monoprotic means that each molecule of an acid will release one proton when it dissociates. Hydrochloric acid (HCl) and nitric acid (HNO_3) are strong acids so they ionise fully:

$$HCl_{(aq)} \rightarrow H^+_{(aq)} + Cl^-_{(aq)}$$

HCl and HNO_3 are also monoprotic, so each mole of acid produces one mole of hydrogen ions. This means the H^+ concentration is the same as the acid concentration. So, if you know the concentration of the acid you know the H^+ concentration and you can calculate the pH.

Examples

Calculate the pH of 0.100 moldm^{-3} hydrochloric acid:

$[HCl] = [H^+] = 0.100$ moldm^{-3}. So:

$$pH = -\log_{10}[H^+]$$
$$= -\log_{10} 0.100$$
$$= 1.00$$

Calculate the pH of 0.050 moldm^{-3} nitric acid:

$[HNO_3] = [H^+] = 0.050$ moldm^{-3}. So:

$$pH = -\log_{10} 0.050$$
$$= 1.30$$

If a solution of hydrochloric acid has a pH of 2.45, what is the concentration of the acid?

$[HCl] = [H^+] = 10^{-pH}$. So:

$$[HCl] = 10^{-2.45}$$
$$= 3.55 \times 10^{-3} \text{ moldm}^{-3}$$

pH of strong diprotic acids

Diprotic means that each molecule of an acid will release two protons when it dissociates. Sulfuric acid is an example of a strong diprotic acid:

$$H_2SO_{4(l)} \rightarrow 2H^+_{(aq)} + SO_4{}^{2-}{}_{(aq)}$$

So, diprotic acids produce two moles of hydrogen ions for each mole of acid, meaning that the H^+ concentration is twice the concentration of the acid.

Examples

Calculate the pH of 0.100 moldm^{-3} sulfuric acid:

$[H^+] = 2 \times [H_2SO_4] = 0.200$ moldm^{-3}. So:

$$pH = -\log_{10}[H^+]$$
$$= -\log_{10} 0.200$$
$$= 0.70$$

Calculate the pH of 0.250 moldm^{-3} sulfuric acid:

$[H^+] = 2 \times 0.250 = 0.500$. So:

$$pH = -\log_{10}[H^+]$$
$$= -\log_{10}[0.500]$$
$$= 0.30$$

pH of strong bases

Sodium hydroxide (NaOH) and potassium hydroxide (KOH) are strong bases that fully ionise in water — they donate one mole of OH^- ions per mole of base. This means that the concentration of OH^- ions is the same as the concentration of the base. So for 0.02 $moldm^{-3}$ sodium hydroxide solution, $[OH^-]$ is also 0.02 $moldm^{-3}$. But to work out the pH you need to know $[H^+]$ — luckily this is linked to $[OH^-]$ through the ionic product of water, K_w:

$$K_w = [H^+][OH^-]$$

So if you know $[OH^-]$ for a strong aqueous base and K_w at a certain temperature, you can work out $[H^+]$ and then the pH. Just follow these steps:

Step 1: Find the values of K_w and $[OH^-]$. You may be told these in the question or you may have to work them out.

Step 2: Rearrange the equation, substitute the values for K_w and $[OH^-]$ into the equation, and solve it to find $[H^+]$.

Step 3: Once you know $[H^+]$, substitute this into the pH equation ($pH = -\log_{10}[H^+]$) and solve it to find out the pH.

Example

The value of K_w at 298 K is 1.0×10^{-14} mol^2dm^{-6}. Find the pH of 0.100 $moldm^{-3}$ NaOH at 298 K.

1. Find the values of K_w and $[OH^-]$:
   - The value of K_w is given in the question as 1.0×10^{-14} mol^2dm^{-6}
   - NaOH is a strong base so will donate one mole of OH^- ions per mole of base. The concentration of NaOH is 0.100 $moldm^{-3}$ so $[OH^-]$ must be 0.100 $moldm^{-3}$.
2. Substitute the values of K_w and $[OH^-]$ into the K_w equation:

$$K_w = [H^+][OH^-]$$

$$\text{So } [H^+] = \frac{K_w}{[OH^-]} = \frac{1.0 \times 10^{-14}}{0.100} = 1.0 \times 10^{-13}\ moldm^{-3}$$

3. Substitute the value of $[H^+]$ into the pH equation:

$$pH = -\log_{10}(1.0 \times 10^{-13}) = 13.00$$

Figure 4: NaOH is a strong base. It can be a solid or an aqueous solution.

Tip: See page 20 for more information on K_w.

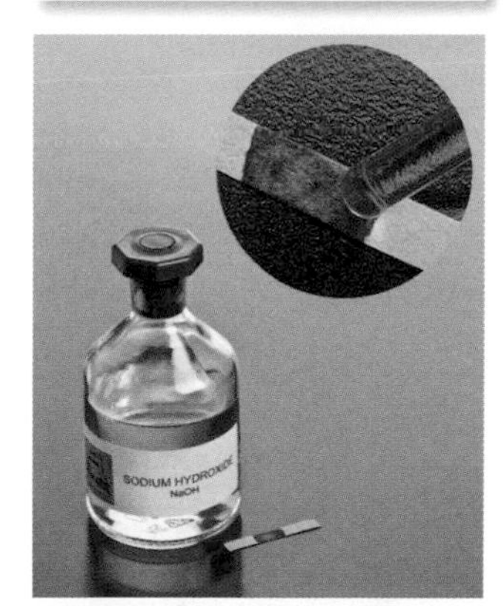

Figure 5: Sodium hydroxide turns this universal indicator paper dark blue, which shows it has a high pH.

Exam Tip

You can use $K_w = [H^+]^2$ (p. 20) to calculate the pH of water. pH will vary with temperature, but if you know K_w at that temperature you can work out $[H^+]$ and then pH.

Exam Tip

Before diving in to answer a question, you might find it useful to highlight the key bits of information in the question that you're likely to use.

Practice Questions — Application

Q1 Hydrochloric acid (HCl) is a strong monoprotic acid. Calculate the pH of a 0.080 $moldm^{-3}$ solution of HCl.

Q2 Sulfuric acid (H_2SO_4) is a strong diprotic acid. Calculate the pH of a 0.025 $moldm^{-3}$ soution of H_2SO_4.

Q3 Potassium hydroxide (KOH) is a strong base. A 0.200 $moldm^{-3}$ solution of KOH was prepared at 50 °C. The value of K_w is 5.48×10^{-14} mol^2dm^{-6} at this temperature. Calculate the pH of this solution.

Practice Questions — Fact Recall

Q1 Write out the expression that defines pH.

Q2 Explain what is meant by the terms monoprotic and diprotic.

Q3 Give the expression for the ionic product of water, K_w.

8. The Acid Dissociation Constant

Calculating the pH of strong acids isn't too bad, but for weak acids things are a bit more complicated — you need to use the acid dissociation constant, K_a.

Learning Objectives:

- Be able to construct an expression, with units, for the dissociation constant K_a for a weak acid.
- Be able to perform calculations relating the pH of a weak acid to the dissociation constant, K_a, and the concentration.
- Know that $pK_a = -\log_{10}K_a$.

Specification Reference 3.4.3

What is the acid dissociation constant?

Weak acids don't ionise fully in solution, so the $[H^+]$ isn't the same as the acid concentration. This makes it a bit trickier to find their pH. You have to use yet another equilibrium constant — the acid dissociation constant, K_a. The units of K_a are moldm^{-3} and the equation for K_a is derived as follows:

For a weak aqueous acid, HA, you get the equilibrium $HA_{(aq)} \rightleftharpoons H^+_{(aq)} + A^-_{(aq)}$. As only a tiny amount of HA dissociates, you can assume that [HA] at the start of the reaction is the same as [HA] at equilibrium. So if you apply the equilibrium law, you get:

$$K_a = \frac{[H^+][A^-]}{[HA]}$$

When dealing with weak acids, you can assume that all the H^+ ions come from the acid, so $[H^+] = [A^-]$. So the formula for K_a can be simplified to:

$$K_a = \frac{[H^+]^2}{[HA]}$$

Tip: K_a is a type of equilibrium constant, so the formula for K_a is based on the expression for K_c.

Finding the pH of weak acids

You can use K_a to find the pH of a weak acid. Just follow these steps.

Step 1: Write an expression for K_a for the weak acid.

Step 2: Rearrange the equation and substitute in the values you know to find $[H^+]^2$.

Step 3: Take the square root of the number to find $[H^+]$.

Step 4: Substitute $[H^+]$ into the pH equation to find the pH.

Figure 1: Lemon juice contains citric acid. It turns this universal indicator paper orange, which shows that it's a weak acid.

Example

Find the pH of a 0.020 moldm^{-3} solution of propanoic acid (CH_3CH_2COOH) at 298K. K_a for propanoic acid at this temperature is 1.30×10^{-5} moldm^{-3}.

1. Write an expression for K_a for the weak acid:

$$K_a = \frac{[H^+][CH_3CH_2COO^-]}{[CH_3CH_2COOH]} = \frac{[H^+]^2}{[CH_3CH_2COOH]}$$

2. Rearrange it to find $[H^+]^2$:

$$[H^+]^2 = K_a[CH_3CH_2COOH] = (1.30 \times 10^{-5}) \times 0.020 = 2.60 \times 10^{-7}$$

3. Take the square root of this number to find $[H^+]$:

$$[H^+] = \sqrt{2.60 \times 10^{-7}} = 5.10 \times 10^{-4} \text{ moldm}^{-3}$$

4. Use $[H^+]$ to find the pH of the acid:

$$pH = -\log_{10}[H^+] = -\log_{10} 5.10 \times 10^{-4} = 3.29$$

Exam Tip

It's really important to show all the steps of your working out when you're answering an exam question — that way the examiner can give you some marks for your method even if your final answer is wrong.

Finding the concentration of weak acids

If you already know the pH you can use K_a to find the concentration of the acid. You don't need to know anything new for this type of calculation — you use the same formulas you used to find the pH.

Step 1: Substitute the pH into the inverse pH equation to calculate $[H^+]$.

Step 2: Write an expression for K_a.

Step 3: Rearrange the equation to give the concentration of the acid.

Step 4: Substitute the values for K_a and $[H^+]$ into the equation and solve it.

Example

The pH of an ethanoic acid (CH_3COOH) solution is 3.02 at 298 K. Calculate the molar concentration of this solution. The K_a of ethanoic acid is 1.75×10^{-5} moldm^{-3} at 298 K.

1. Use the pH of the acid to find $[H^+]$:

$$[H^+] = 10^{-pH} = 10^{-3.02} = 9.55 \times 10^{-4} \text{ moldm}^{-3}$$

2. Write an expression for K_a:

$$K_a = \frac{[H^+][CH_3COO^-]}{[CH_3COOH]} = \frac{[H^+]^2}{[CH_3COOH]}$$

3. Rearrange it to give $[CH_3COOH]$:

$$[CH_3COOH] = \frac{[H^+]^2}{K_a}$$

4. Substitute in K_a and $[H^+]$ and solve the equation to find $[CH_3COOH]$:

$$[CH_3COOH] = \frac{(9.55 \times 10^{-4})^2}{1.75 \times 10^{-5}} = 0.0521 \text{ moldm}^{-3}$$

Figure 2: Ethanoic acid is a weak acid.

Exam Tip
In the exam you might not be given the chemical formula of the acid you're looking at — you may have to work it out for yourself. See pages 46-49 for a recap on nomenclature.

Exam Tip
If you can't work out the chemical formula of an acid, just use HA instead and you might still get the marks.

Finding the K_a of weak acids

If you know both the concentration and the pH, you can use them to find the K_a of the weak acid. Just find $[H^+]$ (as shown in the example above), substitute the values you know into the expression for K_a and solve.

Example

A solution of 0.162 moldm^{-3} HCN has a pH of 5.05 at 298 K. What is the value of K_a for HCN at 298 K?

1. Use the pH of the acid to find $[H^+]$:

$$[H^+] = 10^{-pH} = 10^{-5.05} = 8.91 \times 10^{-6} \text{ moldm}^{-3}$$

2. Write an expression for K_a:

$$K_a = \frac{[H^+][CN^-]}{[HCN]} = \frac{[H^+]^2}{[HCN]}$$

3. Substitute in the values for $[H^+]$ and $[HCN]$:

$$K_a = \frac{[H^+]^2}{[HCN]} = \frac{(8.91 \times 10^{-6})^2}{0.162} = 4.90 \times 10^{-10} \text{ moldm}^{-3}$$

Exam Tip
You need to be able to do all three types of calculation in the exam — any one of them could crop up so make sure you understand these examples.

The logarithmic constant pK_a

The value of K_a varies massively from one acid to the next. This can sometimes make the numbers difficult to manage so to make life easier, scientists often use the pK_a instead. pK_a is calculated from K_a in exactly the same way as pH is calculated from $[H^+]$ — and vice versa:

$$pK_a = -\log_{10}(K_a) \qquad K_a = 10^{-pKa}$$

Tip: Notice how pK_a values aren't annoyingly tiny like K_a values.

So if an acid has a K_a value of 1.50×10^{-7} moldm^{-3}, then:

$$\begin{aligned} pK_a &= -\log_{10}(K_a) \\ &= -\log_{10}(1.50 \times 10^{-7}) \\ &= 6.82. \end{aligned}$$

Tip: The larger the pK_a, the weaker the acid. Strong acids have very small pK_a values.

And if an acid has a pK_a value of 4.32, then:

$$\begin{aligned} K_a &= 10^{-pKa} \\ &= 10^{-4.32} \\ &= 4.79 \times 10^{-5} \text{ moldm}^{-3} \end{aligned}$$

Just to make things that bit more complicated, there might be a pK_a value in a 'find the pH' type of question. If so, you need to convert it to K_a so that you can use the K_a expression.

Tip: These are the same steps as you followed on page 24 but with an extra step (converting the pK_a into K_a) at the beginning.

Example

Calculate the pH of 0.050 moldm^{-3} methanoic acid (HCOOH). Methanoic acid has a pK_a of 3.75 at 298 K.

1. Convert the pK_a value to a K_a value:

$$\begin{aligned} K_a &= 10^{-pKa} \\ &= 10^{-3.75} \\ &= 1.78 \times 10^{-4} \text{ moldm}^{-3} \end{aligned}$$

2. Write out an expression for K_a:

$$K_a = \frac{[H^+][HCOO^-]}{[HCOOH]} = \frac{[H^+]^2}{[HCOOH]}$$

3. Rearrange it to give $[H^+]^2$:

$$\begin{aligned} [H^+]^2 &= K_a[HCOOH] \\ &= 1.78 \times 10^{-4} \times 0.050 \\ &= 8.9 \times 10^{-6} \end{aligned}$$

4. Take the square root to get $[H^+]$:

$$\begin{aligned} [H^+] &= \sqrt{8.9 \times 10^{-6}} \\ &= 2.98 \times 10^{-3} \text{ moldm}^{-3} \end{aligned}$$

5. Substitute $[H^+]$ into the pH equation and solve:

$$\begin{aligned} pH &= -\log(2.98 \times 10^{-3}) \\ &= 2.53 \end{aligned}$$

Exam Tip
pH values for weak acids are usually between 2 and 5. If you get an answer much bigger or smaller than this in your exam, double-check your calculation — you may have gone wrong somewhere.

It works the other way around too. Sometimes you are asked to calculate K_a but have to give your answer as a pK_a value. In this case, you just work out the K_a value as usual and then convert it to pK_a — and Bob's your pet hamster.

Practice Questions — Application

Q1 A solution of the weak acid hydrocyanic acid (HCN) has a concentration of 2.0 $moldm^{-3}$. The K_a of this acid at 25 °C is 4.9×10^{-10} $moldm^{-3}$.

a) Write down an expression for the K_a of this acid.

b) Calculate the pH of this solution at 25 °C

Q2 Some nitrous acid (HNO_2) has a pH of 3.8 in solution at 25 °C. The K_a of this acid at 25 °C is 4.0×10^{-4} $moldm^{-3}$. Determine the concentration of this solution at 25 °C.

Q3 The K_a of lactic acid at 25 °C is 1.38×10^{-4} $moldm^{-3}$. Calculate the pH of a 0.48 $moldm^{-3}$ solution of lactic acid at 25 °C.

Q4 A 0.28 $moldm^{-3}$ solution of a weak acid (HA) has a pH of 4.11 at 25 °C. Calculate the K_a of this acid at 25 °C.

Q5 Methanoic acid (HCOOH) has a K_a of 1.8×10^{-4} $moldm^{-3}$ at 298 K. The pH of a solution of methanoic acid was measured to be 3.67 at 298 K. Determine the concentration of this solution of methanoic acid.

Q6 Ethanoic acid has a pK_a of 4.78 at 298 K. A 0.25 $moldm^{-3}$ solution of ethanoic acid was prepared.

a) Determine the K_a of ethanoic acid at 298 K.

b) Calculate the pH of this solution at 298 K.

Q7 A 0.154 $moldm^{-3}$ weak acid solution has a pH of 4.5 at 45 °C. Calculate the pK_a of this acid at 45 °C.

Q8 The pK_a of hydrofluoric acid (HF) is 3.14 at a certain temperature. Calculate the concentration of a solution of hydroflouric acid that has a pH of 3.2 at this temperature.

Q9 A weak acid (HX) has a pK_a of 4.5 at 25 °C. Calculate the pH of a 0.6 $moldm^{-3}$ solution of this acid at 25 °C.

Exam Tip
You'll almost certainly have to use expressions for terms like pH and pK_a in the exam so you really, really need to make sure that you know the formulas. Have a look at pages 242-243 for a summary of all the formulas in this section.

Practice Questions — Fact Recall

Q1 What are the units for K_a?

Q2 a) Write an expression for the K_a of a general weak acid (HA).

b) Rearrange this equation to give an expression for calculating [HA].

Q3 Give two things that K_a can be used for.

Q4 a) Write out the expression that defines pK_a.

b) Rearrange this equation to give an expression for K_a.

9. Titrations and pH Curves

When acids and bases are mixed together a neutralisation reaction occurs — H^+ ions from the acid join with OH^- ions from the base to create water. If there are equal numbers of H^+ and OH^- ions the mixture will be neutral (pH 7). What do titrations and pH curves have to do with this? Read on...

Learning Objectives:
- Understand the typical shape of pH curves for acid–base titrations in all combinations of weak and strong monoprotic acids and bases.
- Be able to use pH curves to select an appropriate indicator.

Specification Reference 3.4.3

Titrations

Titrations allow you to find out exactly how much alkali is needed to neutralise a quantity of acid. Here's how you do one...

Step 1: You measure out some acid of known concentration using a pipette and put it in a flask, along with some appropriate **indicator** (indicators change colour at a certain pH — see page 30 for more).

Step 2: Do a rough titration — add the alkali to the acid using a burette fairly quickly to get an approximate idea where the solution changes colour. This is the **end point** — the point at which all of the acid is just neutralised. Give the flask a regular swirl to make sure the acid and alkali are mixed properly.

Step 3: Repeat step one and then do an accurate titration. Run the alkali in to within 2 cm^3 of the end point, then add it drop by drop. If you don't notice exactly when the solution changes colour you've overshot and your result won't be accurate.

Step 4: Record the amount of alkali needed to neutralise the acid.

It's best to repeat this process a few times, making sure you get very similar answers each time (within about 0.1 cm^3 of each other).

You can also find out how much acid is needed to neutralise a quantity of alkali. It's exactly the same process as above, but you add acid to alkali instead. The equipment you'll need to do a titration is illustrated in Figure 2.

Tip: Sometimes you'll hear about alkalis being used in titrations, sometimes bases. Don't get yourself in a muddle over it — an alkali is just a type of base, it's a base that's soluble in water.

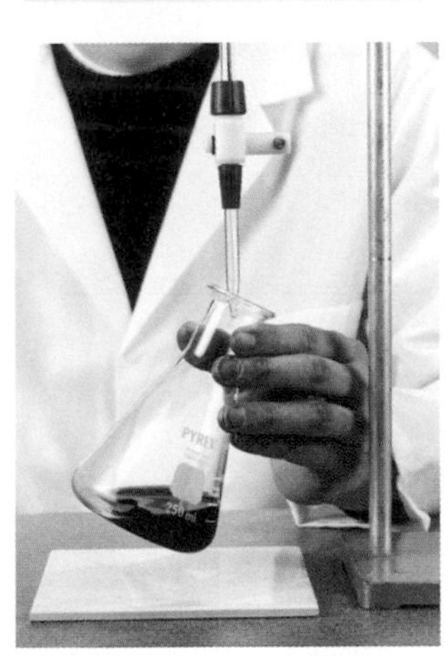

Figure 1: *An acid–base titration experiment.*

Tip: This equipment should look familiar to you. You've probably used it in a practical lesson at some point.

Tip: You need to repeat titrations to make sure your results are reliable — it's all part of How Science Works (see page 236 for more). HOW SCIENCE WORKS

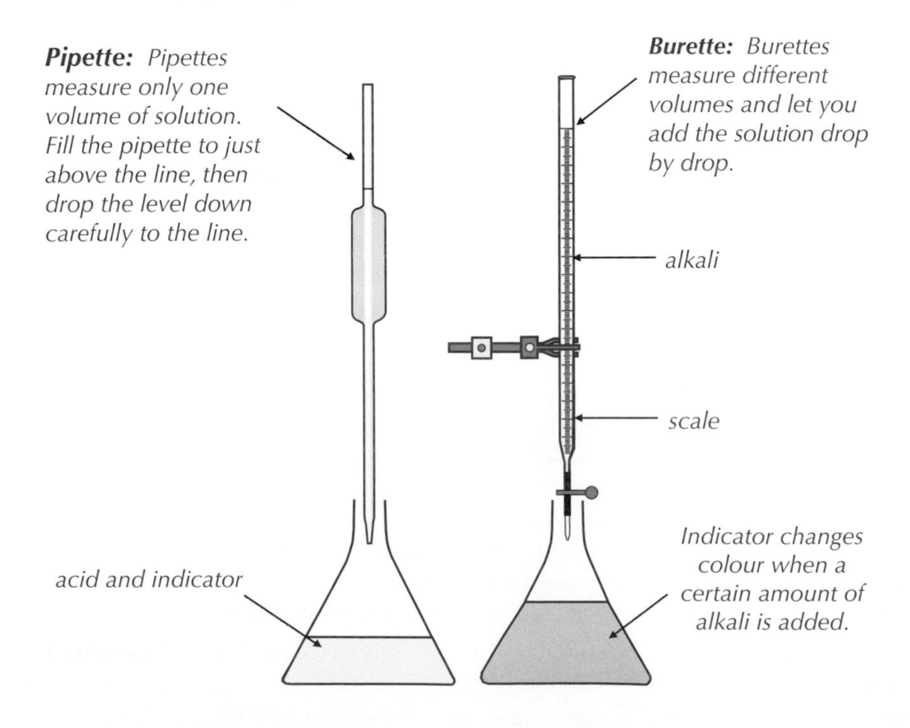

Figure 2: *Equipment needed to perform a titration.*

pH curves

pH curves show the results of titration experiments. They can be made by plotting the pH of the titration mixture against the amount of base added as the titration goes on. The pH of the mixture can be measured using a pH meter and the scale on the burette can be used to see how much base has been added.

The shape of the curve looks a bit different depending on the strengths of the acid and base that were used. The graphs below show the pH curves for the different combinations of strong and weak monoprotic acids and bases:

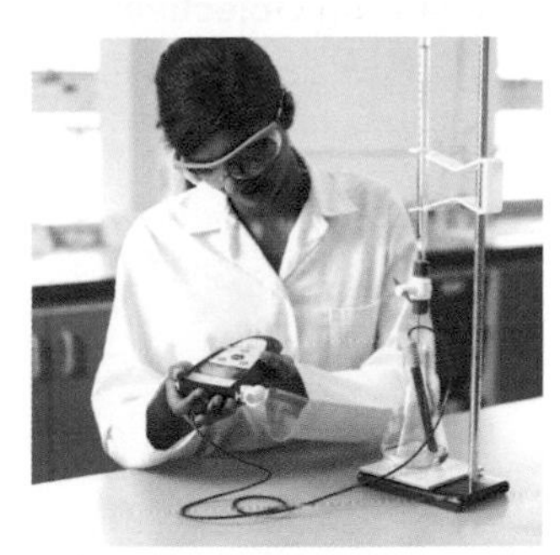

Figure 3: A student using a pH meter to measure pH during an acid–base titration.

Strong acid/strong base

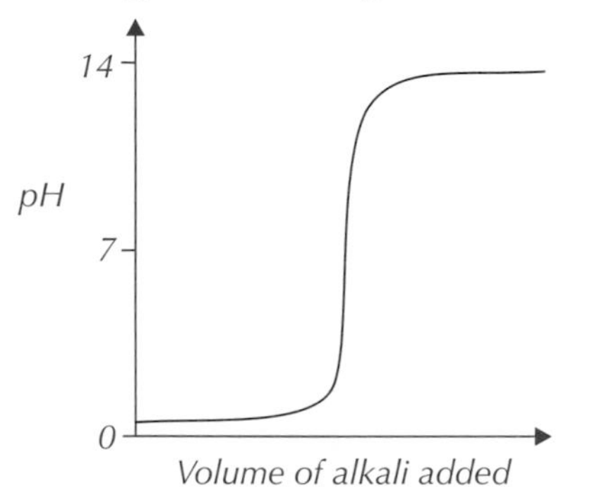

The pH starts around 1, as there's an excess of strong acid.
It finishes up around pH 13, when you have an excess of strong base.

Strong acid/weak base

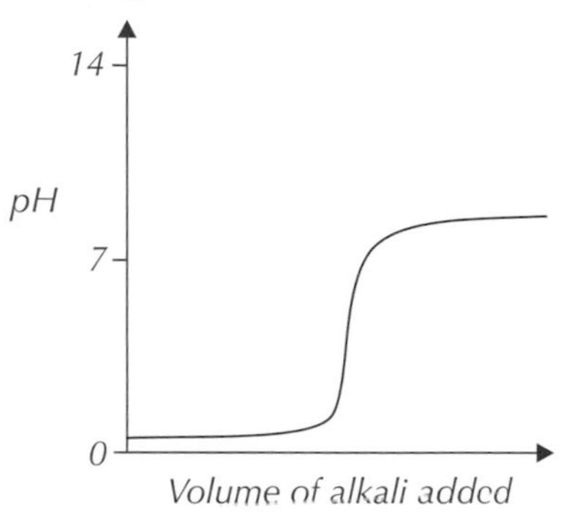

The pH starts around 1, as there's an excess of strong acid.
It finishes up around pH 9, when you have an excess of weak base.

Weak acid/strong base

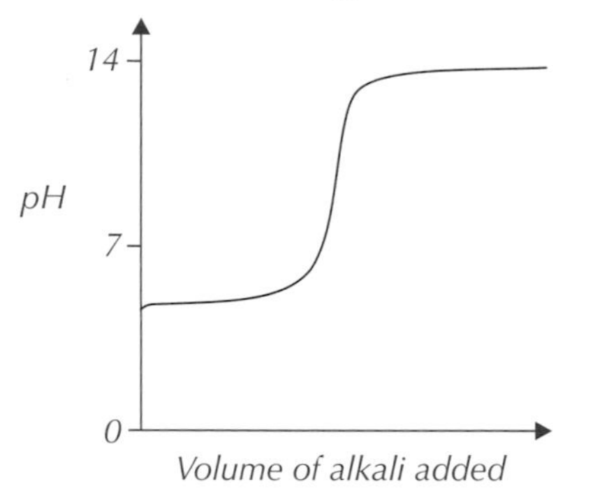

The pH starts around 5, as there's an excess of weak acid.
It finishes up around pH 13, when you have an excess of strong base.

Weak acid/weak base

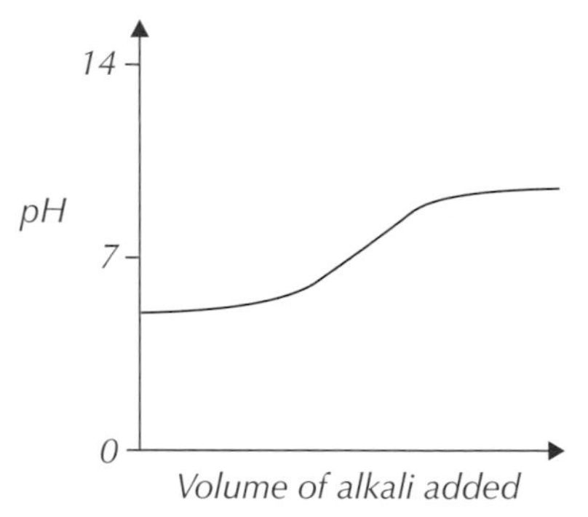

The pH starts around 5, as there's an excess of weak acid.
It finishes up around pH 9, when you have an excess of weak base.

All the graphs apart from the weak acid/weak base graph have a bit that's almost vertical — the mid-point of this vertical section is the equivalence point or end point. At this point, a tiny amount of base causes a sudden, big change in pH — it's here that all the acid is just neutralised.

You don't get such a sharp change in a weak acid/weak base titration. If you used an indicator for this type of titration, its colour would change very gradually, and it would be very tricky to see the exact end point. So you're usually better using a pH meter to find the end point for this type of titration.

Tip: If you titrate a base with an acid instead, the shapes of the curves stay the same, but they're reversed. For example:

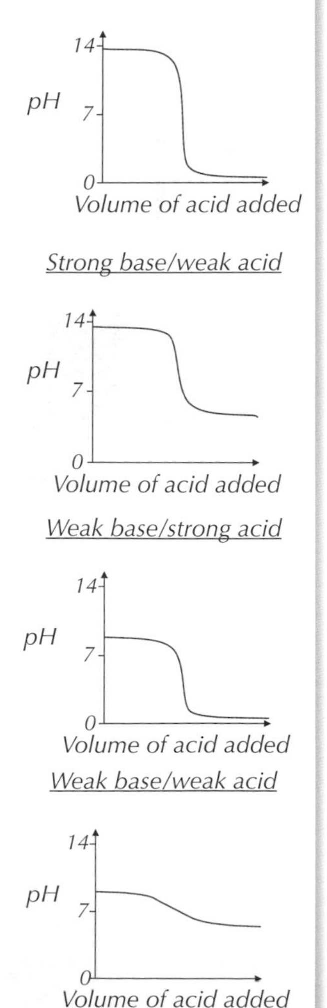

Indicators

When you use an indicator, you need it to change colour exactly at the end point of your titration. So you need to pick one that changes colour over a narrow pH range that lies entirely on the vertical part of the pH curve.
So for the titration shown in Figure 4 (below) you'd want an indicator that changed colour somewhere between pH 8 and pH 11:

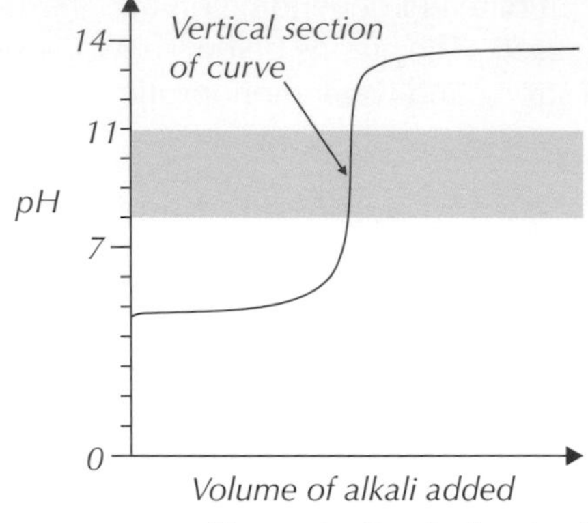

The curve is vertical between pH 8 and pH 11 — so a very small amount of alkali will cause the pH to change from 8 to 11.

So, an indicator that changes colour between pH 8 and pH 11 is needed.

Figure 4: *Graph showing how to select an indicator.*

Figure 5: *The red to yellow colour change of methyl orange.*

Figure 6: *The colourless to pink colour change of phenolphthalein*

Methyl orange and **phenolphthalein** are indicators that are often used for acid–base titrations. They each change colour over a different pH range:

Name of indicator	Colour at low pH	Approx. pH of colour change	Colour at high pH
Methyl orange	red	3.1 – 4.4	yellow
Phenolphthalein	colourless	8.3 – 10	pink

- For a strong acid/strong alkali titration, you can use either of these indicators — there's a rapid pH change over the range for both indicators.
- For a strong acid/weak alkali only methyl orange will do. The pH changes rapidly across the range for methyl orange, but not for phenolphthalein.
- For a weak acid/strong alkali, phenolphthalein is the stuff to use. The pH changes rapidly over phenolphthalein's range, but not over methyl orange's.
- For weak acid/weak alkali titrations there's no sharp pH change, so no indicator will work.

You need to be able to use a pH curve to select an appropriate indicator:

Example

The graph to the right shows the pH curve produced when a strong acid is added to a weak base. From the table below, select an indicator that you could use for this titration.

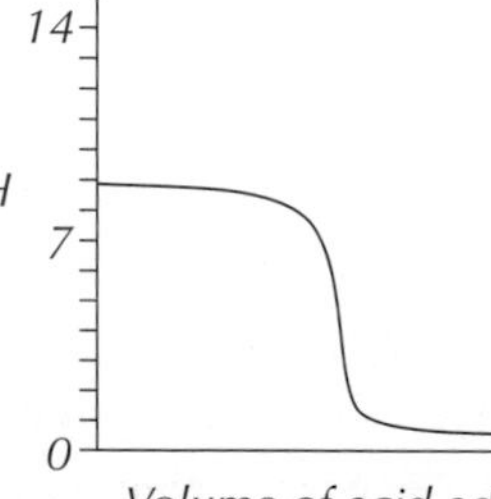

Indicator	pH range
Bromophenol blue	3.0 – 4.6
Litmus	5.0 – 8.0
Cresol purple	7.6 – 9.2

The graph shows that the vertical part of the pH curve is between about pH 2 and pH 6. So you need an indicator with a pH range between 2 and 6. The only indicator that changes colour within this range is bromophenol blue. So in this example, bromophenol blue is the right indicator to choose.

Exam Tip
In your exam, you'll usually be given a table of indicators to choose from, like in this example — so don't worry, you don't have to learn all these indicators and their pH ranges.

Practice Questions — Application

Q1 The graphs below show the pH curves for four different acid–base titrations. For each reaction state what type of acid and base were used and select an appropriate indicator from the table below.

Indicator	pH range
Thymol blue	1.2 – 2.8
Methyl orange	3.1 – 4.4
Litmus	5.0 – 8.0
Cresol purple	7.6 – 9.2
Phenolphthalein	8.3 – 10

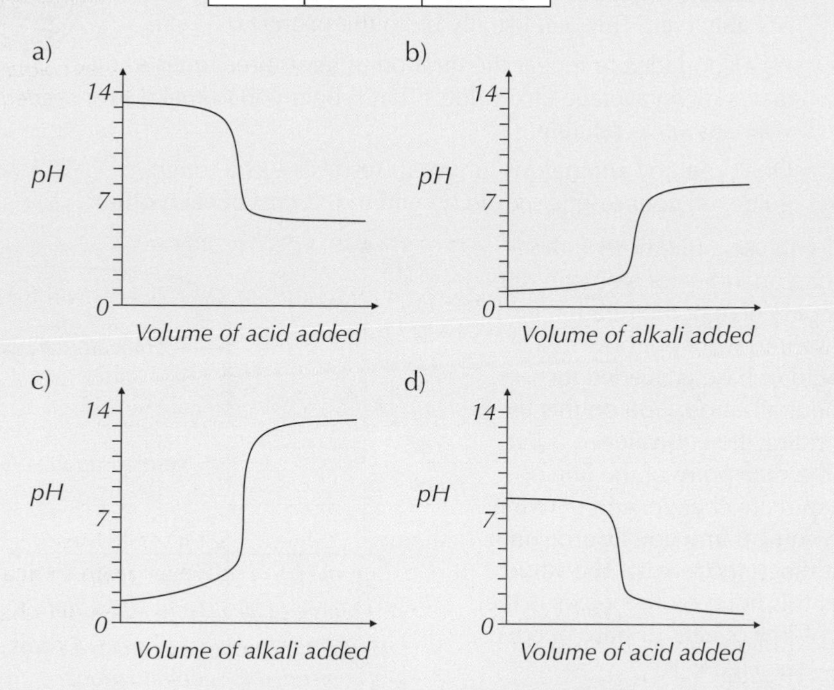

Q2 Neutral red changes colour from red to yellow between pH 6.8 and pH 8.0. Sketch the pH curve for a titration reaction that this indicator could be used for.

Practice Questions — Fact Recall

Q1 Sketch the pH curve produced when:

a) A strong acid neutralises a weak base.

b) A strong base neutralises a strong acid.

c) A weak acid neutralises a strong base.

Q2 a) What happens at the end point of a titration reaction?

b) How can you see that the end point has been reached when you're carrying out a titration?

c) How can you tell the end point has been reached using a pH curve?

Q3 How would you know if an indicator is suitable for a particular titration reaction?

10. Titration Calculations

Learning Objective:

- Be able to perform calculations for the titrations of monoprotic and diprotic acids with sodium hydroxide based on experimental results.

Specification Reference 3.4.3

Now that you've learnt all about titrations it's time to find out what you can do with the results. At A2 there are a few calculations you'll need to be able to do — the next few pages tell you how.

Titration results

When you've done a titration you can use your results to calculate the concentration of your acid or base. There are a few things you can do to make sure your titration results are as accurate as possible:

- Measure the neutralisation volume as **precisely** as you possibly can. This will usually be to the nearest 0.05 cm^3.
- It's a good idea to repeat the titration at least three times and take a mean average titre value. That'll help you to make sure your answer is **reliable**.
- Don't use any **anomalous** (unusual) results — as a rough guide, all your results should be within 0.2 cm^3 of each other.

Tip: Making sure that your results are accurate and reliable is an important part of How Science Works — see page 236 for more on this.

If you use a pH meter rather than an indicator, you can draw a pH curve of the titration and use it to work out how much acid or base is needed for neutralisation. You do this by finding the equivalence point (the mid–point of the line of rapid pH change) and drawing a vertical line downwards until it meets the x-axis. The value at this point on the x-axis is the volume of acid or base needed — see Figure 1.

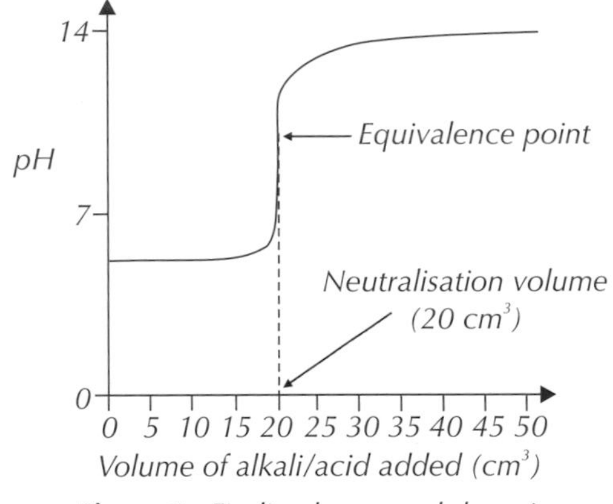

Figure 1: *Finding how much base is needed for neutralisation.*

Figure 2: *A pH meter being used to monitor the pH during a titration.*

Calculating concentrations

Monoprotic acids

Once you know the neutralisation volume you can use it to calculate the concentration of the acid or base. To do this:

Step 1: Write out a balanced equation for the titration reaction.

Step 2: Decide what you know already and what you need to know — usually you'll be given the two volumes and a concentration and you'll have to work out the other concentration.

Step 3: For one reagent you'll know both the concentration and the volume. Calculate the number of moles of this reagent using the equation:

$$\text{moles} = \frac{\text{concentration (moldm}^{-3}) \times \text{volume (cm}^3)}{1000}$$

Step 4: Use the molar ratios in the balanced equation to find out how many moles of the other reagent reacted.

Step 5: Calculate the unknown concentration using the equation:

$$\text{concentration} = \frac{\text{moles} \times 1000}{\text{volume}}$$

in moldm⁻³ (concentration) ... *in cm³* (volume)

Tip: You came across the formula:

$$\textbf{moles} = \frac{\textbf{conc.} \times \textbf{vol.}}{\textbf{1000}}$$

in AS, but you need to know it for A2 as well. The dividing by 1000 bit is to get the volume from cm^3 to dm^3 — if your volume is already in dm^3 then it's just:

moles = conc. × vol.

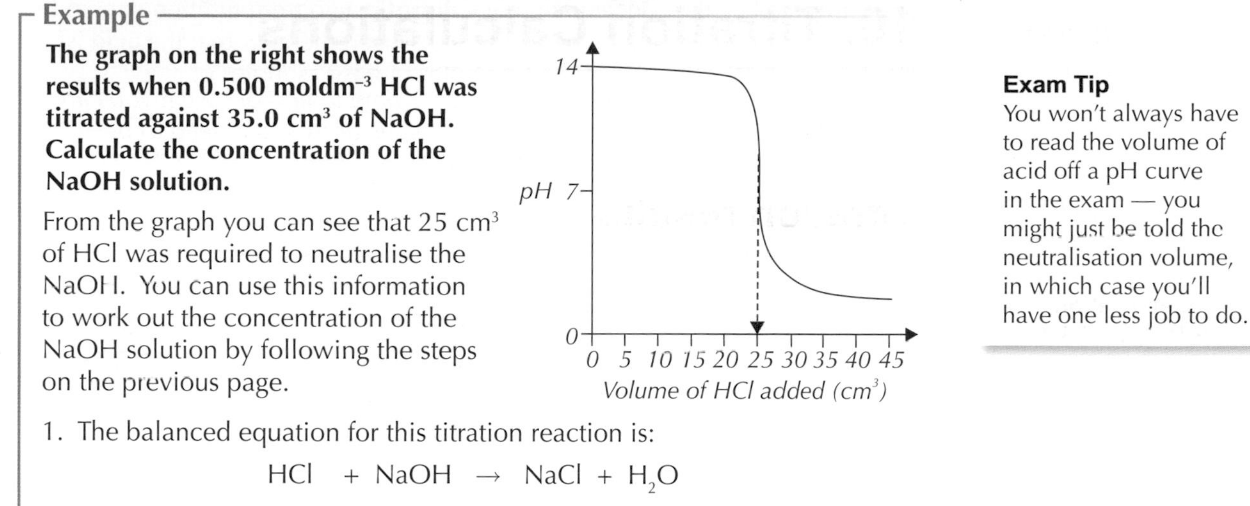

Example

The graph on the right shows the results when 0.500 $moldm^{-3}$ HCl was titrated against 35.0 cm^3 of NaOH. Calculate the concentration of the NaOH solution.

From the graph you can see that 25 cm^3 of HCl was required to neutralise the NaOH. You can use this information to work out the concentration of the NaOH solution by following the steps on the previous page.

1. The balanced equation for this titration reaction is:

$$HCl + NaOH \rightarrow NaCl + H_2O$$

2. You know the concentration of HCl (0.500 $moldm^{-3}$), the volume of HCl (25.0 cm^3) and the volume of NaOH (35.0 cm^3). You need to know the concentration of NaOH.

3. Calculate the moles of HCl:

$$\text{moles HCl} = \frac{\text{concentration} \times \text{volume}}{1000} = \frac{0.500 \times 25.0}{1000} = 0.0125 \text{ moles}$$

4. From the equation, you know 1 mole of HCl neutralises 1 mole of NaOH. So 0.0125 moles of HCl must neutralise 0.0125 moles of NaOH.

5. Calculate the concentration of NaOH:

$$\text{Conc. NaOH} = \frac{\text{moles} \times 1000}{\text{volume}} = \frac{0.0125 \times 1000}{35.0} = 0.357 \text{ moldm}^{-3}$$

Exam Tip
You won't always have to read the volume of acid off a pH curve in the exam — you might just be told the neutralisation volume, in which case you'll have one less job to do.

Tip: In these calculations the units of concentration should always be $moldm^{-3}$.

Diprotic acids

A diprotic acid is one that can release two protons when it's in solution. Ethanedioic acid (HOOC–COOH) is diprotic. When ethanedioic acid reacts with a base like sodium hydroxide, it's neutralised. But the reaction happens in two stages, because the two protons are removed from the acid separately. This means that when you titrate ethanedioic acid with a strong base you get a pH curve with two equivalence points:

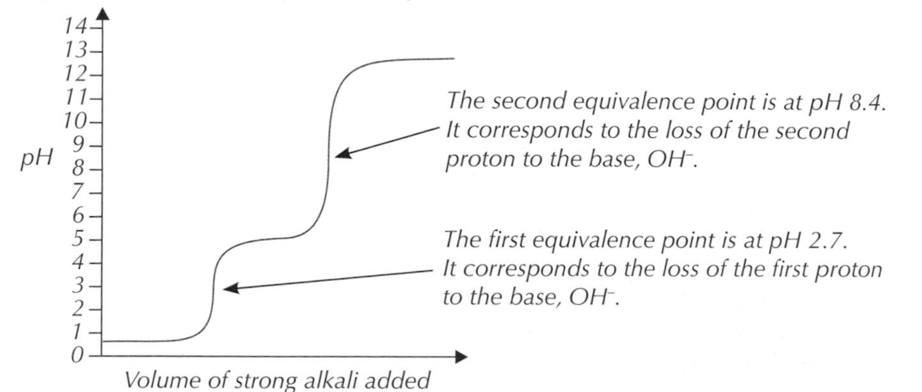

First equivalence point: $HOOC\text{–}COOH_{(aq)} + OH^-_{(aq)} \rightarrow HOOC\text{–}COO^-_{(aq)} + H_2O_{(l)}$

Second equivalence point: $HOOC\text{–}COO^-_{(aq)} + OH^-_{(aq)} \rightarrow {}^-OOC\text{–}COO^-_{(aq)} + H_2O_{(l)}$

Tip: pH curves for diprotic acids look a bit different to those for monoprotic acids. For more on pH curves, see page 29.

Tip: The curve won't always look exactly like this. The pH at the start, end and equivalence points will vary depending on the concentrations of the acid and the base used.

You can calculate the concentration of a **diprotic** acid from titration data in the same way as you did for a monoprotic acid. Just remember that the acid is diprotic so you'll need twice as many moles of base as moles of acid.

Exam Tip
You need to be able to do calculations for both monoprotic and diprotic acids so make sure you understand these two examples.

Example

25.0 cm³ of ethanedioic acid, $C_2H_2O_4$, was completely neutralised by 20.0 cm³ of 0.100 moldm⁻³ NaOH solution. Calculate the concentration of the ethanedioic acid solution.

1. The balanced equation for this titration reaction is:

$$C_2H_2O_4 + 2NaOH \rightarrow Na_2C_2O_4 + 2H_2O$$

2. You know the volume of $C_2H_2O_4$ (25.0 cm³), the volume of NaOH (20.0 cm³) and the concentration of NaOH (0.100 moldm⁻³). You need to know the concentration of $C_2H_2O_4$.

3. Calculate the moles of NaOH:

$$\text{moles NaOH} = \frac{\text{concentration} \times \text{volume}}{1000} = \frac{0.100 \times 20.0}{1000} = 0.002 \text{ moles}$$

Tip: Because it's a diprotic acid, you need twice as many moles of base as moles of acid.

4. You know from the equation that you need 2 moles of NaOH to neutralise 1 mole of $C_2H_2O_4$. So 0.002 moles of NaOH must neutralise (0.002 ÷ 2) = 0.001 moles of $C_2H_2O_4$.

5. Calculate the concentration of $C_2H_2O_4$:

$$\text{Conc. } C_2H_2O_4 = \frac{\text{moles} \times 1000}{\text{volume}} = \frac{0.001 \times 1000}{25} = 0.0400 \text{ moldm}^{-3}$$

Practice Questions — Application

Q1 In a titration, the equivalence point was reached after 13.8 cm³ of a 1.50 moldm⁻³ solution of HCl had been added to 20.0 cm³ of NaOH. Calculate the concentration of the NaOH solution.

Q2 Nitric acid (HNO_3) was added to 30.0 cm³ of a 0.250 moldm⁻³ solution of NaOH in the presence of methyl orange. A colour change was observed after 17.8 cm³ of the acid had been added. Calculate the concentration of the nitric acid solution.

Q3 A 0.250 moldm⁻³ NaOH solution was titrated against 24.0 cm³ of HCl. The experiment was repeated three times and the amount of NaOH required to neutralise the HCl each time is given in the table below.

	Titration 1	Titration 2	Titration 3
Titre volume (cm³ NaOH)	22.38	22.45	22.42

a) Calculate the average titre volume for this titration.

b) Calculate the concentration of the HCl solution.

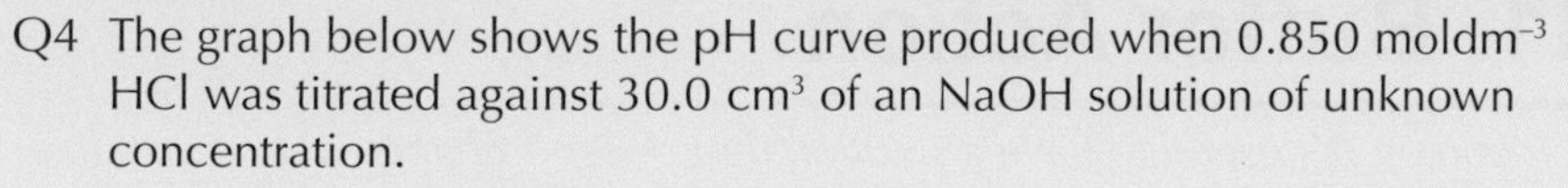

Q4 The graph below shows the pH curve produced when 0.850 $moldm^{-3}$ HCl was titrated against 30.0 cm^3 of an NaOH solution of unknown concentration.

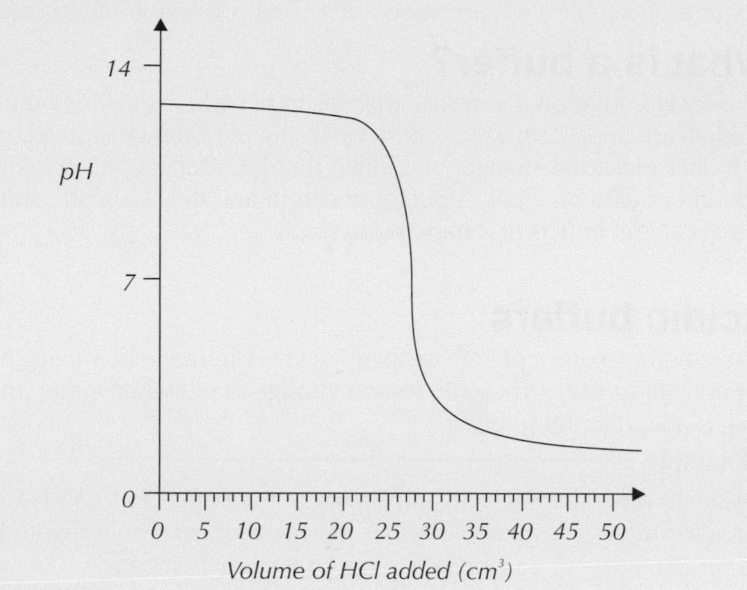

Calculate the concentration of the NaOH solution.

Q5 32.0 cm^3 of a NaOH solution is fully neutralised when 18.0 cm^3 of a 0.400 $moldm^{-3}$ solution of H_2SO_4 is added to it. Calculate the concentration of the NaOH solution.

Q6 When a 1.20 $moldm^{-3}$ solution of NaOH was titrated against 20.0 cm^3 of carbonic acid (H_2CO_3), 26.2 cm^3 of NaOH was required to fully neutralise the acid. Calculate the concentration of the carbonic acid solution.

Tip: When you're writing the equations for a titration remember that it's a neutralisation reaction so the products will be a salt and water.

Practice Questions — Fact Recall

Q1 Write out the equation that links the number of moles, the volume and the concentration of a solution.

Q2 Sketch the pH curve produced when a strong base is added to a strong diprotic acid in a titration.

Q3 Explain why the pH curve for the titration of a diprotic acid is different to a pH curve for the titration of a monoprotic acid.

Q4 How many moles of a diprotic acid does it take to neutralise 1 mole of NaOH?

11. Buffer Action

Sometimes, it's useful to have a solution that doesn't change pH when small amounts of acid or alkali are added to it. That's where buffers come in handy.

Learning Objectives:

- Be able to explain qualitatively the action of acidic and basic buffers.
- Know some applications of buffer solutions.

Specification Reference 3.4.3

What is a buffer?

A buffer is a solution that resists changes in pH when small amounts of acid or alkali are added. A buffer doesn't stop the pH from changing completely — it does make the changes very slight though. Buffers only work for small amounts of acid or alkali — put too much in and they won't be able to cope. You get acidic buffers and basic buffers.

Acidic buffers

Acidic buffers have a pH of less than 7 — they're made by mixing a weak acid with one of its salts. They can resist a change in pH when either an acid or a base is added to the solution.

Tip: The acid has to be a weak acid — you can't make an acidic buffer with a strong acid.

Example

A mixture of ethanoic acid and sodium ethanoate ($CH_3COO^-Na^+$) is an acidic buffer. The ethanoic acid is a weak acid, so it only slightly dissociates:

$$CH_3COOH_{(aq)} \rightleftharpoons H^+_{(aq)} + CH_3COO^-_{(aq)}$$

But the salt fully dissociates into its ions when it dissolves:

$$CH_3COONa_{(s)} \xrightarrow{water} CH_3COO^-_{(aq)} + Na^+_{(aq)}$$

So in the solution you've got heaps of undissociated ethanoic acid molecules ($CH_3COOH_{(aq)}$), and heaps of ethanoate ions ($CH_3COO^-_{(aq)}$) from the salt.

When you alter the concentration of H^+ or OH^- ions in the buffer solution the equilibrium position moves to counteract the change (this is down to Le Chatelier's principle — see page 17). Here's how it all works:

Tip: Acidic buffers work slightly differently to basic buffers, which are covered on the next page — but the principle of how buffers work is the same for both types.

Resisting an acid

The large number of CH_3COO^- ions make sure that the buffer can cope with the addition of acid. If you add a small amount of acid the H^+ concentration increases. Most of the extra H^+ ions combine with CH_3COO^- ions to form CH_3COOH. This shifts the equilibrium to the left, reducing the H^+ concentration to close to its original value. So the pH doesn't change much.

Addition of H^+ (acid) ←

$$CH_3COOH_{(aq)} \rightleftharpoons H^+_{(aq)} + CH_3COO^-_{(aq)}$$

Resisting a base

If a small amount of base (e.g. NaOH) is added, the OH^- concentration increases. Most of the extra OH^- ions react with H^+ ions to form water — removing H^+ ions from the solution. This causes more CH_3COOH to dissociate to form H^+ ions — shifting the equilibrium to the right. There's no problem doing this as there's loads of spare CH_3COOH molecules. The H^+ concentration increases until it's close to its original value, so the pH doesn't change much.

Addition of OH^- (base) →

$$CH_3COOH_{(aq)} \rightleftharpoons H^+_{(aq)} + CH_3COO^-_{(aq)}$$

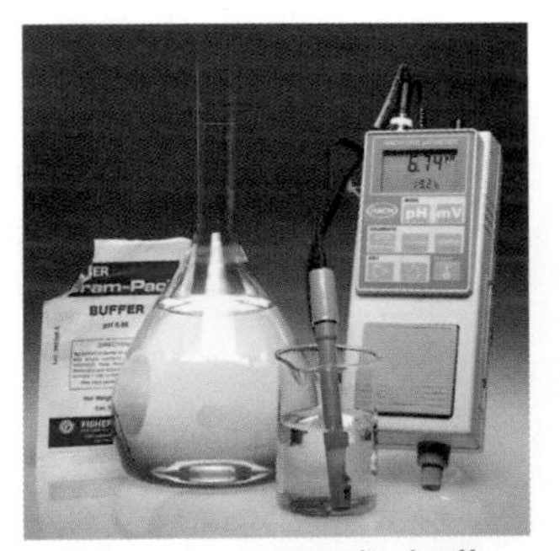

Figure 1: *An acidic buffer solution.*

Basic buffers

Basic buffers have a pH greater than 7 — and they're made by mixing a weak base with one of its salts. They can resist changes in pH when acid or base is added, just like acidic buffers can.

Tip: You can't make basic buffers with strong bases — they have to be weak bases.

Example

A solution of ammonia (NH_3, a weak base) and ammonium chloride (NH_4Cl, a salt of ammonia) acts as a basic buffer.

The salt fully dissociates in solution:

$$NH_4Cl_{(aq)} \rightarrow NH_4^+{}_{(aq)} + Cl^-{}_{(aq)}$$

Some of the NH_3 molecules will also react with water molecules:

$$NH_{3\,(aq)} + H_2O_{(l)} \rightleftharpoons NH_4^+{}_{(aq)} + OH^-{}_{(aq)}$$

So the solution will contain loads of ammonium ions (NH_4^+), and lots of ammonia molecules too. The equilibrium position of this reaction can move to counteract changes in pH:

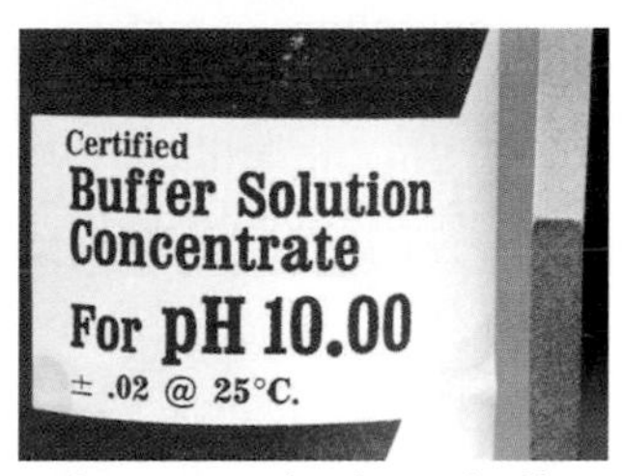

Figure 2: This basic buffer will maintain a pH of 10.00 when small amounts of acid or alkali are added.

Resisting an acid

If a small amount of acid is added, the H^+ concentration increases, making the solution more acidic. Some of the H^+ ions react with OH^- ions to make H_2O. When this happens the equilibrium position moves to the right to replace the OH^- ions that have been used up. This reaction will remove most of the extra H^+ ions that were added — so the pH won't change much.

Addition of H^+ (acid) →

$$NH_{3\,(aq)} + H_2O_{(l)} \rightleftharpoons NH_4^+{}_{(aq)} + OH^-{}_{(aq)}$$

Exam Tip
You don't need to memorise these specific examples but you do need to be able to explain how both acidic and basic buffers work.

Resisting a base

If a small amount of base is added, the OH^- concentration increases, making the solution more alkaline. Most of the extra OH^- ions will react with the NH_4^+ ions, to form NH_3 and H_2O. So the equilibrium will shift to the left, removing OH^- ions from the solution, and stopping the pH from changing much.

Addition of OH^- (base) ←

$$NH_{3\,(aq)} + H_2O_{(l)} \rightleftharpoons NH_4^+{}_{(aq)} + OH^-{}_{(aq)}$$

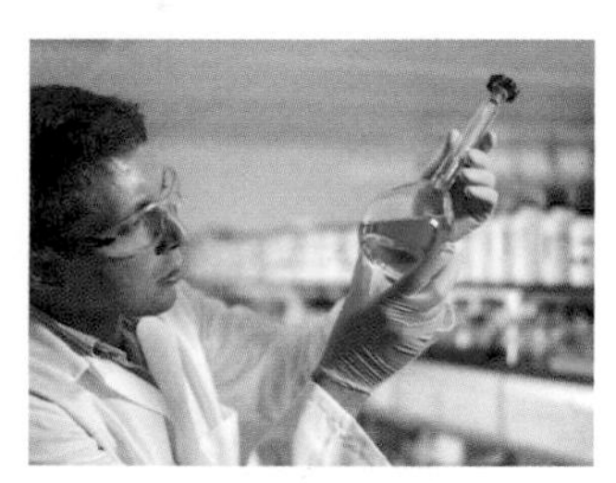

Figure 3: A lovely blue buffer solution being prepared by a lovely blue-gloved scientist.

Acidic and basic buffers — summary

How buffers work can be a bit tricky to get your head round, so here's a nice summary diagram to help you out:

Acidic Buffer

$HA \rightleftharpoons H^+ + A^-$

Acid Added

$[H^+]$ increases.

The rise in $[H^+]$ should decrease the pH but...

Excess H^+ combines with A^- and the equilibrium shifts left.

$[H^+]$ decreases to close to its original value.

Base Added

$[OH^-]$ increases.

OH^- combines with H^+ so $[H^+]$ decreases.

The fall in $[H^+]$ should increase the pH but...

The equilibrium shifts right to replace the lost H^+.

$[H^+]$ increases to close to its original value.

pH stays almost the same

Basic Buffer

$B + H_2O \rightleftharpoons BH^+ + OH^-$

Acid Added

$[H^+]$ increases.

The rise in $[H^+]$ should decrease the pH but...

H^+ combines with OH^- so $[OH^-]$ decreases.

The equilibrium shifts right to replace the lost OH^-.

$[OH^-]$ increases to close to its original value.

Base Added

$[OH^-]$ increases

The rise in $[OH^-]$ should increase the pH but...

Excess OH^- combines with BH^+ and the equilibrium shifts left.

$[OH^-]$ decreases to close to its original value.

pH stays almost the same

Tip: pH is determined by $[H^+]$, but because OH^- will combine with H^+ and remove it from solution, $[OH^-]$ affects $[H^+]$ and so affects pH. A rise in $[OH^-]$ will increase the pH, a fall in $[OH^-]$ will decrease the pH. Unless there's a buffer present, that is.

Applications of buffers

Most shampoos contain a pH 5.5 buffer — it counteracts the alkaline soap in the shampoo. The soap might get your hair squeaky clean, but alkalis don't make your hair look shiny. Biological washing powders contain buffers too. They keep the pH at the right level for the enzymes to work best. There are also lots of biological buffer systems in our bodies, making sure all our tissues are kept at the right pH. For example, it's vital that blood stays at a pH very near to 7.4, so it contains a buffer system.

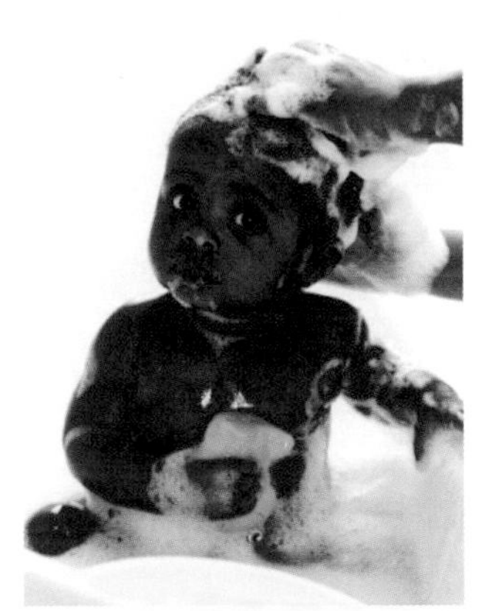

Figure 4: Shampoos contain buffers, so this cute baby will have nice shiny hair.

Practice Questions — Fact Recall

Q1 What is a buffer?

Q2 How are acidic buffers made?

Q3 Explain how an acidic buffer resists changes in pH when:
- a) a small amount of acid is added.
- b) a small amount of base is added.

Q4 How are basic buffers made?

Q5 Explain how a basic buffer resists changes in pH when:
- a) a small amount of acid is added.
- b) a small amount of base is added.

Q6 Give two situations where buffers are used.

12. Calculating the pH of Buffers

You need to be able to calculate the pH of buffer solutions. These calculations look scary, but don't worry — they're not nearly as bad as they look.

Learning Objective:

- Be able to calculate the pH of acidic buffer solutions.

Specification Reference 3.4.3

Calculations using known concentrations

If you know the K_a of the weak acid and the concentrations of the weak acid and its salt, calculating the pH of an acidic buffer isn't too tricky. Here's how to go about it:

Step 1: Write out the expression for the K_a of the weak acid.

Step 2: Rearrange the equation to give an expression for $[H^+]$.

Step 3: Substitute the value for K_a and the concentrations of the acid and salt into the equation.

Step 4: Solve the equation to find a value for $[H^+]$.

Step 5: Substitute your value for $[H^+]$ into the pH equation ($pH = -\log[H^+]$) and solve it to calculate the pH.

Tip: Writing expressions for K_a was covered on page 24. Have a look back if you need a recap.

Tip: See page 21 for a reminder on how to calculate pH.

Example

A buffer solution contains 0.400 moldm^{-3} methanoic acid, HCOOH, and 0.600 moldm^{-3} sodium methanoate, $HCOO^-Na^+$. For methanoic acid, $K_a = 1.6 \times 10^{-4}$ moldm^{-3}. What is the pH of this buffer?

1. Write the expression for K_a of the weak acid:

$$HCOOH_{(aq)} \rightleftharpoons H^+_{(aq)} + HCOO^-_{(aq)} \quad \text{so} \quad K_a = \frac{[H^+][HCOO^-]}{[HCOOH]}$$

2. Rearrange the equation to get $[H^+]$:

$$[H^+] = \frac{K_a \times [HCOOH]}{[HCOO^-]}$$

3. Substitute in the value of K_a and the concentrations given in the question: You have to make a few assumptions here:
   - $HCOO^-Na^+$ is fully dissociated, so assume that the equilibrium concentration of $HCOO^-$ is the same as the initial concentration of $HCOO^-Na^+$.
   - HCOOH is only slightly dissociated, so assume that its equilibrium concentration is the same as its initial concentration.

$$[H^+] = \frac{K_a \times [HCOOH]}{[HCOO^-]} = \frac{(1.6 \times 10^{-4}) \times 0.400}{0.600}$$

Tip: Remember — the concentrations in the expression for K_a all have to be equilibrium concentrations.

4. Solve to find $[H^+]$:

$$[H^+] = \frac{(1.6 \times 10^{-4}) \times 0.400}{0.600} = 1.07 \times 10^{-4} \text{ moldm}^{-3}$$

5. Use your value of $[H^+]$ to calculate the pH:

$$\begin{aligned} pH &= -\log[H^+] \\ &= -\log(1.07 \times 10^{-4}) \\ &= \mathbf{3.97} \end{aligned}$$

Another way to make acidic buffers

Mixing a weak acid with its salt is not the only way to make an acidic buffer. You could also take a weak acid and add a small amount of alkali, so that some of the acid is neutralised to make a salt, but some is left un-neutralised. The reaction mixture would then contain a weak acid and its salt, so would act as an acidic buffer. You can calculate the pH of an acidic buffer that has been made this way by following the steps below:

Step 1: Write out the equation for the neutralisation reaction — remember acid + base → salt + water.

Step 2: Calculate the number of moles of acid and base at the start of the reaction using the volumes and concentrations given in the question.

Step 3: Use the molar ratios in the equation to work out the moles of acid and salt left at the end of the reaction.

Step 4: Calculate the concentration of the acid and salt in the buffer solution by dividing by the volume of the solution — this is the volume of the acid and the base added together.

Step 5: Then you're ready to calculate the pH.

Tip: The molar ratios tell you how many moles of acid will react with a certain number of moles of base, and how many moles of salt are produced. These numbers will always be in the same ratio for a given reaction.

Example

A buffer is formed by mixing 15 cm^3 of 0.1 moldm^{-3} sodium hydroxide (NaOH) and 30 cm^3 of 0.6 moldm^{-3} propanoic acid (CH_3CH_2COOH). Calculate the pH of this buffer solution ($K_a = 1.35 \times 10^{-5}$ moldm^{-3}).

1. Write out the equation for the reaction:

$$CH_3CH_2COOH + NaOH \rightarrow CH_3CH_2COO^-Na^+ + H_2O$$

2. Calculate the number of moles of acid and base:

$$\text{Moles } CH_3CH_2COOH = \frac{\text{Conc.} \times \text{Vol.}}{1000} = \frac{0.6 \times 30}{1000} = 0.018 \text{ moles}$$

$$\text{Moles NaOH} = \frac{\text{Conc.} \times \text{Vol.}}{1000} = \frac{0.1 \times 15}{1000} = 0.0015 \text{ moles}$$

3. The acid is in excess, so all the base reacts. There's 0.0015 moles of NaOH at the start of the reaction. If it all reacts there will be 0.0015 moles of salt at the end of the reaction.

The equation shows us that 1 mole of base will react with 1 mole of acid to give 1 mole of salt. So if there are 0.0015 moles of salt, 0.0015 moles of acid must have been used up.
This leaves 0.018 – 0.0015 = 0.0165 moles of acid.

So, the buffer solution contains 0.0015 moles of $CH_3CH_2COO^-Na^+$ and 0.0165 moles of CH_3CH_2COOH.

4. Calculate the concentration of acid and salt in the buffer solution:

The total volume of the solution is 15 + 30 = 45 cm^3

$$\text{Conc. } CH_3CH_2COOH = \frac{\text{moles} \times 1000}{\text{volume}} = \frac{0.0165 \times 1000}{45}$$
$$= 0.37 \text{ moldm}^{-3}$$

Tip: It's really important that you know equations like:

$$\text{moles} = \frac{\text{conc.} \times \text{vol.}}{1000}$$

You won't be able to do the harder calculations if you haven't got your head around the basics. Check out pages 242-243 for a summary of the equations that you need to know.

Exam Tip
In the exam you'll only be asked to calculate the pH of an acidic buffer — so you don't need to worry about calculating the pH of basic buffers.

$$\text{Conc. } CH_3CH_2COO^-Na^+ = \frac{\text{moles} \times 1000}{\text{volume}} = \frac{0.0015 \times 1000}{45}$$

$$= 0.033 \text{ moldm}^{-3}$$

5. Work out the pH as before:

$$CH_3CH_2COOH \rightleftharpoons H^+ + CH_3CH_2COO^- \text{ so } K_a = \frac{[H^+][CH_3CH_2COO^-]}{[CH_3CH_2COOH]}$$

$$[H^+] = \frac{K_a \times [CH_3CH_2COOH]}{[CH_3CH_2COO^-]} = \frac{(1.35 \times 10^{-5}) \times 0.37}{0.033} = 1.51 \times 10^{-4} \text{ moldm}^{-3}$$

$$pH = -\log[H^+] = -\log(1.51 \times 10^{-4}) = 3.82$$

Tip: This step was covered in more detail on page 39 — have a look back if you need a quick reminder of what's going on.

Practice Questions — Application

Q1 An acidic buffer solution contains 0.200 moldm^{-3} propanoic acid (CH_3CH_2COOH) and 0.350 moldm^{-3} potassium propanoate. For propanoic acid, $K_a = 1.35 \times 10^{-5}$ moldm^{-3}.

a) Write an expression for the K_a of propanoic acid.

b) Calculate the concentration of H^+ ions in this buffer solution.

c) Calculate the pH of this buffer solution.

Q2 A buffer solution contains 0.150 moldm^{-3} ethanoic acid and 0.250 moldm^{-3} potassium ethanoate. For ethanoic acid $K_a = 1.74 \times 10^{-5}$ moldm^{-3}. Calculate the pH of this buffer.

Q3 A buffer is made by mixing 30.0 cm^3 of 0.500 moldm^{-3} propanoic acid (CH_3CH_2COOH) with 20.0 cm^3 of 0.250 moldm^{-3} potassium hydroxide (KOH). For propanoic acid, $K_a = 1.35 \times 10^{-5}$ moldm^{-3}.

a) Write an equation to show the reaction of propanoic acid with potassium hydroxide.

b) Calculate the number of moles of propanoic acid and potassium hydroxide at the beginning of the reaction.

c) Calculate the concentration of propanoic acid and potassium propanoate in the buffer solution.

d) Calculate the concentration of H^+ ions in this buffer solution.

e) Calculate the pH of the buffer solution.

Q4 A buffer is formed by mixing together 25.0 cm^3 of 0.200 moldm^{-3} methanoic acid (HCOOH) and 15.0 cm^3 of 0.100 moldm^{-3} sodium hydroxide (NaOH). For methanoic acid, $K_a = 1.6 \times 10^{-4}$ moldm^{-3}. Calculate the pH of this buffer.

Section Summary

Make sure you know...

- That reaction rate is the change in the amount of reactants or products per unit time.
- How to work out reaction rates from concentration–time graphs.
- How to derive the rate equation for a reaction — for the reaction A + B → C + D, rate = $k[A]^m[B]^n$.
- What each of the terms in the rate equation means.
- That the rate constant, k, is always the same for a certain reaction at a particular temperature.
- That increasing the temperature increases the rate constant.
- How to calculate the rate constant and its units, using the rate equation and experimental data.
- How to use the initial rates method to work out the orders of a reaction.
- That the rate-determining step is the slowest step in a reaction mechanism.
- How to use the rate equation to determine which step in a reaction is the rate-determining step.
- How knowing the rate-determining step can help in working out reaction mechanisms.
- That a dynamic equilibrium exists when the forward and backward reactions in a reversible reaction are happening at exactly the same rate, so the concentration of reactants and products doesn't change.
- That K_c is the equilibrium constant.
- How to derive expressions for the equilibrium constant, K_c.
- How to calculate K_c and its units from the equilibrium concentrations and molar ratios for a reaction.
- How to use K_c to find unknown equilibrium concentrations for a reaction.
- That increasing the temperature of exothermic reactions will decrease K_c.
- That increasing the temperature of endothermic reactions will increase K_c.
- That changing the concentrations of reactants or adding a catalyst has no effect on the value of K_c.
- That a Brønsted–Lowry acid is a proton donor and a Brønsted–Lowry base is a proton acceptor.
- That strong acids/bases dissociate fully in water while weak acids/bases only partially dissociate.
- That acid–base reactions involve the transfer of protons — $HA + B \rightleftharpoons BH^+ + A^-$.
- That water is weakly dissociated and the ionic product of water is $K_w = [H^+][OH^-]$ which is equivalent to $[H^+]^2$ for pure water.
- That $pH = -\log[H^+]$ where $[H^+]$ is the concentration of H^+ ions in $mol dm^{-3}$.
- How to convert pH into $[H^+]$ and vice versa.
- How to calculate the pH of a strong acid from its concentration.
- How to calculate the pH of a strong base from its concentration, using K_w.
- That K_a is the dissociation constant for a weak acid, and how to write expressions for K_a.
- How to calculate the pH of a weak acid from its concentration and K_a.
- How to calculate the concentration of a weak acid from its pH and K_a.
- How to calculate K_a for a weak acid from its pH and concentration.
- That $pK_a = -\log(K_a)$ and how to convert K_a to pK_a and vice versa.
- What the pH curves for all the different combinations of weak and strong acids and bases look like.
- How to use pH curves to select an appropriate pH indicator to use in a titration.
- How the pH curves for a monoprotic and a diprotic acid are different.
- How to calculate the concentration of monoprotic and diprotic acids using the results of a titration.
- What a buffer is and how both acidic and basic buffers can resist changes in pH.
- That buffers are used in shampoos, biological washing powders and biological systems.
- How to calculate the pH of an acidic buffer.

Exam-style Questions

1 Under certain conditions the following reaction occurs between nitrogen monoxide (NO) and hydrogen (H_2):

$$2NO_{(g)} + 2H_{2(g)} \rightarrow N_{2(g)} + 2H_2O_{(g)}$$

The table below shows the results of a series of initial rate experiments for this reaction.

Experiment number	[NO] ($moldm^{-3}$)	[H_2] ($moldm^{-3}$)	Initial rate ($moldm^{-3}s^{-1}$)
1	3.0×10^{-3}	6.0×10^{-3}	4.50×10^{-3}
2	3.0×10^{-3}	3.0×10^{-3}	2.25×10^{-3}
3	6.0×10^{-3}	1.5×10^{-3}	4.50×10^{-3}

1 (a) Determine the orders of reaction with respect to NO and H_2.

(2 marks)

1 (b) Write out the rate equation for this reaction.

(1 mark)

1 (c) Using the data above, calculate the rate constant (k) for this reaction and give its units.

(3 marks)

1 (d) What would the rate of reaction be if 4.5×10^{-3} $moldm^{-3}$ NO were mixed with 2.5×10^{-3} $moldm^{-3}$ H_2 under the same conditions as the experiment above?

(If you were unable to answer 1 (c), use $k = 6.5 \times 10^5$.)

(2 marks)

1 (e) Using the rate equation, explain why a one-step mechanism is not possible for this reaction.

(2 marks)

2 The following equilibrium establishes at temperature X:

$$CH_{4(g)} + 2H_2O_{(g)} \rightleftharpoons CO_{2(g)} + 4H_{2(g)} \qquad \Delta H = +165\ kJmol^{-1}$$

At equilibrium the mixture was found to contain 0.080 $moldm^{-3}$ CH_4, 0.320 $moldm^{-3}$ H_2O, 0.200 $moldm^{-3}$ CO_2 and 0.280 $moldm^{-3}$ H_2.

2 (a) (i) Write an expression for K_c for this equilibrium.

(1 mark)

2 (a) (ii) Calculate the value of K_c at temperature X, and give its units.

(3 marks)

At a different temperature, Y, the value of K_c was found to be 0.08 and the equilibrium concentrations were as follows:

Gas	CH_4	H_2O	CO_2	H_2
Concentration ($moldm^{-3}$)	?	0.560	0.420	0.480

2 (b) (i) Calculate the equilibrium concentration of CH_4 at this temperature.

(2 marks)

2 (b) (ii) At another temperature, Z, the value of K_c was found to be 1.2×10^{-3}. Suggest whether temperature Z is higher or lower than temperature Y. Explain your answer.

(3 marks)

2 (c) State how the value of K_c would change if a catalyst was added to the reaction. Explain your answer.

(2 marks)

3 The concentrations of strong acids and strong bases can be found by carrying out titrations. Titrations are usually done at room temperature (25 °C). The value of K_w at 25 °C is 1.0×10^{-14} $moldm^{-3}$.

3 (a) (i) Give the expression for K_w.

(1 mark)

3 (a) (ii) Give the expression for pH.

(1 mark)

3 (b) Calculate the pH of a 0.15 $moldm^{-3}$ solution of NaOH at 25 °C.

(3 marks)

3 (c) In a titration reaction at 25 °C, 25 cm^3 of this 0.15 $moldm^{-3}$ solution of NaOH was neutralised by 18.5 cm^3 of a HCl solution of unknown concentration.

3 (c) (i) Which of the graphs below (A, B and C) shows the pH curve for this reaction?

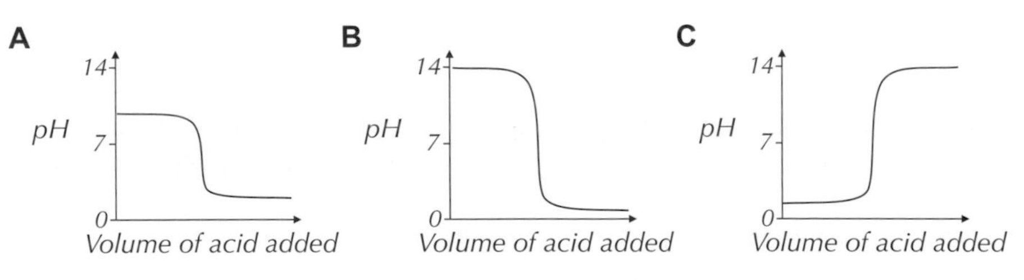

(1 mark)

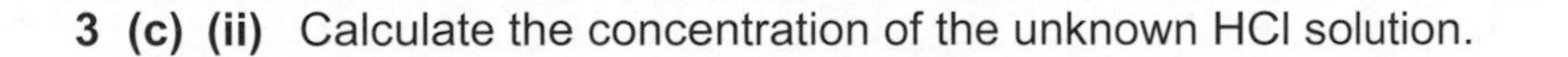

3 (c) (ii) Calculate the concentration of the unknown HCl solution.

(3 marks)

3 (c) (iii) Calculate the pH of the HCl solution.

(2 marks)

3 (d) The pH curve for another titration is shown below.

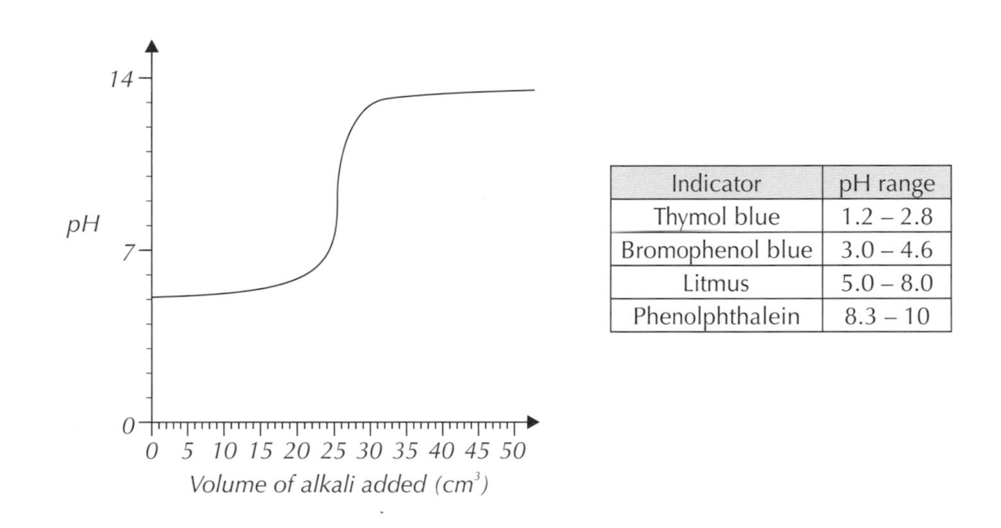

Indicator	pH range
Thymol blue	1.2 – 2.8
Bromophenol blue	3.0 – 4.6
Litmus	5.0 – 8.0
Phenolphthalein	8.3 – 10

3 (d) (i) Suggest an acid and a base that could have been used in this titration.

(2 marks)

3 (d) (ii) From the table above, suggest an indicator that would be suitable for this titration.

(1 mark)

4 Methanoic acid (HCOOH) is a weak acid. A 0.24 $moldm^{-3}$ solution of HCOOH has a pH of 2.2 at 25 °C.

4 (a) (i) Write out the equation for the dissociation of CHOOH.

(1 mark)

4 (a) (ii) Write out an expression for K_a for this acid.

(1 mark)

4 (a) (iii) Calculate the pK_a of methanoic acid at 25 °C.

(3 marks)

4 (b) A buffer solution can be formed by mixing 30 cm^3 of this 0.24 $moldm^{-3}$ methanoic acid with 20 cm^3 of 0.15 $moldm^{-3}$ sodium hydroxide (NaOH).

4 (b) (i) Calculate the pH of this buffer.

(6 marks)

4 (b) (ii) Explain how this buffer resists changes in pH when an acid is added.

(3 marks)

Learning Objective:
- Be able to apply IUPAC rules for nomenclature to simple organic compounds, limited to chains with up to 6 carbon atoms.

Specification Reference 3.4.4

1. Nomenclature

Organic chemistry is the study of carbon-containing compounds. These compounds could be made up of just a few hydrogen and carbon atoms or they could contain thousands. However many atoms they contain, it's important that we can talk about them without getting confused — that's where nomenclature comes in. Nomenclature is just a fancy word for naming organic compounds.

Naming organic compounds

The IUPAC system for naming organic compounds is the agreed international language of chemistry. Years ago, organic compounds were given whatever names people fancied, such as acetic acid and ethylene. But these names caused confusion between different countries.

The IUPAC system means scientific ideas can be communicated across the globe more effectively. So it's easier for scientists to get on with testing each other's work, and either confirm or dispute new theories.

You need to be able to name all the organic molecules found in this book using the IUPAC system for naming organic compounds. Here are the rules for some simple organic compounds to get you started.

Exam Tip
You have to spell the IUPAC names of compounds correctly in the exam to get the marks. Always double check your spelling to make sure you haven't made any silly mistakes.

Straight chain alkanes

There are two parts to the name of a straight chain **alkane**. The first part — the stem, states how many carbon atoms there are in the molecule (see Figure 1).

Number of Carbon Atoms	Stem
1	*meth-*
2	*eth-*
3	*prop-*
4	*but-*
5	*pent-*
6	*hex-*

Figure 1: *Stems for naming organic compounds.*

Tip: These pages are a bit of a recap of stuff you learnt for AS. Unfortunately, you're going to get tested on it for A2 as well, so make sure you know it all.

The second part (the suffix) is always "-ane". It's the "-ane" bit that lets people know it's an alkane.

Example

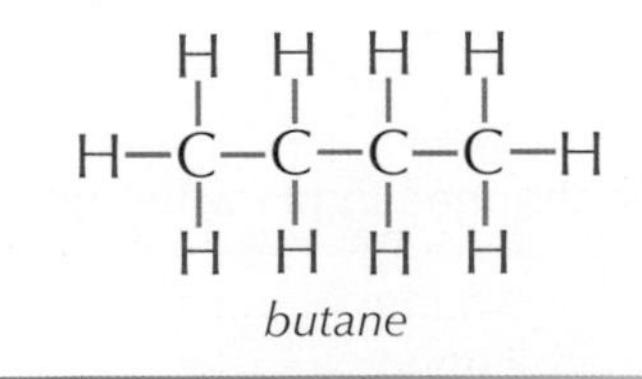

butane

There are four carbon atoms so the stem is 'but-' — the alkane is called butane.

Branched alkanes

Branched alkanes have side chains. These are the carbon atoms that aren't part of the longest continuous chain. To name branched alkanes you first need to count how many carbon atoms are in the longest chain and work out the stem (just like you would for a straight chain alkane). Once you've done that you can name the side chains. The side chains are named according to how many carbon atoms they have (see Figure 2) and which carbon atom they are attached to. If there's more than one side chain in a molecule, you place them in alphabetical order. So but- groups come before eth- groups which come before meth- groups.

Number of Carbon Atoms	Side Chain Prefix
1	*methyl-*
2	*ethyl-*
3	*propyl-*
4	*butyl-*
5	*pentyl-*
6	*hexyl-*

Figure 2: *Names of carbon side chains.*

Tip: Naming cycloalkanes is pretty similar to naming alkanes. You just have to add the prefix cyclo- before the stem. So, the molecule below would be cyclopentane.

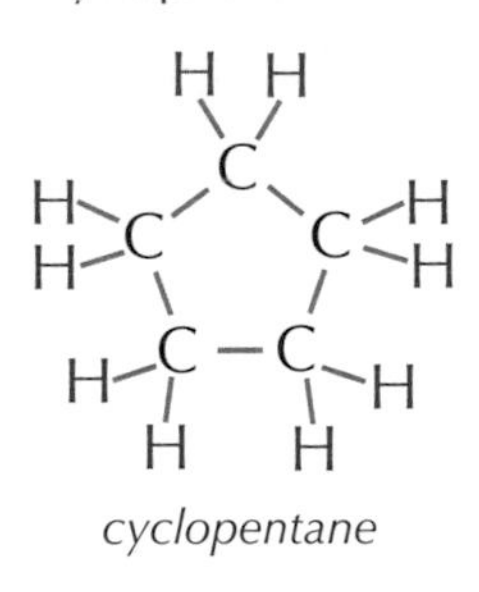

cyclopentane

Example

The longest continuous carbon chain is six carbon atoms, so the stem is hexane.

There are two side chains.

One side chain is a methyl group joined to the 2nd carbon atom: 2-methyl-.

The other is an ethyl group (two carbons) joined to the 4th carbon atom: 4-ethyl-.

Side chains go in alphabetical order, so the alkane is 4-ethyl-2-methylhexane.

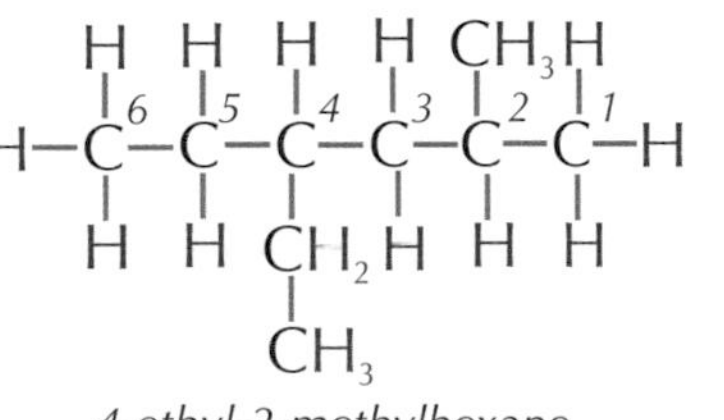

4-ethyl-2-methylhexane

Tip: Always number the carbons in the longest carbon chain so that the carbon with the main functional group attached has the lowest possible number.
If there's more than one longest chain, pick the one with the most side-chains.

If there are two or more side chains of the same type then you add a prefix of di- for two, tri- for three etc.

Example

The longest carbon chain is six atoms long, so the stem is hexane.

There are two methyl groups on the 3rd carbon atom and one methyl on the 5th carbon atom: 3,3,5-trimethyl-.

The alkane is called 3,3,5-trimethylhexane.

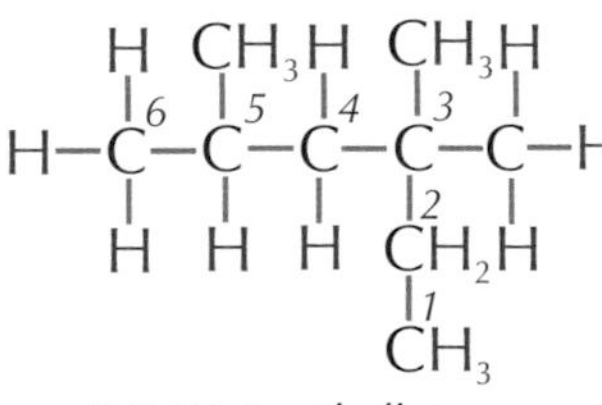

3,3,5-trimethylhexane

Tip: When you're naming molecules you put commas between numbers (e.g. 2,2) and dashes between a number and a letter (e.g. 3-methyl).

Haloalkanes

Haloalkanes are just alkanes where one or more hydrogens have been swapped for a halogen. You name them in exactly the same way that alkanes are named but you have to add in a prefix before the name of the alkane (see Figure 3). The prefixes are always placed in alphabetical order.

Halogen	Prefix
Fluorine	*fluoro-*
Chlorine	*chloro-*
Bromine	*bromo-*
Iodine	*iodo-*

Figure 3: *Prefixes for naming haloalkanes.*

Tip: Always number the carbon chain so that the lowest numbers possible are in the name. For example, the molecule on the right could be named 1-bromo-1-chloro-2,2,2-trifluoroethane but this would have higher numbers in the name, so would be wrong.

Example

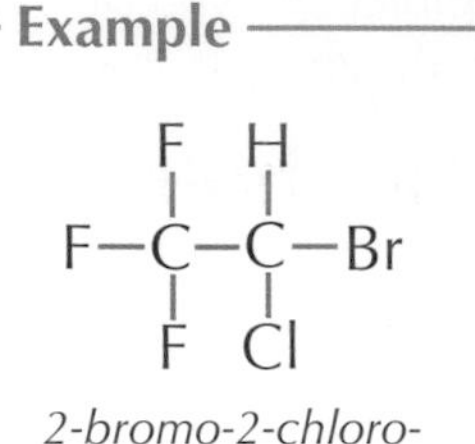

2-bromo-2-chloro-1,1,1-trifluoroethane

There are only two carbon atoms so the stem is ethane.

There's one bromine atom and one chlorine atom attached to the second carbon atom so it has a 2-bromo-2-chloro- prefix.

There are three fluorine atoms attached to the 1st carbon atom so there's a 1,1,1-trifluoro- prefix.

So this is 2-bromo-2-chloro-1,1,1-trifluoroethane.

Alkenes

Alkenes have at least one double bond between carbon atoms in their carbon chain. They're named in the same way as alkanes but the -ane ending is changed to an -ene ending. For alkenes with more than three carbons, you need to say which carbon the double bond starts from.

Tip: In alkenes, you need to use the longest continuous carbon chain containing the carbon-carbon double bond to find the stem of the name.

Example

The longest chain is five carbons, so the stem of the name is pent-.

The functional group is C=C, so it's pentene.

Number the carbons from right to left (so the double bond starts on the lowest possible number). The first carbon in the double bond is carbon 1.

So this molecule is pent-1-ene.

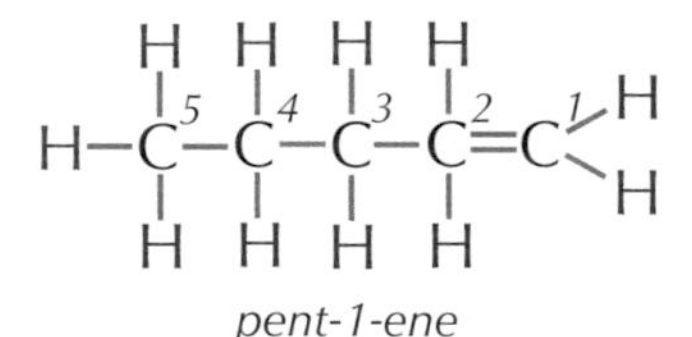

pent-1-ene

If the alkene has two double bonds the suffix becomes diene. The stem of the name usually gets an extra 'a' too (e.g. buta-, penta- not but-, pent-) when there's more than one double bond. And you might see the numbers written first.

Tip: If there's more than one double bond in an alkene the stem comes from the carbon chain that contains the most double bonds (even if it's not the longest chain).

Example

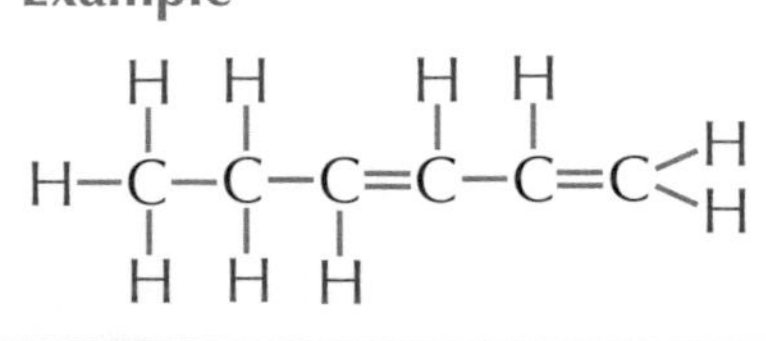

This molecule can be named as hexa-1,3-diene or 1,3-hexadiene.

Alcohols

Alcohols are named using the same IUPAC naming rules found on pages 46-47 but the suffix -ol is added in place of the -e on the end of the name. You also need to indicate which carbon atom the alcohol functional group is attached to — the carbon number(s) comes before the -ol suffix. If there are two –OH groups the molecule is a -diol and if there are three it's a -triol.

Example

The longest continuous carbon chain is three carbon atoms, so the stem is propane.

There's one –OH group attached to the 1st carbon atom so the suffix is -1-ol

There are two methyl groups attached to the 2nd carbon atom so there's a 2,2-dimethyl prefix.

So, the alcohol is called 2,2-dimethylpropan-1-ol.

2,2-dimethylpropan-1-ol

Tip: If the alcohol functional group isn't the most important one in the molecule then you can also use the hydroxy- prefix to name alcohols. For example, the molecule below would be 1-hydroxypropanone.

1-hydroxypropanone

Primary, secondary and tertiary alcohols

An alcohol is primary, secondary or tertiary, depending on which carbon atom the hydroxyl group –OH is bonded to. **Primary alcohols** are given the notation 1° and the –OH group is attached to a carbon with one alkyl group attached (see Figure 4). **Secondary alcohols** are given the notation 2° and the –OH group is attached to a carbon with two alkyl groups attached. **Tertiary alcohols** are given the notation 3° (you can see where I'm going with this) and the –OH group is attached to a carbon with three alkyl groups attached.

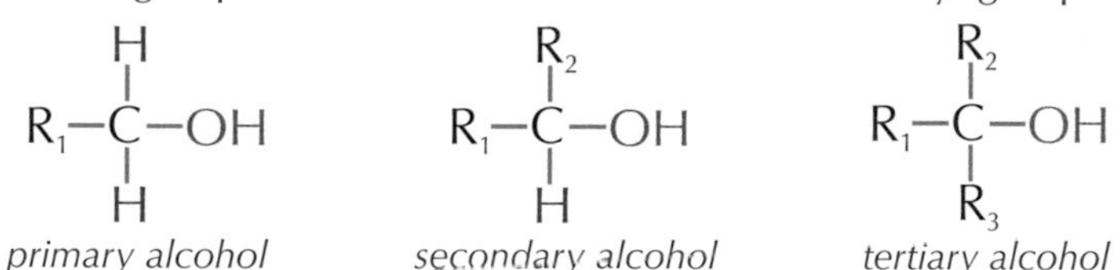

Figure 4: *Diagrams of 1°, 2° and 3° alcohols. R = alkyl group.*

Tip: An alkyl group is just an alkane with one hydrogen taken off, for example CH_3. You can use the letter R to represent an alkyl group in a molecule.

Example

Propan-1-ol is a primary (1°) alcohol because the carbon the –OH group is attached to is only attached to one other alkyl group (CH_3CH_2).

propan-1-ol

Practice Question — Application

Q1 Name the following molecules.

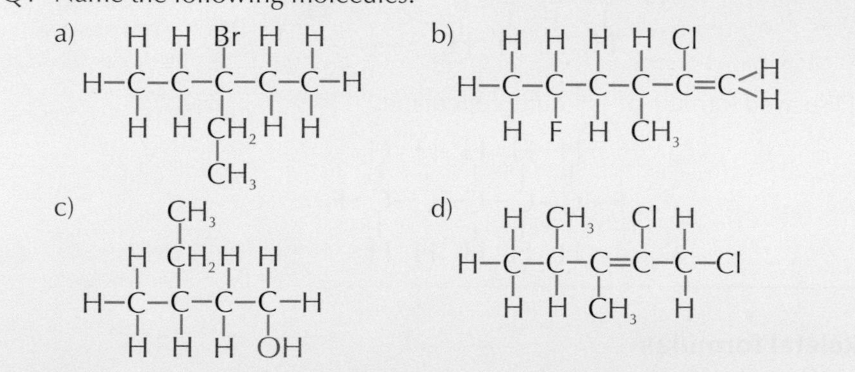

Practice Questions — Fact Recall

Q1 What suffix is used to show that a molecule is an alkane?

Q2 State the prefix used for naming a haloalkane that contains chlorine.

Q3 What is the suffix used to show there's an alcohol functional group?

Q4 What is a primary alcohol?

2. Formulas

Learning Objective:

- Be able to draw the structural formulas and displayed formulas of isomers.

Specification Reference 3.4.4

You've studied most of these types of formulas at AS-Level but you need to know them for your A2 exams too. Don't be tempted to skip over them — they're really important. And look out for skeletal formulas — they're new.

Types of formulas

Molecular formulas

A molecular formula is the actual number of atoms of each element in a molecule.

Examples

Hexene has the molecular formula C_6H_{12} — it's made up of six carbon atoms and 12 hydrogen atoms.

1,5-difluoropentane has the molecular formula $C_5H_{10}F_2$ — it's made up of five carbon atoms, ten hydrogen atoms and two fluorine atoms.

Tip: You can use formulas to work out the functional groups found in a molecule. A functional group is the reactive part of a molecule that gives it its properties. For example, the functional group of a bromoalkane is -Br.

Structural formulas

A structural formula shows the atoms carbon by carbon, with the attached hydrogens and functional groups.

Examples

Hex-1-ene has the structural formula $CH_3CH_2CH_2CH_2CHCH_2$.

1,5-difluoropentane has the structural formula $FCH_2CH_2CH_2CH_2CH_2F$.

Tip: You can show long chains of carbon atoms in structural formulas by using brackets. For example, butane can be written $CH_3CH_2CH_2CH_3$ or $CH_3(CH_2)_2CH_3$.

Displayed formulas

A displayed formula shows how all the atoms are arranged, and all the bonds between them.

Examples

Displayed formula of hex-1-ene:

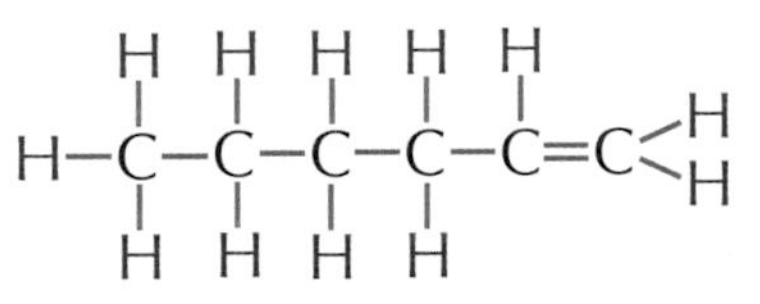

Displayed formula of 1,5-difluoropentane:

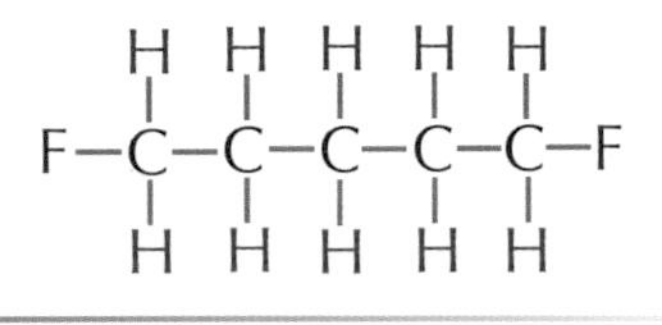

Tip: When you're drawing out displayed formulas make sure you show <u>all</u> the bonds. Writing CH_3 at the end of a bond isn't good enough when you've specifically been asked for a displayed formula. This is how it should be drawn:

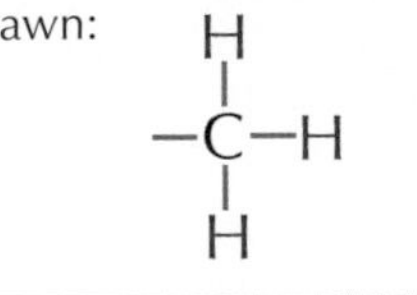

Skeletal formulas

A skeletal formula shows the bonds of the carbon skeleton only, with any functional groups. The hydrogen and carbon atoms aren't shown. This is handy for drawing large complicated structures, like cyclic hydrocarbons. The carbon atoms are found at each junction between bonds and at the end of bonds (unless there's already a functional group there). Skeletal formulas don't show the hydrogen atoms but don't forget about them — each carbon atom has enough hydrogen atoms attached to make the total number of bonds from the carbon up to four.

Examples

Displayed and skeletal formulas of 1,5-difluoropentane:

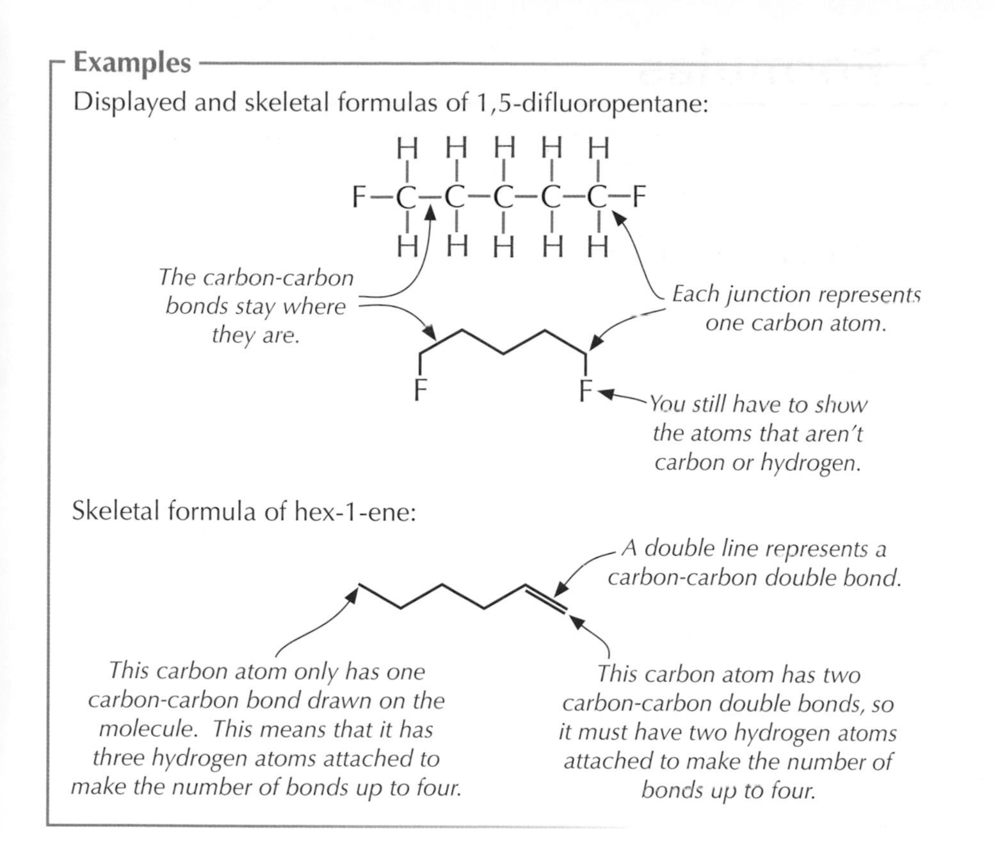

Exam Tip
Skeletal formulas are notoriously difficult to draw in an exam without making any mistakes... If you're not 100% happy with them stick to displayed formulas — you don't want to introduce silly errors into your answers.

Empirical formulas

An empirical formula is the simplest ratio of whole number atoms of each element in a compound. To find the empirical formula you have to divide the molecular formula by the smallest number of atoms for a given element in the molecule. Sometimes the empirical formula will be the same as the molecular formula. This happens when you can't divide the molecular formula by the smallest number of atoms and still end up with whole numbers of atoms.

Examples

Name	Molecular Formula	Divide by...	Empirical Formula
hex-1-ene	C_6H_{12}	6	CH_2
1,5-difluoropentane	$C_5H_{10}F_2$		$C_5H_{10}F_2$
1,2-dichlorohexane	$C_6H_{12}Cl_2$	2	C_3H_6Cl

In the second example in the table, the molecular formula is the same as the empirical formula — you can't divide by the smallest number of atoms for a given element and still get whole numbers.

Tip: Molecular formulas with only one atom of an element in them have to be the empirical formula too — they can't be simplified any further.

C_3H_6O is an empirical formula — there's only 1 oxygen atom.

General formulas and homologous series

A general formula is an algebraic formula that can describe any member of a family of compounds. A homologous series is a bunch of organic compounds which have the same general formula and similar chemical properties. Each member differs by $-CH_2-$.

Exam Tip
You need to make sure you know which type of formula is which. You won't get any marks for writing a structural formula when the examiner wants a displayed one.

Example

The general formula for alkanes is C_nH_{2n+2}. You can use this formula to work out how many hydrogen atoms there are in any alkane if you know the number of carbon atoms. For example...

If an alkane has 2 carbon atoms, n = 2.
This means the alkane will have (2 × 2) + 2 = 6 hydrogen atoms.

If an alkane has 10 carbon atoms, n = 10.
This means the alkane will have (2 × 10) + 2 = 22 hydrogen atoms.

Practice Questions — Application

Q1 Write down the molecular formula of the following compounds:

a) 2-methylpropan-1-ol
b) 1,2,3-trichloropentane
c) hexan-3-one
d) 2-chloro-2,3-dimethylbutane

Tip: An -one suffix shows that the molecule is a ketone. Ketones have the functional group: R—C(=O)—R

Q2 Write down the structural formulas of the molecules in Q1.

Q3 Draw the displayed formula of 3-bromobutan-2-ol.

Tip: Remember to draw out all of the bonds when you're drawing a displayed formula.

Q4 Draw the skeletal formulas of the molecules below:

a) propane
b) 2-methylpentan-3-ol
c) 3-ethyl-2-methylhexane
d) 1-chloroethane

Q5 Write down the names of the molecules below.

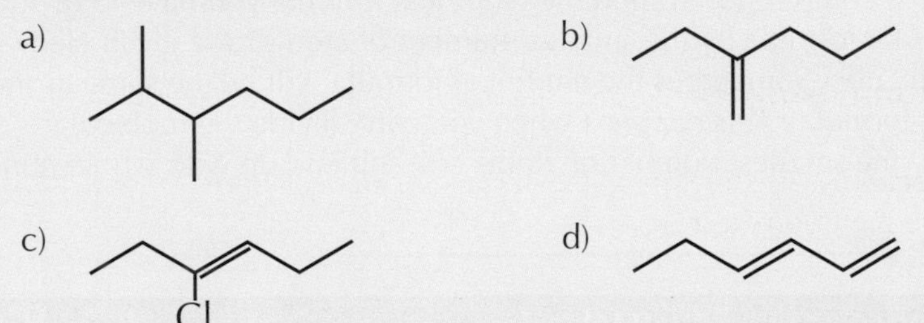

Exam Tip
It's unlikely that you'll be asked to draw a skeletal formula in the exam but you might have to interpret what one means or use one to answer a question so you'd better get good at recognising them.

Q6 Write down the empirical formulas of the following molecules:

a) $C_8H_{16}O_2$
b) $C_2H_4F_2$
c) $C_9H_{17}Cl_3$

Practice Questions — Fact Recall

Q1 What does a structural formula show?
Q2 What does a displayed formula show?
Q3 What is a skeletal formula?
Q4 What is a general formula?

3. Isomers

There was quite a lot on isomers at AS-Level and there's a bit more to learn here. These pages cover everything you need to know about the three different types of structural isomerism, and E/Z-stereoisomerism as well.

Learning Objectives:

- Know and understand the meaning of the term structural isomerism.
- Know that E/Z-isomerism is a form of stereoisomerism.
- Be able to draw the structural formulas and displayed formulas of isomers.

Specification Reference 3.4.4

Structural isomers

In **structural isomers** the atoms are connected in different ways. But they still have the same molecular formula. There are three types of structural isomers — chain isomers, position isomers and functional group isomers.

1. Chain isomers

Chain isomers have different arrangements of the carbon skeleton. Some are straight chains and others are branched in different ways.

Example

There are different chain isomers of C_6H_{14}. The diagrams below show the straight chain isomer hexane and a branched chain isomer 2,3-dimethylbutane.

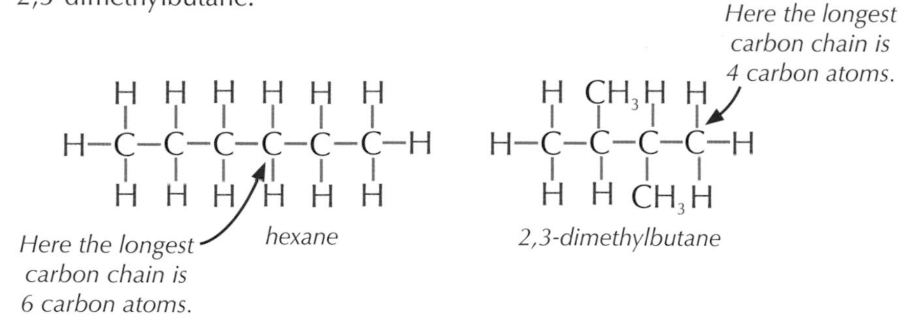

Tip: You could draw isomers using skeletal formulas instead of displayed formulas, for example:

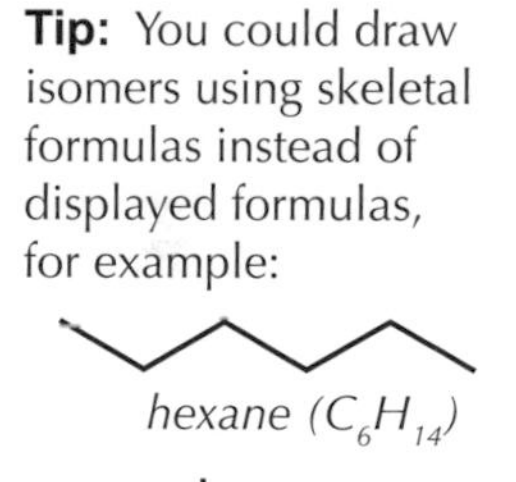

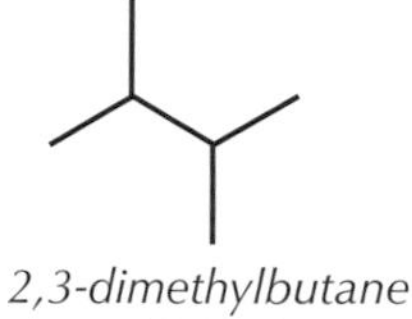

2. Positional isomers

Positional isomers have the same skeleton and the same atoms or groups of atoms attached. The difference is that the atom or group of atoms is attached to a different carbon atom.

Example

There are two position isomers of C_4H_9Br. The bromine atom is attached to different carbon atoms in each isomer.

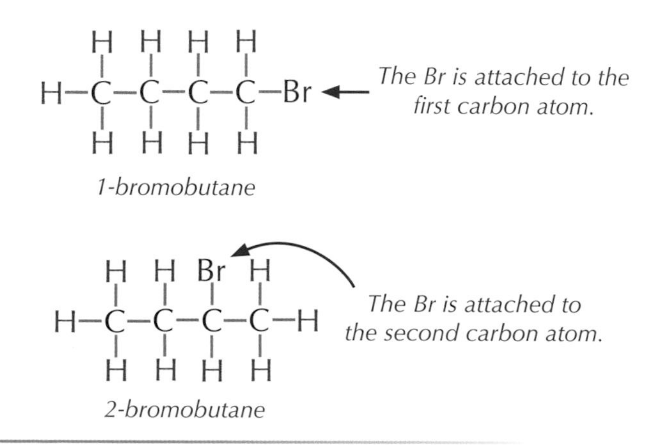

Tip: Always number the carbon atoms in a molecule — it makes it easier to name them and identify isomers:

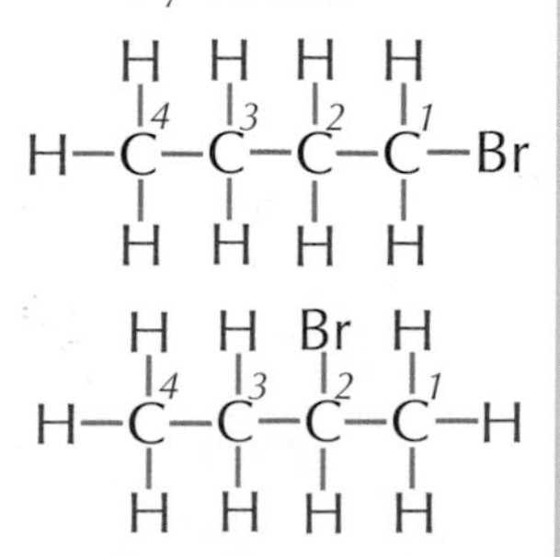

3. Functional group isomers

Functional group isomers have the same atoms arranged into different functional groups.

Example

The formulas below show two functional group isomers of C_3H_6O.

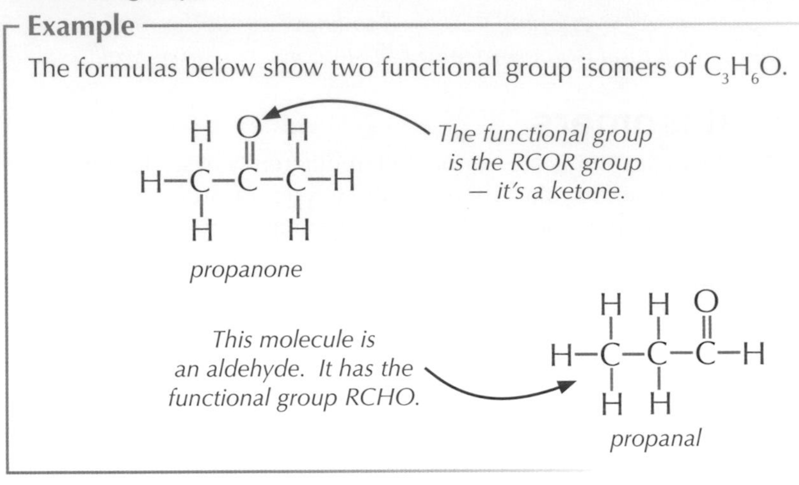

Exam Tip
E/Z-isomerism is one type of stereoisomerism that you have to know for your exam, but you also need to know about optical isomerism. That's covered on pages 56-60.

Stereoisomers

Stereoisomers have the same structural formula but a different arrangement of atoms in space. You can twist and rotate a molecule any way you like around a single bond. But a double bond has a fixed position — you can't rotate the rest of the molecule around it. Because of the lack of rotation around the double bond, some alkenes have E/Z-isomers. E/Z-isomers occur when each double-bonded carbon atom has two different atoms or groups attached to it. Then you get an '**E-isomer**' and a '**Z-isomer**'.

The E-isomer is the one that has the highest priority groups across the double bond from each other. The Z-isomer is the one which has the highest priority groups both above or both below the double bond (see Figure 1).

Tip: The group with the highest priority is the one that has the highest molecular mass. For example, CH_2CH_3 will be higher priority than a CH_3 group.

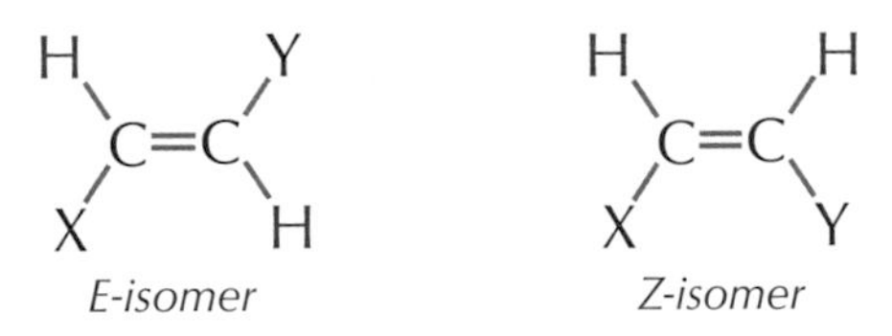

Figure 1: *E- and Z-isomers. In these diagrams X and Y are the largest groups.*

Example

In 1,2-dibromoethene ($C_2H_2Br_2$), both of the double-bonded carbon atoms have an H and a Br group attached to them.

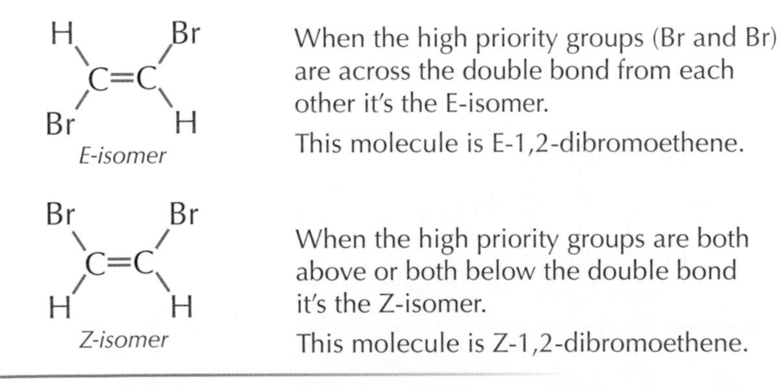

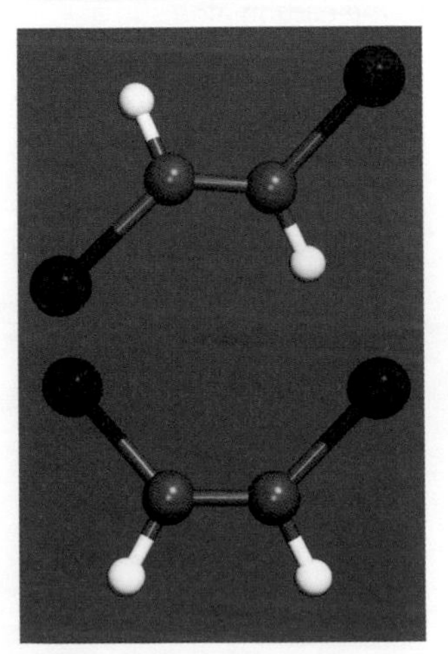

Figure 2: *E-isomer (top) and Z-isomer (bottom) of 1,2-dibromoethene.*

Practice Questions — Application

Q1 Draw three different chain isomers of C_6H_{14}.

Q2 State the type of isomerism shown in the following pairs of molecules.

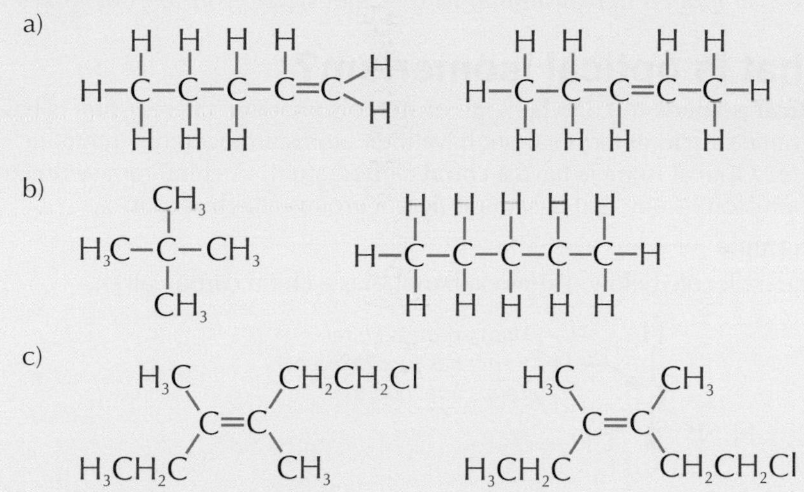

Q3 Draw one functional group isomer of butanone.
The structure of butanone is shown below.

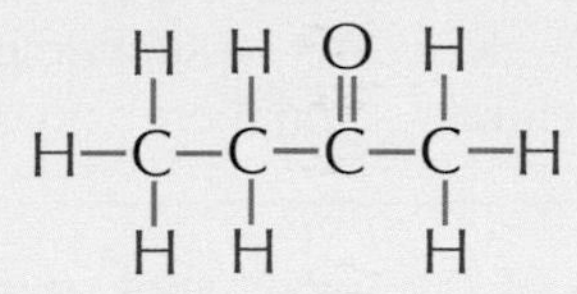

Q4 State whether the following molecules are E-isomers or Z-isomers.

Q5 Draw the E- and Z-stereoisomers of the following molecule.

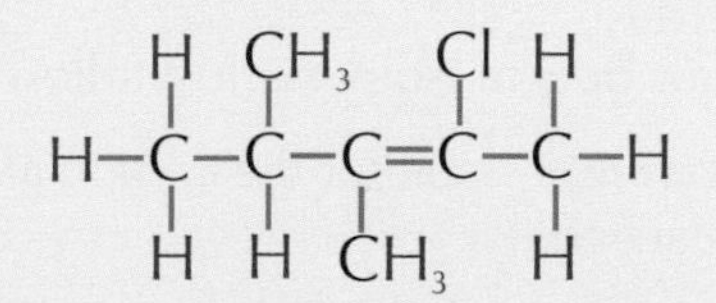

Practice Questions — Fact Recall

Q1 What is a chain isomer?

Q2 What is a stereoisomer?

Q3 When do you get E-/Z-isomerism in a molecule? Explain your answer.

Exam Tip
You don't always have to draw all of the bonds when you're drawing a molecule. Writing CH_3 or NH_2 next to a bond is just as good as drawing out all the bonds — unless you've been asked for a displayed formula that is.

Tip: When you're drawing functional group isomers you need to double check that you've put in exactly the same number of each type of atom — it's very easy to miscount hydrogen atoms.

Exam Tip
If you're asked to give the full IUPAC name of E- and Z-isomers in the exam don't forget to put E- or Z- at the front. You'll lose easy marks if you don't.

4. Optical Isomerism

There's more on isomers coming up in this topic. If you're struggling to get your head around all the different types of isomers try and find some molecular models to play around with — they'll help you sort out what's what.

Learning Objectives:

- Know that optical isomerism is a form of stereoisomerism.
- Know that an asymmetric carbon atom is chiral and gives rise to optical isomers which exist as non super-imposable mirror images and differ only in their effect on plane polarised light.
- Understand the meaning of the terms enantiomer and racemate.
- Understand why racemates are formed.
- Appreciate that drug action may be determined by the stereochemistry of the molecule and that different optical isomers may have very different effects.

Specification Reference 3.4.4

Tip: Stereochemistry is just the relative positions of atoms and groups of atoms in space.

What is optical isomerism?

Optical isomerism is another type of **stereoisomerism**. Stereoisomers have the same structural formula, but have their atoms arranged differently in space. Optical isomers have a **chiral** carbon atom. A chiral (or asymmetric) carbon atom is one that has four different groups attached to it.

Example

The molecule below, 1-aminoethanol, has a chiral carbon atom.

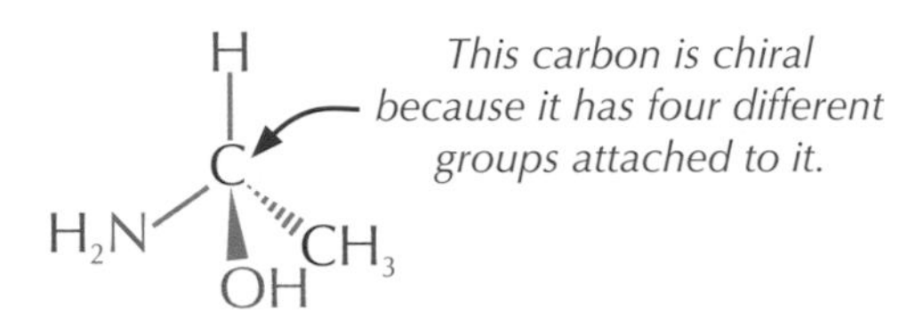

It's possible to arrange the groups in two different ways around chiral carbon atoms so that two different molecules are made — these molecules are called **enantiomers** or optical isomers. The enantiomers are mirror images and no matter which way you turn them, they can't be superimposed. (If molecules can be superimposed, they're **achiral** — and there's no optical isomerism.)

Example

Here are the two enantiomers of 1-aminoethanol. It doesn't matter how many times you turn and twist them, they can't be superimposed.

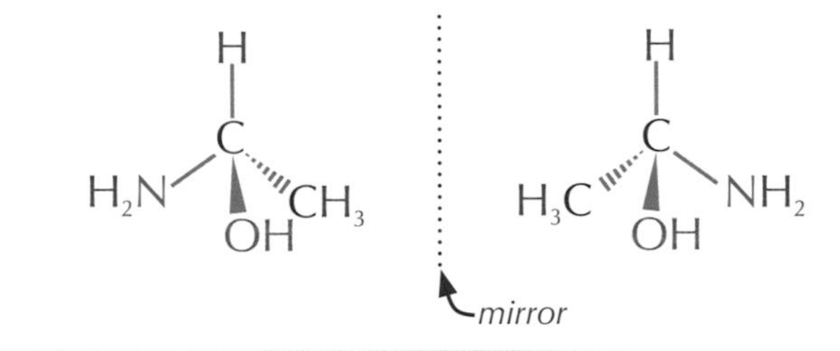

You have to be able to draw optical isomers. Just follow these steps each time:

1. Locate the chiral centre — look for the carbon atom with four different groups attached.
2. Draw one enantiomer in a tetrahedral shape — put the chiral carbon atom at the centre and the four different groups in a tetrahedral shape around it. Don't try to draw the full structure of each group — it gets confusing.
3. Draw the mirror image of the enantiomer — put in a mirror line next to the enantiomer and then draw the mirror image of the enantiomer on the other side of it.

Don't panic. There are some examples coming up on the next page to help you get to grips with this.

Figure 1: *Left handed and right handed scissors. These pairs of scissors are mirror images of each other — look closely and you'll see that they can't be superimposed on each other.*

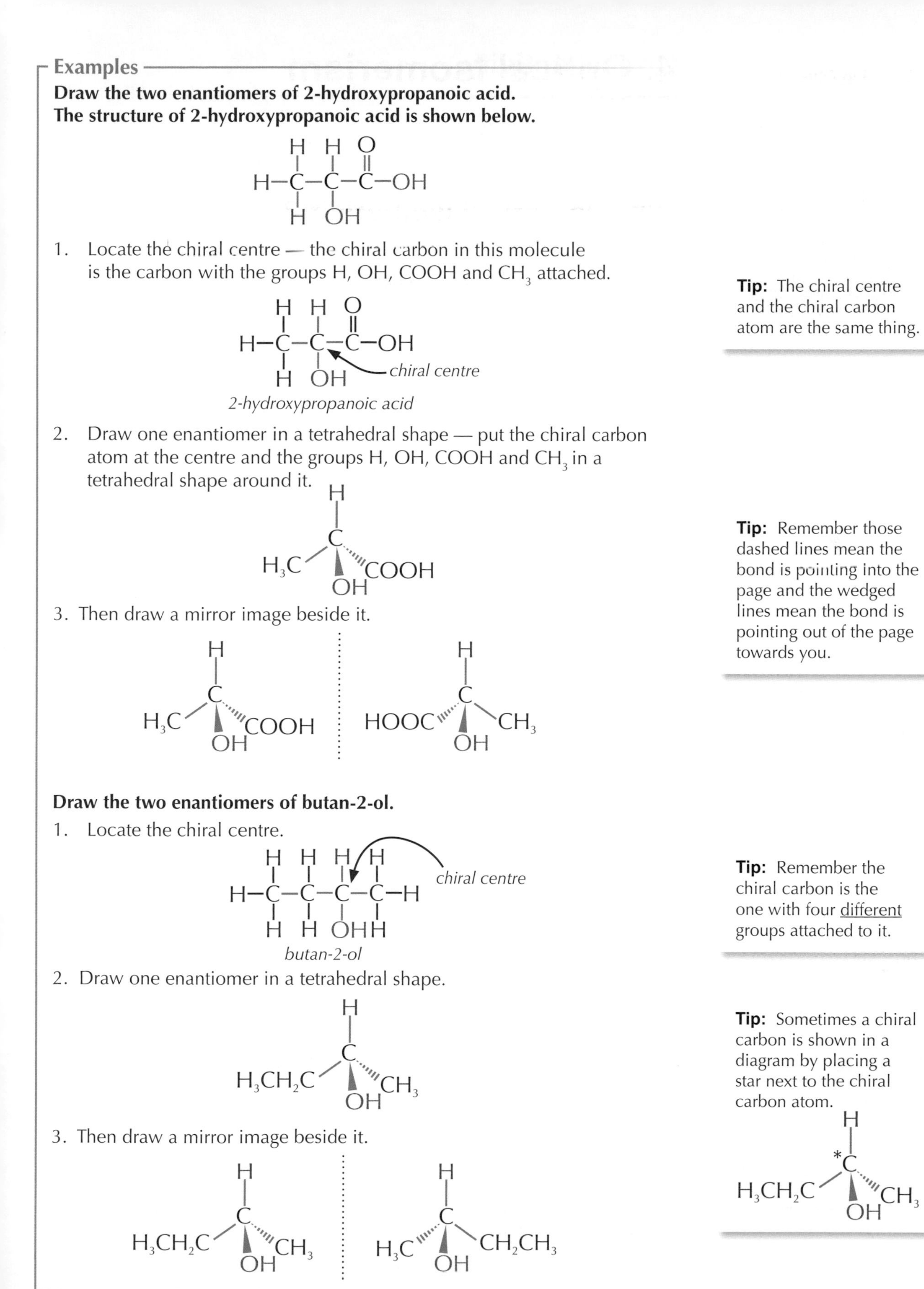

Examples

Draw the two enantiomers of 2-hydroxypropanoic acid.
The structure of 2-hydroxypropanoic acid is shown below.

1. Locate the chiral centre — the chiral carbon in this molecule is the carbon with the groups H, OH, COOH and CH_3 attached.

2-hydroxypropanoic acid

2. Draw one enantiomer in a tetrahedral shape — put the chiral carbon atom at the centre and the groups H, OH, COOH and CH_3 in a tetrahedral shape around it.

3. Then draw a mirror image beside it.

Tip: The chiral centre and the chiral carbon atom are the same thing.

Tip: Remember those dashed lines mean the bond is pointing into the page and the wedged lines mean the bond is pointing out of the page towards you.

Draw the two enantiomers of butan-2-ol.

1. Locate the chiral centre.

butan-2-ol

2. Draw one enantiomer in a tetrahedral shape.

3. Then draw a mirror image beside it.

Tip: Remember the chiral carbon is the one with four <u>different</u> groups attached to it.

Tip: Sometimes a chiral carbon is shown in a diagram by placing a star next to the chiral carbon atom.

Figure 2: *Etienne Malus. The French physicist who developed the idea of plane-polarised light.*

Optical activity

Optical isomers are optically active — they rotate **plane-polarised light**.

Plane-polarised light

Normal light vibrates in all directions — some of it vibrates up and down, some of it vibrates side to side and some wiggles all over the place. If normal light is passed through a polarising filter it becomes plane-polarised, this means all the light is vibrating in the same plane (for example, only up and down or only side to side).

Rotation of plane-polarised light

When you pass plane-polarised light through an optically active mixture, the molecules interact with the light and rotate the plane of the vibration of the light. The two enantiomers of an optically active molecule will rotate the plane-polarised light in opposite directions. One enantiomer rotates it in a clockwise direction, and the other rotates it in an anticlockwise direction.

Exam Tip
Don't worry, you won't need to give all this detail about vibrations in the exam. All you need to know is that optical isomers are optically active and will rotate plane-polarised light.

Racemates

A **racemate** (or racemic mixture) contains equal quantities of each enantiomer of an optically active compound. Racemates don't show any optical activity — the two enantiomers cancel each other's light-rotating effect. Chemists often react two achiral things together and get a racemic mixture of a chiral product. This is because when two molecules react there's an equal chance of forming each of the enantiomers.

Examples

Here's the reaction between butane and chlorine:

H_3CH_2C–C(H)(H)–CH_3 + Cl_2 ⟶ **HCl** + H–C(H)(H)–C(H)(H)–C(Cl)(H)–C(H)(H)–H

butane *2-chlorobutane*

A chlorine atom replaces one of the H groups, to give 2-chlorobutane. Either of the H's directly attached to the central carbon can be replaced, so the reaction produces a mixture of the two possible enantiomers.

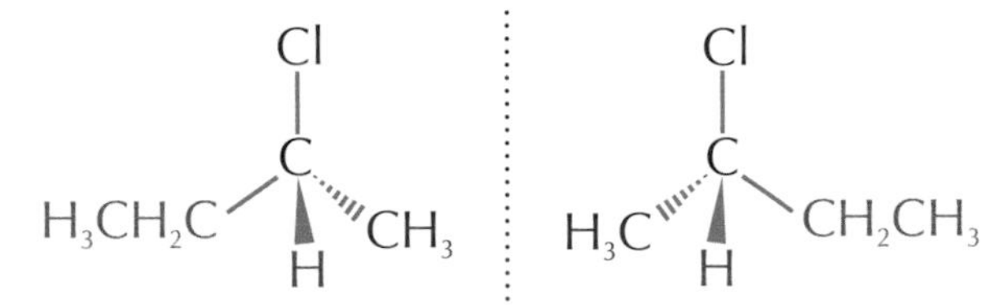

Each hydrogen has a fifty-fifty chance of being replaced, so the two optical isomers are formed in equal amounts — you get a racemic mixture.

Here's the reaction between propanal and HCN. The nitrile group adds to the carbonyl group to form 2-hydroxybutanenitrile.

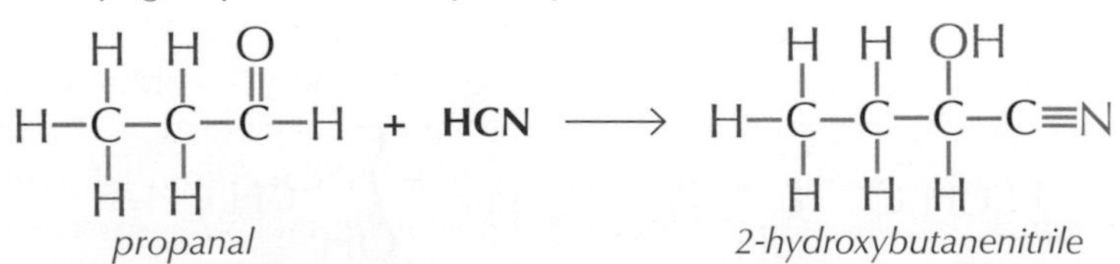

Tip: Butane is achiral because it doesn't have four <u>different</u> groups attached to the central carbon atom — two of the groups are hydrogen atoms.

Tip: Not all reactions that produce chiral compounds will produce racemates. Sometimes one enantiomer will be favoured over another enantiomer and you'll get an <u>enantiomerically pure product</u> — a product that contains only one enantiomer.

2-hydroxybutanenitrile has two enantiomers (shown below). They are equally likely to form via this reaction and so the two enantiomers are formed in equal amounts — you get a racemic mixture.

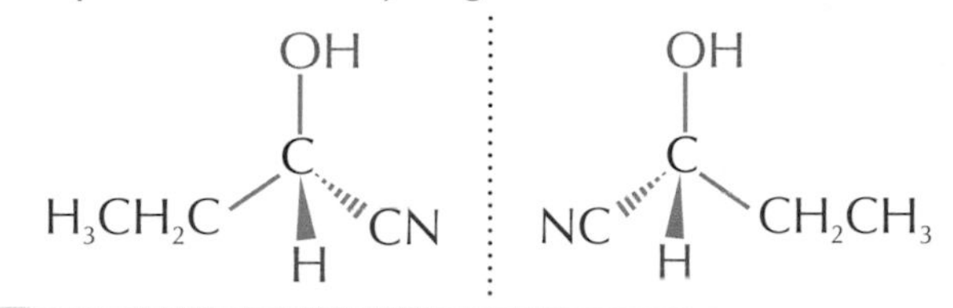

You can modify a reaction to produce a single enantiomer using chemical methods, but it's difficult and expensive.

Pharmaceutical drugs

Drugs work by changing chemical reactions that are taking place in the body. Most drugs do this by binding to an active site — usually on an enzyme or a specific receptor molecule. A drug must be exactly the right shape to fit into the correct active site — only one enantiomer will do. The other enantiomer could fit into a different enzyme, and might cause harmful side-effects or have no effect at all.

It's still sometimes possible to use a racemic mixture of the drug to treat patients. However, the patient may have to take double the dose to achieve the same effect as taking an enantiomerically pure version of the drug. There are some benefits to using racemic mixtures as drugs though — there's no need to separate out the enantiomeric products, which will reduce the difficulty and cost of producing the drug.

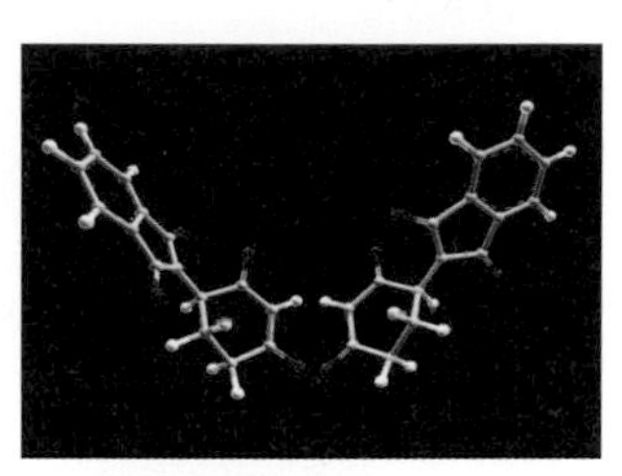

Figure 3: *The two enantiomers of thalidomide. One enantiomer is an effective anti-sickness drug, the other can cause birth defects.*

Example

Thalidomide is an example of a drug whose optical isomers have different effects.

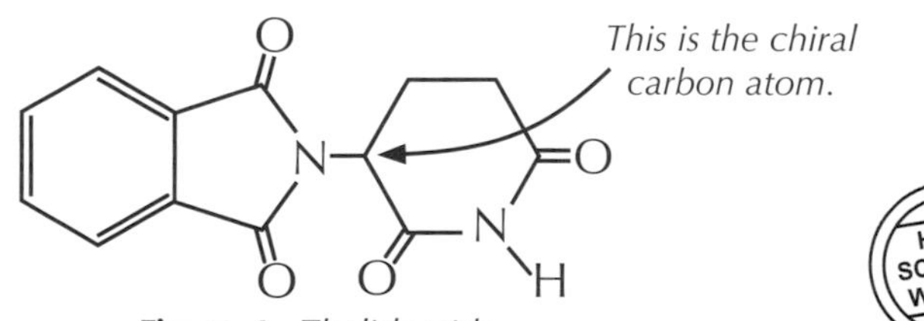

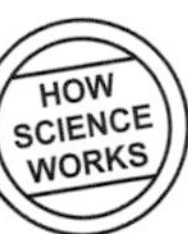

Figure 4: *Thalidomide.*

Thalidomide was developed in the 1950s as a sedative drug. Early tests seemed to show that it had few side effects, and so it was launched as a prescription drug. Thalidomide also proved to be an effective anti-sickness drug. It was widely prescribed to pregnant women in the late 1950s and early 1960s to combat morning sickness. At the same time babies began to be born with malformed limbs — thalidomide was shown to be causing these symptoms, and its use was banned.

The drug had not been tested thoroughly enough, particularly in relation to its possible effects on the developing foetus. Further studies demonstrated that the two optical isomers have different effects in the body. One is an effective anti-sickness drug. The other can cause birth defects. In this case even if a pure dose of the safe isomer is given, the body will convert some of it to the harmful isomer. More recent research has shown that thalidomide can be useful for treating other diseases, such as some types of cancer. Patients can now be treated with thalidomide, but very strict controls are in place to ensure that it is never taken by anyone who is pregnant.

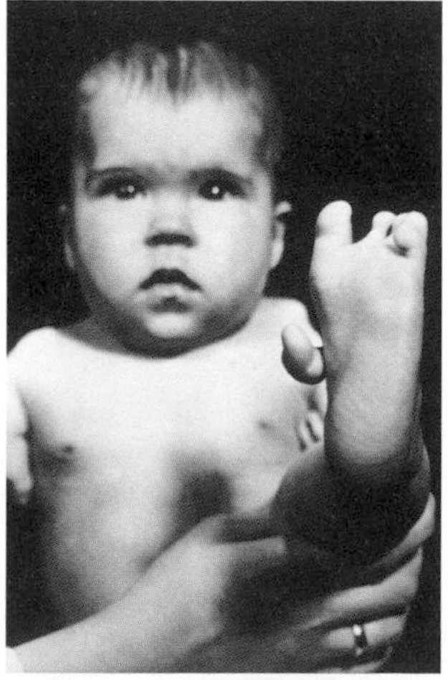

Figure 5: *Toddler with a deformed foot. This birth defect resulted from the drug thalidomide.*

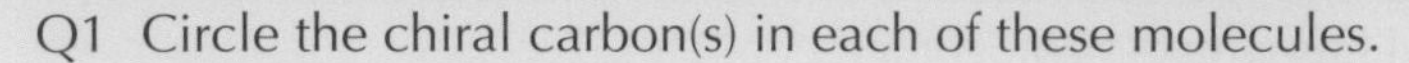

Practice Questions — Application

Q1 Circle the chiral carbon(s) in each of these molecules.

a) b)

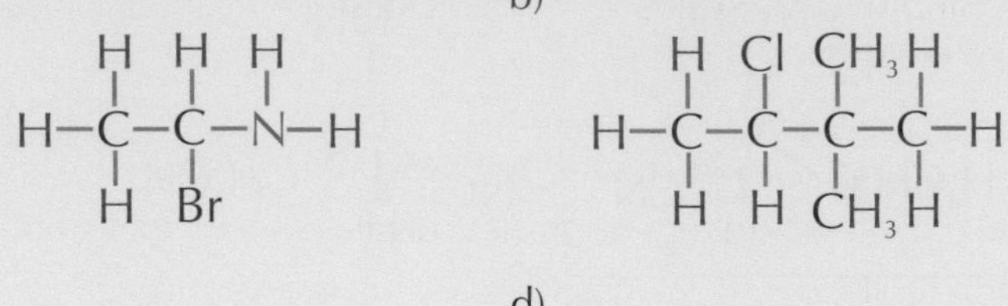

c) d)

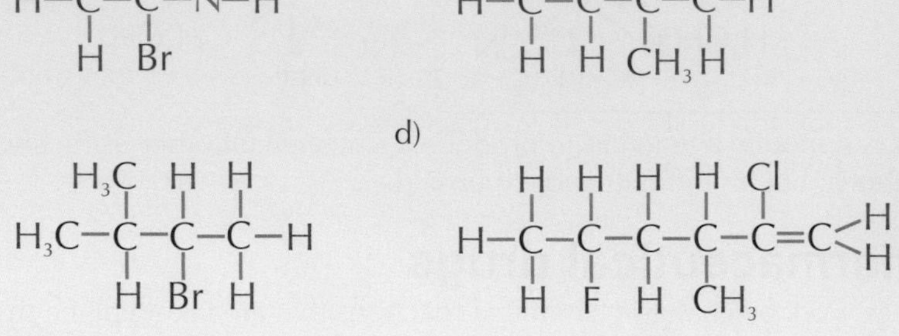

Q2 Draw the two enantiomers of the following molecules.

a) b)

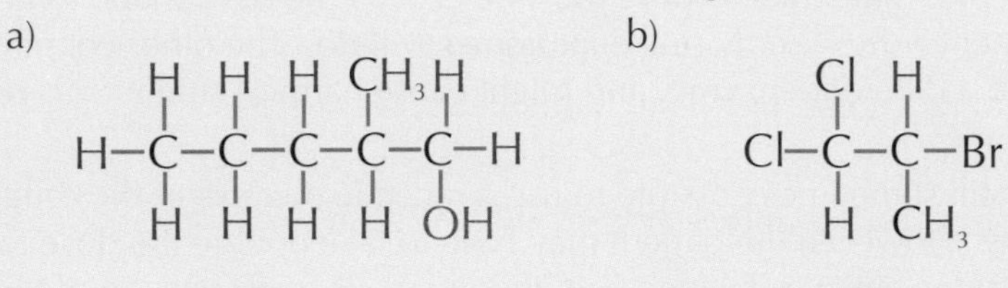

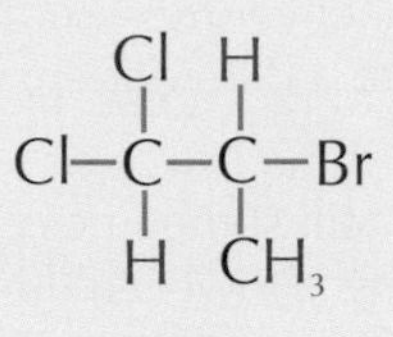

c) d)

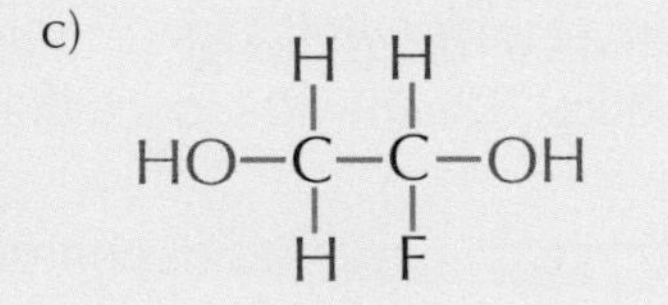

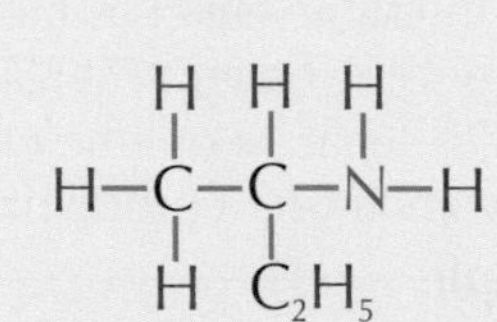

Tip: When you're drawing out the enantiomers for molecules just write out the structural formula of each group — don't try and draw the displayed formula for each one or your diagram will become too confusing.

Q3 Here is an equation for the reaction between butanone and HCN.

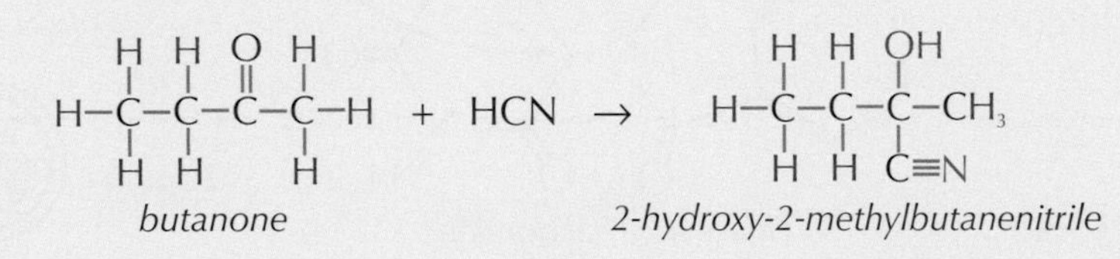

butanone *2-hydroxy-2-methylbutanenitrile*

Draw the two optical isomers that can be formed via this reaction.

Practice Questions — Fact Recall

Q1 What is optical isomerism?

Q2 What is a chiral carbon?

Q3 What does it mean if a molecule is 'optically active'?

Q4 Explain why racemic mixtures are not optically active.

Q5 Explain why it is important that some drugs consist of only one enantiomer.

Q6 Give an example of a drug that has a different effect on the body depending on which enantiomer you use.

Section Summary

Make sure you know...

- How to apply IUPAC rules for nomenclature to alkanes, haloalkanes, alkenes and alcohols, limited to chains with up to 6 carbon atoms.
- What molecular formulas, structural formulas, displayed formulas, skeletal formulas, empirical formulas, general formulas and homologous series are.
- How to draw the structural formulas, displayed formulas and skeletal formulas of isomers.
- That structural isomers have the same molecular formula as each other but that their atoms are connected in different ways.
- That chain isomers, positional isomers and functional group isomers are all types of structural isomers.
- How to recognise and draw chain isomers, positional isomers and functional group isomers.
- That stereoisomers are molecules with the same structural formula but that their atoms have a different arrangement in space.
- That E/Z- isomerism is a form of stereoisomerism.
- How to recognise, draw and name E- and Z-isomers.
- That optical isomerism is a form of stereoisomerism.
- That chiral carbon atoms are carbon atoms with four different groups attached, and that optical isomers have chiral carbon atoms.
- That enantiomers (optical isomers) are molecules with a chiral carbon atom and the same structural formula that exist as non super-imposable mirror images.
- How to draw optical isomers.
- That enantiomers rotate plane-polarised light in opposite directions.
- That a racemic mixture contains equal quantities of each enantiomer of an optically active compound.
- That racemic mixtures are optically inactive.
- That different enantiomers may have different effects on the body so some drugs need to be enantiomerically pure.

Exam-style Questions

1 Molecule **A** will react with bromine gas to produce molecule **B**.
The reaction is shown below.

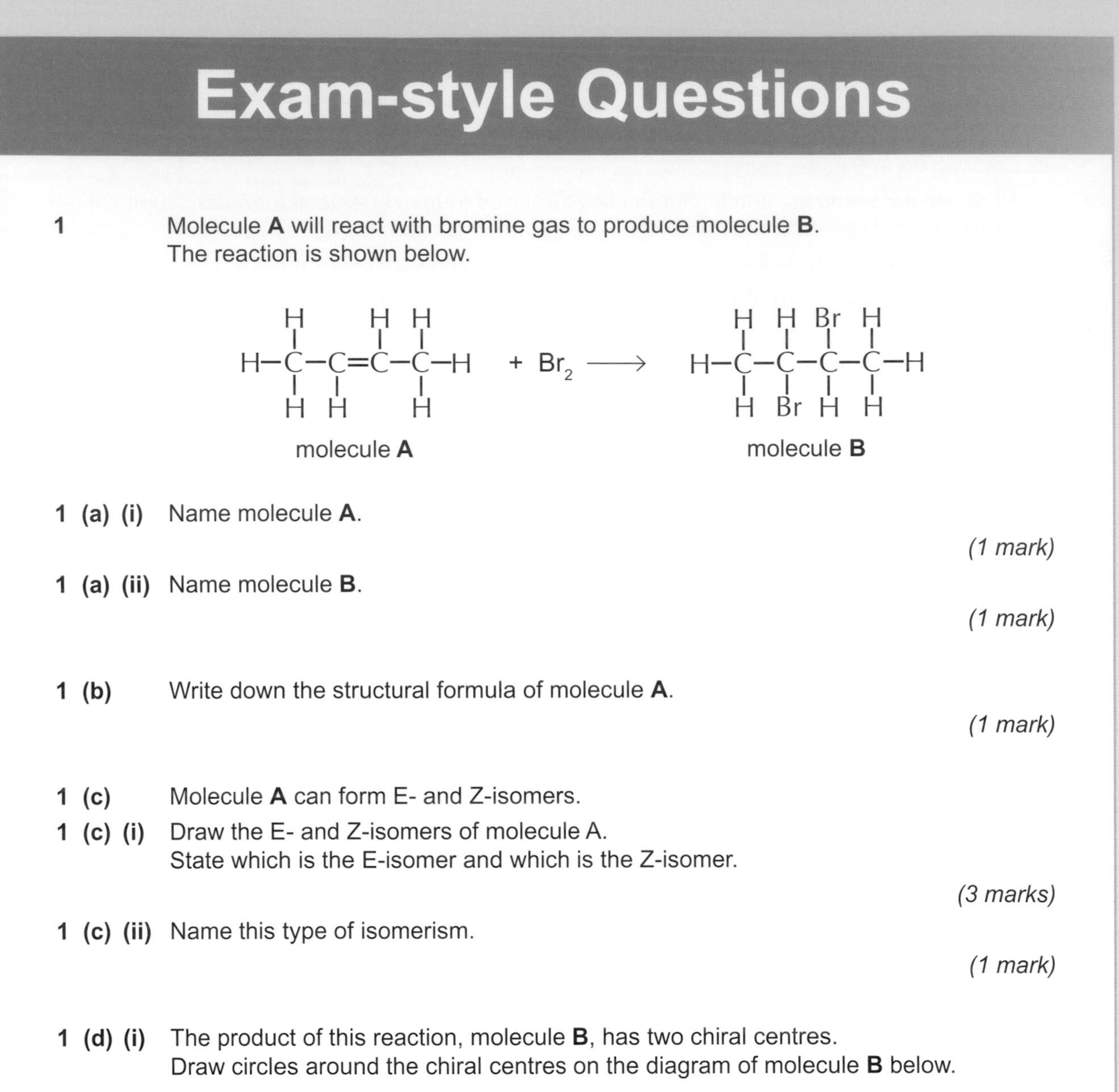

molecule **A** molecule **B**

1 (a) (i) Name molecule **A**.

(1 mark)

1 (a) (ii) Name molecule **B**.

(1 mark)

1 (b) Write down the structural formula of molecule **A**.

(1 mark)

1 (c) Molecule **A** can form E- and Z-isomers.

1 (c) (i) Draw the E- and Z-isomers of molecule A.
State which is the E-isomer and which is the Z-isomer.

(3 marks)

1 (c) (ii) Name this type of isomerism.

(1 mark)

1 (d) (i) The product of this reaction, molecule **B**, has two chiral centres.
Draw circles around the chiral centres on the diagram of molecule **B** below.

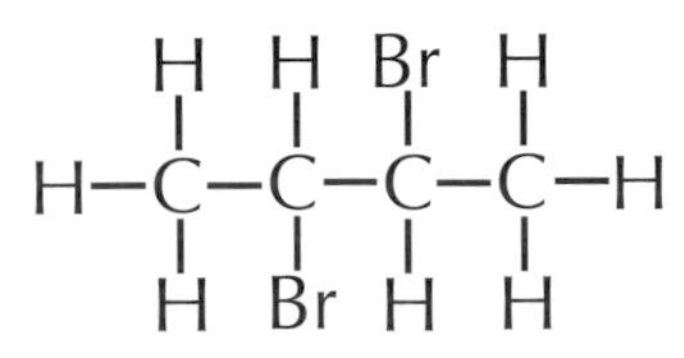

(2 marks)

1 (d) (ii) Draw two enantiomers of molecule **B**.

(2 marks)

2 (a) Draw the displayed formula of 2,4-dibromohex-3-ene.

(1 mark)

2 (b) Write down the structural formula of 2,4-dibromohex-3-ene.

(1 mark)

2 (c) 2,4-dibromohex-3-ene contains two different forms of stereoisomerism.

2 (c) (i) What is a stereoisomer?

(1 mark)

2 (c) (ii) Draw two optical isomers and two E/Z-isomers of 2,4-dibromohex-3-ene.

(4 marks)

3 Optical isomerism is a type of stereoisomerism involving chiral carbon atoms.

3 (a) What is a chiral carbon atom?

(1 mark)

3 (b) Molecule **X** contains one chiral carbon atom.
The structure of molecule **X** is shown below.

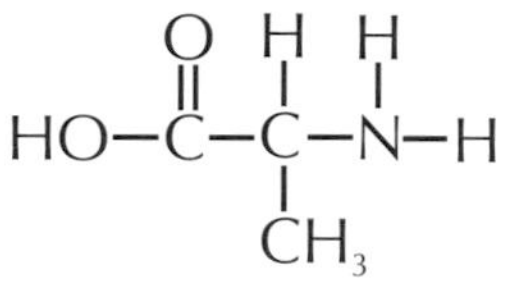

```
     O  H  H
     ‖  |  |
HO—C—C—N—H
        |
        CH3
```

molecule **X**

Draw the two enantiomers of molecule **X** by locating the chiral carbon atom.

(2 marks)

3 (c) The enantiomers of **X** are optically active.

3 (c) (i) Explain what the term 'optically active' means.

(1 mark)

3 (c) (ii) Explain why the product of a reaction to produce molecule **X** might not be optically active.

(3 marks)

3 (d) Identify the molecules below that would have optical isomers.

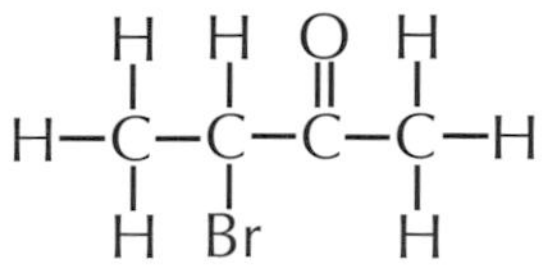

```
  H  H  O  H
  |  |  ‖  |
H—C—C—C—C—H
  |  |     |
  H  Br    H
```

molecule **A**

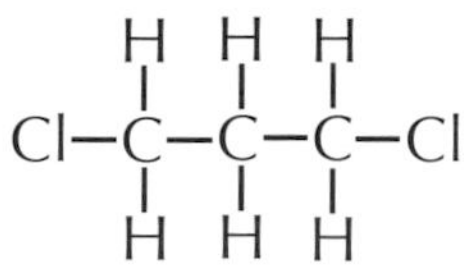

```
   H  H  H
   |  |  |
Cl—C—C—C—Cl
   |  |  |
   H  H  H
```

molecule **B**

```
  H  H  O  H  H
  |  |  ‖  |  |
H—C—C—C—C—C—H
  |  |     |  |
  H  Br    F  H
```

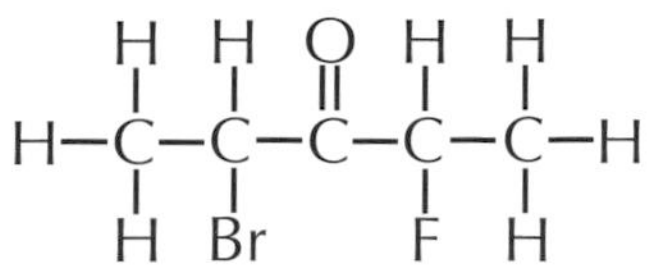

molecule **C**

(2 marks)

4 Escitalopram and citalopram are widely available antidepressant drugs. Citalopram is a racemic mixture and escitalopram is an enantiomerically pure form of citalopram. The structure of escitalopram is shown below.

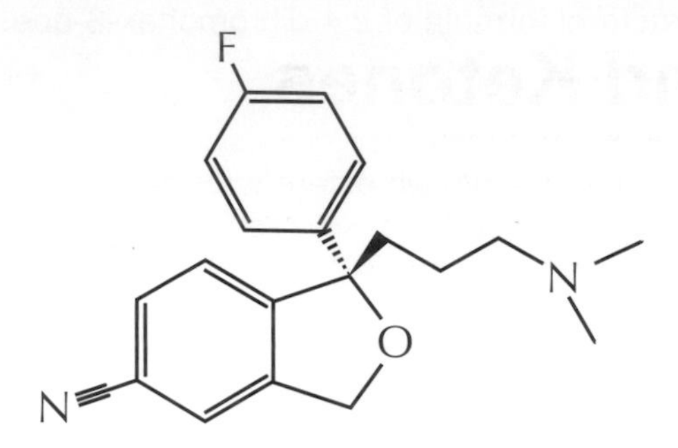

escitalopram

4 (a) Explain what the terms racemic mixture and enantiomer mean.

(2 marks)

4 (b) Both enantiomers of this compound can be used in antidepressant drugs. Give two reasons why, for many pharmaceutical drugs, only one enantiomer is present in the drug.

(2 marks)

4 (c) How could you identify escitalopram from citalopram if given a sample of both?

(2 marks)

4 (d) Escitalopram can be synthesised via the precursor molecule shown below.

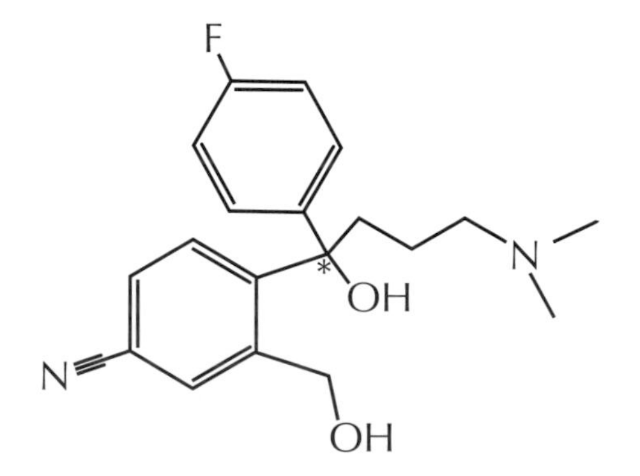

precursor molecule

Explain why the starred carbon in the molecule is chiral.

(1 mark)

1. Aldehydes and Ketones

Aldehydes and ketones are compounds that are made by oxidising alcohols. Aldehydes are made by oxidising primary alcohols and ketones are made by oxidising secondary alcohols. You met aldehydes and ketones at AS-level, but now it's time to cover them in a bit more detail.

Learning Objectives:
- Be able to apply IUPAC rules for naming aldehydes and ketones.
- Know that aldehydes are readily oxidised to carboxylic acids and that this forms the basis of a simple chemical test to distinguish between aldehydes and ketones (e.g. Fehling's solution and Tollens' reagent).
- Know that aldehydes can be reduced to primary alcohols and ketones to secondary alcohols using reducing agents such as $NaBH_4$ (mechanisms are required).

Specification Reference 3.4.4, 3.4.5

What are aldehydes and ketones?

Aldehydes and **ketones** are both **carbonyl compounds** as they both contain the carbonyl functional group, C=O. The difference is, they've got their carbonyl groups in different positions. Aldehydes have their carbonyl group at the end of the carbon chain. Ketones have their carbonyl group in the middle of the carbon chain, see Figure 1.

Figure 1: *The difference between an aldehyde and a ketone. 'R' represents a carbon chain of any length.*

Nomenclature

Before you can study aldehydes and ketones you need to know how to name them. Aldehydes have the suffix -al. You don't have to say which carbon the functional group is on — it's always on carbon-1. Naming aldehydes follows very similar rules to the naming of alcohols (see pages 48-49).

Tip: This is all a recap of stuff you learnt at AS-level so if it's not looking familiar, you might want to have a look back at your AS notes.

Example

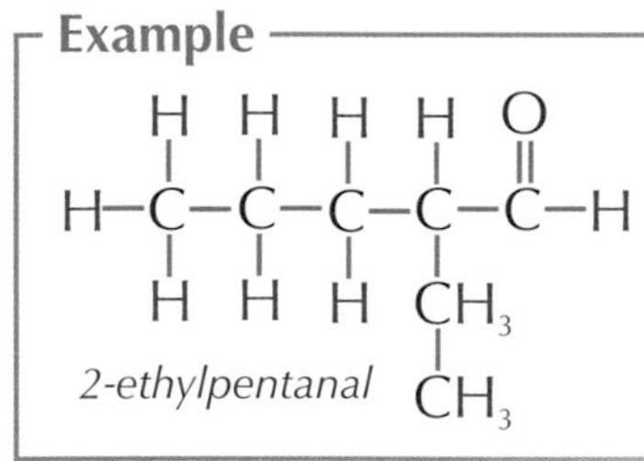

The longest carbon chain containing the aldehyde functional group is 5 carbon atoms, so the stem is pentane.

There's an ethyl- group attached to the second carbon atom so there's a 2-ethyl- prefix.

So, the aldehyde is called 2-ethylpentanal.

The suffix for ketones is -one. For ketones with five or more carbons, you always have to say which carbon the functional group is on. (If there are other groups attached, such as methyl groups, you have to say it for four-carbon ketones too.)

Example

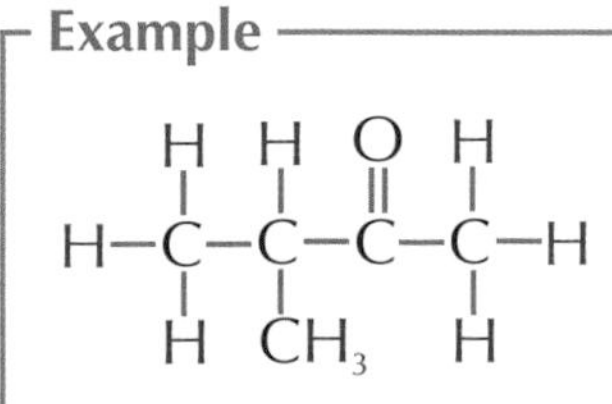

The longest continuous carbon chain is 4 carbon atoms, so the stem is butane.

The carbonyl is found on the second carbon atom and there is a methyl group on the third carbon.

So, the ketone is called 3-methylbutan-2-one.

Tip: When naming ketones, the carbonyl group is the highest priority, so you always number the carbons from the end that means the carbonyl group carbon has the lowest number.

Testing for aldehydes and ketones

Tip: Remember — oxidation is the loss of electrons and reduction is the gain of electrons. See page 169 for more on oxidation and reduction.

Tip: In these equations [O] is used to represent an oxidising agent.

There are a few tests to distinguish between aldehydes and ketones. They all work on the idea that an aldehyde can be easily oxidised to a carboxylic acid, but a ketone can't. Aldehydes can be easily oxidised to carboxylic acids because there's a hydrogen attached to the carbonyl group:

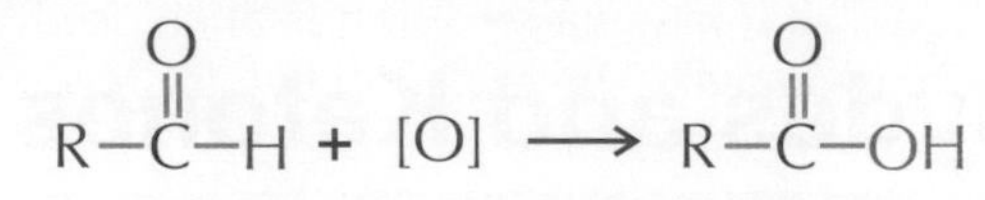

The only way to oxidise a ketone would be to break a carbon-carbon bond so ketones are not easily oxidised:

$$R-C(=O)-R + [O] \longrightarrow \text{Nothing happens}$$

As an aldehyde is oxidised, another compound is reduced — so a reagent is used that changes colour as it's reduced. There are three main reagents that can be used to distinguish between aldehydes and ketones — Tollens' reagent, Fehling's solution and Benedict's solution.

Tollens' reagent

Tollens' reagent is a colourless solution of silver nitrate dissolved in aqueous ammonia. If it's heated in a test tube with an aldehyde, a silver mirror forms after a few minutes (see Figure 2). As the aldehyde is oxidised, the diaminesilver ions in the Tollens' reagent are reduced, producing silver and ammonia:

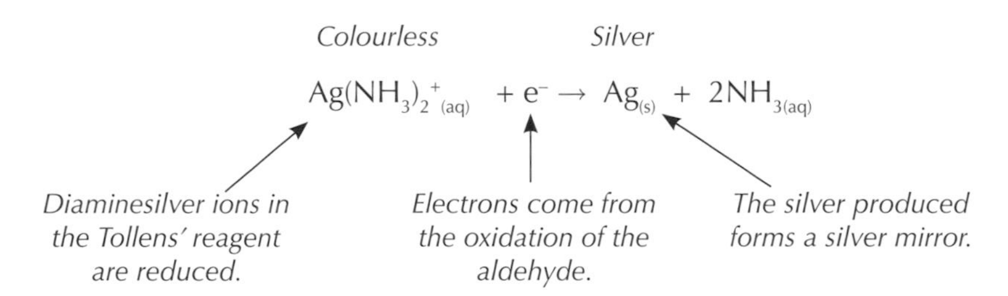

Figure 2: Tollens' reagent. The test-tube on the left shows the unreacted Tollens' reagent. The test-tube on the right shows the result of a reaction with an aldehyde.

Aldehydes and ketones are flammable, so they must be heated in a water bath rather than over a flame.

Fehling's solution or Benedict's solution

Fehling's solution is a blue solution of complexed copper(II) ions dissolved in sodium hydroxide. If it's heated with an aldehyde the copper(II) ions are reduced to a brick-red precipitate of copper(I) oxide (see Figure 3):

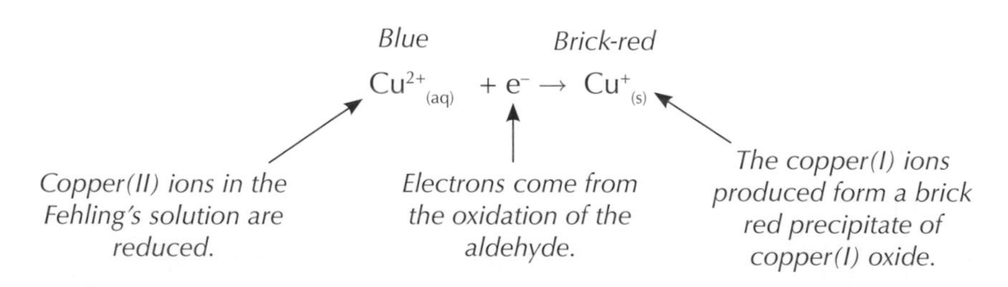

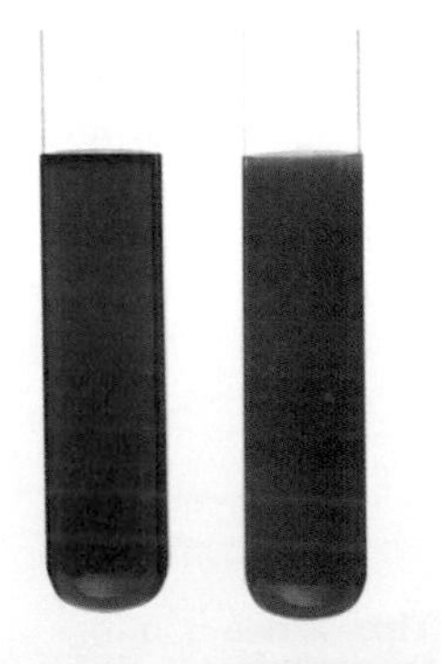

Figure 3: Fehling's solution. The test-tube on the left shows the unreacted Fehling's solution. The test-tube on the right shows the result of the reaction of Fehling's solution with an aldehyde.

Benedict's solution is exactly the same as Fehling's solution except the copper(II) ions are dissolved in sodium carbonate instead. You still get a brick-red precipitate of copper(I) oxide though.

Reducing aldehydes and ketones

In AS Chemistry you saw how primary alcohols can be oxidised to produce aldehydes and carboxylic acids, and how secondary alcohols can be oxidised to make ketones. Using a reducing agent you can reverse these reactions. $NaBH_4$ (sodium tetrahydridoborate(III) or sodium borohydride) is usually the reducing agent used. But in equations, [H] is often used to indicate a hydrogen from a reducing agent. The equation below shows the reduction of an aldehyde to a primary alcohol:

$$R{-}\overset{\overset{\displaystyle O}{\|}}{C}{-}H + 2[H] \longrightarrow R{-}\overset{\overset{\displaystyle OH}{|}}{\underset{\underset{\displaystyle H}{|}}{C}}{-}H$$

And here's the reduction of a ketone to a secondary alcohol:

$$R{-}\overset{\overset{\displaystyle O}{\|}}{C}{-}R + 2[H] \longrightarrow R{-}\overset{\overset{\displaystyle OH}{|}}{\underset{\underset{\displaystyle H}{|}}{C}}{-}R$$

Figure 4: $NaBH_4$ *powder. This is dissolved in water with methanol to produce a commonly used reducing agent.*

Exam Tip
When you're writing equations like this in an exam make sure you balance the [H]'s as well as the molecules.

Nucleophilic addition reactions

You need to understand the reaction mechanisms for the reduction of aldehydes and ketones back to alcohols. These are **nucleophilic addition** reactions — a H^- ion from the reducing agent acts as a nucleophile and adds on to the δ^+ carbon atom of a carbonyl group. You haven't covered nucleophilic addition reactions before so here's the mechanism...

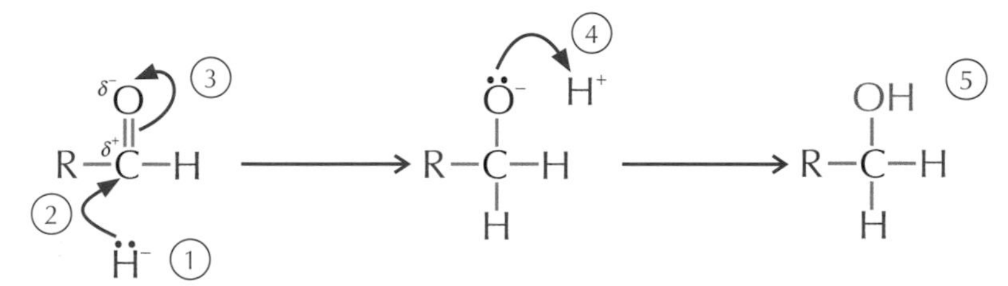

Tip: In reaction mechanisms, the curly arrows show the movement of an electron pair.

1. The C=O bond is polar so the $C^{\delta+}$ attracts the negatively charged lone pair of electrons on the H^- ion.
2. The H^- ion attacks the slightly positive carbon atom and donates its lone pair of electrons forming a bond with the carbon.
3. As carbon can only have 4 bonds, the addition of the H^- ion causes one of the carbon-oxygen bonds to break. This forces a lone pair of electrons from the C=O double bond onto the oxygen.
4. The oxygen donates its lone pair of electrons to a H^+ ion (this H^+ ion usually comes from water but sometimes a weak acid is added as a source of H^+).
5. A primary alcohol is produced.

The mechanism for the reduction of a ketone is the same as for an aldehyde — you just get a secondary alcohol at the end instead of a primary alcohol:

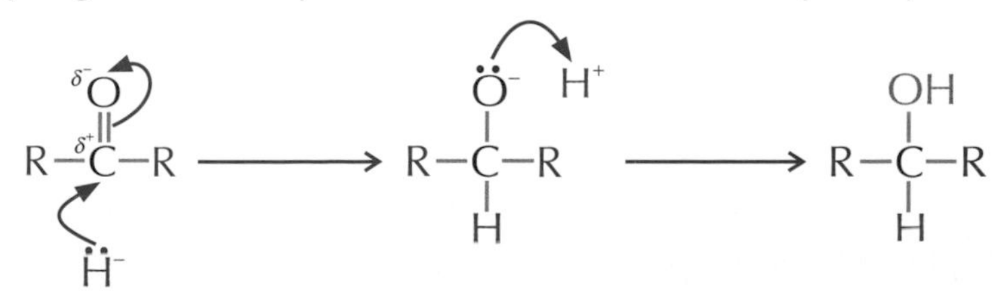

Exam Tip
You need to be able to draw the mechanism for the reduction of any aldehyde or ketone — so make sure you understand all the steps of these nucleophilic addition reactions.

This reaction mechanism can be applied to any aldehyde or ketone.

Examples

Propanal can be reduced to propan-1-ol:

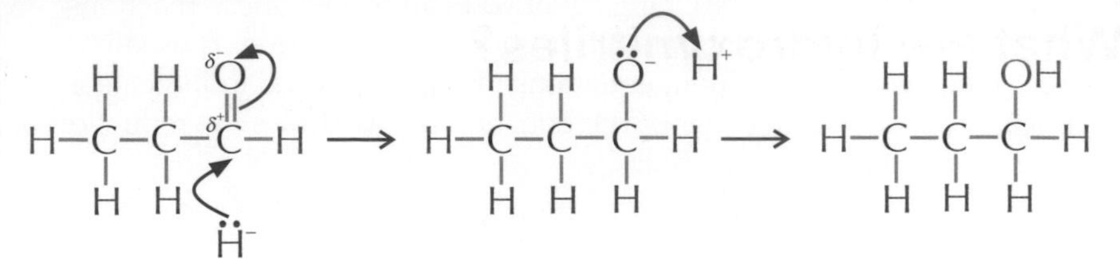

Butanone can be reduced to butan-2-ol:

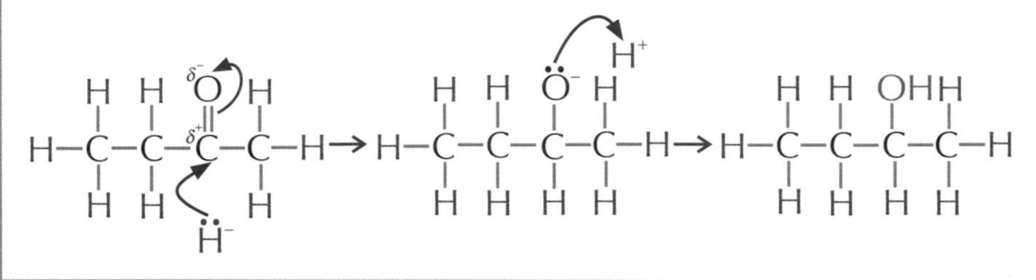

Exam Tip
You must draw the curly arrows coming from the lone pair of electrons. If you don't — you won't get the marks for the mechanism in the exam.

Practice Questions — Application

Q1 Name these molecules:

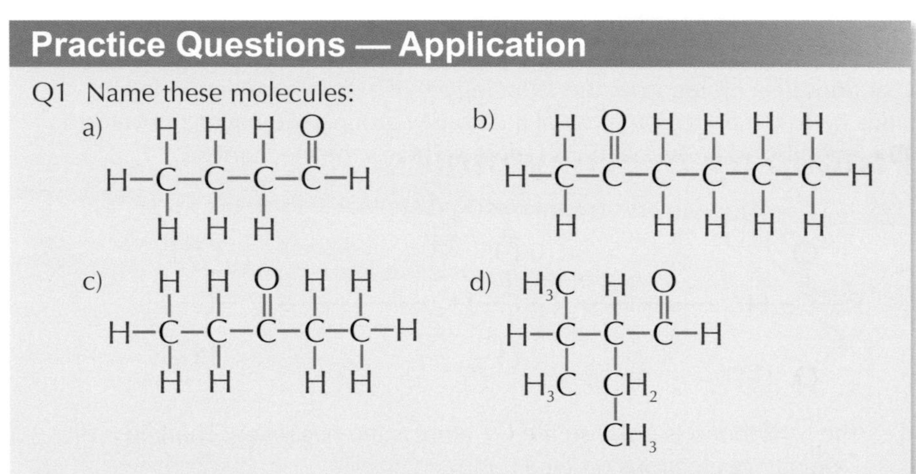

Q2 Draw the mechanisms for the reduction of each molecule in Q1 to an alcohol.

Q3 Write an equation for the reduction of pentan-2-one to pentan-2-ol. Use [H] to represent a reducing agent.

Tip: Don't forget — aldehydes are reduced to primary alcohols and ketones are reduced to secondary alcohols.

Practice Questions — Fact Recall

Q1 What is the difference between an aldehyde and a ketone?

Q2 What type of compound is produced when an aldehyde is oxidised?

Q3 Explain why ketones cannot be easily oxidised.

Q4 Describe what you would observe if you used the following to distinguish between an aldehyde and a ketone:

a) Tollens' reagent.

b) Fehling's solution.

Q5 Identify a reducing agent which could be used to reduce an aldehyde to a primary alcohol.

Tip: Sometimes you might see primary, secondary and tertiary alcohols written as 1°, 2° and 3° alcohols.

2. Hydroxynitriles

Aldehydes and ketones can be used to produce another set of molecules known as hydroxynitriles.

What are hydroxynitriles?

Hydroxynitriles are molecules which contain a hydroxyl group (OH) and a nitrile group (CN) — see Figure 1.

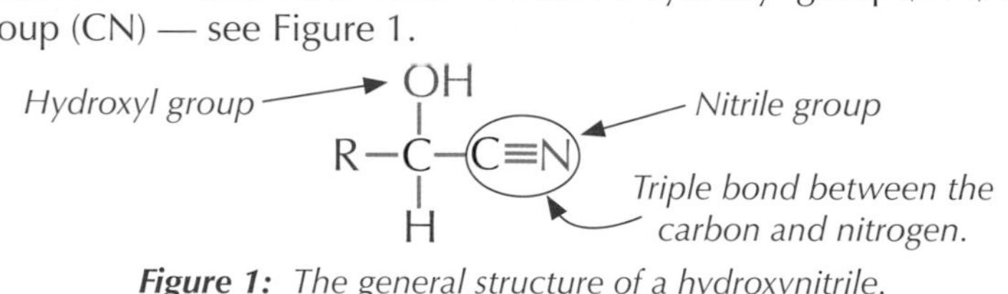

***Figure 1:** The general structure of a hydroxynitrile.*

When naming hydroxynitriles the nitrile group is the most important so the suffix is -nitrile and the carbon that's attached to the nitrogen is always carbon-1. There's also a hydroxy- prefix because of the OH group. After that naming hydroxynitriles is just the same as naming any other compound.

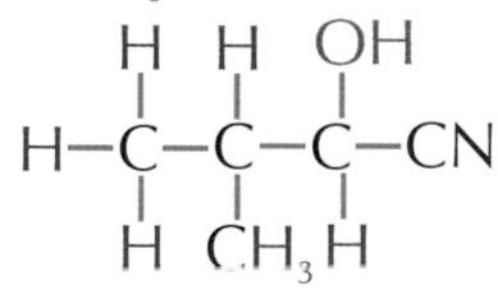

The longest continuous carbon chain is 4 carbon atoms, so the stem is butane. The OH group is on carbon-2 and there is a methyl group on carbon-3. So, this is 2-hydroxy-3-methylbutanenitrile.

Producing hydroxynitriles

Hydroxynitriles can be produced by reacting aldehydes or ketones with hydrogen cyanide (HCN). This is another example of a nucleophilic addition reaction — a nucleophile attacks the molecule, causing an extra group to be added. Here's the mechanism for the reaction:

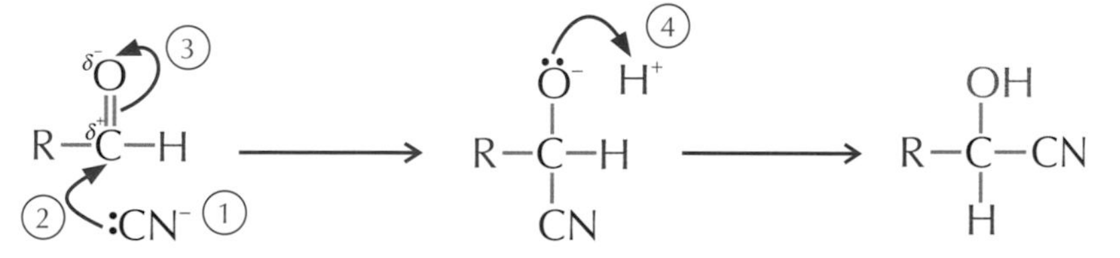

1. Hydrogen cyanide's a weak acid — it partially dissociates in water to form H^+ ions and CN^- ions: $HCN \rightleftharpoons H^+ + CN^-$.
2. The CN^- ion from the HCN attacks the partially positive carbon atom and donates a pair of electrons forming a bond with the carbon.
3. A pair of electrons from the C=O double bond is pushed onto the oxygen.
4. The oxygen bonds to a H^+ ion (from either hydrogen cyanide or water) to form the hydroxyl group (OH) and a hydroxynitrile is produced.

Example

Propanone and HCN react to form 2-hydroxy-2-methylpropanenitrile. The mechanism for this reaction is shown below:

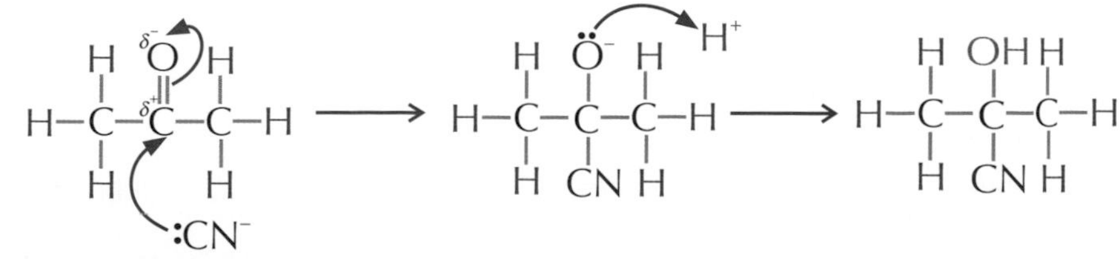

Learning Objectives:
- Be able to apply IUPAC rules for naming hydroxynitriles.
- Understand the mechanism of the reaction of carbonyl compounds with HCN as a further example of nucleophilic addition producing hydroxynitriles.
- Be able to appreciate the hazards of synthesis using HCN/KCN.

Specification Reference 3.4.4, 3.4.5

Tip: When you're naming hydroxynitriles don't forget to count the carbon atom found in the nitrile group as carbon-1.

Tip: This mechanism is exactly the same as the nucleophilic addition mechanism on page 67, except we're using CN^- instead of H^-.

Exam Tip
Don't forget to add a negative sign to the oxygen after step three.

Exam Tip
In the exam, you could be asked to apply this mechanism to show how any aldehyde or ketone reacts with HCN.

Figure 2: Warning labels on the bottles of chemicals warn you if a chemical is dangerous.

Exam Tip
You need to learn the risks associated with using HCN and why KCN is usually used instead.

Risk assessments

A **risk assessment** involves reviewing the hazards of the reacting chemicals, the products and any conditions needed, such as heat. You don't have to wrap yourself in cotton wool, but you do have to take all reasonable precautions to reduce the risk of an accident.

Example

Here's a bit of a risk assessment for reacting hydrogen cyanide with a carbonyl compound:

Hydrogen cyanide (HCN) is an extremely toxic gas. So to reduce the risk, potassium cyanide (KCN) is used instead. KCN is also toxic but it can be stored more safely. Acidified potassium cyanide is used for the reaction to supply both the CN^- ions and the H^+ ions needed. However, the reaction should still be done in a fume cupboard as there is still a risk of some HCN gas being released from the solution. Also, the organic compounds are flammable, so if you need to heat them use a water bath or electric mantle.

Practice Questions — Application

Q1 a) Draw the structure of the hydroxynitrile that would be produced if 2-methylpropanal was reacted with HCN. The structure of 2-methylpropanal is shown below:

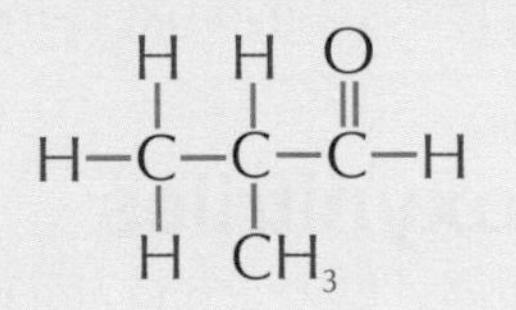

b) Draw the mechanism for this reaction.

Q2 The diagram below shows a hydroxynitrile:

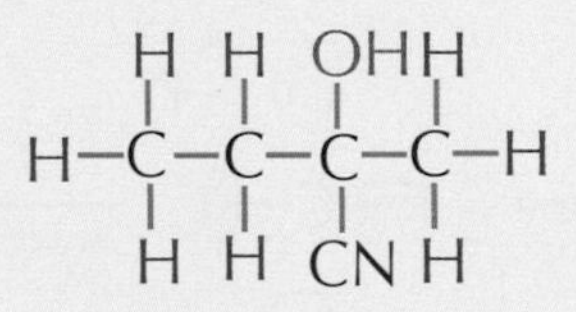

a) Name this hydroxynitrile.

b) Draw the structure of the carbonyl compound that could be used to produce this hydroxynitrile.

c) Name this carbonyl compound.

d) Draw the mechanism for the production of this hydroxynitrile.

Practice Questions — Fact Recall

Q1 What is a hydroxynitrile?

Q2 Name the mechanism for the production of hydroxynitriles from carbonyl compounds and HCN.

Q3 a) What is a risk assessment?

b) Explain why risk assessments are important.

Q4 Scientists often use KCN in place of HCN when producing hydroxynitriles. Explain why.

3. Carboxylic Acids and Esters

Carboxylic acids and esters are two more types of carbonyl compound that you need to know about for A2-level chemistry. Read on to learn all about them.

Learning Objectives:

- Be able to apply IUPAC rules for naming carboxylic acids and esters.
- Know that carboxylic acids are weak acids but will liberate CO_2 from carbonates.
- Know that carboxylic acids and alcohols react, in the presence of a strong acid catalyst, to give esters.

Specification Reference 3.4.4, 3.4.5

What are carboxylic acids?

Carboxylic acids contain the carboxyl functional group –COOH.

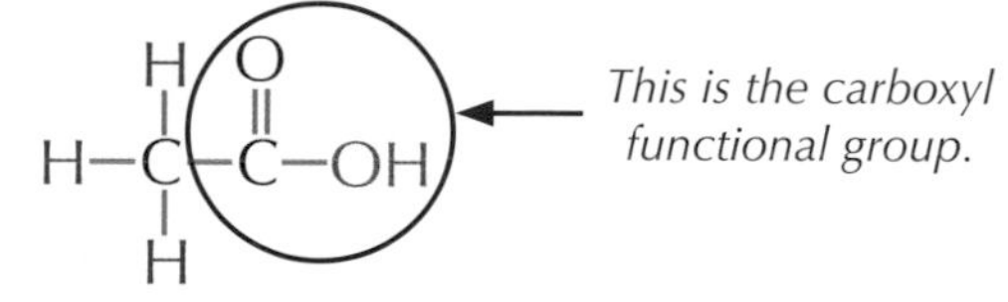

To name them, you find and name the longest alkane chain, take off the 'e' and add '–oic acid'. The carboxyl group is always at the end of the molecule and when naming it's more important than other functional groups — so all the other functional groups in the molecule are numbered starting from this carbon.

Example

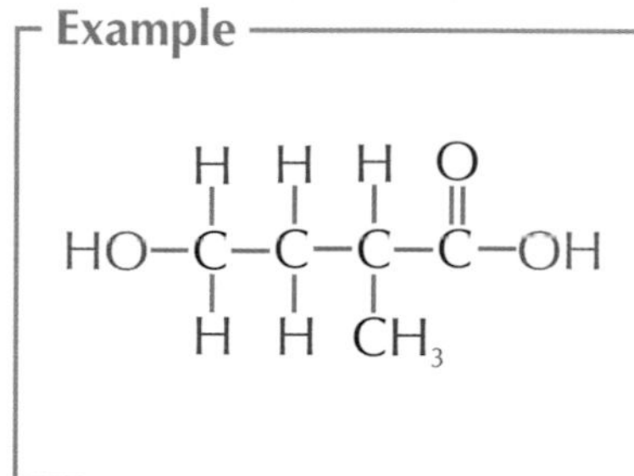

The longest continuous carbon chain is 4 carbon atoms, so the stem is butane.

Numbering of the carbons starts at the COOH group so there's a COOH group on carbon-1, a methyl group on carbon-2 and a hydroxyl group on carbon-4.

So, this is 4-hydroxy-2-methylbutanoic acid.

Tip: A carboxyl group contains a carbonyl group and a hydroxyl group on the same carbon atom.

Dissociation of carboxylic acids

Carboxylic acids are weak acids — in water they partially dissociate into a carboxylate ion and an H^+ ion.

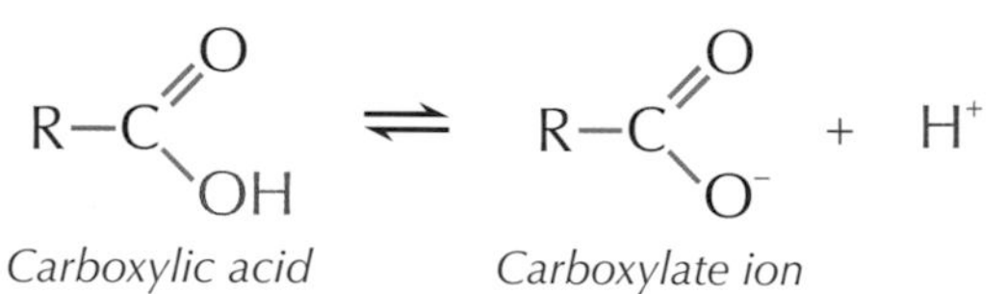

Carboxylic acid *Carboxylate ion*

This reaction is reversible but the equilibrium lies to the left because most of the molecules don't dissociate.

Tip: See page 19 for more on the dissociation of weak acids.

Reaction with carbonates

Carboxylic acids react with carbonates (CO_3^{2-}) or hydrogencarbonates (HCO_3^-) to form a salt, carbon dioxide and water.

Examples

$$2CH_3COOH_{(aq)} + Na_2CO_{3(s)} \rightarrow 2CH_3COONa_{(aq)} + H_2O_{(l)} + CO_{2(g)}$$

Ethanoic acid — *Sodium carbonate* — *Sodium ethanoate*

$$HCOOH_{(aq)} + NaHCO_{3(s)} \rightarrow HCOONa_{(aq)} + H_2O_{(l)} + CO_{2(g)}$$

Methanoic acid — *Sodium hydrogencarbonate* — *Sodium methanoate*

In these reactions, carbon dioxide fizzes out of the solution.

Tip: When you're writing equations for the reaction of carboxylic acids with carbonates, always remember to balance the equation at the end.

Esterification reactions

If you heat a carboxylic acid with an alcohol in the presence of a strong acid catalyst, you get an **ester**. It's called an **esterification** reaction.

Tip: Esterification reactions are also condensation reactions because they release a small molecule (water) when the carboxylic acid and alcohol join.

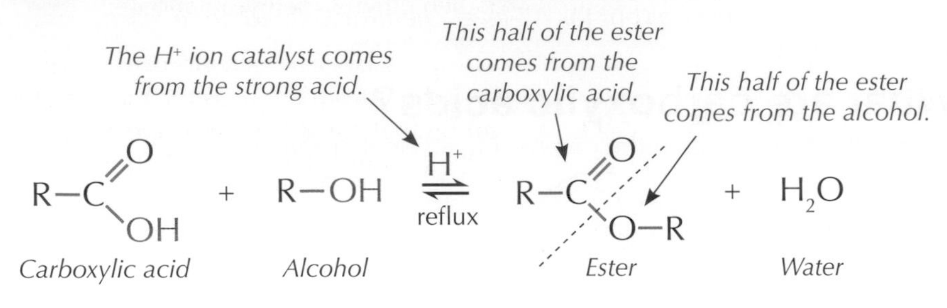

Concentrated sulfuric acid (H_2SO_4) is usually used as the acid catalyst but other strong acids such as HCl or H_3PO_4 can also be used.

Figure 1: *Model showing the structure of the ester ethyl ethanoate.*

Naming esters

You've just seen that an ester is formed by reacting an alcohol with a carboxylic acid. Well, the name of an ester is made up of two parts — the first bit comes from the alcohol, and the second bit from the carboxylic acid.

To name an ester, just follow these steps:

1. Look at the alkyl group that came from the alcohol. This is the first bit of the ester's name.
2. Now look at the part that came from the carboxylic acid. Swap its '-oic acid' ending for 'oate' to get the second bit of the name.
3. Put the two parts together.

Example

Ethanoic acid reacts with methanol to produce the ester shown below:

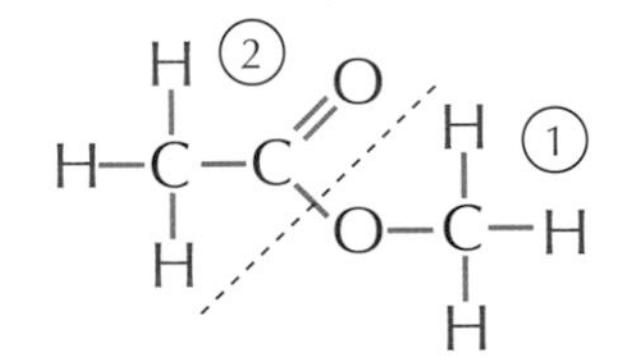

1. This part of the ester came from the alcohol. It's a methyl group so the first part of the ester's name is methyl-.
2. This part of the ester came from the carboxylic acid. It came from ethanoic acid so the second part of the ester's name is - ethanoate.
3. So this ester is methyl ethanoate.

Tip: Be careful — the name of the ester is written the opposite way round to the formula.

The same rules apply even if the carbon chains are branched or if the molecule has a benzene ring attached. Always number the carbons starting from the carbon atoms in the C–O–C bond.

Examples

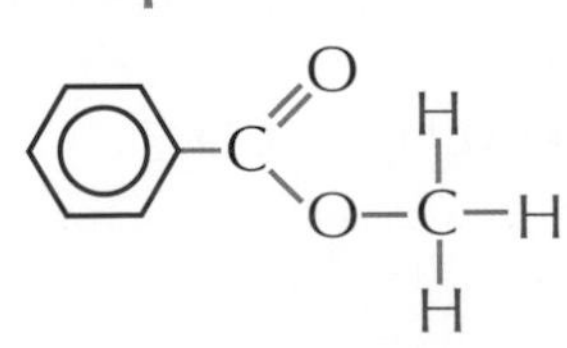

This ester has a methyl group that came from the alcohol so the name begins with methyl-.

There is a benzene ring that came from benzoic acid so the name ends in -benzoate.

So this is methyl benzoate.

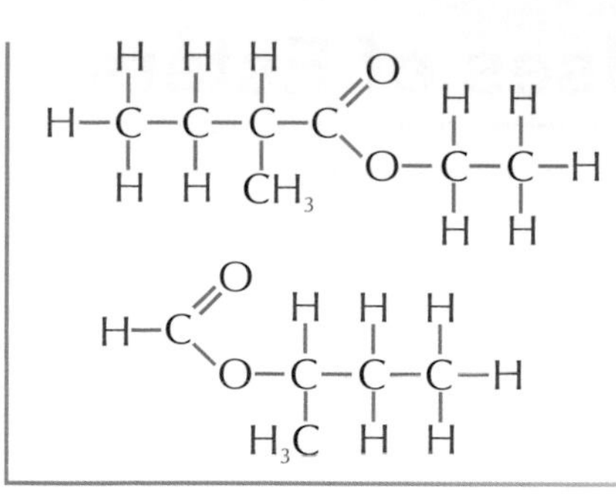

This ester has an ethyl group that came from the alcohol and a 2-methyl butanyl group that came from the acid so is called ethyl 2-methylbutanoate.

This ester has a 1-methylpropyl group that came from the alcohol and a methyl group that came from the acid so is called 1-methylpropyl methanoate.

Sometimes you may be asked to predict which alcohol and which carboxylic acid are needed to form a particular ester.

Example

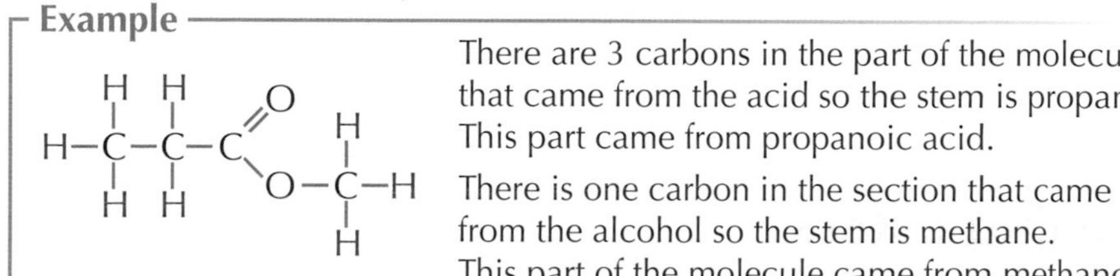

There are 3 carbons in the part of the molecule that came from the acid so the stem is propane. This part came from propanoic acid.

There is one carbon in the section that came from the alcohol so the stem is methane. This part of the molecule came from methanol.

Tip: The rules about naming esters only apply if the alcohol is a primary alcohol — if it's a secondary alcohol the first part of the name will be different. E.g. 1-methylpropyl methanoate is formed from methanoic acid and butan-2-one, not 1-methyl propanone.

Practice Questions — Application

Q1 Below are two carboxylic acids:

(i) $H-C(=O)-OH$

(ii)

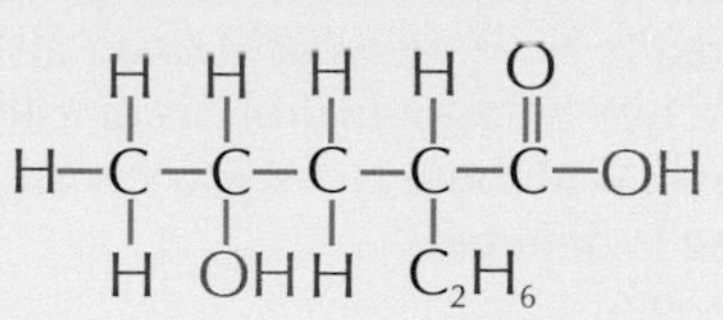

a) Name these carboxylic acids.

b) Write a balanced equation for the reaction of carboxylic acid (i) with sodium carbonate (Na_2CO_3).

Q2 Below are two esters:

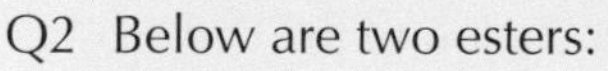

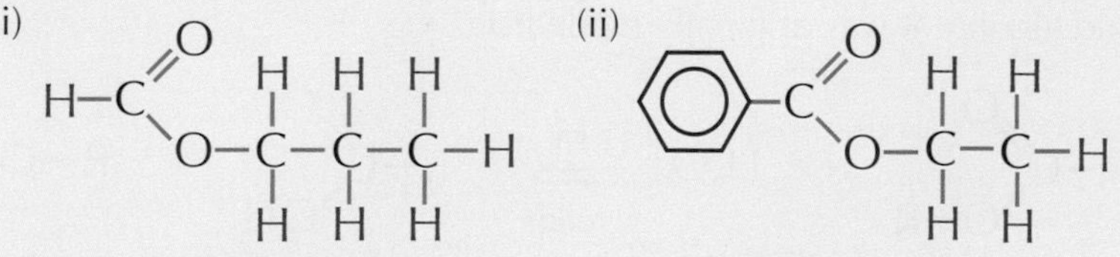

a) Name these esters

b) State which carboxylic acid and which alcohol have reacted to form each of these esters.

Q3 1-methylethyl methanoate is an ester.

a) Draw the structure of this ester.

b) Write an equation to show the formation of this ester from an acid and an alcohol.

Exam Tip

Sometimes examiners will try and throw you by drawing esters the opposite way round, e.g.

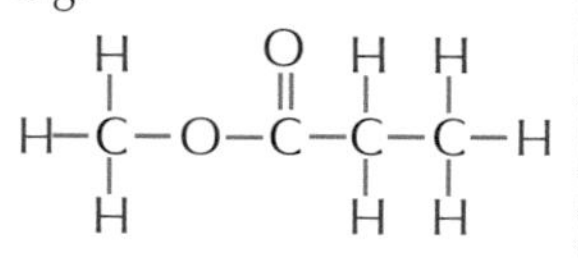

Try not to get confused when naming esters — always think about the position of the O and C=O groups rather than just thinking about left and right. This ester is methyl propanoate.

Practice Questions — Fact Recall

Q1 Name the three products that are produced when a carboxylic acid reacts with a carbonate or a hydrogen carbonate.

Q2 Carboxylic acids react with alcohols to form esters.

a) What is the name given to this type of reaction?

b) What type of catalyst is used for this reaction? Give an example.

4. Reactions and Uses of Esters

Esters are extremely useful molecules. In fact — you've probably used an ester at some point today without even realising it. Read on to find out more.

Learning Objectives:

- Know that esters can have pleasant smells.
- Know the common uses of esters (e.g. in solvents, plasticizers, perfumes and food flavourings).
- Know that esters can be hydrolysed.
- Know that vegetable oils and animal fats are esters of propane-1,2,3-triol (glycerol).
- Understand that vegetable oils and animal fats can be hydrolysed to give soap, glycerol and long chain carboxylic (fatty) acids.
- Know that biodiesel is a mixture of methyl esters of long chain carboxylic acids.
- Know that vegetable oils can be converted into biodiesel by reaction with methanol in the presence of a catalyst.

Specification Reference 3.4.5

Tip: The nice fragrances and flavours of lots of flowers and fruits come from esters.

Useful properties of esters

Esters have a number of properties that make them very useful.

- Esters have a sweet smell — it varies from gluey sweet for smaller esters to a fruity 'pear drop' smell for the larger ones. This makes them useful in perfumes. The food industry uses esters to flavour things like drinks and sweets too.
- Esters are polar liquids so lots of polar organic compounds will dissolve in them. They've also got quite low boiling points, so they evaporate easily from mixtures. This makes them good solvents in glues and printing inks.
- Esters are used as plasticisers — they're added to plastics during polymerisation to make the plastic more flexible. Over time, the plasticiser molecules escape though, and the plastic becomes brittle and stiff.

Hydrolysis of esters

Hydrolysis is when a substance is split up by water — but using just water is often really slow, so an acid or an alkali is often used to speed it up. There are two types of hydrolysis of esters — acid hydrolysis and base hydrolysis. With both types you get an alcohol, but the second product in each case is different.

Acid hydrolysis

Acid hydrolysis splits the ester into an acid and an alcohol — it's the reverse of the reaction on page 72. You have to reflux the ester with a dilute acid, such as hydrochloric or sulfuric. The ester will then split back into the carboxylic acid and alcohol it was originally made from.

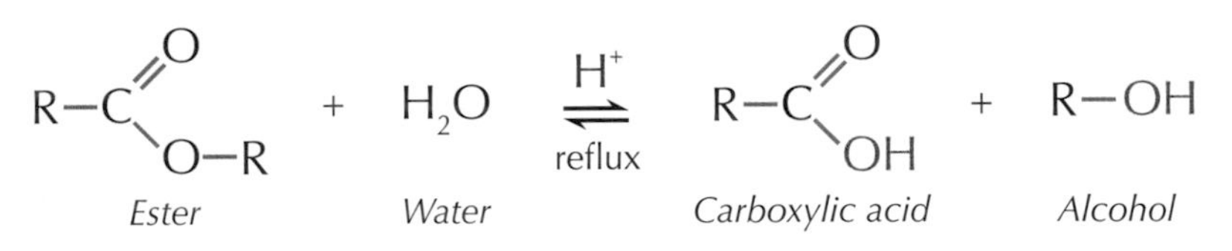

Example

Acid hydrolysis of methyl ethanoate produces ethanoic acid and methanol:

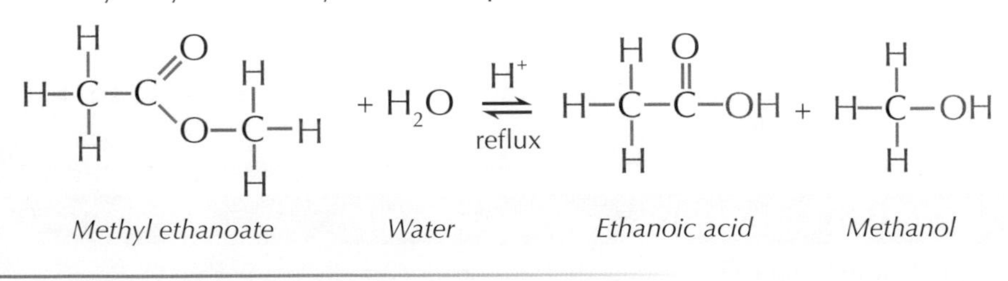

Exam Tip
Don't worry, you don't need to know the mechanism for these reactions — just knowing the equations is enough.

As these acid hydrolysis reactions are reversible you need to use lots of water to push the equilibrium over to the right so you get lots of product. See page 13 for more on reversible reactions and equilibria.

Base hydrolysis

For a base hydrolysis reaction you have to reflux the ester with a dilute alkali, such as sodium hydroxide. OH^- ions from the base react with the ester and you get a carboxylate ion and an alcohol.

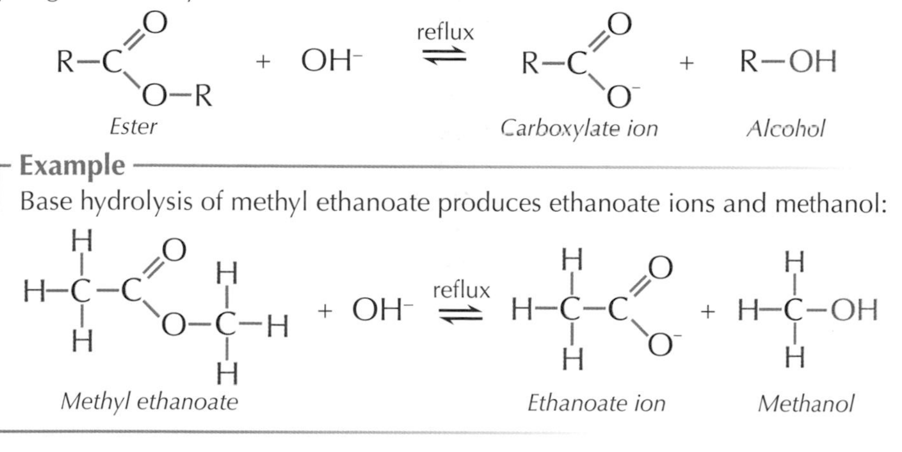

Tip: Make sure you know the difference between the two different types of hydrolysis — acid hydrolysis produces a carboxylic acid and base hydrolysis produces a carboxylate ion.

Tip: The negatively charged carboxylate ions bond with the positively charged ions from the base (e.g. Na^+ ions if the base is NaOH) to form salts like the one shown below:

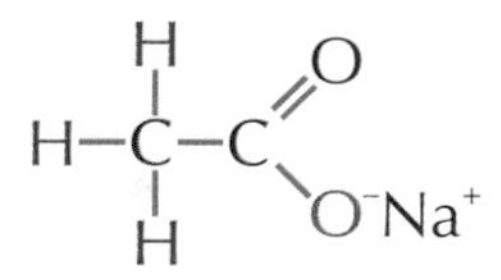

This is sodium ethanoate.

Fats and oils

Fats and oils are esters of glycerol and **fatty acids**. Fatty acids are long chain carboxylic acids. They combine with glycerol (propane-1,2,3-triol) to make fats and oils — see Figure 1. The fatty acids can be **saturated** (no double bonds) or **unsaturated** (with C=C double bonds). Most of a fat or oil is made from fatty acid chains — so it's these that give them many of their properties.

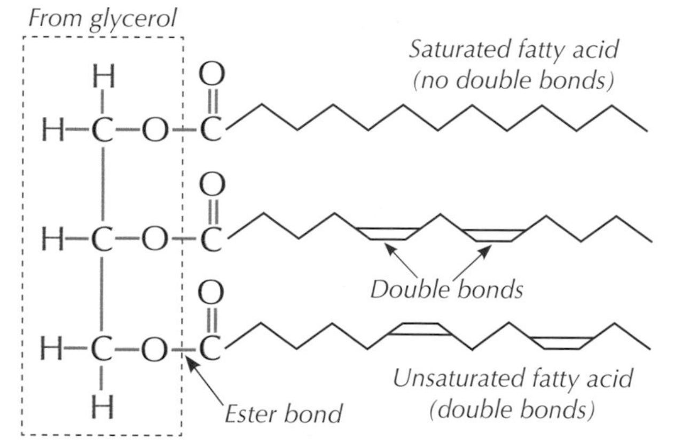

Figure 1: Diagram showing the structure of a fat/oil.

Figure 2: Fats and oils are esters formed from glycerol (propane-1,2,3-triol) and long chain carboxylic acids.

'Fats' have mainly saturated hydrocarbon chains — they fit neatly together, increasing the van der Waals forces between them (see Figure 3). This means higher temperatures are needed to melt them and they're solid at room temperature.

Figure 3: The arrangement of hydrocarbon chains in a fat.

'Oils' have unsaturated hydrocarbon chains — the double bonds mean the chains are bent and don't pack together well, decreasing the effect of the van der Waals forces (see Figure 4). So they're easier to melt and are liquids at room temperature.

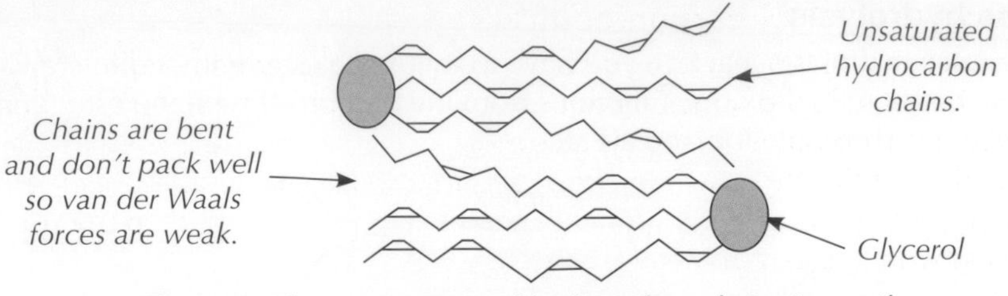

***Figure 4:** The arrangement of hydrocarbon chains in an oil.*

Tip: See the previous page for more on the base hydrolysis of esters.

Hydrolysis of fats and oils

Like any ester, you can hydrolyse oils and fats by heating them with sodium hydroxide. This is a type of base hydrolysis. OH^- ions from the sodium hydroxide react with the fat/oil to form a carboxylate ion and an alcohol. The alcohol that is formed is glycerol (propane-1,2,3-triol) and the carboxylate ions combine with Na^+ ions from the sodium hydroxide to form a sodium salt. And you'll never guess what the sodium salt produced is — a soap.

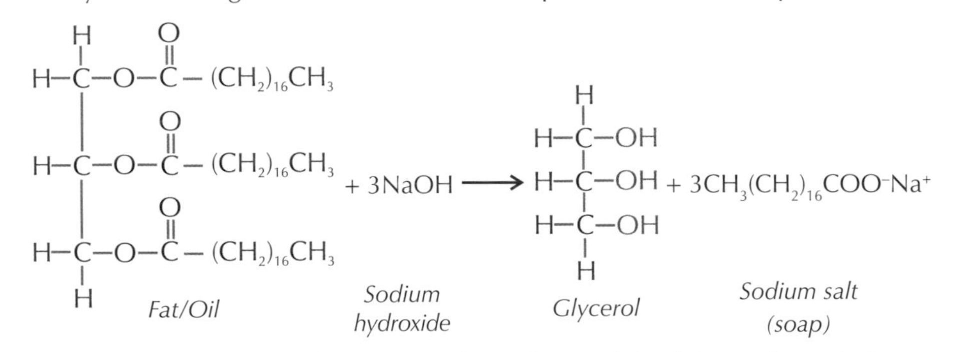

***Figure 5:** Student making soap by heating vegetable oil with sodium hydroxide.*

If you want to, you can then convert the sodium salt back into a long chain carboxylic acid (fatty acid) by adding an acid such as HCl. H^+ ions from the acid displace the Na^+ ions in the salt to form a carboxylic acid, which releases a free Na^+ ion. This reaction is shown below:

$$CH_3(CH_2)_{16}COO^-Na^+ + H^+ \rightarrow CH_3(CH_2)_{16}COOH + Na^+$$

sodium salt (soap) *fatty acid*

Biodiesel

Vegetable oils, e.g. rapeseed oil, make good vehicle fuels, but you can't burn them directly in engines. The oils must be converted into **biodiesel** first. This involves reacting them with methanol, using a strong alkali (e.g. potassium hydroxide or sodium hydroxide) as a catalyst. You get a mixture of methyl esters of fatty acids — this is biodiesel.

Exam Tip
Questions about biodiesel come up a lot so make sure you know the equation for the formation of biodiesel.

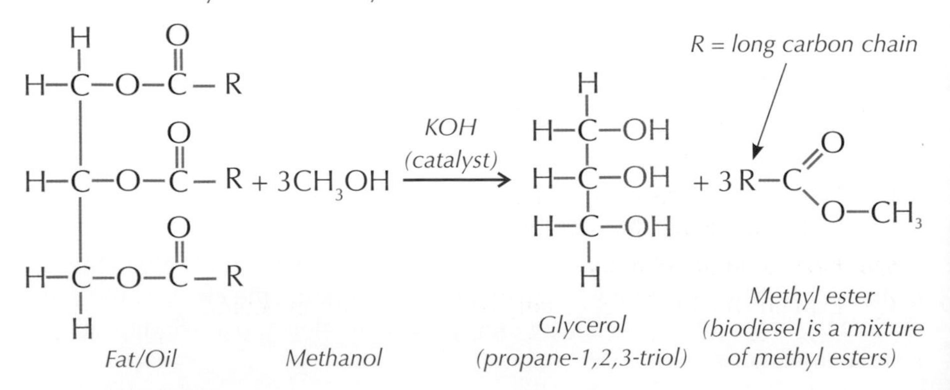

Is biodiesel 100% carbon neutral?

HOW SCIENCE WORKS

Biodiesel can be thought of as carbon neutral, because when crops grow they absorb the same amount of CO_2 as they produce when they're burned. But it's not quite as simple as that — energy is used to make the fertilizer to grow the crops, and it's used in planting, harvesting and converting the oil. If this energy comes from fossil fuels, then the process won't be carbon neutral overall.

Figure 6: *A biodiesel fuel pump.*

Practice Questions — Application

Q1 Below is the ester methyl propanoate:

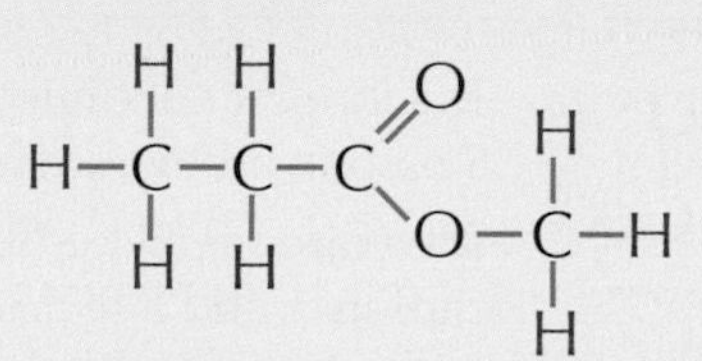

Write an equation to show:

a) the acid hydrolysis of this ester.

b) the base hydrolysis of this ester.

Q2 Stearic acid ($CH_3(CH_2)_{16}COOH$) is a long chain carboxylic acid found in most animal fats.

a) Draw the triester that would be produced if three molecules of stearic acid reacted with glycerol.

b) Write an equation for the production of soap from this triester.

c) Explain how soap could be converted back into glycerol and stearic acid.

Q3 Below is an ester commonly found in vegetable oils.

$$\begin{array}{l} CH_2OOC(CH_2)_{14}CH_3 \\ | \\ CH_2OOC(CH_2)_{14}CH_3 \\ | \\ CH_2OOC(CH_2)_{14}CH_3 \end{array}$$

a) Write an equation for the conversion of this ester into biofuel.

b) Suggest a suitable catalyst for this reaction.

Exam Tip

If you don't recognise the structure of a molecule in your exam, try re-drawing it in a different way — it might start to look more familiar.

Practice Questions — Fact Recall

Q1 Give three common uses of esters.

Q2 What two products are produced when an ester is broken down by:

a) acid hydrolysis?

b) base hydrolysis?

Q3 What two things are fats and oils made of?

Q4 Explain why the properties of fats and oils are different.

Q5 Fats can be hydrolysed by heating them with NaOH. What are the products of this reaction?

Q6 How is biodiesel made?

Q7 Explain why biodiesel usually isn't 100% carbon neutral.

5. Acyl Chlorides

Learning Objectives:

- Be able to apply IUPAC rules for naming acyl chlorides.
- Know the reactions of water, alcohols, ammonia and primary amines with acyl chlorides.
- Understand the mechanism of nucleophilic addition–elimination reactions between water, alcohols, ammonia and primary amines with acyl chlorides.

Specification Reference 3.4.4, 3.4.5

Acyl chlorides are a particularly useful type of carbonyl compound because they are good starting points for making lots of different types of molecule.

What are acyl chlorides?

Acyl (or acid) chlorides have the functional group COCl — their general formula is $C_nH_{2n-1}OCl$. Naming acyl chlorides is similar to naming carboxylic acids. All their names end in –oyl chloride and the carbon atoms are numbered from the end with the acyl functional group.

Example

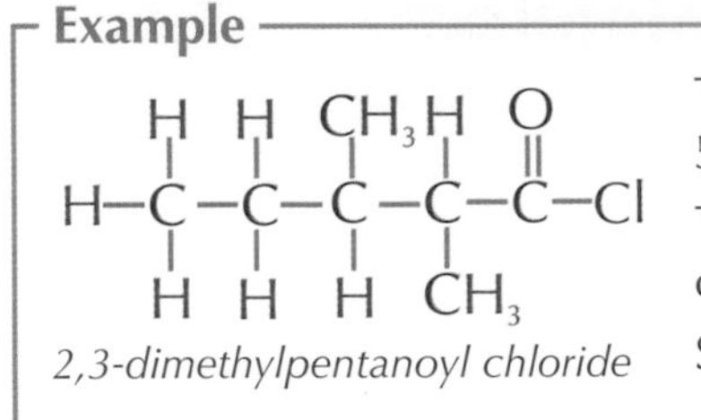

2,3-dimethylpentanoyl chloride

The longest continuous carbon chain is 5 carbon atoms, so the stem is pentane.

There are methyl groups on carbon-2 and carbon-3 and a hydroxyl group on carbon-4.

So, it's 2,3-dimethylpentanoyl chloride.

Reactions of acyl chlorides

Acyl chlorides can react with a wide range of different molecules. In each of these reactions, Cl is substituted by an oxygen or nitrogen group and misty fumes of hydrogen chloride are given off. The key reactions involving acyl chlorides that you need to know are:

Reaction with water

Acyl chlorides react vigorously with cold water, producing a carboxylic acid.

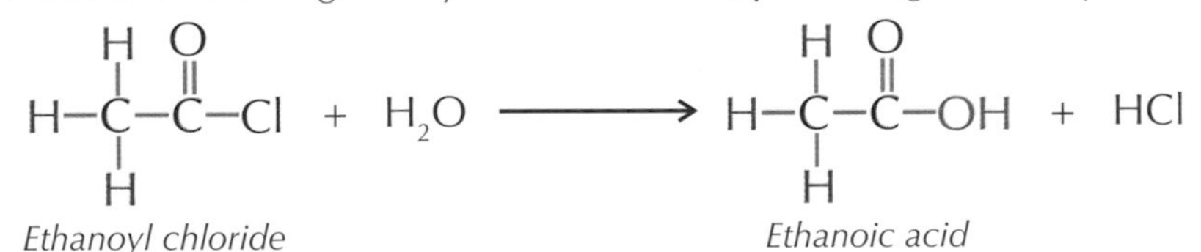

Ethanoyl chloride *Ethanoic acid*

Figure 1: *The reaction of an acyl chloride with water. You can see the misty fumes of HCl that are being given off.*

Reaction with alcohols

Acyl chlorides react vigorously with alcohols at room temperature, producing an ester.

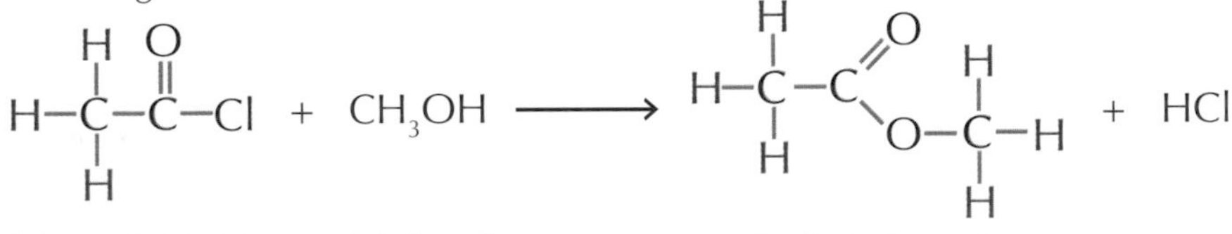

Ethanoyl chloride *Methanol* *Methyl ethanoate*

This irreversible reaction is a much easier, faster way to produce an ester than esterification (see page 72).

Reaction with ammonia

Acyl chlorides react vigorously with ammonia at room temperature, producing an **amide**.

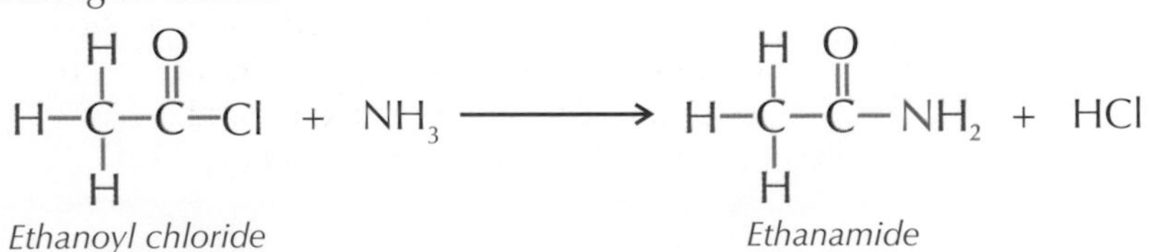

Ethanoyl chloride *Ethanamide*

Reaction with amines

Acyl chlorides react vigorously with **amines** at room temperature, producing an **N-substituted amide**.

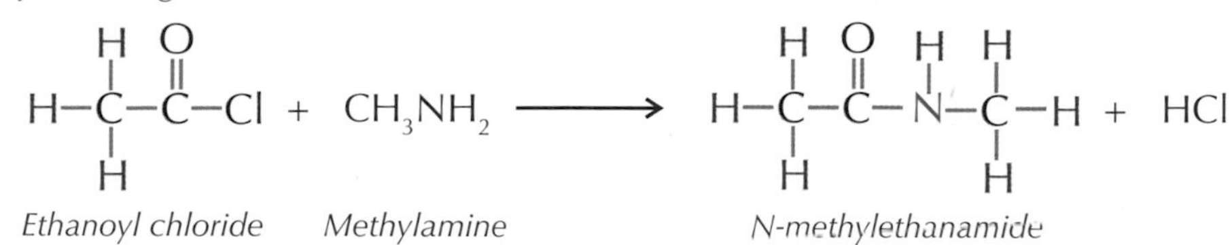

Tip: See pages 94-100 for more on amines and amides.

Nucleophilic addition-elimination

All of the reactions involving acyl chlorides shown on this page and the previous page follow the same mechanism — they are all **nucleophilic addition-elimination** reactions. Acyl chloride nucleophilic addition-elimination reactions have two steps:

1. The nucleophile adds onto the acyl chloride displacing a Cl^- ion.
2. The Cl^- ion steals a hydrogen ion from the nucleophile and HCl is eliminated.

Tip: A nucleophile is a molecule that can donate a lone pair of electrons.

Step 1:

In acyl chlorides, both the chlorine and the oxygen atoms draw electrons towards themselves, so the carbon has a slight positive charge — meaning it's easily attacked by nucleophiles.

Tip: The slight positive charge on the carbon in acyl chlorides is bigger than the slight positive charge on the carbon in carboxylic acids, so acyl chlorides are more reactive compounds.

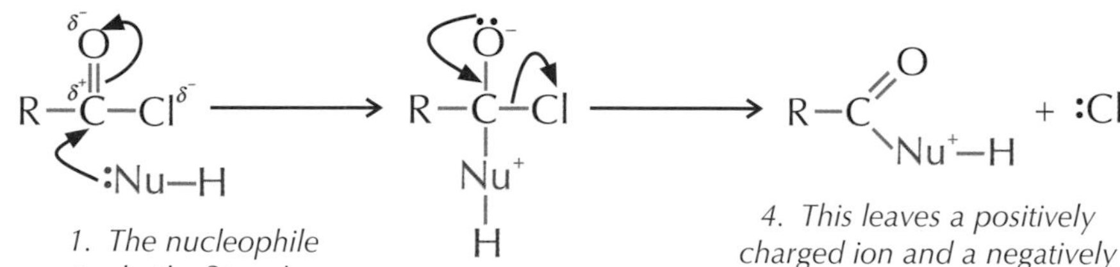

Exam Tip
Sometimes you will be asked to apply this mechanism to a nucleophilic reaction that you haven't studied before so make sure you really understand it — it won't be enough to just learn the examples.

Step 2:

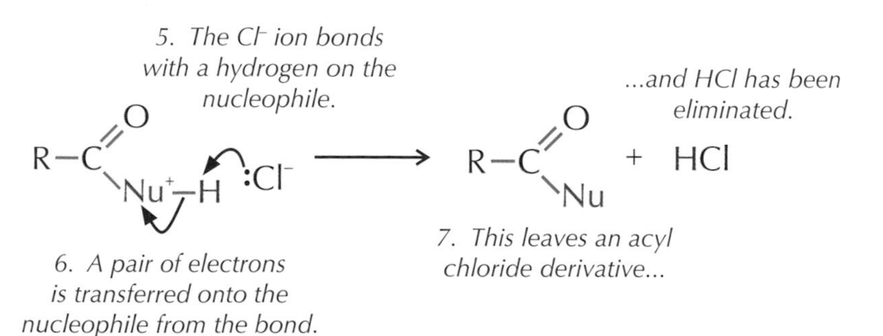

Tip: An acyl chloride derivative is just something that is made from an acyl chloride.

All the reactions that you need to know involving acyl chlorides work in exactly the same way. You just need to change the nucleophile (Nu) to water (H_2O:), an alcohol (e.g. $CH_3\ddot{O}H$), ammonia ($\dot{N}H_3$) or an amine (e.g. $CH_3\dot{N}H_2$).

Example

Below is the mechanism for the reaction of ethanoyl chloride with methanol:

Step 1:

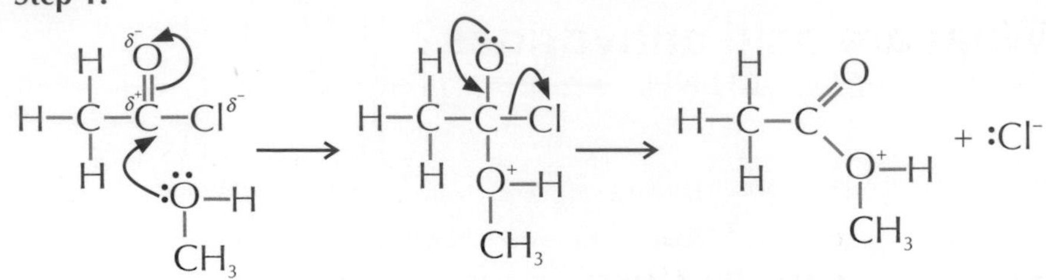

Methanol is the nucleophile here. It attacks the partially positive carbon on the ethanoyl chloride, and a pair of electrons from the C=O bond are transferred to the oxygen. Then the pair of electrons on the oxygen reform the double bond and the chlorine's kicked off.

Exam Tip
You don't have to show the two steps separately in your exam — drawing them one after the other is fine.

Step 2:

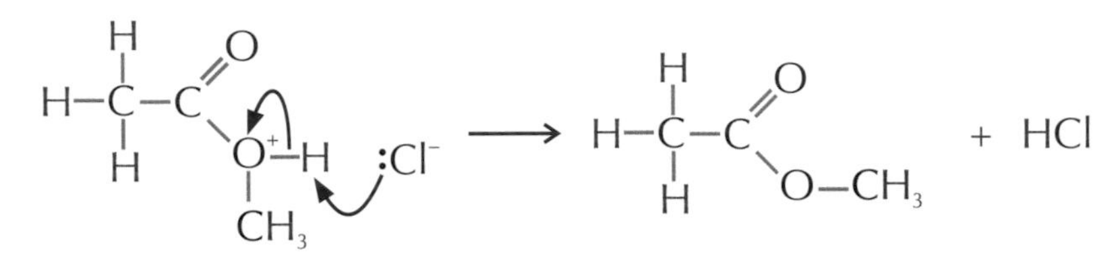

The chlorine bonds with the hydrogen in the hydroxyl group of methanol and hydrogen chloride's eliminated leaving methyl ethanoate.

Tip: Any nucleophile could be involved in a nucleophilic addition-elimination reaction — not just the ones shown here.

Practice Questions — Application

Q1 Name the acyl chlorides that are shown below:

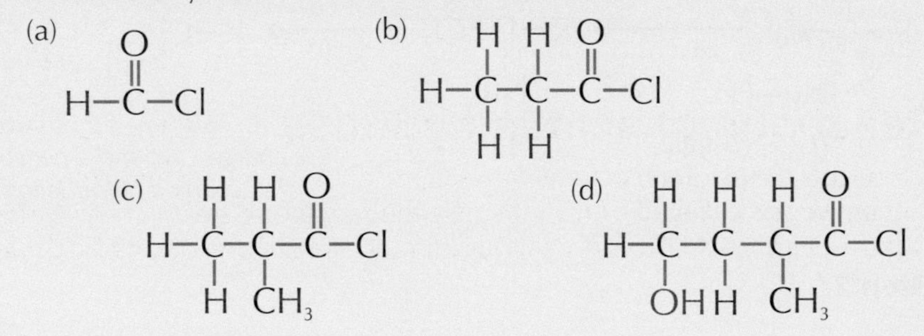

Q2 Draw the mechanisms for the following reactions:

a) acyl chloride (a) with methanol.

b) acyl chloride (b) with water.

c) acyl chloride (c) with ammonia.

d) acyl chloride (d) with methylamine.

Practice Questions — Fact Recall

Q1 What is the general formula for an acyl chloride?

Q2 What are the products when an acyl chloride is reacted with:

a) water? b) an alcohol? c) ammonia? d) an amine?

Q3 What is the name given to the mechanism for the reactions of acyl chlorides with water, alcohols, ammonia and amines?

6. Acid Anhydrides

Acid anhydrides are compounds that react in a similar way to acyl chlorides.

Learning Objectives:

- Be able to apply IUPAC rules for naming acid anhydrides.
- Know the reactions of water, alcohols, ammonia and primary amines with acid anhydrides.
- Understand the industrial advantages of ethanoic anhydride over ethanoyl chloride in the manufacture of the drug aspirin.

Specification Reference 3.4.4, 3.4.5

What are acid anhydrides?

An **acid anhydride** is made from two identical carboxylic acid molecules. The two carboxylic acid molecules are joined together via an oxygen with the carbonyl groups on either side. This oxygen has come from the OH group of one of the carboxylic acids. The other OH group and the spare hydrogen are released as water. The formation of an acid anhydride is shown below.

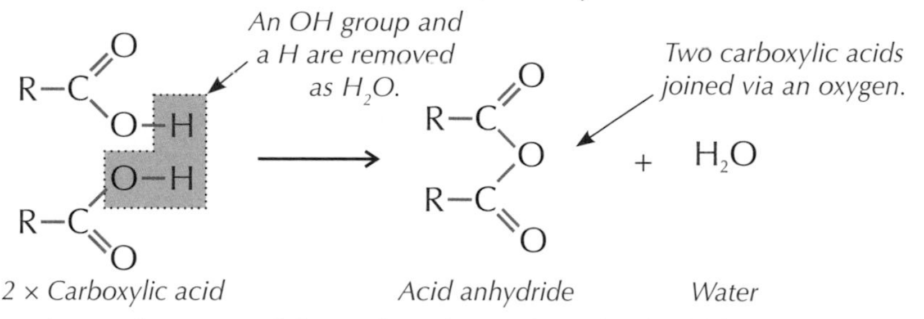

If you know the name of the carboxylic acid, acid anhydrides are easy to name — just take away 'acid' and add 'anhydride'. So methanoic acid gives methanoic anhydride, ethanoic acid gives ethanoic annhydride, etc..

Tip: See page 71 for how to name carboxylic acids.

Example

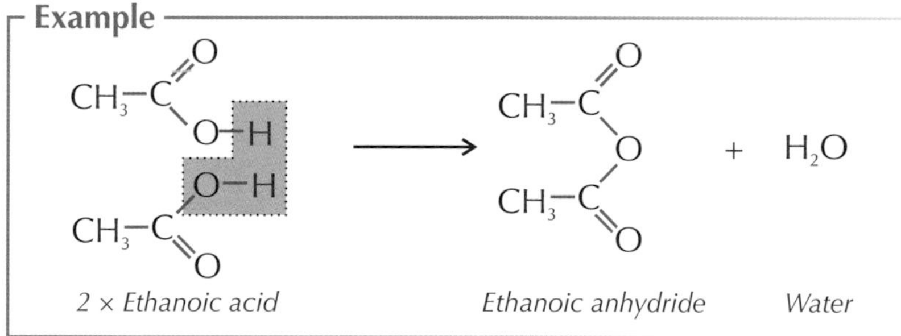

Reactions of acid anhydrides

You need to know the reactions of water, alcohol, ammonia and amines with acid anhydrides. Luckily, they're almost the same as those of acyl chlorides — the reactions are just less vigorous and you get a carboxylic acid formed instead of HCl.

Tip: See pages 78-80 for more on the reactions of acyl chlorides.

Examples

Acid anhydrides react with water, producing a carboxylic acid.

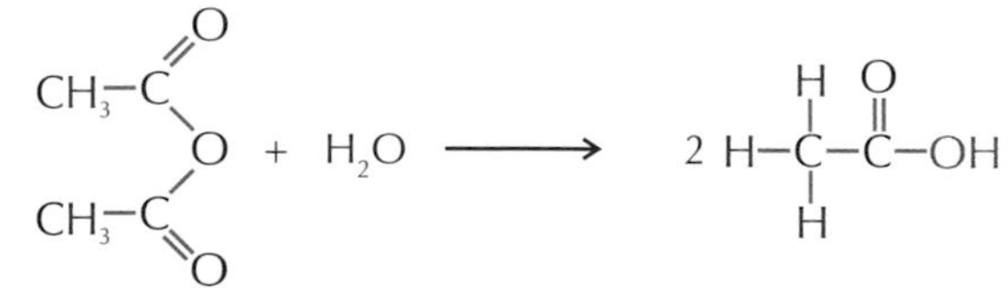

Acid anhydrides react with alcohols, producing an ester.

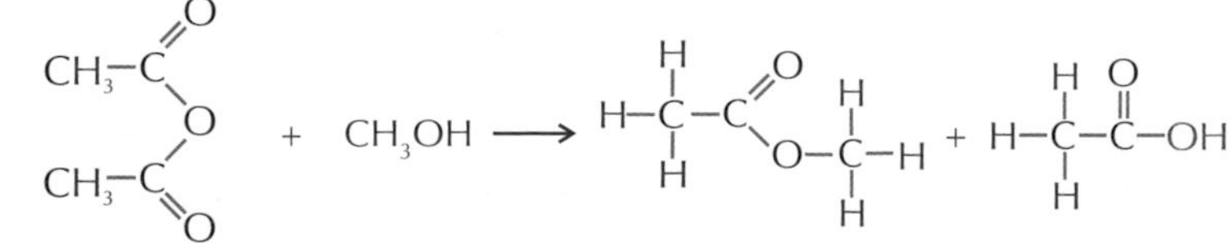

Tip: All of these reactions are nucleophilic addition-elimination reactions — the same as with the acyl chlorides.

Tip: The carboxylic acid formed at the end of all these reactions is the same as the carboxylic acid that would have made the anhydride.

Acid anhydrides react with ammonia, producing an amide.

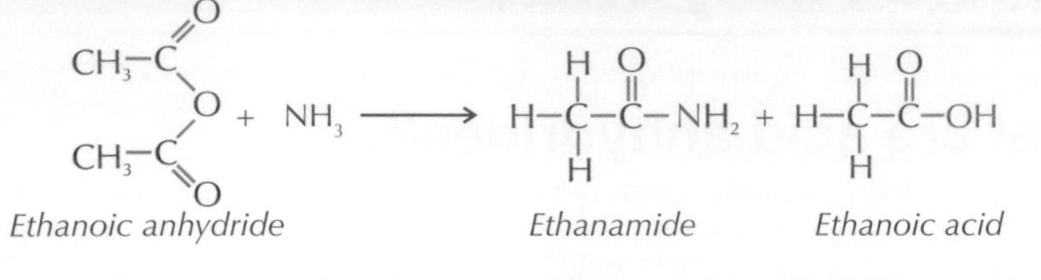

Acid anhydrides react with amines, producing an N-substituted amide.

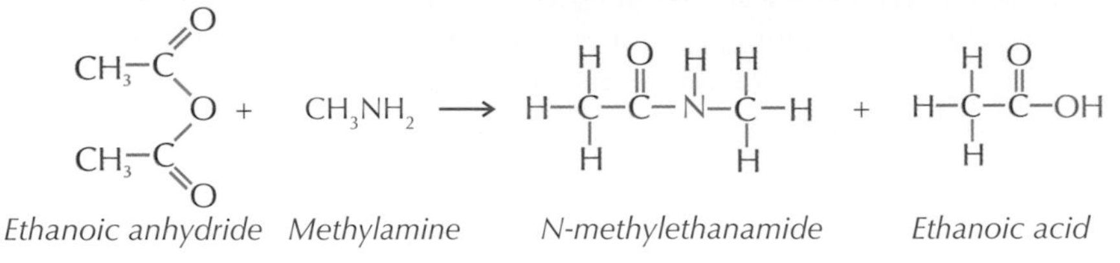

Tip: Aspirin is a drug used to relieve symptoms such as minor aches and pains, fever and swelling.

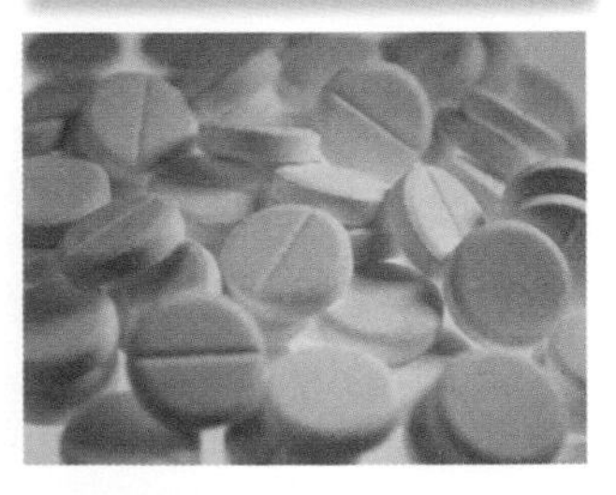

Figure 1: *Aspirin tablets.*

Tip: In these reactions salicylic acid is behaving like an alcohol so everything you've just learnt about the reactions of acid anhydrides/acyl chlorides with alcohols applies here too.

Manufacture of aspirin

Aspirin is an ester — it can be made by reacting salicylic acid (which has an alcohol group) with either ethanoic anhydride or ethanoyl chloride. Ethanoic anhydride is used in industry because it's cheaper than ethanoyl chloride. It's also safer to use than ethanoyl chloride as it's less corrosive, reacts more slowly with water, and doesn't produce dangerous hydrogen chloride fumes (see Figure 2).

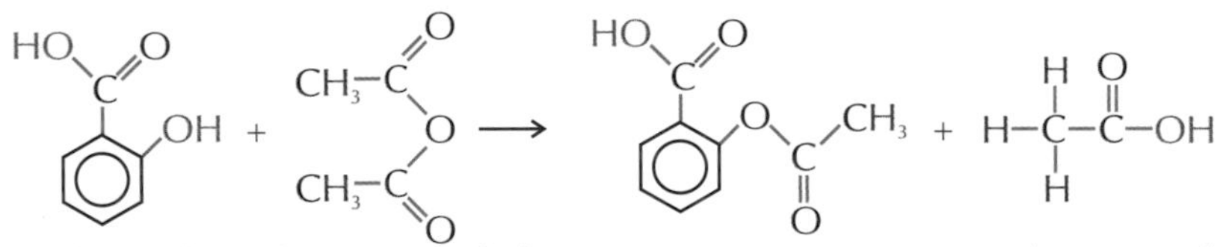

Figure 2: *Using ethanoic anhydride to produce asprin.*

Practice Questions — Application

Q1 Draw the following anhydrides:
 a) propanoic anhydride
 b) 2-ethylpentanoic anhydride
 c) 4-hydroxy-2,3-dimethylbutanoic anhydride

Q2 Write an equation for the following reactions:
 a) propanoic anhydride with water
 b) 2-ethylpentanoic anhydride with methanol
 c) 4-hydroxy-2,3-dimethylbutanoic anhydride with ammonia

Q3 Write the equation for the production of asprin from salicylic acid and ethanoyl chloride.

Practice Questions — Fact Recall

Q1 What is released when two carboxylic acids come together to form an acid anhydride?

Q2 Give two reason why ethanoic anhydride is used instead of ethanoyl chloride when producing aspirin.

Section Summary

Make sure you know...

- The difference between aldehydes and ketones — aldehydes have their carbonyl group at the end of the carbon chain and ketones have their carbonyl group in the middle.
- How to name aldehydes and ketones.
- That aldehydes are easily oxidised to form carboxylic acids but ketones aren't.
- How Tollens' reagent, Fehling's solution and Benedict's solution can be used to test for aldehydes and ketones.
- That aldehydes and ketones can be reduced to alcohols using reducing agents such as $NaBH_4$.
- The nucleophilic addition reaction mechanism for the reduction of aldehydes and ketones.
- What hydroxynitriles are and how to name them.
- That aldehydes and ketones react with HCN to produce hydroxynitriles.
- That the production of hydroxynitriles using aldehydes/ketones and HCN is another example of nucleophilic addition.
- That KCN is often used in place of HCN in reactions with carbonyls because HCN is highly toxic.
- How to name carboxylic acids.
- That carboxylic acids are weak acids that partially dissociate in water.
- That carboxylic acids react with carbonates and hydrogencarbonates to form a salt, CO_2 and H_2O.
- That carboxylic acids react with alcohols in the presence of a strong acid catalyst (e.g. HCl, H_2SO_4 or H_3PO_4) to form esters — this is called an esterification reaction.
- What esters are and how to name them.
- That esters can have pleasant smells so are often used in perfumes and as food flavourings.
- That esters can also be used as plasticisers and solvents.
- That esters can undergo acid hydrolysis to give carboxylic acids and alcohols.
- That esters can undergo base hydrolysis to give carboxylate ions and alcohols.
- That fats/oils are esters of glycerol (propane-1,2,3-triol) and long chain carboxylic acids (fatty acids).
- The difference between fats and oils — fats contain mainly saturated fatty acids while oils contain mostly unsaturated fatty acids.
- Why fats are solid at room temperature when oils are liquid.
- That fats and oils can be hydrolysed to form glycerol and sodium salts which can be used as soap.
- That vegetable oils react with methanol in the presence of a KOH catalyst to form methyl esters which are used in biodiesel.
- Why biodiesel isn't always 100% carbon neutral.
- What acyl chlorides are and how to name them.
- The reactions of acyl chlorides with water, alcohols, ammonia and amines — including the nucleophilic addition-elimination mechanism for these reactions.
- What acid anhydrides are and how to name them.
- The reactions of acid anhydrides with water, alcohols, ammonia and amines.
- That aspirin can be made by reacting salicylic acid with ethanoic anhydride or ethanoyl chloride.
- That ethanoic anhydride is used in industry to produce asprin because it is cheaper and safer to work with than ethanoyl chloride.

Exam-style Questions

1 The two compounds, A and B, shown below are structurally very similar, but a simple test can be used to distinguish between them.

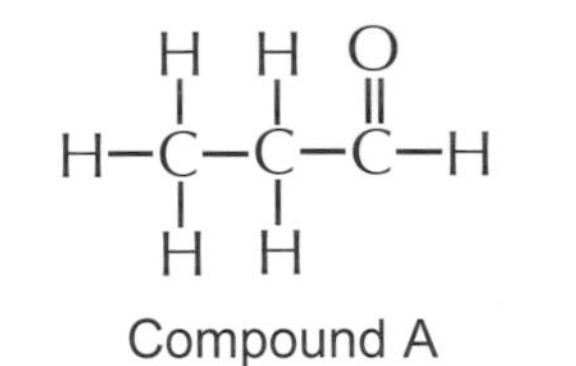

Compound A

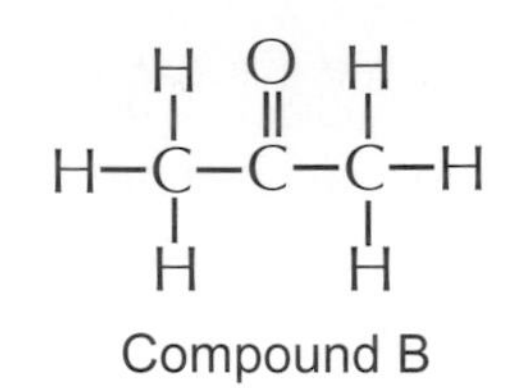

Compound B

1 (a) Give the IUPAC names for these two compounds.

(2 marks)

1 (b) Describe a test that could be used to differentiate between these compounds.

(2 marks)

1 (c) Compound A can be reduced to form a primary alcohol.

1 (c) (i) Suggest a suitable reducing agent for this reaction.

(1 mark)

1 (c) (ii) Outline the mechanism for this reduction reaction.

(3 marks)

1 (d) Compound B can react with hydrogen cyanide (HCN).

1 (d) (i) Name and outline the mechanism for this reaction.

(4 marks)

1 (d) (ii) Give the IUPAC name for the product formed.

(1 mark)

1 (d) (iii) Hydrogen cyanide is toxic. Suggest an alternative reagent that could be used instead of HCN in this reaction.

(1 mark)

2 2-methylpropanoic acid is a carboxylic acid.

2 (a) Draw the structure of this carboxylic acid.

(1 mark)

2 (b) Write an equation for the reaction of 2-methylpropanoic acid with sodium carbonate (Na_2CO_3).

(2 marks)

2 (c) Carboxylic acids react with alcohols to form esters.

2 (c) (i) Draw the structure of the ester that would be formed if 2-methylpropanoic acid reacted with methanol.

(1 mark)

2 (c) (ii) Give the IUPAC name for this ester.

(1 mark)

2 (c) (iii) Suggest a suitable catalyst for this reaction.

(1 mark)

2 (c) (iv) Write an equation for the hydrolysis of this ester with dilute alkali. Show the structure of the reactants and products in your answer.

(2 marks)

2 (d) Give one common use of esters.

(1 mark)

3 Fats and oils are esters formed from glycerol (propane-1,2,3-triol) and fatty acids (long chain carboxylic acids).

3 (a) Explain why fats are usually solid at room temperature while oils are normally liquid.

(3 marks)

3 (b) The structure below shows a naturally occurring triester commonly found in fats and oils.

$$\begin{array}{l} CH_2OOC(CH_2)_{16}CH_3 \\ | \\ CH_2OOC(CH_2)_{16}CH_3 \\ | \\ CH_2OOC(CH_2)_{16}CH_3 \end{array}$$

3 (b) (i) Write an equation to show how this ester could be converted to a sodium salt.

(3 marks)

3 (b) (ii) Suggest a use for this sodium salt.

(1 mark)

3 (c) Biodiesel can be produced from fats and oils.

3 (c) (i) What is biodiesel?

(1 mark)

3 (c) (ii) Write an equation to show how biodiesel could be produced from the ester shown in part (b).

(3 marks)

3 (c) (iii) What is the role of KOH in this reaction?

(1 mark)

4 This question is about acyl chlorides and acid anhydrides.

4 (a) The structure below shows the acyl chloride 2,3-dimethylbutanoyl chloride.

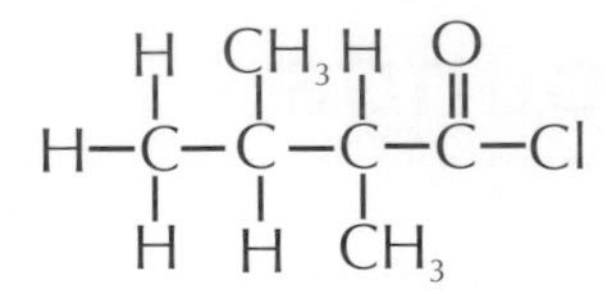

4 (a) (i) Write an equation to show the reaction of this acyl chloride with ammonia.

(2 marks)

4 (a) (ii) Name and outline the mechanism for this reaction.

(6 marks)

4 (b) Acid anhydrides have very similar properties to acyl chlorides but they are structurally very different.

4 (b) (i) Draw the structure of ethanoic anhydride.

(1 mark)

4 (b) (ii) Write an equation to show the reaction of this acid anhydride with water.

(2 marks)

4 (c) Ethanoic anhydride can be reacted with salicylic acid to produce aspirin. The structure of salicylic acid is shown below.

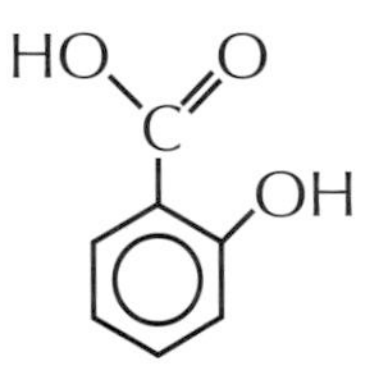

Salicylic acid has an OH group and behaves like an alcohol when reacting with ethanoic anhydride.

4 (c) (i) Using your knowledge of the reactions of acid anhydrides with alcohols, write an equation showing the formation of aspirin from ethanoic anhydride and salicylic acid.

(2 marks)

4 (c) (ii) Aspirin can also be produced by reacting ethanoyl chloride with salicylic acid.

Which method of aspirin production is favoured in industry?
Explain your answer.

(3 marks)

1. Aromatic Compounds

You didn't come across aromatic compounds at AS-level so don't worry if you don't know what they are. The next few pages tell you all about them.

Benzene

Aromatic compounds are compounds that contain a benzene ring, so before you can dive in and learn all about them, you need to know what a benzene ring actually is.

Benzene has the formula C_6H_6. It has a cyclic structure as its six carbon atoms are joined together in a ring. The ring itself is planar (flat) and the hydrogens all stick out in the same plane. There are two main models to explain the structure of the benzene ring — the Kekulé model and the delocalised model.

The Kekulé model

This was proposed by German chemist Friedrich August Kekulé in 1865. He came up with the idea of a ring of C atoms with alternating single and double bonds between them (see Figure 1).

HOW SCIENCE WORKS

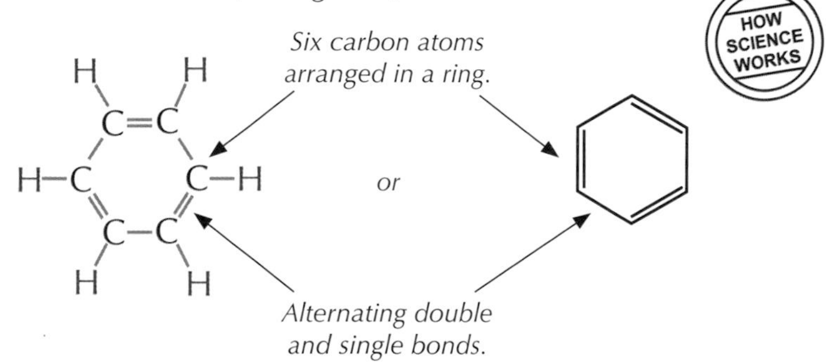

Figure 1: *The structure of benzene according to Kekulé.*

He later adapted the model to say that the benzene molecule was constantly flipping between two forms (isomers) by switching over the double and single bonds (see Figure 2).

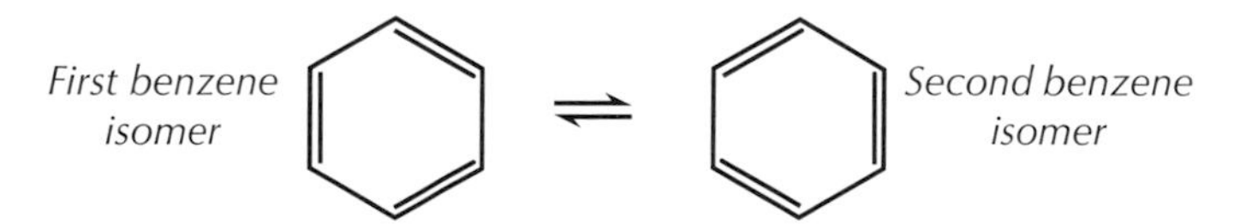

Figure 2: *Benzene flipping between two forms in the adapted Kekulé model.*

If the Kekulé model was correct, you'd expect there to always be three bonds with the length of a C–C bond (147 pm) and three bonds with the length of a C=C bond (135 pm). However X-ray diffraction studies have shown that all the carbon-carbon bonds in benzene have the same length (140 pm) — so they're between the length of a single bond and a double bond. So the Kekulé structure can't be quite right, but it's still used today as it's useful for drawing reaction mechanisms.

Learning Objectives:

- Understand the nature of the bonding in a benzene ring, limited to planar structure and bond length intermediate between single and double.
- Understand that delocalisation confers stability to aromatic rings.
- Be able to use thermochemical evidence from enthalpies of hydrogenation to illustrate the stability of aromatic rings.
- Be able to apply IUPAC rules for naming aromatic compounds.

Specification Reference 3.4.4, 3.4.6

Tip: In simple line diagrams like this one...

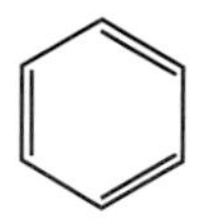

...there is a carbon atom at each corner and you work out the positions of the hydrogens by looking at the number of bonds coming from each carbon atom. There should be four — if there aren't, add one or more hydrogens in.

Tip: pm stands for picometre. A picometre is 1×10^{-12} metres — that's very small indeed.

The delocalised model

Tip: Have a look at your AS notes for a recap on p-orbitals.

The bond-length observations are explained by the delocalised model. In this model, each carbon donates an electron from its p-orbital. These electrons combine to form a ring of delocalised electrons (see Figure 3).

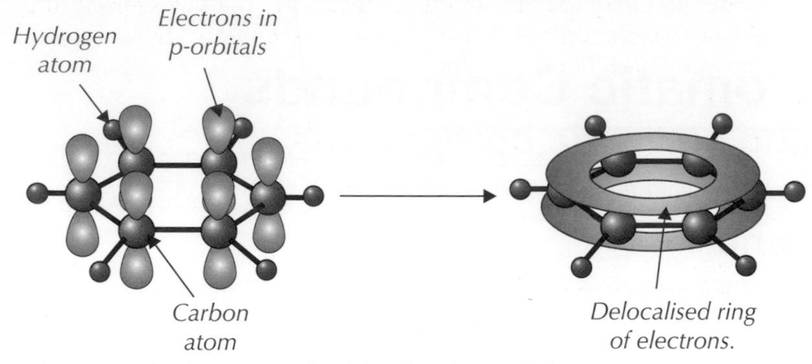

Figure 3: *The formation of a delocalised ring of electrons in benzene.*

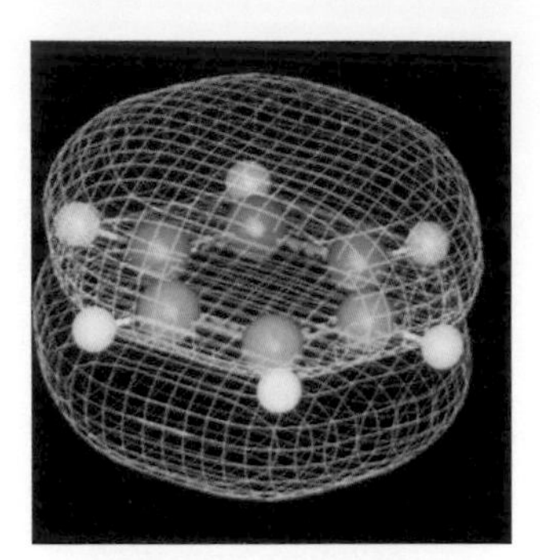

Figure 4: *A computer graphic showing the structure of benzene.*

All the carbon-carbon bonds in the ring are the same, so they are the same length. The electrons in the rings are said to be delocalised because they don't belong to a specific carbon atom. They are represented as a circle in the ring of carbons rather than as double or single bonds (see Figure 5).

Tip: A model is a representation of a situation — scientists use them to try and explain observations. There needs to be evidence to support a model before it's accepted by the scientific community. See pages 1-3 for more.

HOW SCIENCE WORKS

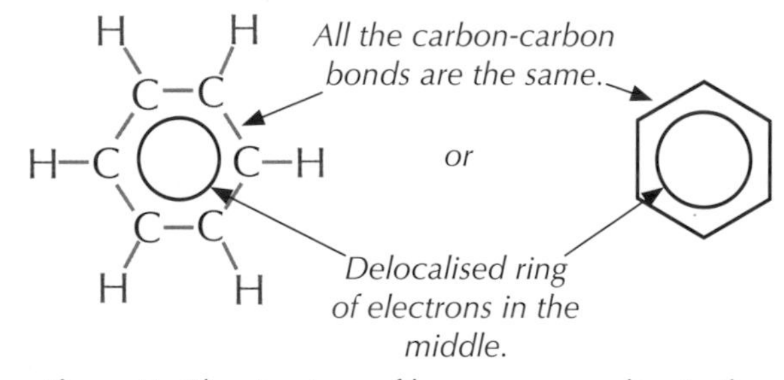

Figure 5: *The structure of benzene according to the delocalised model.*

Evidence for delocalisation

Tip: See page 146 for more on enthalpies.

All the carbon-carbon bonds in benzene are the same length. This is good evidence for the delocalisation model (see above), but even more evidence for this model comes from enthalpy change data.

Cyclohexene has one double bond. When it's hydrogenated, the enthalpy change is –120 $kJmol^{-1}$. If benzene had three double bonds (as in the Kekulé structure), you'd expect it to have an enthalpy of hydrogenation of –360 $kJmol^{-1}$. But the experimental enthalpy of hydrogenation of benzene is –208 $kJmol^{-1}$ — far less exothermic than expected (see Figure 6).

Tip: Cyclohexa-1,3,5-triene (a six-carbon ring with three double bonds) is a theoretical molecule (it doesn't actually exist), so we can't measure its enthalpy of hydrogenation directly. We can only predict it from the enthalpy of hydrogenation for cyclohexene.

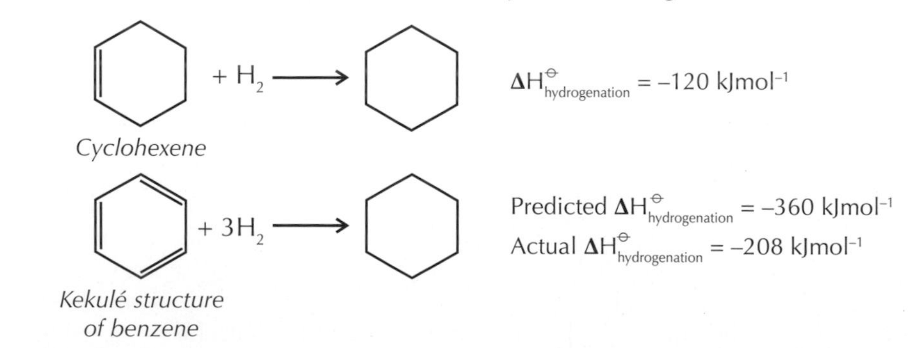

Figure 6: *Enthalpies of hydrogenation providing further evidence for delocalisation.*

Energy is put in to break bonds and released when bonds are made. So more energy must have been put in to break the bonds in benzene than would be needed to break the bonds in the Kekulé structure. This difference indicates that benzene is more stable than the Kekulé structure would be. This is thought to be due to the delocalised ring of electrons. In a delocalised ring the electron density is shared over more atoms, which means the energy of the molecule is lowered and it becomes more stable.

Naming aromatic compounds

Aromatic compounds all contain a benzene ring, but naming them isn't that simple. They're named in two ways:

1. In some cases, the benzene ring is the main functional group and the molecule is named as a substituted benzene ring — the suffix is -benzene and there are prefixes to represent any other functional groups.

Examples

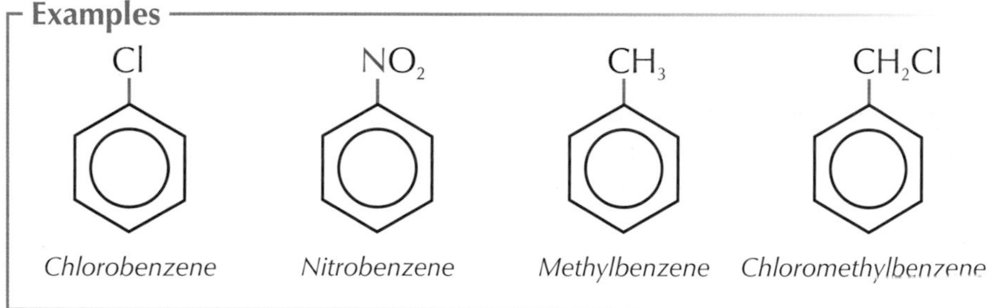

2. In other cases, the benzene ring is not the main functional group and the molecule is named as having a phenyl group (C_6H_5) attached. Phenyl- is used as a prefix to show the molecule has a benzene ring and the suffix comes from other functional groups on the molecule (e.g. -ol if it's an alcohol, -amine if it's an amine).

Examples

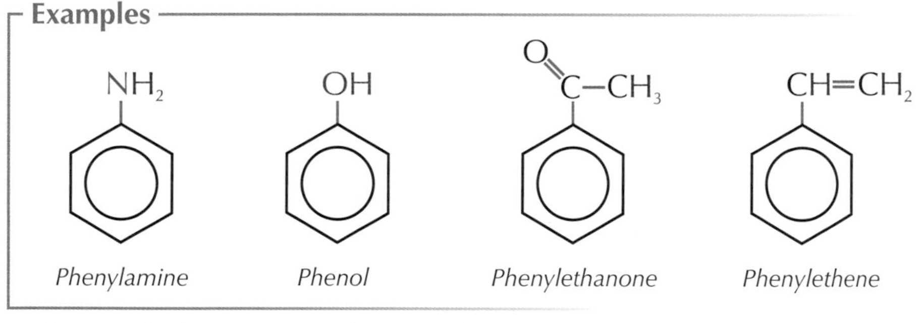

Unfortunately there's no simple rule to help you remember which molecules should be something–benzene and which molecules should be phenyl–something. You just have to learn these examples.

Numbering the benzene ring

If there is more than one functional group attached to the benzene ring you have to number the carbons to show where the groups are. If all the functional groups are the same, pick any group to start from and count round either clockwise or anticlockwise — whichever way gives the smallest numbers. If the functional groups are different, start from whichever functional group gives the molecule its suffix (e.g. the –OH group for a phenol) and continue counting round whichever way gives the smallest numbers. If there's no suffix from a functional group, start numbering from whichever group is first alphabetically.

Tip: Aromatic compounds are also known as arenes, so don't get confused if you see this term around.

Tip: Non-aromatic molecules are called aliphatic molecules — don't get the terms aromatic and aliphatic mixed up.

Tip: If there is only one functional group you don't have to number the carbons because all the positions around the carbon ring are the same.

Exam Tip
You're unlikely to be asked to name anything too complicated in the exam. If you need to give the product of a reaction, don't try and name it unless they specifically ask for the name — giving the structure should be enough to get the marks.

Examples

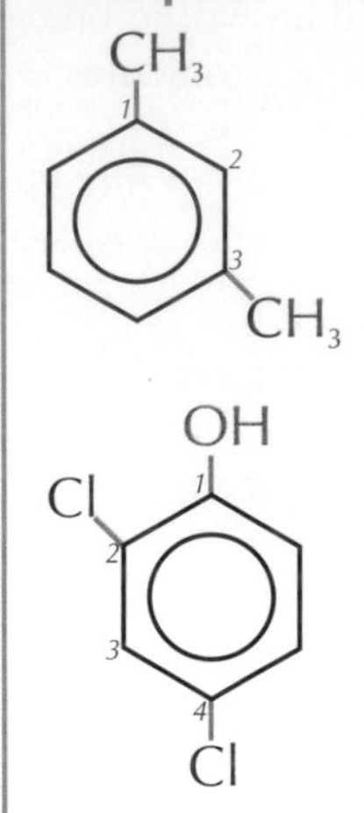

This benzene ring only has methyl groups attached so it will be named as a substituted benzene ring.

Starting from the methyl group at the top and counting clockwise there is another methyl group on carbon-3.

So this is 1,3-dimethylbenzene.

This benzene ring has an OH group attached so the stem is phenol.

Starting from the OH group (the group which gives the molecule its name) and counting anticlockwise there are chlorines on carbon-2 and carbon-4.

So this is 2,4-dichlorophenol.

Practice Questions — Application

Q1 Name these aromatic compounds:

a) b) c)

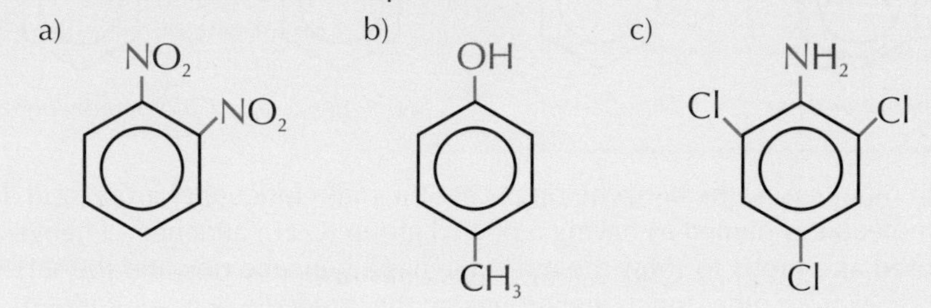

Q2 The graph below shows the enthalpies of hydrogenation of cyclohexene and benzene.

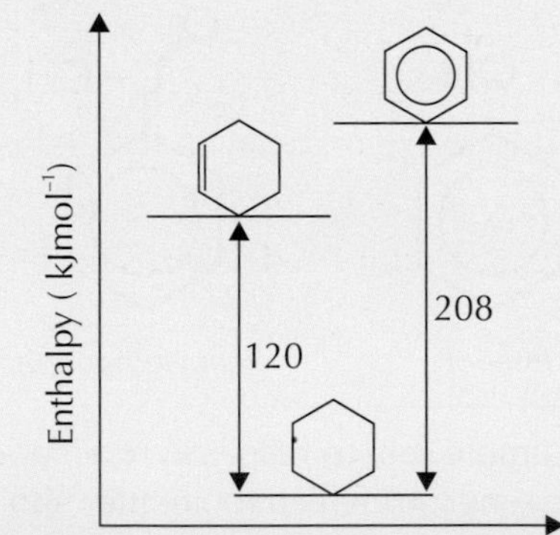

a) Describe Kekulé's model for the structure of benzene.

b) Use the information in the graph to explain why Kekulé's model for the structure of benzene was incorrect.

Practice Questions — Fact Recall

Q1 What are aromatic compounds?

Q2 Describe the structure of benzene according to the delocalisation model.

Q3 Explain how information on the bond lengths in benzene provides support for the delocalisation model.

2. Reactions of Aromatics

You need to know some of the main reactions of aromatic compounds — plus, there's another reaction mechanism for you to learn.

Learning Objectives:

- Understand that electrophilic attack in arenes results in substitution.
- Understand the mechanism of nitration, including the formation of the nitronium ion.
- Understand that nitration is an important step in synthesis (e.g. manufacture of explosives and formation of amines from which dyestuffs are manufactured).
- Understand that Friedel–Crafts acylation reactions are important steps in synthesis.
- Understand the mechanism of acylation using $AlCl_3$ as a catalyst.

Specification Reference 3.4.6

Electrophilic substitution

The benzene ring is a region of high electron density, so it attracts electrophiles. Electrophiles are electron pair acceptors — they are usually a bit short of electrons so are attracted to areas of high electron density. Common electrophiles include positively charged ions (e.g. H^+ or NO_2^+), and polar molecules (e.g. carbonyl compounds), which have a partial positive charge.

As the benzene ring's so stable, it tends to undergo **electrophilic substitution** reactions, which preserve the delocalised ring. The general mechanism for electrophilic substitution on a benzene ring is shown below:

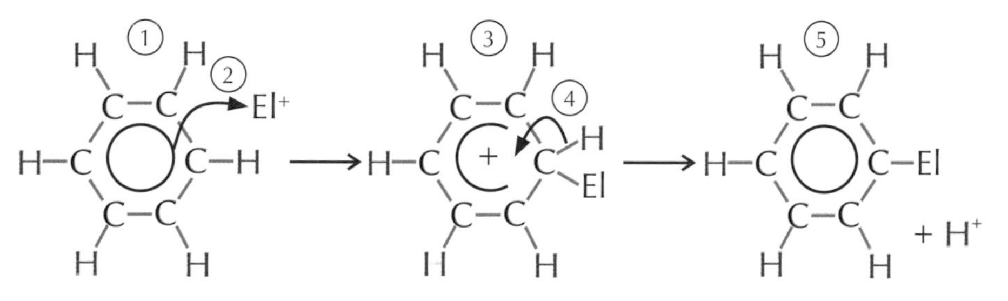

1. The electron dense region at the centre of the benzene ring attracts an electrophile (El^+).
2. The electrophile steals a pair of electrons from the centre of the benzene ring and forms a bond with one of the carbons.
3. This partially breaks the delocalised electron ring and gives the molecule a positive charge.
4. To regain the stability of the benzene ring, the carbon which is now bound to the electrophile loses a hydrogen.
5. So you get the substitution of an H^+ with the electrophile.

You need to know two electrophilic substitution mechanisms for benzene — the nitration reaction (below) and Friedel-Crafts acylation (page 92).

Tip: Don't get confused between electrophiles and nucleophiles. Just remember, electrophiles love electrons.

Nitration

When you warm benzene with concentrated nitric acid and concentrated sulfuric acid, you get nitrobenzene. The overall equation for this reaction is:

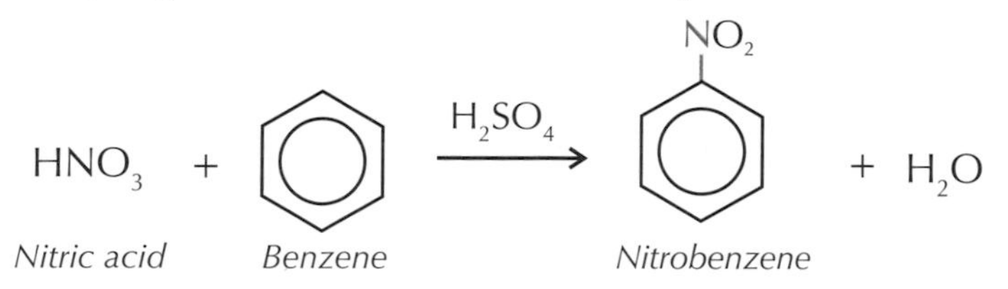

Sulfuric acid acts as a catalyst — it helps to make the nitronium ion, NO_2^+, which is the electrophile. The formation of the nitronium ion is the first step of the reaction mechanism. The equation for this reaction is shown below:

$$HNO_3 + H_2SO_4 \rightarrow HSO_4^- + NO_2^+ + H_2O$$

Once the nitronium ion has been formed, it can react with benzene to form nitrobenzene. This is the electrophilic substitution step in the reaction.

Exam Tip
In your exam, you'll often be asked to write out the equation for the formation of the nitronium ion before giving the rest of the mechanism for nitration — so make sure you learn it.

Here's the mechanism for the electrophilic substitution part of the reaction:

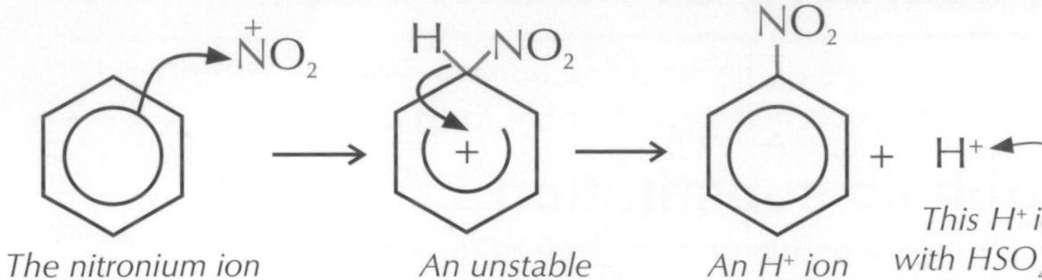

If you only want one NO_2 group added (mononitration), you need to keep the temperature below 55 °C. Above this temperature you'll get lots of substitutions.

Figure 1: *Blocks of TNT explosives.*

Uses of nitration reactions

Nitro compounds can be reduced to form aromatic amines (see page 100). These are used to manufacture dyes and pharmaceuticals. Nitro compounds decompose violently when heated, so they are used as explosives — such as 2,4,6-trinitromethylbenzene (trinitrotoluene (TNT) — see Figures 1 and 2).

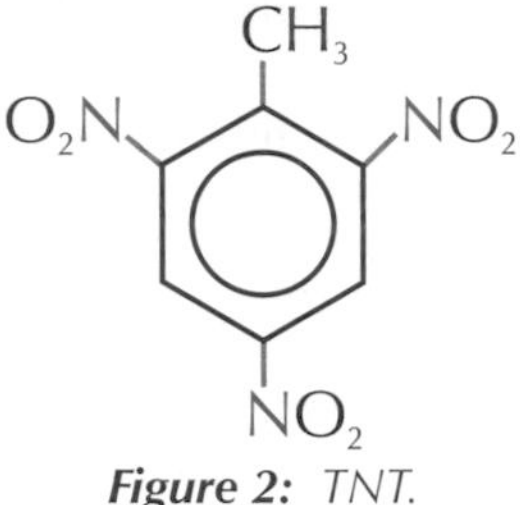

Figure 2: *TNT.*

Friedel-Crafts acylation

Many useful chemicals such as dyes and pharmaceuticals contain benzene rings, but because benzene is so stable, it's fairly unreactive. Friedel-Crafts acylation reactions are used to add an acyl group (–C(=O)–R) to the benzene ring. The products of the reaction are HCl and a phenylketone. The reactants need to be heated under reflux in a non-aqueous environment for the reaction to occur. Here's the equation for the reaction:

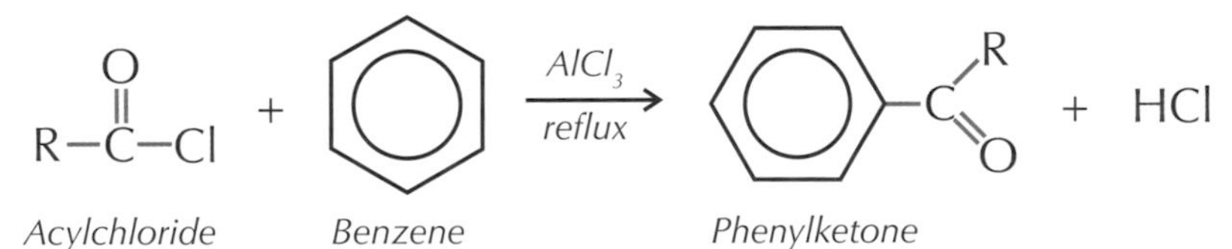

Figure 3: *Charles Friedel — co-developer of Friedel-Crafts acylation.*

Once an acyl group has been added, the side chains can be modified by further reactions to produce useful products.

An electrophile has to have a pretty strong positive charge to be able to attack the stable benzene ring — most just aren't polarised enough. But some can be made into stronger electrophiles using a catalyst called a **halogen carrier**.

Friedel-Crafts acylation uses an acyl chloride to provide the electrophile and a halogen carrier such as $AlCl_3$. $AlCl_3$ accepts a lone pair of electrons from the acyl chloride. As the lone pair of electrons is pulled away, the polarisation in the acyl chloride increases and it forms a carbocation. This makes it a much, much stronger electrophile, and gives it a strong enough charge to react with the benzene ring. The formation of the carbocation is the first step in the reaction mechanism and is shown below:

Acyl chlorides are weak electrophiles. *The halogen carrier accepts a lone pair of electrons from the acyl chloride.* *The carbocation generated is a much stronger electrophile than the acyl chloride.*

$$R-\overset{\delta^- O}{\overset{\|}{C^{\delta+}}}-Cl^{\delta-}: + AlCl_3 \longrightarrow R-\overset{O}{\overset{\|}{C^+}} + AlCl_4^-$$

Tip: There are other types of halogen carrier, but $AlCl_3$ is the only one you need to know about.

Exam Tip
The formation of the carbocation is part of the reaction mechanism so make sure you include it in the exam.

And here's the second step in the reaction mechanism, the electrophilic substitution bit:

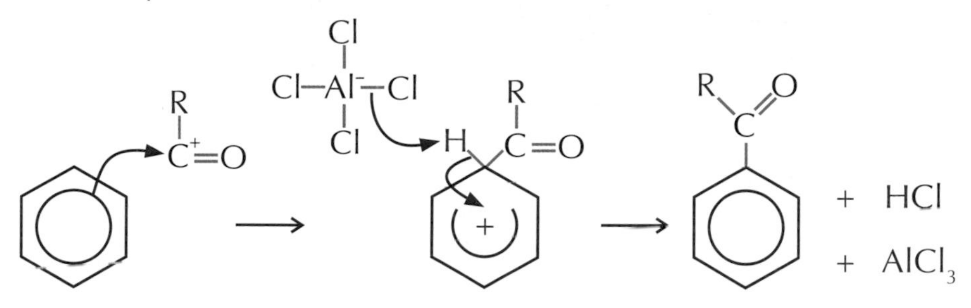

Electrons in the benzene ring are attracted to the positively charged carbocation. Two electrons from the benzene bond with the carbocation. This partially breaks the delocalised ring and gives it a positive charge.

The negatively charged $AlCl_4^-$ ion is attracted to the positively charged ring. One chloride ion breaks away from the aluminium chloride ion and bonds with the hydrogen. This removes the hydrogen from the ring, forming HCl. It also allows the catalyst to reform. Any acyl chloride can react with benzene in this way.

Example

Ethanoyl chloride reacts with benzene to produce phenyl ethanone:

$$CH_3COCl + AlCl_3 \rightarrow CH_3CO^+ + AlCl_4^-$$

Exam Tip
You could draw out the full structure of benzene when writing out this equation — but these simplified diagrams are a lot quicker and could save you valuable time in your exam.

Exam Tip
When drawing the intermediates of these reactions, make sure the horseshoe in the middle of the benzene ring only extends from carbon-2 to carbon-6.

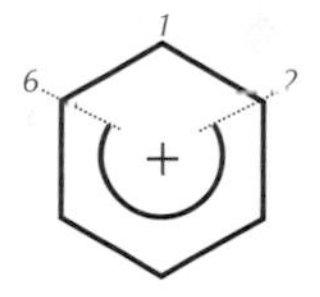

If you make it any bigger you'll lose marks.

Exam Tip
When drawing these mechanisms in your exam, make sure your curly arrows clearly go from the delocalised ring of electrons to the carbocation and from the C-H bond back to the delocalised electron ring. Just drawing your curly arrows to/from the centre of benzene won't be enough to get you all the marks.

Practice Questions — Application

Q1 Phenylmethanone can be produced using Friedel-Craft acylation.
  a) Write out an equation for this reaction.
  b) Suggest a suitable catalyst for this reaction.
  c) Name and outline the mechanism for this reaction.

Q2 a) Draw the mechanism for the formation of nitrobenzene from benzene and concentrated nitric acid.
  b) What two conditions are needed for this reaction to occur?

Practice Questions — Fact Recall

Q1 Explain why electrophiles are attracted to aromatic compounds.

Q2 Give two uses of nitro compounds produced by nitration of benzene.

Q3 Explain the role of $AlCl_3$ in Friedel-Crafts acylation.

Learning Objectives:

- Be able to apply IUPAC rules for naming amines and amides.
- Know that quaternary ammonium salts can be used as cationic surfactants.
- Be able to explain the difference in base strength between ammonia, primary aliphatic and primary aromatic amines in terms of the availability of a lone pair on the N atom.

Specification Reference 3.4.4, 3.4.7

3. Amines and Amides

Amines and amides are produced from ammonia (NH_3). You probably met amines at AS-level, but now you need to know a bit more about them. The next couple of pages are all about amines, amides and why they're useful.

What are amines?

If one or more of the hydrogens in ammonia (NH_3) is replaced with an organic group, you get an **amine**. If one hydrogen is replaced with an organic group, you get a primary amine — if two are replaced, it's a secondary amine, three means it's a tertiary amine and if a fourth organic group is added it's called a quaternary ammonium ion (see Figure 1).

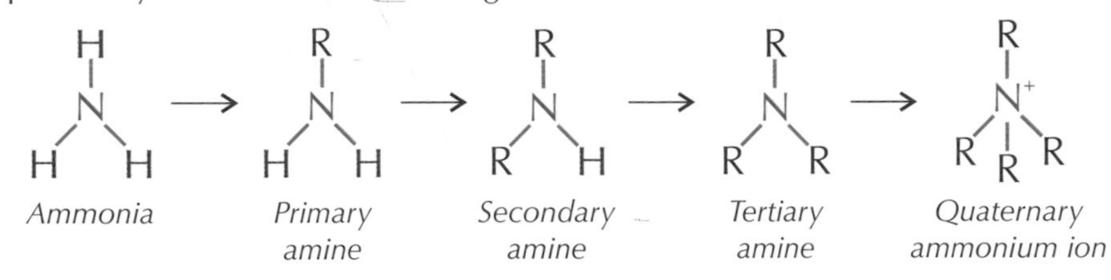

Figure 1: *Diagram showing the different types of amine.*

Because quaternary ammonium ions are positively charged, they will hang around with any negative ions that are near. The complexes formed are called quaternary ammonium salts — like tetramethylammonium chloride ($(CH_3)_4N^+Cl^-$). Small amines smell similar to ammonia, with a slightly 'fishy' twist. Larger amines smell very 'fishy'. (Nice.)

Naming amines

Naming amines is similar to naming other organic compounds. The suffix is -amine (or -amine ion if it's a quaternary ammonium ion). The prefix depends on what organic groups are attached. If the organic groups are all the same you also need to add di- for secondary amines, tri- for tertiary amines and tetra- for quaternary ammonium ions.

Tip: See pages 46-49 for info. on how to name other organic groups.

Examples

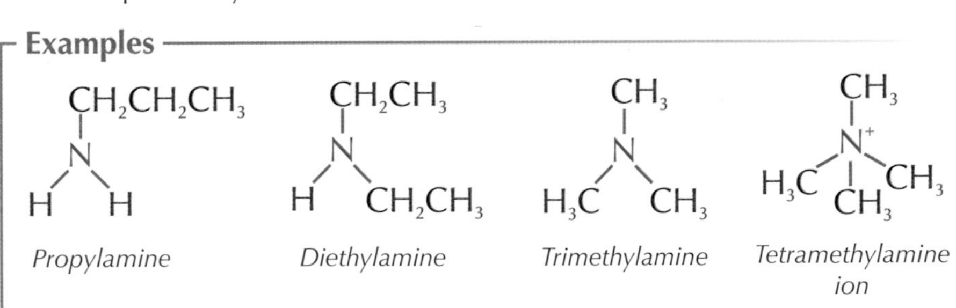

If the amine has more than one type of organic group attached, you list the different groups in alphabetical order.

Example

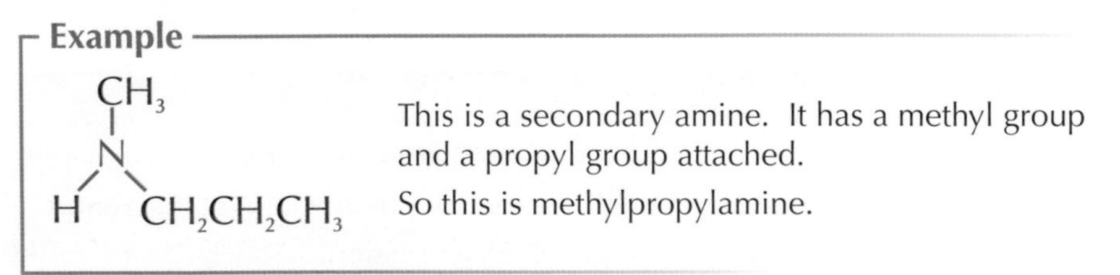

This is a secondary amine. It has a methyl group and a propyl group attached.

So this is methylpropylamine.

You can also get aromatic amines. See page 89 for how to name these.

Tip: Aliphatic amines are amines without a benzene ring. Aromatic amines are amines with a benzene ring.

Cationic surfactants

Surfactants are compounds which are partly soluble and partly insoluble in water. Some quaternary ammonium compounds can be used as **cationic surfactants** (surfactants which are positively charged). These compounds are quaternary ammonium salts with at least one long hydrocarbon chain. The long hydrocarbon chain is insoluble in water and the positively charged head group is soluble (see Figure 2).

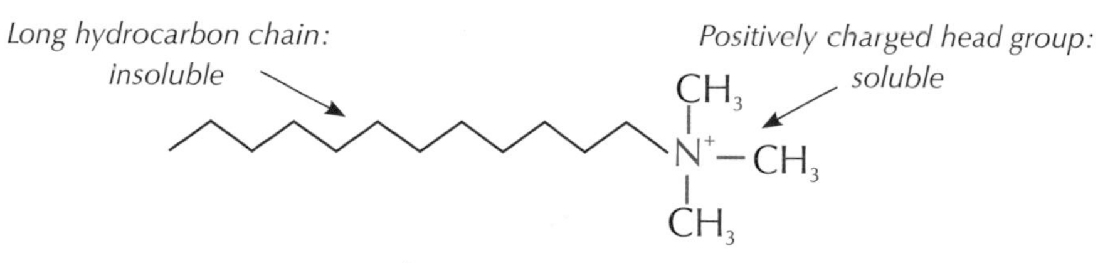

Figure 2: *A cationic surfactant.*

Figure 3: *Fabric softeners contain cationic surfactants.*

Cationic surfactants are used in things like fabric conditioners and hair products. When hair or fabric get wet they pick up negative charges on their surface. The positively charged part of the surfactant is attracted to these negatively charged surfaces and forms a coating over the surface. This coating prevents the build-up of static electricity. In fabric conditioners this is important to keep the fabric smooth and in hair products it helps to keep hair flat.

Forming dative covalent bonds

Amines act as Brønsted-Lowry bases because they accept protons. There's a lone pair of electrons on the nitrogen atom that forms a **dative covalent** (coordinate) bond with an H^+ ion (see Figure 4).

Tip: See page 19 for more on Brønsted-Lowry acids and bases.

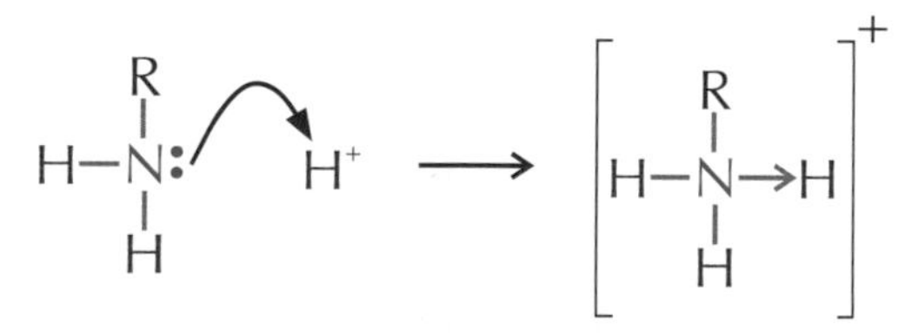

Figure 4: *Formation of a dative bond between a primary amine and an H^+ ion.*

Tip: A dative bond is a type of covalent bond where both of the electrons have been provided by the same atom (in this case the nitrogen atom).

The strength of the base depends on how available the nitrogen's lone pair of electrons is. A lone pair of electrons will be more available if its electron density is higher. The more available the lone pair is, the more likely the amine is to accept a proton, and the stronger a base it will be.

Aromatic amines are weak bases. This is because the benzene ring draws electrons towards itself and the nitrogen's lone pair gets partially delocalised onto the ring. So the electron density on the nitrogen decreases. This makes the lone pair much less available.

Primary aliphatic amines are strong bases. This is because alkyl groups push electrons onto attached groups. So the electron density on the nitrogen atom increases. This makes the lone pair more available.

The strength of ammonia as a base lies somewhere in between. This is because ammonia doesn't have an aromatic group to pull the lone pair of electrons away, or an alkyl group to push the lone pair of electrons forward — see Figure 5.

Exam Tip
You need to be able to explain the difference in base strength between ammonia, primary aromatic amines and primary aliphatic amines — so make sure you understand these explanations.

Areas of highest electron density

Weakest Base
Lone pair least available → ***Strongest Base***
Lone pair most available

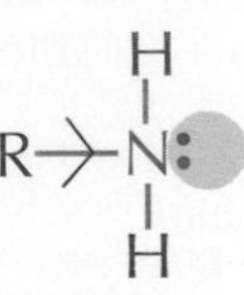

The benzene ring draws electrons towards itself, making the lone pair of electrons less available.

The alkyl group pushes electrons away from itself, making the lone pair of electrons more available.

Figure 5: *Diagram showing why aromatic amines are weaker bases than ammonia and why aliphatic primary amines are stronger bases than ammonia.*

Tip: The effect of an alkyl group on a lone pair of electrons is sometimes called the inductive effect.

Amides

Amides are derivatives of carboxylic acids. They contain the functional group $-CONH_2$. The carbonyl group pulls electrons away from the NH_2 group, so amides behave differently from amines. Here's the general structure of an amine:

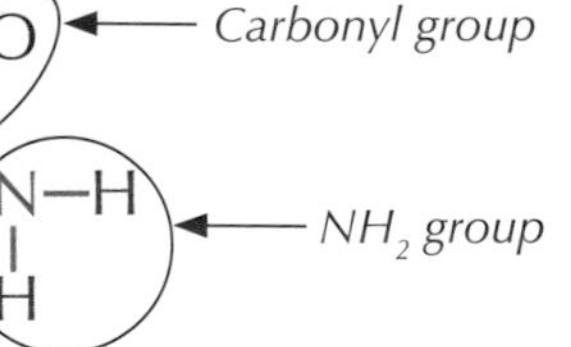

Carbonyl group

The carbonyl group pulls electrons away from the NH_2 group.

NH_2 group

Tip: Don't get confused between amides and amines. Just remember, ami<u>d</u>es contain a C=O <u>d</u>ouble bond — ami<u>n</u>es contain <u>n</u>o double bonds.

Naming amides is pretty easy — the suffix is always -amide and the prefix comes from the alkyl group (R).

Examples

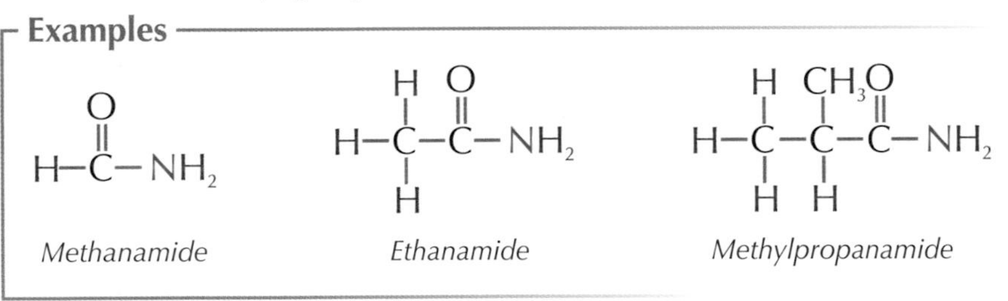

You can also get **N-substituted amides**. These are amides where one of the hydrogens attached to the nitrogen has been substituted with an alkyl group. When naming N-substituted amides, you have to add an extra bit onto the beginning of the name. The name starts with N-something (e.g. N-methyl, N-ethyl, N-propyl) — whatever the alkyl group that's been added onto the nitrogen is.

Tip: Amides can be made by reacting acyl chlorides with ammonia and N-substituted amides can be made by reacting acyl chlorides with amines. See pages 78 and 79 for more.

Examples

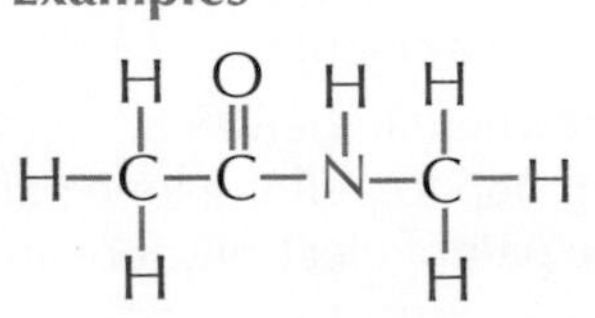

This molecule is based on ethanamide.

One of the hydrogens attached to the nitrogen has been substituted with a methyl group.

So this is N-methylethanamide.

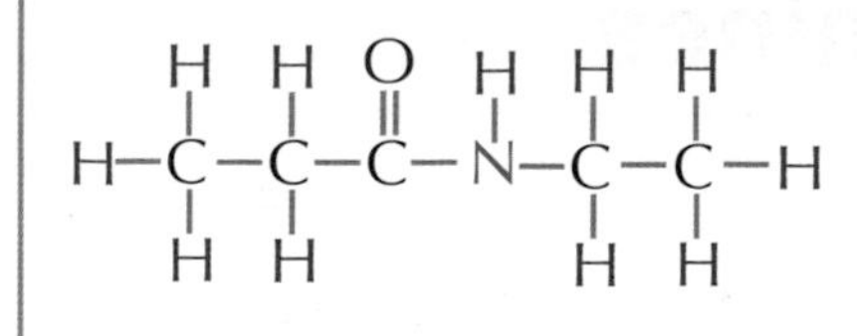

This is based on propanamide.

One of the hydrogens attached to the nitrogen has been substituted with an ethyl group.

So this is N-ethylpropanamide.

Exam Tip

You don't need to know much about amides. As long as you can name them and know how they can be produced from acyl chlorides (see pages 78-79) or acid anhydrides (see page 82) you should be fine in your exam.

Practice Questions — Application

Q1 Name these amines:

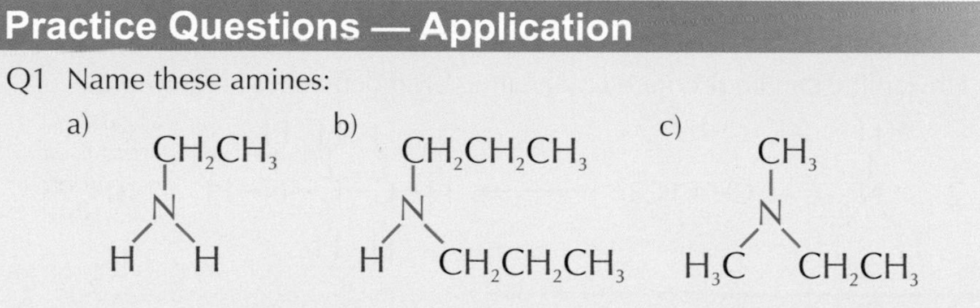

Q2 Ammonia, phenylamine and ethylamine, shown below, can all act as Brønsted-Lowry bases:

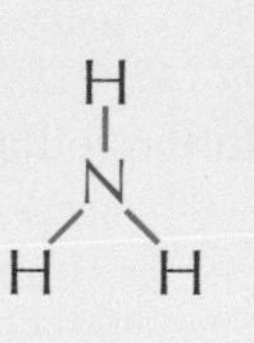

Ammonia

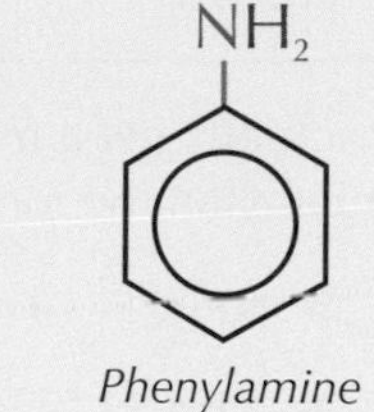

Phenylamine

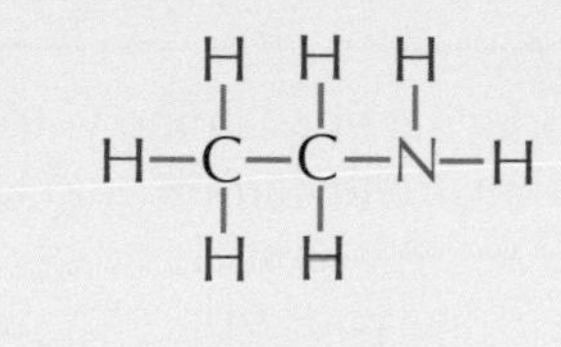

Ethylamine

a) Which of these is the strongest base? Explain your answer.

b) Which of these is the weakest base? Explain your answer.

Q3 Name these amides:

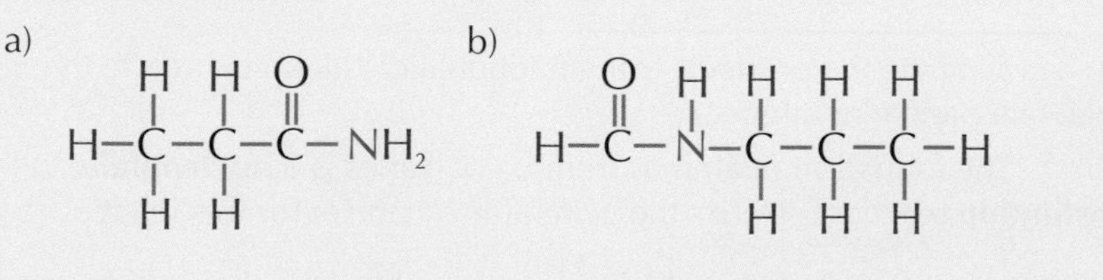

Practice Questions — Fact Recall

Q1 What is a quaternary ammonium ion?

Q2 a) What type of ammonium compound can be used as a cationic surfactant?

b) Give one use of cationic surfactants.

Q3 Amines can act as bases. What determines the strength of the base?

4. Reactions of Amines

The previous section was all about amines and why they are useful. This section covers how amines are made from other organic compounds.

Learning Objectives:

- Understand that the nucleophilic substitution reactions (including mechanism) of ammonia and amines with haloalkanes form primary, secondary, tertiary amines and quaternary ammonium salts.
- Know that primary aliphatic amines can be prepared from haloalkanes and by the reduction of nitriles.
- Know that aromatic amines are prepared by the reduction of nitro compounds.

Specification Reference 3.4.7

Formation of amines from haloalkanes

There are two ways to produce aliphatic amines — the first uses haloalkanes. Amines can be made by heating a haloalkane with excess ammonia.

Example

Ethylamine can be produced by heating bromoethane with ammonia:

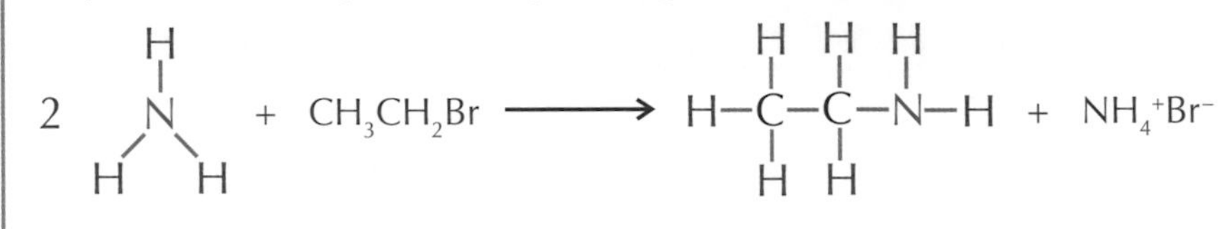

But, things aren't that simple. You'll actually get a mixture of primary, secondary and tertiary amines, and quaternary ammonium salts, as more than one hydrogen is likely to be substituted.

Example

When producing ethylamine you'll actually get a mixture of ethylamine, diethylamine, triethylamine and tetraethylamine ions:

$$NH_3 + CH_3CH_2Br \rightarrow \begin{cases} NH_2CH_3CH_2 \\ NH(CH_3CH_2)_2 \\ N(CH_3CH_2)_3 \\ N(CH_3CH_2)_4^+ \end{cases} + NH_4^+Br^-$$

Tip: See pages 47 and 48 for more on haloalkanes.

You can separate the products using fractional distillation if you're trying to make one particular amine.

The formation of amines from haloalkanes is a **nucleophilic substitution** reaction. Here's the general mechanism for this reaction:

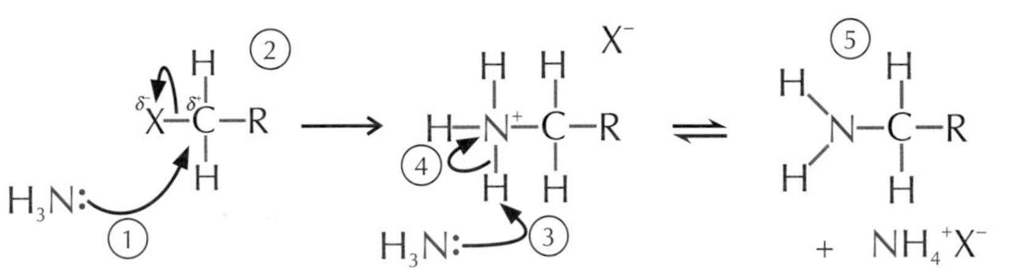

Tip: The nitrogen in the amine has a lone pair of electrons on it. This means it can accept a hydrogen and form an alkylammonium salt — so the conversion of an alkylammonium salt to an amine is reversible.

1. NH_3 (the nucleophile) attacks the δ^+ carbon on the haloalkane and donates its lone pair of electrons, forming a bond with the carbon.
2. As carbon can only have four bonds, the addition of ammonia causes the C–X bond to break, releasing a negatively charged halide ion and leaving an alkylammonium salt.
3. A second ammonia molecule then donates its lone pair of electrons to one of the hydrogens attached to the nitrogen.
4. This hydrogen breaks off from the alkyl ammonium salt and joins ammonia to form an NH_4^+ ion.
5. This leaves a primary amine. The NH_4^+ ion forms an ionic bond with the X^- ion to produce $NH_4^+X^-$.

Example

Here's the mechanism for the formation of ethylamine from ammonia and bromoethane:

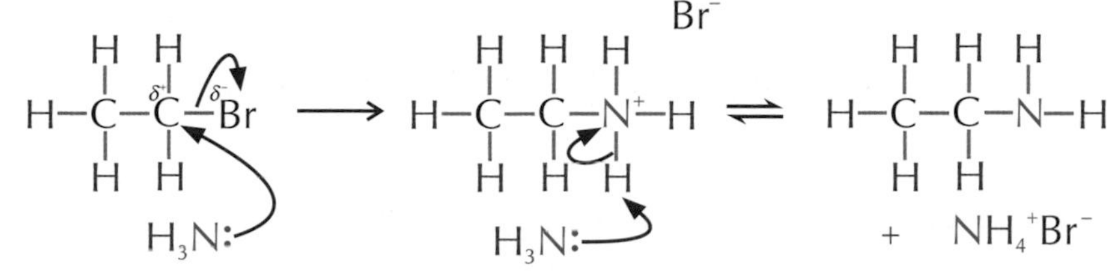

> **Exam Tip**
> You could be asked to name and outline the mechanism for the production of any amine from a haloalkane, so make sure you understand this mechanism — just learning the example won't be enough.

The amine product still has a lone pair of electrons on the nitrogen, so it is still a nucleophile. This means that further substitutions can take place. They keep happening until you get a quaternary ammonium salt, which can't react any further as it doesn't have a lone pair of electrons (see Figure 1).

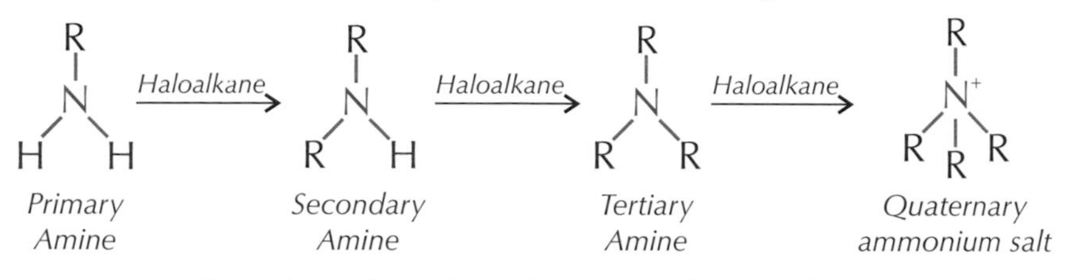

Figure 1: *Further substitutions lead to the formation of secondary, tertiary and quaternary amines.*

> **Tip:** The number of further substitutions that happen can be reduced by increasing the amount of ammonia — the more ammonia there is, the less likely it is that a haloalkane will meet and react with an amine rather than ammonia.

The mechanism for these further substitutions is the same — you just use an amine instead of ammonia.

Example

Here's the mechanism for the formation of dimethylamine from methylamine and bromomethane:

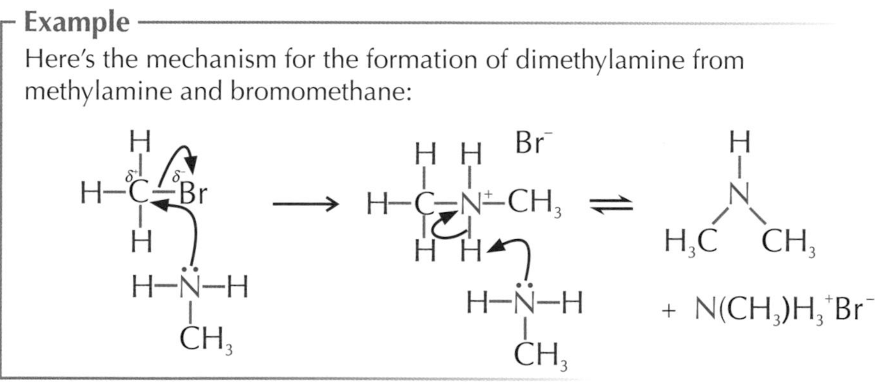

> **Tip:** Amines and ammonia can both act as nucleophiles in nucleophilic substitution reactions because they both have a lone pair of electrons.

Formation of amines from nitriles

The second way to produce aliphatic amines uses nitriles. You can reduce a nitrile to an amine using a strong reducing agent such as lithium aluminium hydride ($LiAlH_4$) followed by some dilute acid.

Example

Here's the equation for the formation of ethylamine from ethanenitrile:

$$\underset{\textit{Ethanenitrile}}{CH_3C{\equiv}N} + 4[H] \xrightarrow[\textit{2. Dilute acid}]{\textit{1. LiAlH}_4} \underset{\textit{Ethylamine}}{CH_3CH_2NH_2}$$

> **Tip:** Forming amines by reducing nitriles is useful if you just want the primary amine because you can't get further substitutions — the primary amine is the only product.

Another way is to reflux the nitrile with sodium metal and ethanol. These are great in the lab, but $LiAlH_4$ and sodium are too expensive for industrial use. Industry uses a metal catalyst such as platinum or nickel at a high temperature and pressure — it's called **catalytic hydrogenation**.

Example

Here's the equation for the formation of ethylamine from ethanenitrile using catalytic hydrogenation:

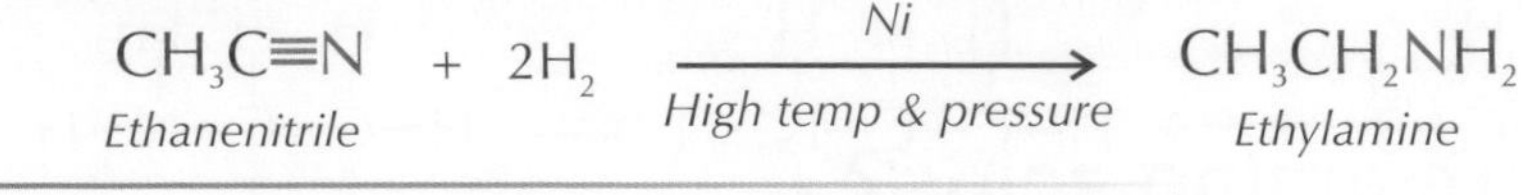

$$CH_3C{\equiv}N + 2H_2 \xrightarrow[\text{High temp \& pressure}]{Ni} CH_3CH_2NH_2$$

Ethanenitrile → *Ethylamine*

Formation of aromatic amines

Aromatic amines are produced by reducing a nitro compound, such as nitrobenzene. There are two steps to the method:

- First you need to heat a mixture of a nitro compound, tin metal and concentrated hydrochloric acid under reflux — this makes a salt.
- Then to turn the salt into an aromatic amine, you need to add an alkali, such as sodium hydroxide solution.

Tip: See page 91 for more on nitrobenzene and how it is made.

Example

Phenylamine can be made by reducing nitrobenzene:

- Mixing nitrobenzene with tin and concentrated HCl and heating under reflux produces the salt $C_6H_5NH_3^+ Cl^-$.
- Adding NaOH to this salt then releases phenylamine.

Here's the overall equation for the reaction:

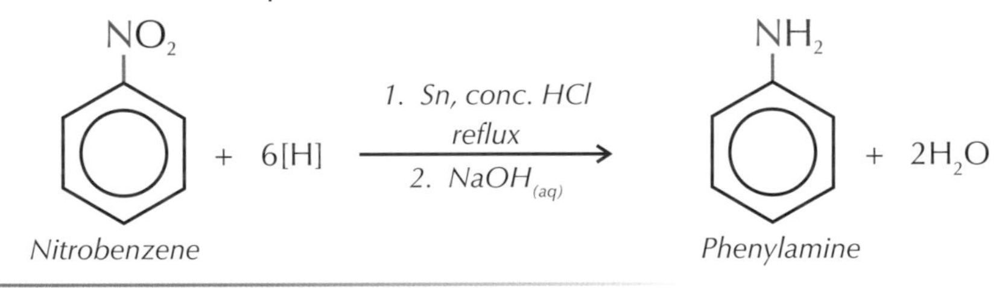

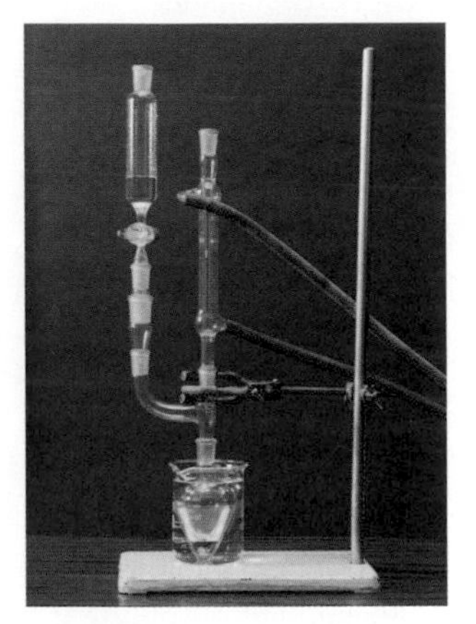

Figure 2: *The reflux equipment used to make phenylamine.*

Practice Questions — Application

Q1 a) Write an equation to show the formation of methylamine from chloromethane.

b) Name and outline the mechanism for this reaction.

Q2 a) Write an equation to show the formation of propylamine from propanenitrile by catalytic hydrogenation.

b) What conditions are required for this reaction?

Q3 Write an equation to show the formation of 3-methylphenylamine from 3-methylnitrobenzene.

Practice Questions — Fact Recall

Q1 a) How can amines be produced from haloalkanes?

b) Explain why a mixture of primary, secondary, tertiary and quaternary amines are produced in these reactions.

c) How can the products of these reactions be separated?

Q2 a) Give three ways that amines can be produced from nitriles.

b) Which of these methods is used in industry, and why?

Q3 Describe how aromatic amines can be produced.

5. Amino Acids and Proteins

This is where chemistry and biology start to overlap. Proteins are an important component of any living organism. The building blocks of proteins are called amino acids. Read on to find out all about them.

Learning Objectives:

- Understand that amino acids have both acidic and basic properties.
- Be able to apply IUPAC rules for naming amino acids.
- Understand that amino acids can form zwitterions.
- Know that mixtures of amino acids can be separated by chromatography.
- Understand that proteins are sequences of amino acids joined by peptide links.
- Understand that hydrolysis of the peptide link produces the constituent amino acids.
- Understand the importance of hydrogen bonding in proteins (detailed structures not required).

Specification Reference 3.4.4, 3.4.8

What are amino acids?

An **amino acid** has two functional groups — an amino group (NH_2) and a carboxyl group (COOH). The structure of all amino acids is the same apart from an alkyl side chain (R) that is different in each. The general structure of an amino acid is given in Figure 1.

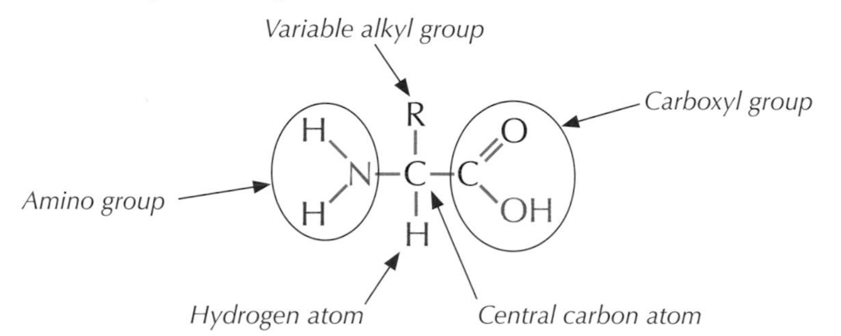

Figure 1: *The general structure of an amino acid.*

Amino acids are interesting molecules because they are **amphoteric** — this means they've got both acidic and basic properties. They can act as acids because the carboxyl group is acidic — it can donate a proton:

$$\text{-COOH} \rightleftharpoons \text{-COO}^- + \text{H}^+$$

They can act as bases because the amino group is basic — it can accept a proton:

$$\text{-NH}_2 + \text{H}^+ \rightleftharpoons \text{-NH}_3^+$$

Amino acids are chiral molecules because the carbon usually has four different groups attached. So a solution of a single amino acid enantiomer will rotate polarised light — see Figure 2.

Tip: See pages 56-59 for more on optical isomerism and chirality.

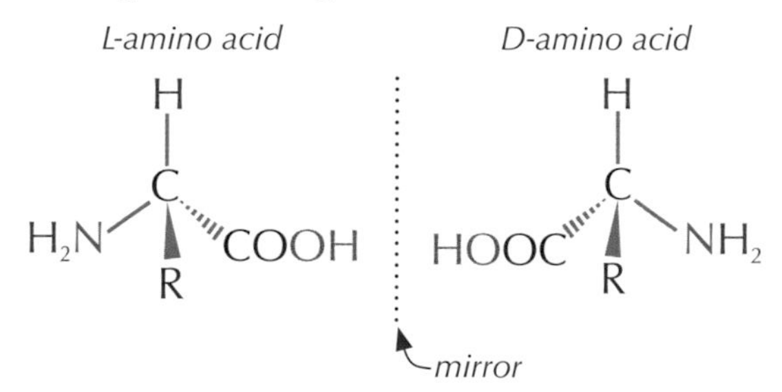

Figure 2: *The two different amino acid enantiomers.*

Tip: The only amino acid that isn't chiral is glycine because its alkyl side chain is just a hydrogen — so there are two hydrogens attached to the central carbon.

Tip: In nature the vast majority of amino acids are in the L-form, but some D-form amino acids do exist.

Naming amino acids

Amino acids often have a common and a systematic name. There's no way of working out the common names, but you can work out the systematic names. To name an amino acid systematically just follow these steps:

1. Find the longest carbon chain that includes the carboxylic acid group and write down its name.
2. Number the carbons in the chain starting with the carbon in the carboxylic acid group as number 1.

3. Write down the positions of any NH_2 groups and show that they are NH_2 groups with the word 'amino'.
4. Write down the names of any other functional groups and say which carbon they are on.

Exam Tip
Don't worry about learning the common names of the amino acids. If you're asked to name an amino acid in your exam just give the systematic name — you can work this out without having to memorise them all.

Examples

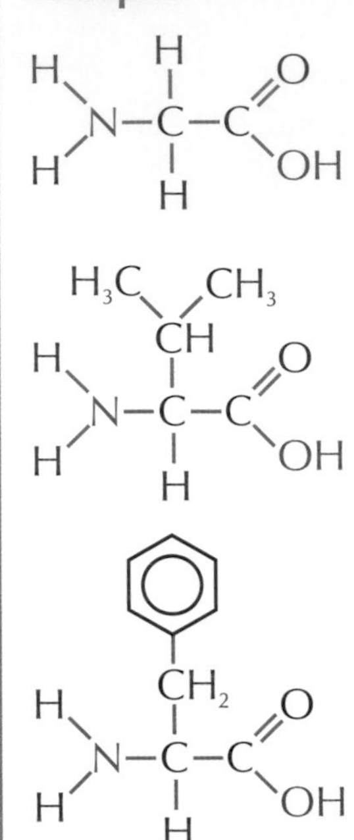

The common name for this amino acid is glycine.
The longest carbon chain is two carbons long so the stem is ethane and the amino group is on carbon-2.
So the systematic name is 2-aminoethanoic acid.

The common name for this amino acid is valine.
The longest carbon chain is four carbons long so the stem is butane. The amino group is on carbon-2 and there is a methyl group on carbon-3.
So this is 2-amino-3-methylbutanoic acid.

The common name for this amino acid is phenylalanine.
The longest carbon chain is three carbons long so the stem is propane. The amino group is on carbon-2 and there is a phenyl group on carbon-3.
So this is 2-amino-3-phenylpropanoic acid.

Exam Tip
The amino acid side chains can get really complicated, but don't worry — you won't be asked to name anything too complicated in your exam.

Zwitterions

Amino acids can exist as **zwitterions**. A zwitterion is a dipolar ion — it has both a positive and a negative charge in different parts of the molecule. Zwitterions only exist near an amino acid's **isoelectric point**. This is the pH where the average overall charge on the amino acid is zero. It's different for different amino acids — it depends on their R-group.

An amino acid becomes a zwitterion when its amino group is protonated to NH_3^+ and its OH group is deprotonated to OH^-.

- In conditions more acidic than the isoelectric point, the $-NH_2$ group is likely to be protonated but the –COOH group will be unchanged — so the amino acid will carry a positive charge but not a negative charge.
- In conditions more basic than the isoelectric point, the –COOH group is likely to lose its proton but the $-NH_2$ group will be unchanged — so the amino acid will carry a negative charge but not a positive charge.
- Only at or near the isoelectric point are both the carboxyl group and the amino group likely to be ionised — forming a zwitterion (see Figure 3).

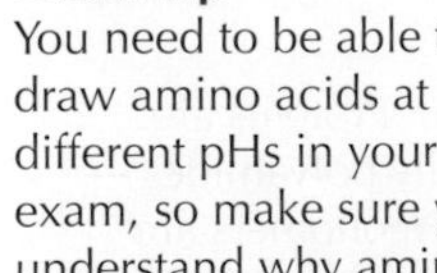

Exam Tip
You need to be able to draw amino acids at different pHs in your exam, so make sure you understand why amino acids have different charges at different pHs.

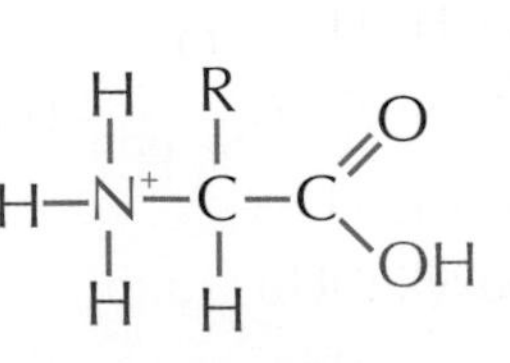

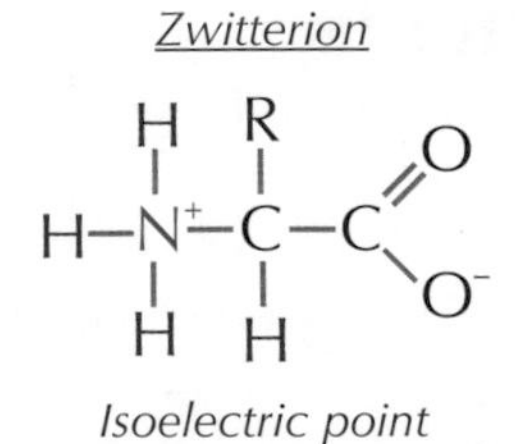

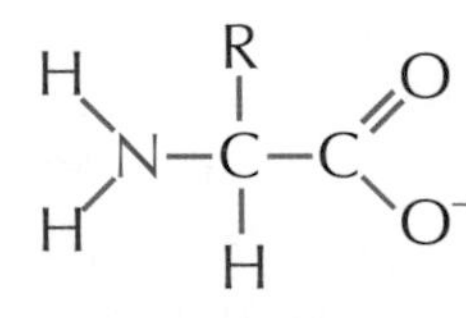

Figure 3: *Formation of a zwitterion.*

Separating mixtures of amino acids

If you have a solution containing a mixture of amino acids, you can use **paper chromatography** to separate them out and identify the different amino acids that make up your solution — see Figure 5. Here's how you do it:

- Draw a pencil line near the bottom of a piece of chromatography paper and put a concentrated spot of the mixture of amino acids on it.
- Dip the bottom of the paper (not the spot) into a solvent.
- As the solvent spreads up the paper, the different amino acids move with it, but at different rates, so they separate out.
- You can identify each amino acid by looking at how far it moves in relation to the solvent and comparing it to a standard.
- Amino acids aren't coloured — so you have to spray ninhydrin solution on the paper to turn them purple.

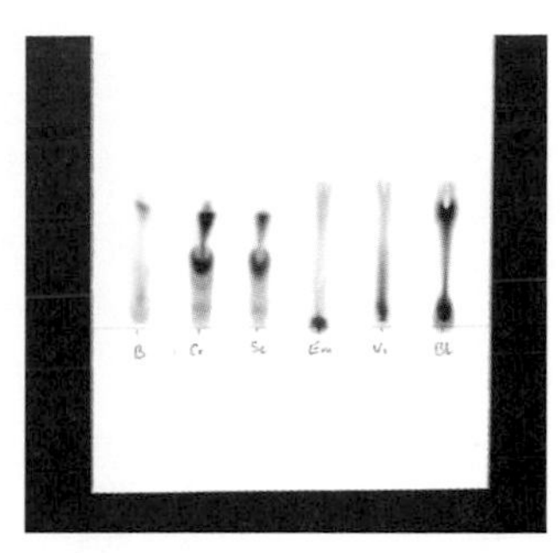

Figure 4: Paper chromatography of coloured dyes. You can see how the dyes move up the paper with the solvent and separate — just like the amino acids do.

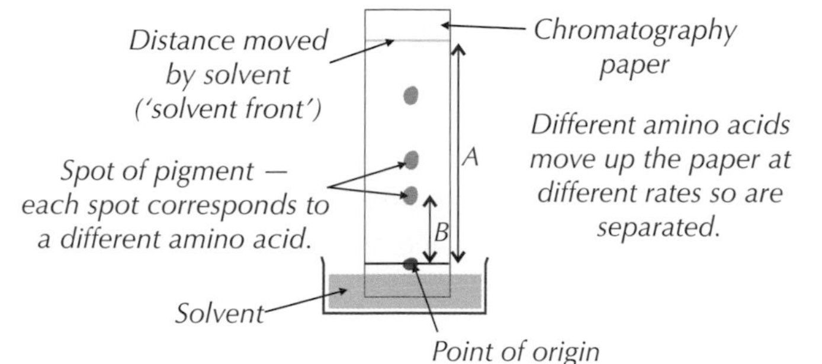

Figure 5: Paper chromatography can be used to separate mixtures of amino acids.

Forming proteins

Proteins are condensation polymers of amino acids — they are made up of lots of amino acids joined together by peptide links. The chain is put together by condensation reactions and broken apart by hydrolysis reactions.
Here's how two amino acids join together to make a dipeptide:

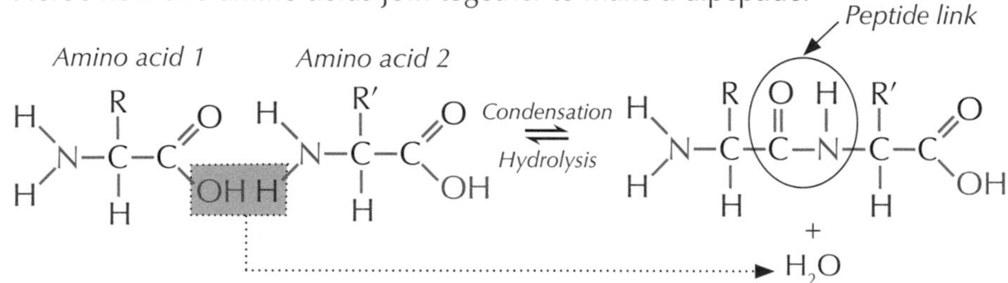

If the two amino acids that are combining are different, then two different dipeptides will be formed because the amino acids can join either way round.

Example

A molecule of alanine and a molecule of glycine could join to form either of these dipeptides:

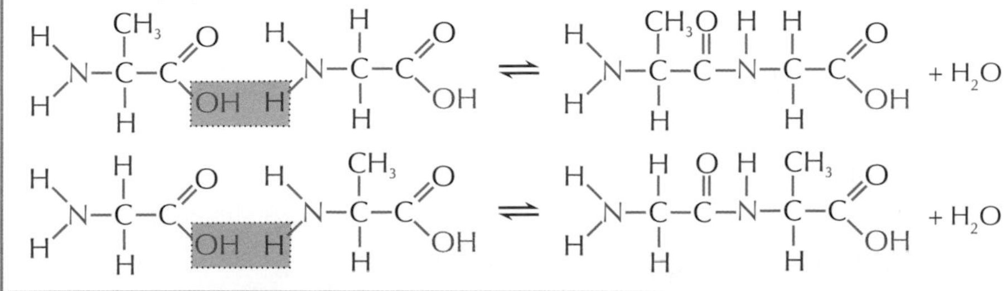

Tip: Some proteins are made from more than one amino acid chain.

Tip: A condensation reaction is a reaction which joins two molecules together and releases water.
A hydrolysis reaction is a reaction that splits a larger molecule into two smaller molecules using water.

Tip: Proteins are really polyamides — the monomers are joined by amide groups. In proteins these are called peptide links.

Tip: Proteins hold living organisms together so it's really important that they're difficult to break down — otherwise we'd just fall to pieces.

To break up the protein (hydrolyse it) you need to use pretty harsh conditions. Aqueous 6 M hydrochloric acid is added, and the mixture is heated under reflux for 24 hours. The final mixture is then neutralised.

Hydrogen bonding in proteins

Proteins are not just straight chains of amino acids. Instead, the chains fold or twist due to intermolecular and intramolecular forces. **Hydrogen bonding** is one type of force that holds proteins in shape. Hydrogen bonds exist between polar groups — e.g. $-OH$ and $-NH_2$. These groups contain electronegative atoms which induce a partial positive charge on the hydrogen atom. This hydrogen is then attracted to lone pairs of electrons on adjacent polar groups and a hydrogen bond is formed — see Figure 6.

Tip: Hydrogen bonding was covered at AS level, so get your old AS notes out if you need a bit of a reminder.

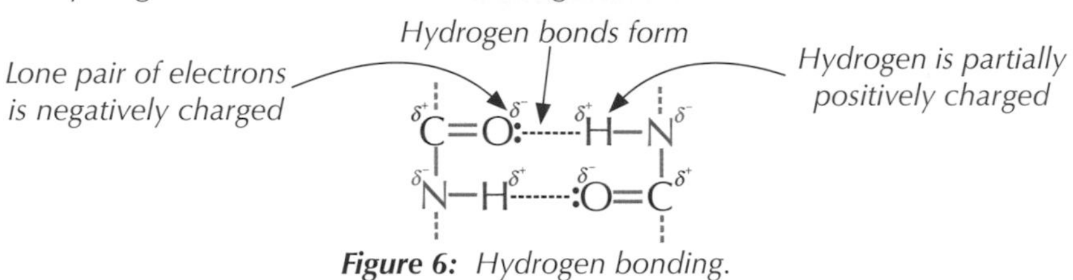

Figure 6: *Hydrogen bonding.*

Their 3-dimensional shape is vital to how proteins function. For example, changing the shape of a protein that acts as an enyzme can stop it working. Factors such as heat and pH can affect hydrogen bonding and so can change the shape of proteins.

Practice Question — Application

Q1 Below are two amino acids (**A** and **B**):

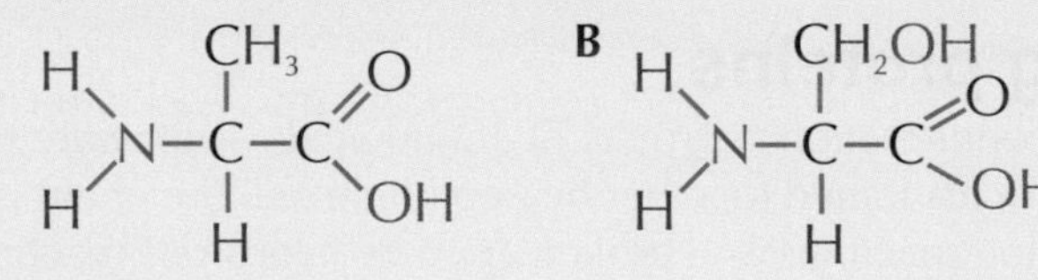

a) Name these amino acids.

b) Draw species **A** at:

(i) low pH (ii) its isoelectric point (iii) high pH

c) Draw the two possible dipeptides that could be formed by joining amino acids **A** and **B**.

Practice Questions — Fact Recall

Q1 Explain why amino acids are amphoteric.

Q2 a) What is a zwitterion?

b) When do amino acids form zwitterions?

Q3 Describe how paper chromatography can be used to separate out a mixture of amino acids.

Q4 By what type of reaction are:

a) amino acids joined to form dipeptides?

b) dipeptides broken down to form amino acids?

Q5 What conditions are needed to break up a protein?

Q6 a) What type of bonds join the amino acids in proteins together?

b) Name a type of bond that holds proteins in a precise 3D shape?

6. Polymers

Lots of small molecules (called monomers) can join together to form really long molecules (called polymers). There are two main types of polymer you need to know about — addition polymers and condensation polymers.

Learning Objectives:

- Be able to draw the repeating unit of addition polymers from monomer structures and vice versa.
- Understand that condensation polymers may be formed by reactions between dicarboxylic acids and diols, between dicarboxylic acids and diamines and between amino acids.
- Know the linkage of the repeating units of polyesters (e.g. Terylene) and polyamides (e.g. nylon 6,6 and Kevlar).

Specification Reference 3.4.9

Addition Polymers

The double bonds in alkenes can break and then join together to make long chains called **addition polymers**. It's like they're holding hands in a big line. The individual, small alkenes are called **monomers**.

Example

Polyphenylethene is a polymer that is made by joining lots of phenylethene monomers together:

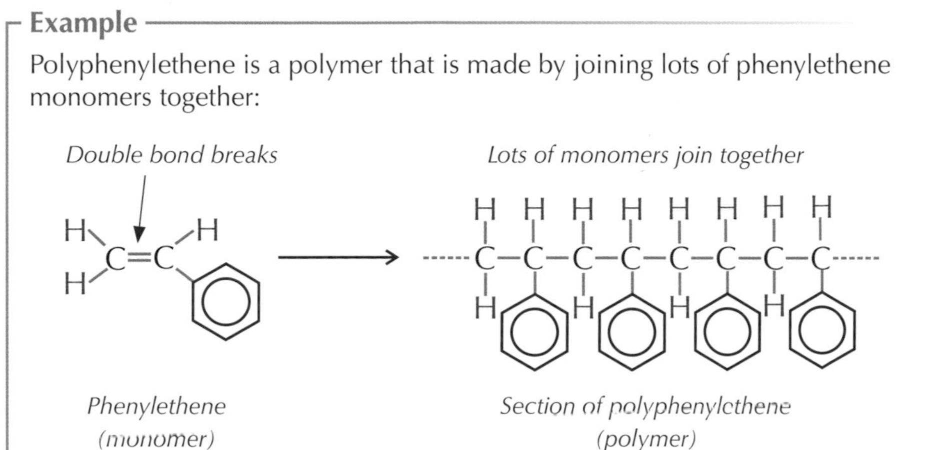

Addition polymers are made up of repeating units (a bit of molecule that repeats over and over again). The repeating unit looks very similar to the monomer but the double bond has opened out. You need to be able to draw repeating units from the structure of a monomer and vice versa.

Tip: The names of polymers can be written with or without the brackets — e.g. poly(chloroethene) or polychloroethene.

Examples

Polychloroethene is made from chloroethene. To draw the repeating unit of polychloroethene just replace the double bond in chloroethene with a single bond and add a bond to each of the carbons:

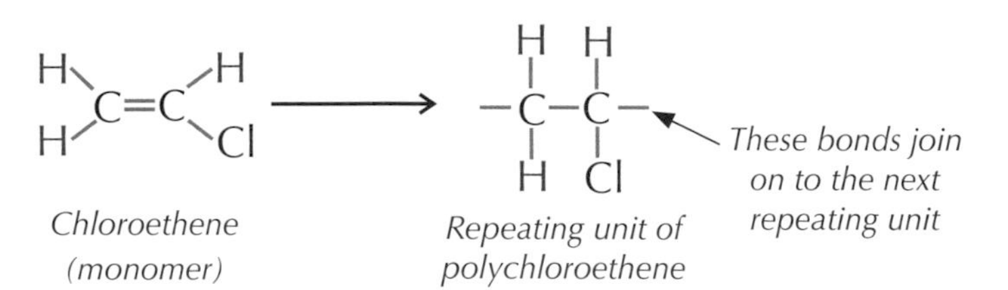

Figure 1: Polychloroethene is also known as PVC. It's used to make loads of things — like credit cards.

The repeating unit of polypropene is shown below. To draw the monomer of polypropene just remove the empty bonds (which join on to the next repeating unit) and replace the central carbon-carbon bond with a double bond:

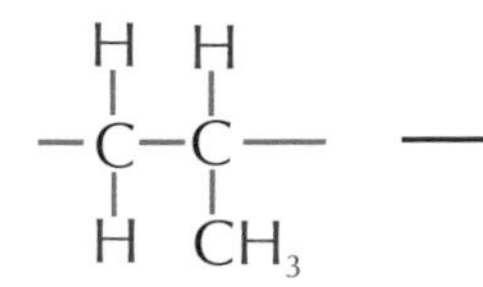

Repeating unit of polypropene

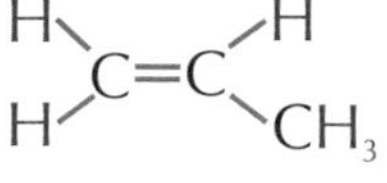

Propene (monomer)

Condensation polymers

Condensation polymerisation usually involves two different types of monomer. Each monomer has at least two functional groups. Each functional group reacts with a group on another monomer to form a link, creating polymer chains. Each time a link is formed, a small molecule is lost (water) — that's why it's called condensation polymerisation. Examples of condensation polymers include polyamides, polyesters and polypeptides (or proteins).

Tip: The formation of polypeptides is covered on page 103.

Formation of polyamides

Reactions between dicarboxylic acids and diamines make polyamides. The carboxyl groups of dicarboxylic acids react with the amino groups of diamines to form amide links — see Figure 2.

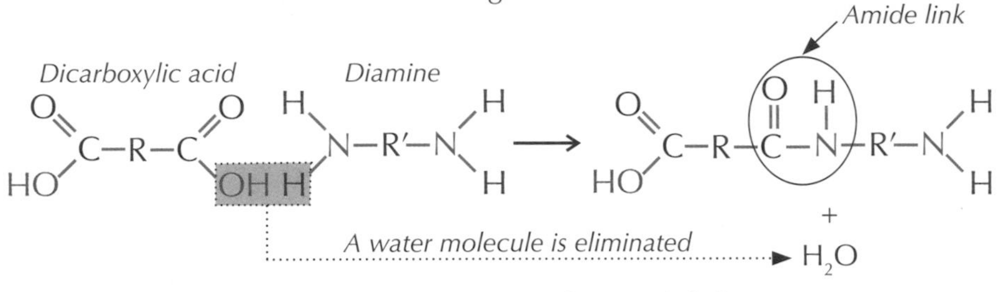

Figure 2: *The formation of an amide link.*

Dicarboxylic acids and diamines have functional groups at both ends, which means that they can form two amide links and long chains can form. There are two polyamides you need to learn the repeating units for:

- Nylon 6,6 — made from 1,6-diaminohexane and hexanedioic acid:

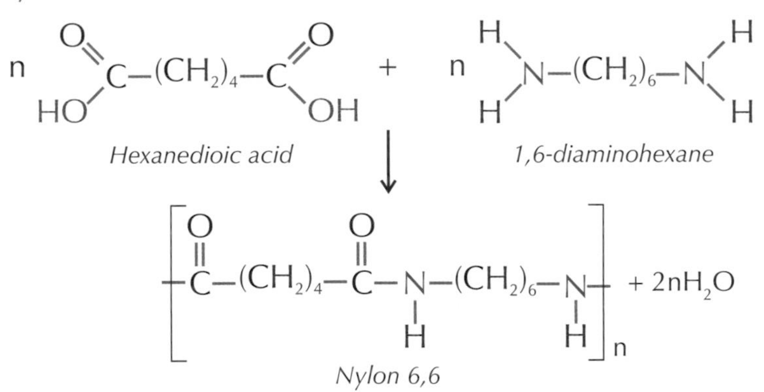

Tip: If you're struggling to remember the repeating units of nylon 6,6 and Kevlar®, just remember — nylon 6,6 has 6 carbons between each NH group and Kevlar® has benzene between each functional group.

- Kevlar® — made from benzene-1,4-dicarboxylic acid and benzene-1,4-diamine:

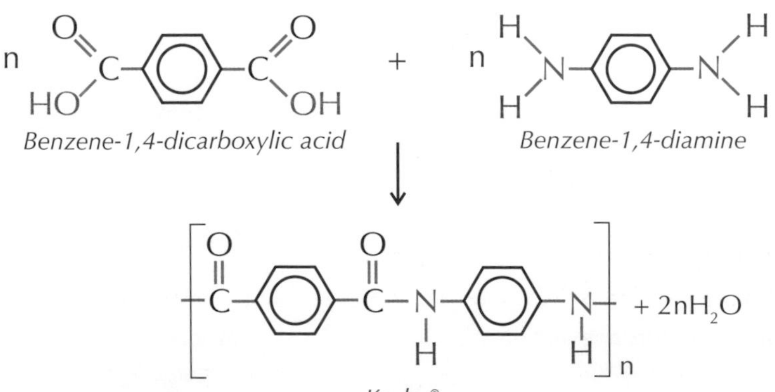

Figure 3: *Kevlar® is used to make bulletproof clothing.*

Formation of polyesters

The carboxyl groups of dicarboxylic acids can react with the hydroxyl groups of diols to form ester links — see Figure 4.

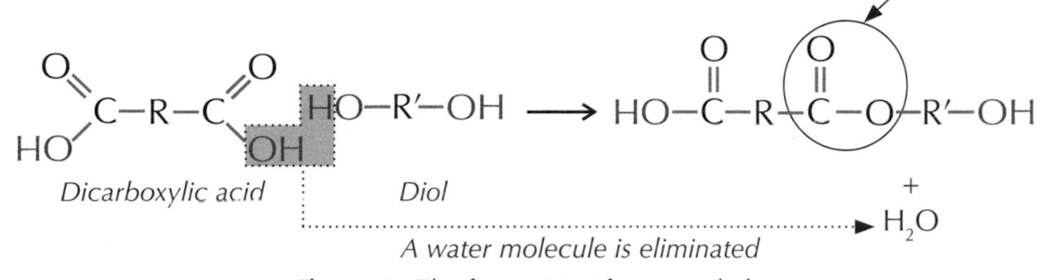

Figure 4: *The formation of an ester link.*

Tip: The formation of polyesters is very similar to the formation of polyamides and polypeptides.

Polymers joined by ester links are called polyesters — an example is Terylene™ (PET). Terylene™ is formed from benzene-1,4-dicarboxylic acid and ethane-1,2-diol.

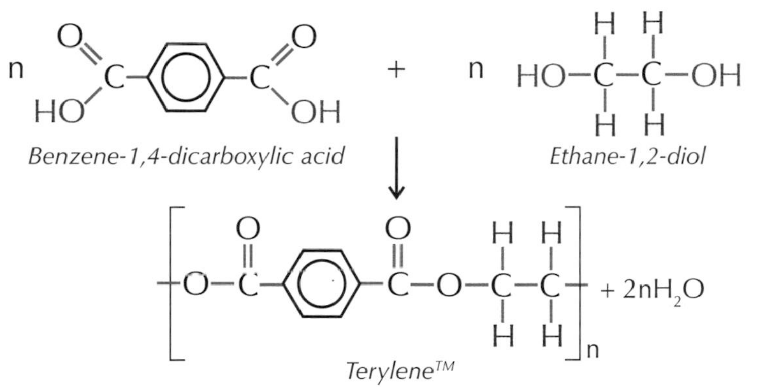

Figure 5: *The containers that microwave meals come in are made of Terylene™.*

Practice Questions — Application

Q1 Teflon® is a polymer commonly used to coat non-stick pans. The structure of a short stretch of Teflon® is shown below.

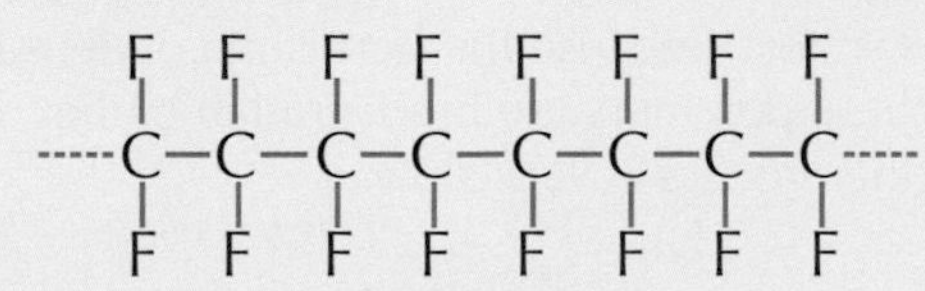

a) What type of polymer is Teflon®?

b) Draw the structure of the monomer that's used to make Teflon®.

Q2 Draw the repeating unit of the polymer made from this alkene:

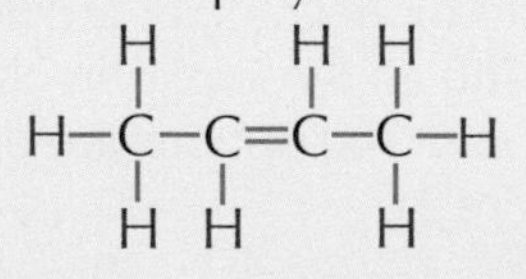

Practice Questions — Fact Recall

Q1 What are monomers?

Q2 Reactions between which types of molecules give rise to:

a) polyamides? b) polyesters?

Q3 What type of reaction gives rise to polyamides and polyesters?

Q4 Draw the repeating units of:

a) Nylon 6,6 b) Kevlar® c) Terylene™

7. Disposing of Polymers

Learning Objectives:
- Understand that polyalkenes are chemically inert and therefore non-biodegradable.
- Understand that polyesters and polyamides can be broken down by hydrolysis and are, therefore, biodegradable.
- Appreciate the advantages and disadvantages of different methods of disposal of polymers.
- Appreciate the advantages and disadvantages of recycling polymers.

Specification Reference 3.4.9

Polymers are really useful — loads of things are made from them. But unfortunately, disposing of polymers once they've been used can be a tad tricky. Read on to find out why.

The widespread use of polymers

Synthetic polymers have loads of advantages, so they're incredibly widespread these days — we take them pretty much for granted. Just imagine what you'd have to live without if there were no polymers (see Figure 1).

Figure 1: *Some of the many items that are made out of synthetic polymers.*

Biodegradability of polymers

Addition polymers such as poly(ethene) and polystyrene are chemically inert (very unreactive). This is because the bonds between the repeating units are non-polar, so they aren't susceptible to attack by nucleophiles. Being chemically inert is an advantage when polymers are being used (e.g. a polystyrene cup won't react with your coffee), but it has the disadvantage of making them non-biodegradable (the bonds in the polymer can't be hydrolysed and won't break down naturally).

Condensation polymers such as PET (a polyester that's used to make fizzy drinks bottles and carrier bags amongst other things) and nylon (a polyamide) can be broken down by hydrolysis. This is because the bonds between the repeating units are polar and so are susceptible to attack by nucleophiles such as water. Because the bonds in condensation polymers can be hydrolysed, these polymers are biodegradable (they will break down naturally), although the process is very slow.

Exam Tip
You need to be able to explain why polyalkenes are non-biodegradable while polyamines and polyesters are biodegradable — it's all to do with the bonding and the polarity of the polymers.

Disposing of waste plastics

It's estimated that in the UK we throw away over 3 million tons of plastic (i.e. synthetic polymers) every year. Because plastics either take a very long time to biodegrade or are non-biodegradable, the question of what to do with all those plastic objects when we've finished using them is an important one. The options are burying, burning or sorting for reusing or recycling (Figure 2).

Tip: A ton is just over 1000 kg (1016.047 kg to be exact) so 3 million tons is an awful lot of plastic to dispose of.

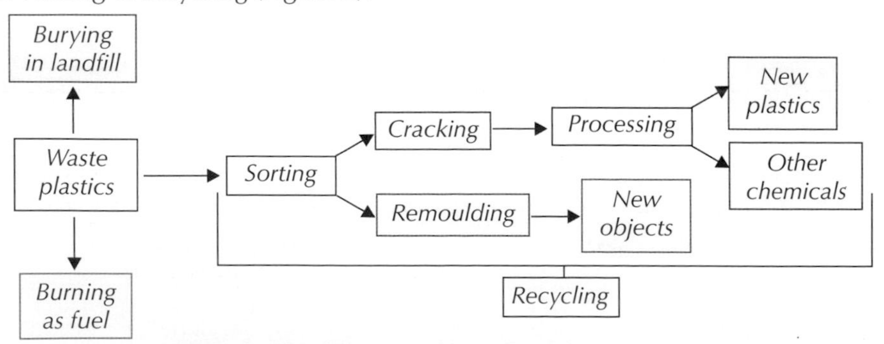

Figure 2: *The different methods for disposing of waste plastic.*

None of these methods is an ideal solution — they all have advantages and disadvantages associated with them.

Burying waste plastic

Landfill is one option for dealing with waste plastics. It is generally used when the plastic is difficult to separate from other waste, not in sufficient quantities to make separation financially worthwhile or too difficult technically to recycle. Landfill is a relatively cheap and easy method of waste disposal, but there are disadvantages to burying waste plastic too:

- It requires areas of land.
- As the waste decomposes it can release methane — a greenhouse gas.
- Leaks from landfill sites can also contaminate water supplies.

The amount of waste we generate is becoming more and more of a problem, so there's a need to reduce landfill as much as possible.

Figure 3: A landfill site — burying waste plastic is one way of disposing of it.

Burning waste plastic

Waste plastics can be burned and the heat used to generate electricity. This process needs to be carefully controlled to reduce toxic gases. For example, polymers that contain chlorine (such as PVC) produce HCl when they're burned — this has to be removed. So, waste gases from the combustion are passed through scrubbers which can neutralise gases such as HCl by allowing them to react with a base. But, the waste gases, e.g. carbon dioxide, will still contribute to the greenhouse effect.

Tip: The disposal of plastics is an example of a situation where society needs to use evidence provided by scientists to decide on the best course of action. (See page 4 for more on science and decision making.)

Recycling plastics

Because many plastics are made from non-renewable oil-fractions, it makes sense to recycle plastics as much as possible. There's more than one way to recycle plastics. After sorting into different types some plastics (poly(propene), for example) can be melted and remoulded, while others can be cracked into monomers which can be used to make more plastics or other chemicals. Plastic products are usually marked to make sorting easier. The different numbers show different polymers.

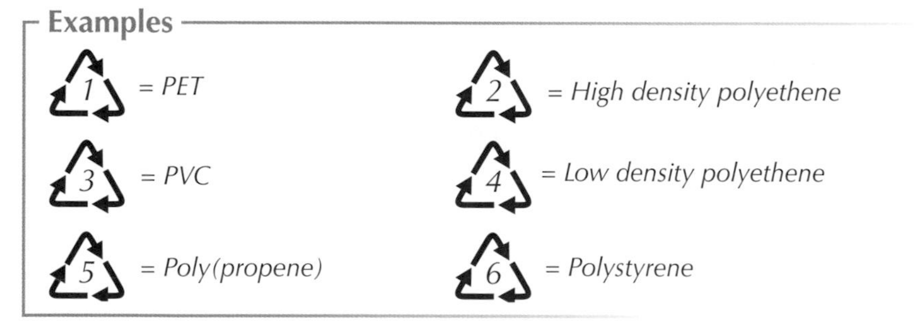

Figure 4: The recycling symbol on the bottom of a plastic bottle.

Like other disposal methods, there are advantages and disadvantages to recycling plastics:

Advantages	Disadvantages
It reduces the amount of waste going into landfill.	It is technically difficult to recycle plastics.
It saves raw materials — which is important because oil is non-renewable.	Collecting, sorting and processing the plastic is more expensive than burning/landfill.
The cost of recycling plastics is lower than making the plastics from scratch.	You often can't remake the plastic you started with — you have to make something else.
It produces less CO_2 emissions than burning the plastic.	The plastic can be easily contaminated during the recycling process.

Exam Tip
When answering a question on advantages and disadvantages of recycling plastics, don't just say cost — you need to justify your answer because the cost can be an advantage and a disadvantage.

Figure 5: A reusable plastic bag or 'bag for life' sold by a supermarket.

Environmental considerations

Plastics are so useful that it's very unlikely we'll stop using them anytime soon, despite the disposal problems. However, greater awareness of the problems may change how we use plastics.

Example

Supermarkets have been criticised for the amount of plastic waste they create. They've responded by:

- Trying to reduce the amount of plastic packaging on food items.
- Employing scientists to develop plastics that biodegrade quickly, e.g. food packaging that biodegrades in just one year.
- Encouraging us to reuse plastics by selling 'bags for life' that can be used over and over again or by charging for carrier bags.

Practice Question — Application

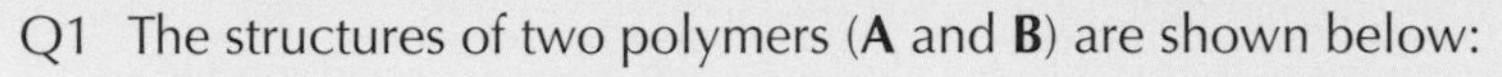

Q1 The structures of two polymers (**A** and **B**) are shown below:

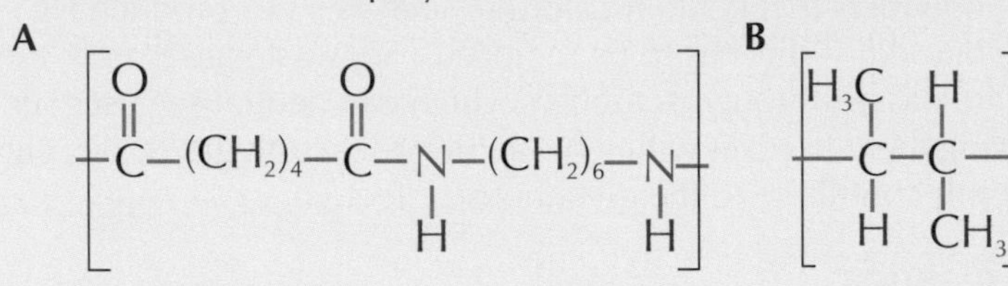

Which of these polymers is biodegradable?

Practice Questions — Fact Recall

Q1 a) Explain why addition polymers are chemically inert.

b) Why is it good for addition polymers to be chemically inert?

c) What does being chemically inert mean for the biodegradability of the plastic?

Q2 a) Are condensation polymers biodegradable or non-biodegradable?

b) Explain why the biodegradabilities of addition and condensation polymers are different.

Q3 Disposing of waste plastic in landfill sites is cheap and easy. Give three disadvantages of using landfill sites.

Q4 Burning plastic produces toxic gases. How can these toxic gases be removed?

Q5 a) Give two ways in which plastics can be recycled.

b) How is the sorting of plastics made easier?

c) Give two advantages and two disadvantages of recycling waste plastics.

Section Summary

Make sure you know...

- That benzene has the chemical formula C_6H_6 with six carbons joined together in a planar (flat) ring.
- The two different models for the structure of benzene — Kekulé's model and the delocalised model.
- That the carbon-carbon bonds in benzene are all the same length (intermediate between double and single bonds) and that this doesn't fit with Kekulé's model.
- How enthalpies of hydrogenation provide further evidence for the delocalised model.
- Why the delocalisation of electrons makes aromatic compounds more stable.
- What aromatic compounds are and how to name them.
- That the benzene ring is a region of high electron density so it attracts electrophiles.
- That electrophilic attack on benzene rings usually results in substitution because the ring is so stable.
- That Friedel-Crafts acylation and nitration are both electrophilic substitution reactions, and how to draw the mechanism for these reactions.
- That nitration is used to add nitro groups onto benzene rings.
- The role of H_2SO_4 as a catalyst for nitration reactions.
- That nitro compounds are used to make explosives and aromatic amines (which are used to manufacture dyes and pharmaceuticals).
- That Friedel-Crafts acylation adds an acyl group onto benzene rings, producing a phenylketone.
- The role of halogen carriers such as $AlCl_3$ as catalysts in Friedel-Crafts acylation.
- What amines are and how to name them.
- That quaternary ammonium salts can be used as cationic surfactants.
- That amines can act as Brønsted-Lowry bases because they can accept protons.
- Why aromatic amines are weaker bases than ammonia and why aliphatic amines are stronger bases.
- What amides are and how to name them.
- That amines can be formed by heating a haloalkane with an excess of ammonia.
- That nucleophilic substitution reactions produce a mixture of primary, secondary, tertiary and quaternary amines because more than one hydrogen is likely to be substituted.
- The mechanism for nucleophilic substitution reactions.
- That amines can also be formed by reducing nitriles.
- That aromatic amines are formed by reducing nitro compounds such as nitrobenzene.
- What amino acids are and how to name them.
- That amino acids are amphoteric — they have both acidic and basic properties.
- That amino acids can form zwitterions.
- That mixtures of amino acids can be separated using paper chromatography.
- That proteins are sequences of amino acids joined by peptide links.
- That proteins can be hydrolysed to re-produce the constituent amino acids.
- That hydrogen bonding is important in maintaining the 3-dimensional structure of proteins.
- What addition polymers and condensation polymers are.
- How to draw the repeating units of addition polymers from monomer structures and vice versa.
- How polyamides, polyesters and polypeptides are formed.
- Why addition polymers are non-biodegradable and condensation polymers are biodegradable.
- The advantages and disadvantages of disposing of waste plastic in landfill and burning waste plastic.
- The advantages and disadvantages of recycling waste plastics.

Exam-style Questions

1 Benzene is an extremely important molecule in the synthesis of aromatic compounds. In 1865, Kekulé proposed that the structure of benzene consists of a ring of carbon atoms with alternating single and double bonds between them.

1 (a) Describe one piece of evidence that suggests Kekulé's model for the structure of benzene is incorrect.

(3 marks)

1 (b) The benzene ring is very stable and as a result benzene is fairly unreactive. Friedel-Crafts acylation reactions are used to add acyl side chains onto the benzene ring which can then be modified to make useful products.

1 (b) (i) Write an equation to show the production of phenylpropanone by Friedel-Crafts acylation. Show the structure of phenylpropanone.

(2 marks)

1 (b) (ii) Friedel-Crafts acylation uses an $AlCl_3$ catalyst. Explain its role.

(2 marks)

1 (b) (iii) Outline the mechanism for this reaction.

(4 marks)

1 (c) Nitro groups can be added to the benzene ring via nitration reactions. If methylbenzene is heated with concentrated nitric and sulfuric acids, 2,4,6-trinitromethylbenzene (TNT) can be produced.

1 (c) (i) Write an equation to show the formation of a nitronium ion from concentrated nitric and sulfuric acids.

(1 mark)

1 (c) (ii) Outline the mechanism for the addition of one nitro group onto the benzene ring of methylbenzene.

(3 marks)

1 (d) Nitro compounds can be reduced to give aromatic amines.

1 (d) (i) Write an equation to show the reduction of nitrobenzene to phenylamine.

(2 marks)

1 (d) (ii) Describe the conditions needed for this reaction.

(3 marks)

2 The diagrams below show two amines (**X** and **Y**).

2 (a) Give the IUPAC names for these two amines.

(2 marks)

2 (b) Aliphatic amines such as amine **X** can be produced by heating haloalkanes with an excess of ammonia.

2 (b) (i) Write an equation to show the formation of amine **X** from a bromoalkane.

(2 marks)

2 (b) (ii) Name and outline the mechanism for this reaction.

(5 marks)

2 (c) Preparations of amine **X** from a haloalkane are usually impure and contain a number of different products.

2 (c) (i) State why a mixture of different products can be produced in these reactions.

(1 mark)

2 (c) (ii) Draw the structure of one of the other products likely to be in the mixture with amine **X**.

(1 mark)

2 (c) (iii) Suggest how the amount of amine **X** in the mixture could be increased.

(1 mark)

2 (d) Amine **X** can also be made by reducing a nitrile with a strong reducing agent such as $LiAlH_4$.

2 (d) (i) Write an equation to show the reduction of a nitrile to amine **X**.

(1 mark)

2 (d) (ii) Explain why the amine **X** produced via this reaction is purer than the amine **X** made from a haloalkane.

(2 marks)

2 (e) Amines **X** and **Y** can both act as bases.

2 (e) (i) State why amines are able to act as bases.

(1 mark)

2 (e) (ii) Which of these two amines is the stronger base? Explain your answer.

(4 marks)

3 The diagrams below show the structure of an amino acid at three different pHs.

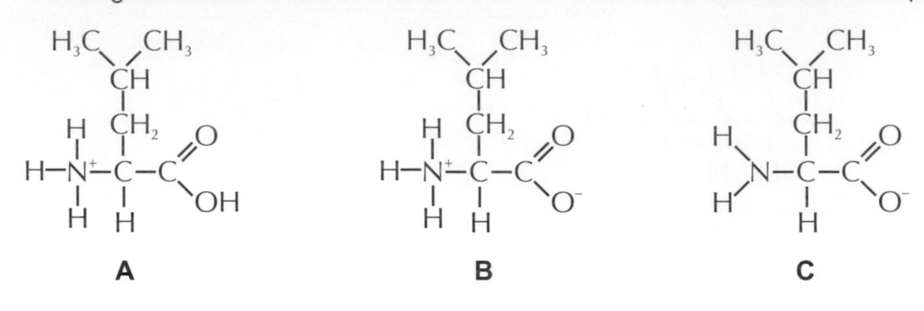

3 (a) Give the systematic name for the amino acid from which all of these species are derived.

(1 mark)

3 (b) (i) Which of these species **A**, **B** or **C** forms at the isoelectric point for this amino acid?

(1 mark)

3 (b) (ii) What is the name given to describe this species?

(1 mark)

3 (c) The diagram below shows the structure of a dipeptide.

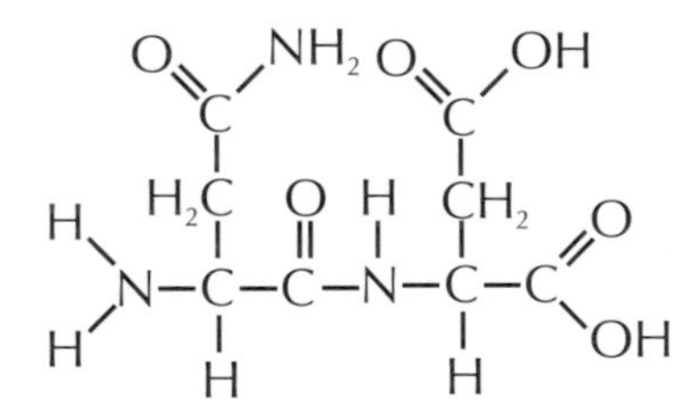

3 (c) (i) Draw the two amino acids which have joined together to make this dipeptide.

(2 marks)

3 (c) (ii) What conditions are required to hydrolyse a peptide bond?

(2 marks)

4 Nylon 6,6 is made from hexanedioic acid and 1,6-diaminohexane.

4 (a) What type of polymer is nylon 6,6?

(1 mark)

4 (b) Draw the repeating unit of nylon 6,6.

(1 mark)

4 (c) Is nylon 6,6 biodegradable or non-biodegradable? Explain you answer.

(4 marks)

4 (d) Discuss the advantages and disadvantages of recycling objects made from nylon 6,6.

(4 marks)

1. Organic Synthesis

Organic synthesis is the part of chemistry that deals with how to make organic compounds using different chemical reactions. Organic synthesis is one of the most important branches of chemistry as it provides ways to create materials and chemicals like pharmaceutical drugs, fertilisers and plastics.

Learning Objectives:
- Be able to identify organic functional groups using the reactions in the AS- and A2-Level Chemistry courses.
- Be able to deduce how to synthesise organic compounds using the reactions covered in the AS- and A2-Level Chemistry courses.

Specification Reference 3.4.10

Organic synthesis in the exam

In your Unit 4 chemistry exam you could be asked to provide a step-wise synthesis for the production of one chemical from another. You might have to use any of the reactions you've learnt in AS- or A2-Level chemistry so it's really important that you learn them all really well. If you're asked how to make one compound from another in the exam, make sure you include:

- Any special procedures, such as refluxing.
- The conditions needed, e.g. high temperature or pressure, or the presence of a catalyst.
- Any safety precautions, e.g. do it in a fume cupboard. (If there are things like hydrogen chloride or hydrogen cyanide around, you really don't want to go breathing them in. Stuff like bromine and strong acids and alkalis are corrosive, so you don't want to splash them on your bare skin.)

The next few pages cover some of the stuff you should know to help you get through those tricky organic synthesis questions.

Tip: A synthesis is just a method detailing how to create a chemical.

Tests for alcohols, aldehydes and ketones

To find out which sort of alcohol you've got, you warm it with the oxidising agent acidified potassium dichromate(VI). Then you watch for a colour change...

- **Primary** — the orange dichromate slowly turns green as an aldehyde forms (then eventually a carboxylic acid).
- **Secondary** — the orange dichromate slowly turns green as a ketone forms.
- **Tertiary** — nothing happens. Boring, but easy to remember.

The test shows the same result for primary and secondary alcohols — you have to perform another test to find out if you have produced an aldehyde or a ketone.

You can distinguish between an aldehyde and a ketone using Tollens' reagent (an aldehyde forms a silver mirror, no reaction with a ketone), or with either Fehling's solution or Benedict's solution (an aldehyde gives a brick red precipitate, no reaction with a ketone). There's more about these tests on page 66.

Tip: The colour change is the orange dichromate(VI) ion, $Cr_2O_7^{2-}$, being reduced to the green chromium(III) ion, Cr^{3+}.

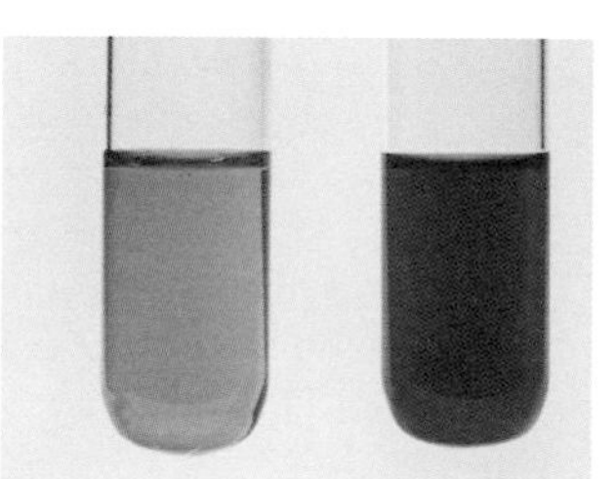

Figure 1: *Alcohol oxidation. The acidified potassium dichromate(VI) ion turns from orange to green when it oxidises a primary alcohol to a carboxylic acid.*

Test for unsaturation

To see if a compound is unsaturated (contains any double bonds), all you need to do is shake it with orange bromine solution. The solution will quickly decolourise if the substance is unsaturated.

Figure 2: *Bromine water has been added to two test-tubes. The one on the right contains a compound with a C=C, that has decolourised the bromine water. The one on the left contains a substance that doesn't react with bromine.*

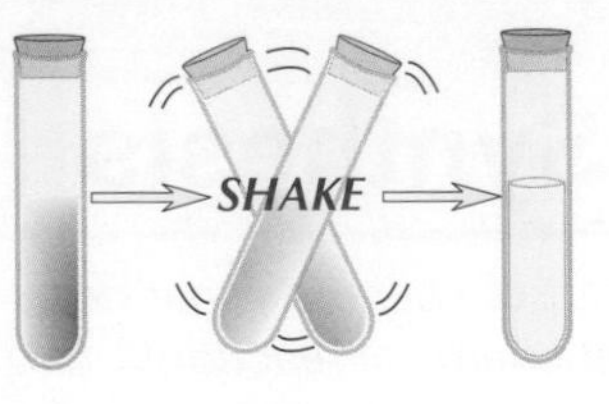

Figure 3: *Adding bromine water to a solution containing a carbon-carbon double bond decolourises the bromine water.*

Distinguishing between haloalkanes

At AS you learned that you could identify halide ions using silver nitrate solution. Well, you can use this test to distinguish between different haloalkanes. You first need to get the halogen off the haloalkane and into solution as a halide ion — so add sodium hydroxide.

$$CH_3CH_2X + OH^- \rightarrow CH_3CH_2OH + X^-$$

X is a halogen

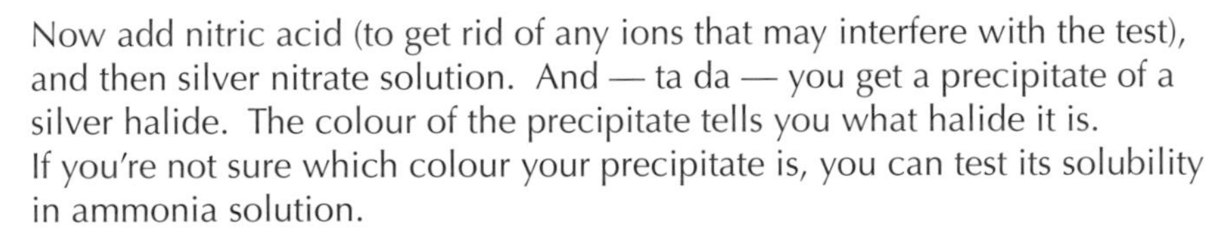

Now add nitric acid (to get rid of any ions that may interfere with the test), and then silver nitrate solution. And — ta da — you get a precipitate of a silver halide. The colour of the precipitate tells you what halide it is.
If you're not sure which colour your precipitate is, you can test its solubility in ammonia solution.

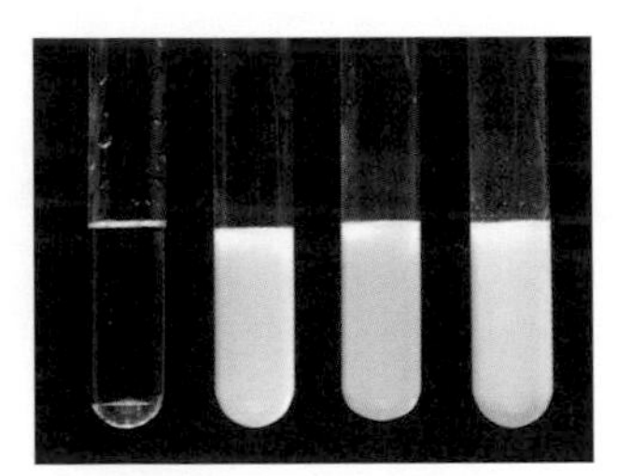

Figure 4: *Results of silver nitrate tests for solutions containing (L-R) fluoride, chloride, bromide and iodide ions.*

Halide	With silver nitrate	Solubility of precipitate in ammonia solution
F^-	no precipitate	—
Cl^-	white precipitate	dissolves in dilute ammonia solution
Br^-	cream precipitate	dissolves in concentrated ammonia solution
I^-	yellow precipitate	insoluble in concentrated ammonia solution

Figure 5: *Summary table for the tests to distinguish between haloalkanes.*

Percentage yield and atom economy

Examiners love to squidge calculations into organic synthesis questions. Make sure that you've not forgotten how to calculate percentage yield and atom economy:

$$\%\ \text{yield} = \frac{\text{actual yield}}{\text{theoretical yield}} \times 100$$

The theoretical yield is how much product you expect to get from the reactants (you can work this out from the balanced equation).

$$\%\ \text{atom economy} = \frac{\text{mass of desired product}}{\text{total mass of reactants}} \times 100$$

The atom economy is the proportion of reactant atoms that become part of the desired product. A low atom economy means a reaction is very wasteful — and wasteful reactions aren't sustainable.

Tip: If you need to calculate the masses for the atom economy expression, use the M_r of the products and reactants multiplied by the number of moles of each given in the balanced equation.

Functional groups

Here's a summary of all the functional groups you've seen in organic chemistry at A-Level. Make sure you know what they are and how to draw them.

Homologous series	Functional group	Prefix or suffix	Examples
alkanes	n/a	-ane	propane $CH_3CH_2CH_3$
branched alkanes	n/a	alkyl- (-yl)	methylpropane $CH_3CH(CH_3)CH_3$
alkenes	C=C	-ene	propene $CH_3CH{=}CH$
alcohols	–OH	-ol	ethanol CH_3CH_2OH
aldehydes	–C(=O)–H	-al	ethanal CH_3CHO
ketones	–C(=O)–	-one	propanone CH_3COCH_3
esters	–C(=O)–O–	alkyl -oate	ethyl ethanoate $CH_3COOCH_2CH_3$
carboxylic acids	–C(=O)–OH	-oic acid	ethanoic acid CH_3COOH
cycloalkanes	n/a	cyclo- -ane	cyclohexane C_6H_{12}
arenes	benzene ring (–C with C–H groups)	phenyl- (-benzene)	phenylamine $C_6H_5NH_2$ ethylbenzene $C_6H_5C_2H_5$
amines	$-NH_2$	-amine (primary)	methylamine CH_3NH_2
	–NH (with one further bond)	di- -amine (secondary)	dimethylamine $(CH_3)_2NH$
	–N– (with one further bond)	tri- -amine (tertiary)	trimethylamine $N(CH_3)_3$
amides	$-C(=O)-NH_2$	-amide	ethanamide CH_3CONH_2
acyl chlorides	–C(=O)–Cl	-oyl chloride	ethanoyl chloride CH_3COCl

Exam Tip
You need to learn all of these functional groups off by heart — they won't be given to you in the exam.

Synthesis routes

Chemists have got to be able to make one compound from another. It's vital for things like designing medicines. It's also good for making imitations of useful natural substances when the real things are hard to extract. Chemists use synthesis routes to show the reagents, conditions and any special procedures needed to get from one compound to another. The reaction scheme on the next two pages shows the synthesis routes you've come across in the AS- and A2-Level Chemistry course. These reactions are covered elsewhere in the book, or in your AS notes, so check back for extra details.

Exam Tip
You will be asked to recall some of the synthesis routes in your exam, so it's important that you know them all. But when you turn the page, don't freak out — there's nothing new to learn there, it's just a summary of what you've already learnt. Make sure you know them all using the 'cover the page, scribble them out and check' method. Repeat until you can do it from memory.

Synthesis routes for making organic compounds

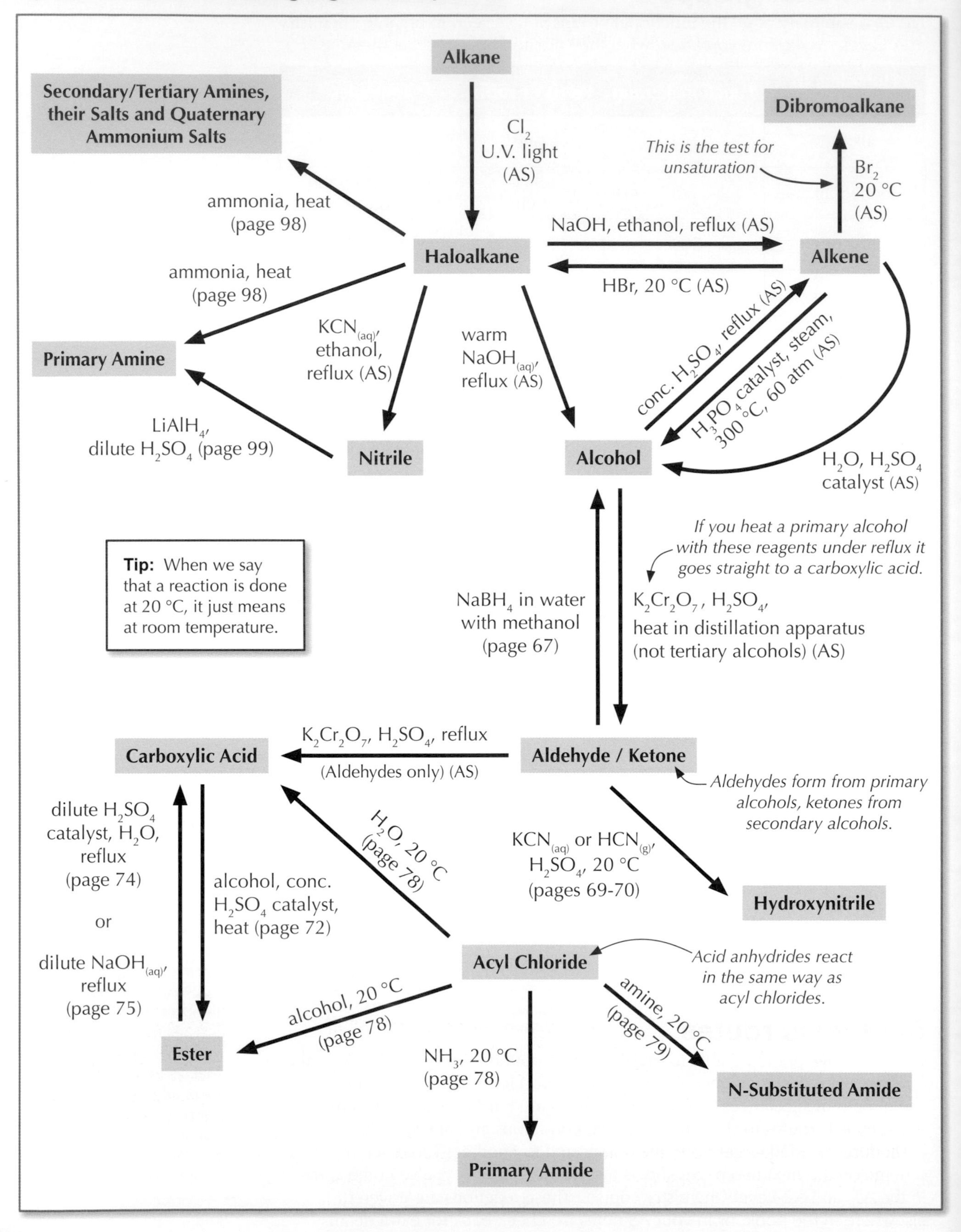

Synthesis routes for aromatic compounds

There are not so many of these reactions to learn — so make sure you know all the itty-bitty details. If you can't remember any of the reactions, look back to the relevant pages and take a quick peek over them.

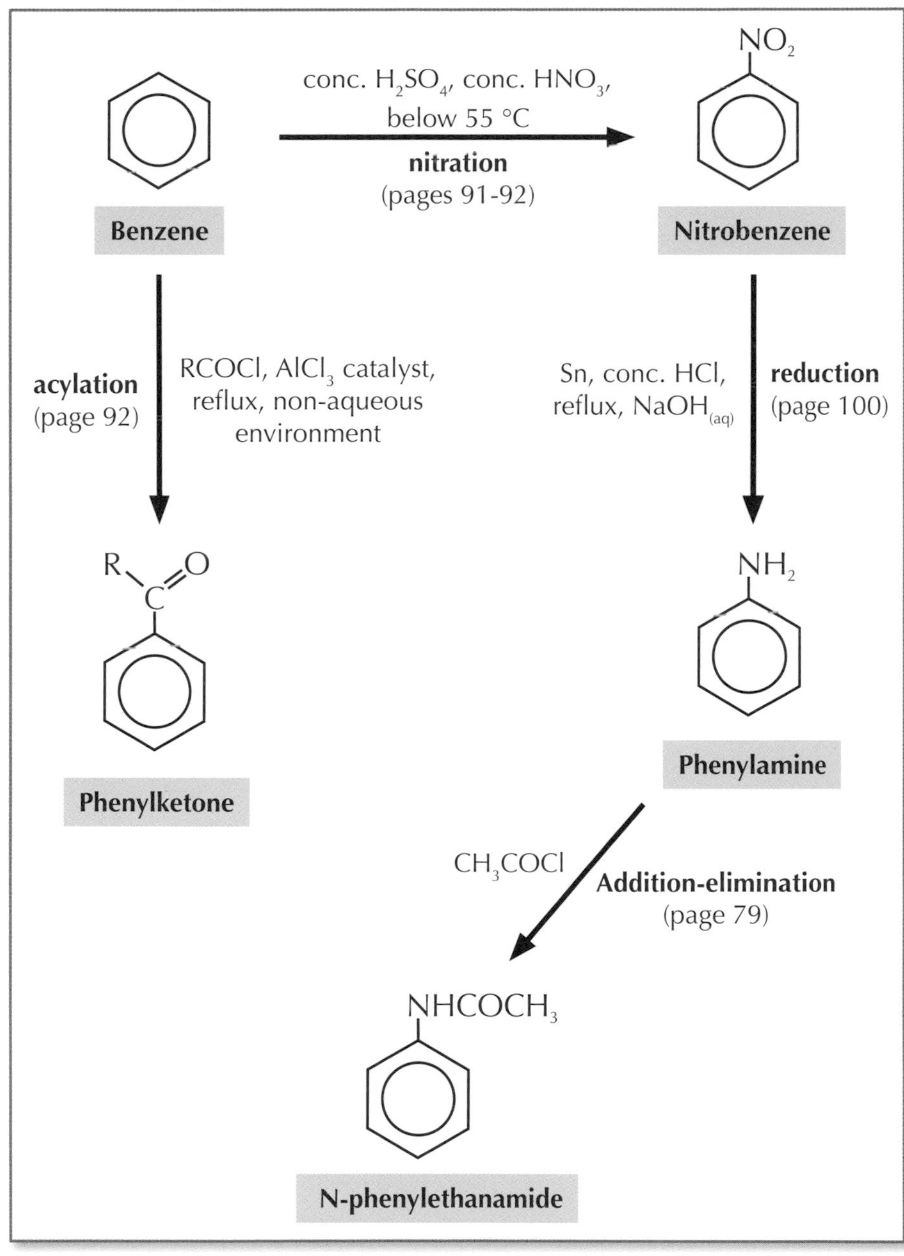

Exam Tip
When you're writing down a step-wise synthesis in the exam don't forget to put the conditions as well as the reagents. You might lose marks if you don't.

Exam Tip
For acylation questions in the exam don't just put RCOCl — you need to specify what the R group is.

Exam technique

In the exam you may be asked to 'identify' the name of a reagent used in a synthesis step. A reagent is just a chemical that can be used straight out of a bottle or container, for example, hydrochloric acid (HCl) or potassium cyanide (KCN). You must be really careful about this...

Example

Identify the reagents used to transform a haloalkane into a nitrile.

Giving the reagent CN^- in this case would be incorrect as you can't just take it out of a bottle. The correct answer would be KCN and ethanol.

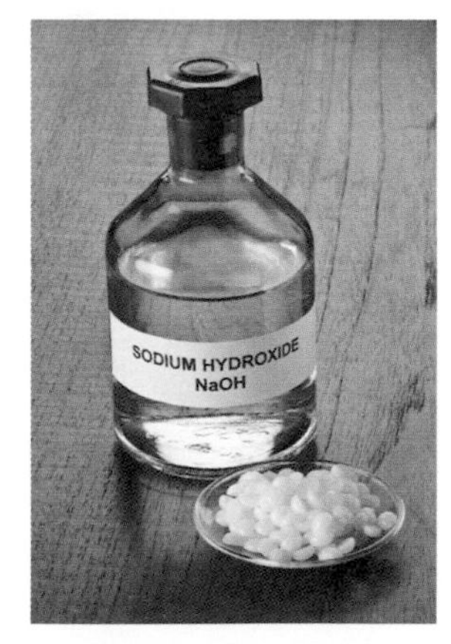

Figure 6: *Reagents are chemicals that can be taken from bottles or containers.*

Practice Questions — Application

Q1 Write down the reagents and conditions you would use to carry out the following organic syntheses.

a) Making ethanol from ethene using steam hydration.

b) Forming chloromethane from methane.

c) Creating phenylethanone from benzene.

d) Turning 2-chloropropane into a secondary amine.

Exam Tip
For questions like these you don't have to give the mechanisms or equations for the reactions.

Q2 The following syntheses require a two-step organic synthesis. Write down the reagents and conditions you would use to carry out each step in the following organic syntheses.

a) Forming phenylamine from benzene.

b) Creating propanal from 1-bromopropane.

c) Turning ethane into propanenitrile.

d) Making methyl butanoate from butanal.

Exam Tip
You need to be specific when you're talking about reagents in the exam. Make sure you write down exactly what you need to use — writing 'an alcohol' when you really mean 'ethanol' just won't get you all of the marks.

Q3 Give a three-step synthesis of N-phenylethanamide starting from benzene. In your second synthesis step you should form phenylamine. For each step, give the reagents and conditions you would use to carry out the reaction.

Q4 Give a three-step synthesis of ethyl ethanoate starting from chloroethane. In your first synthesis step you should form ethanol. For each step, give the reagents and conditions you would use to carry out the reaction.

Practice Questions — Fact Recall

Q1 What reagent would you use to distinguish between a primary and a tertiary alcohol?

Q2 What reagent would you use to test for unsaturation?

Q3 What would you observe if you added sodium hydroxide followed by nitric acid and silver nitrate to 1-bromopropane?

Q4 Write down the formula that you would use to calculate the percentage yield of a reaction.

Q5 Write down the formula for calculating % atom economy.

Q6 Write down the functional group of an aldehyde.

Q7 What homologous series has the functional group $-NH_2$?

2. Mass Spectrometry

Analytical techniques are the methods that chemists use to find out more about the physical and chemical properties of substances. There are quite a few different techniques covered in this section — first up is mass spectrometry.

Learning Objective:

- Be able to use data from mass spectrometry to determine the structure of specified compounds.

Specification Reference 3.4.11

Finding relative molecular mass

Mass spectrometry can be used to find the relative molecular mass, M_r, of a compound. Electrons in the spectrometer bombard the sample molecules and break electrons off, forming ions. A mass spectrum is produced, showing the relative amounts of ions with different mass-to-charge ratios. To find the relative molecular mass (M_r) of a compound you look at the molecular ion peak (the M peak). This peak is due to the molecular ion, which is formed by the loss of one electron.

Tip: If you can't remember how a mass spectrometer works have a quick look back at your AS notes.

Examples

The equation below shows the formation of the molecular ion from butane.

$$C_4H_{10} \rightarrow [C_4H_{10}]^+ + e^-$$

The equation below shows the formation of the molecular ion from ethanol.

$$C_2H_5OH \rightarrow [C_2H_5OH]^+ + e^-$$

Figure 1: Mass spectrometer.

The mass/charge value of the molecular ion peak is the molecular mass (assuming the ion has 1^+ charge, which it normally will have).

Example

Here's the mass spectrum of butane.

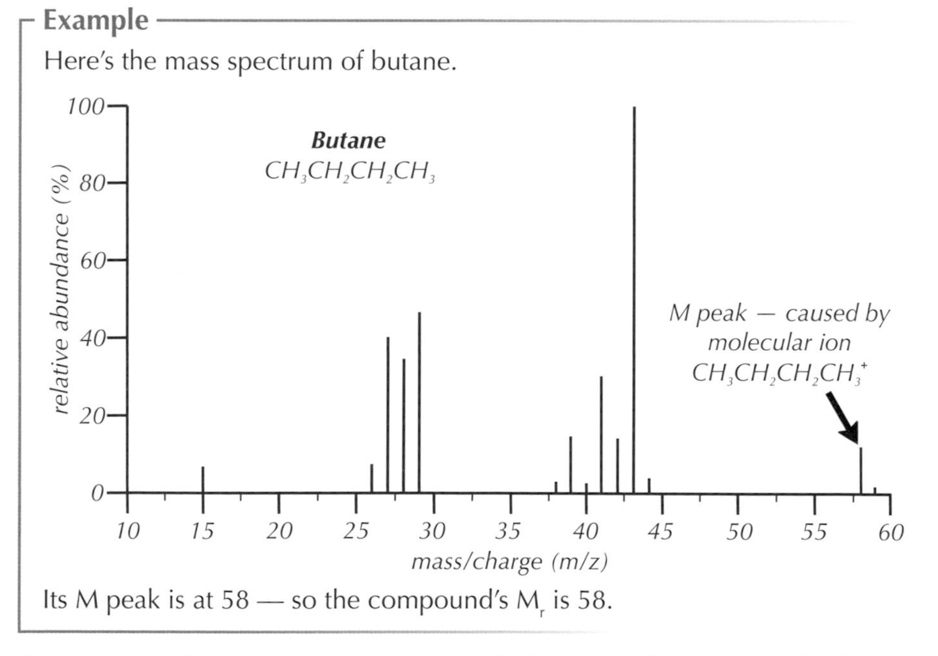

Its M peak is at 58 — so the compound's M_r is 58.

For most organic compounds the M peak is the one with the second highest mass/charge ratio. (The smaller peak to the right of the M peak is called the M+1 peak — there's more about the M+1 peak coming up.)

Tip: The mass to charge ratio (m/z) is found along the x-axis of a mass spectrum. For these spectrums you can assume that the charge on all the ions is 1+ (which means that their m/z is just the same as their mass).

The M+1 peak

The peak 1 unit to the right of the M peak is called the M+1 peak. It's mostly due to the carbon-13 isotope which exists naturally and makes up about 1.1% of carbon. You can use the M+1 peak to find out how many carbon atoms there are in the molecule. There's even a handy formula for this (as long as the molecule's not too huge):

$$\text{number of carbon atoms in an organic compound} = \frac{\text{height of M+1 peak}}{\text{height of M peak}} \times 100$$

Example

If a molecule has a molecular peak with a relative abundance of 44.13%, and an M+1 peak with a relative abundance of 1.41%, how many carbon atoms does it contain?

Use the formula for finding the number of carbon atoms in an organic compound and just plug the numbers in.

$$\text{number of carbon atoms in an organic compound} = \frac{\text{height of M+1 peak}}{\text{height of M peak}} \times 100$$

$$= (1.41 \div 44.13) \times 100 = 3.195$$

So the molecule contains 3 carbon atoms.

Tip: This equation won't give you a nice whole number answer. Just round the answer you get to the nearest whole number.

The M+2 peak

If a molecule's got either chlorine or bromine in it you'll get an M+2 peak as well as an M peak and an M+1 peak. It's because chlorine and bromine have natural isotopes with different masses and they all show up on the spectrum.

Compounds containing chlorine

Chlorine's two isotopes, Cl-35 and Cl-37, occur in the ratio of 3:1. So if a molecule contains chlorine, it will give an M peak and an M+2 peak with heights in the ratio 3:1.

Example

Here is part of the mass spectrum of chloroethane.

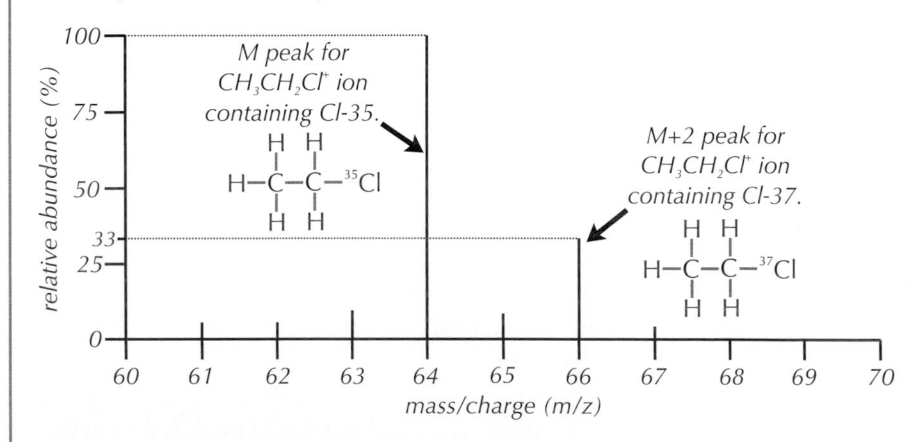

The M and M+2 peak heights in this spectrum are in the ratio 3 : 1 because of the Cl-35 and Cl-37 isotopes.

Tip: Remember the M peak gives you the molecular mass of the compound and so the M+2 peak is the molecular mass of the compound with the extra mass of 2 from the heavier halogen isotope.

Compounds containing Bromine

Bromine's got two isotopes, Br-79 and Br-81, that occur in equal amounts. So if a molecule contains bromine, the M peak and M+2 peak will both have the same height.

Example

Here is part of the mass spectrum of bromoethane.

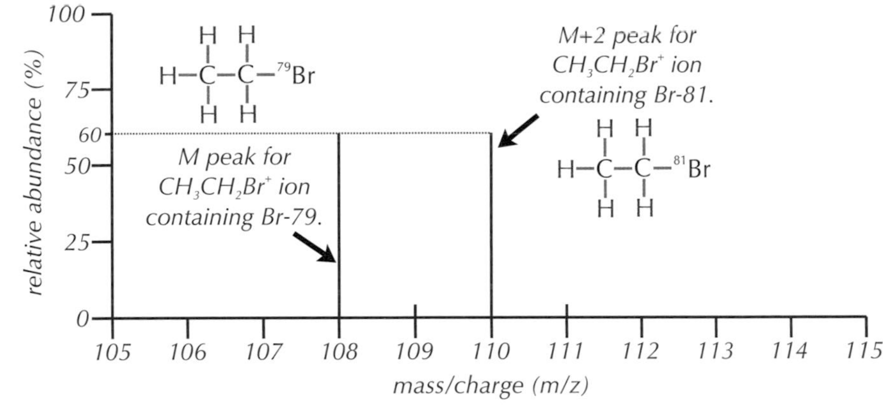

The M and M+2 peaks are in the ratio 1 : 1 because of the equal abundance of Br-79 and Br-81 isotopes.

Tip: These won't be the only peaks with a larger m/z than the M peak you'll find on a mass spectrum but you don't need to worry about any of the others at A-Level.

Tip: The M+1, M+2 and M+4 peaks all count as molecular ion peaks too, because they're all made by knocking one electron off a molecule.

If you spot an M+4 peak it's because the molecule contains two atoms of the halogen. (This changes the ratios of the M and M+2 peaks though.)

Example

The mass spectrum of dibromoethane will have an M peak, an M+2 peak and an M+4 peak. These peaks correspond to the following molecules:

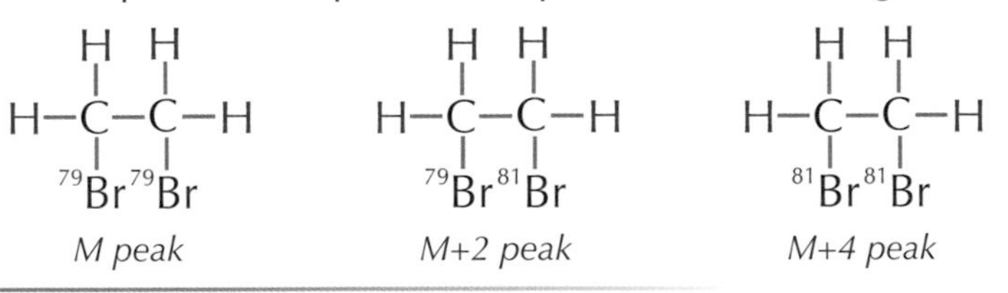

Exam Tip
You could be asked to predict the number of molecular ion peaks found on the mass spectrum of a haloalkane molecule. Just work out the number of different possible combinations of isotope masses. For example, for three atoms of bromine there are four possible combinations:
1: ^{79}Br, ^{79}Br, ^{79}Br
2: ^{79}Br, ^{79}Br, ^{81}Br
3: ^{79}Br, ^{81}Br, ^{81}Br
4: ^{81}Br, ^{81}Br, ^{81}Br
So, there will be 4 molecular ion peaks.

Practice Questions — Application

Q1 Write down the equation for the formation of a molecular ion from propanone.

Q2 If a molecule has an M peak with a relative abundance of 53.04%, and an M+1 peak with a relative abundance of 3.16%, how many carbon atoms does it contain?

Q3 Predict the number of molecular ion peaks found in a molecule that contains three chlorine atoms.

Practice Questions — Fact Recall

Q1 What information does the molecular ion peak on a mass spectrum give you?

Q2 If a molecule contains one chlorine atom, in what ratio will the heights of the M and M+2 peaks appear on a mass spectrum?

Q3 What does the appearance of an M+4 peak on a spectrum indicate?

3. More Mass Spectrometry

Learning Objectives:

- Be able to use data from mass spectrometry to determine the structure of specified compounds.
- Understand that the fragmentation of a molecular ion gives rise to a characteristic relative abundance spectrum that may give information about the structure of the molecule.
- Know that the more stable X^+ species give higher peaks, limited to carbocation and acylium ions.

Specification Reference 3.4.11

There's loads more lovely stuff on mass spectrometry coming up in this topic.

Fragmentation

In the mass spectrometer, the bombarding electrons make some of the molecular ions break up into **fragments**. The fragments that are ions show up on the mass spectrum, making a fragmentation pattern. Fragmentation patterns can be used to identify molecules and even their structures.

Example

For butane ($CH_3CH_2CH_2CH_3$), the molecular ion is $CH_3CH_2CH_2CH_3^+$, and the fragments it breaks into include CH_3^+ (M_r = 15) and $CH_3CH_2^+$ (M_r = 29).

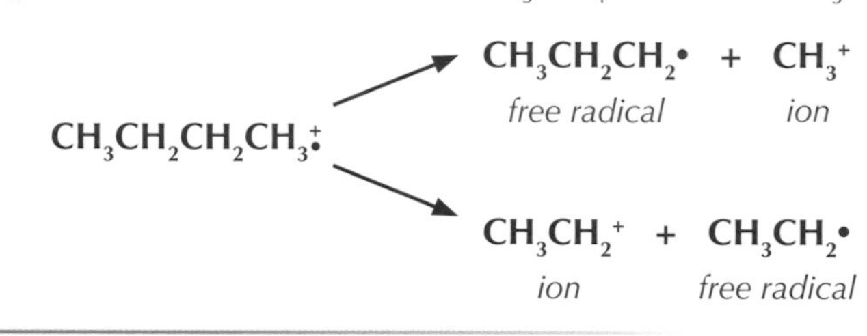

To work out the structural formula, you've got to work out what ion could have made each peak from its m/z value. (You assume that the m/z value of a peak matches the mass of the ion that made it.)

Tip: Remember that only the ions show up on the mass spectrum — the free radicals don't show up because they are uncharged.

Example

The mass spectrum below is for a molecule with the molecular formula C_3H_8O. Use the mass spectrum to work out the structure of the molecule:

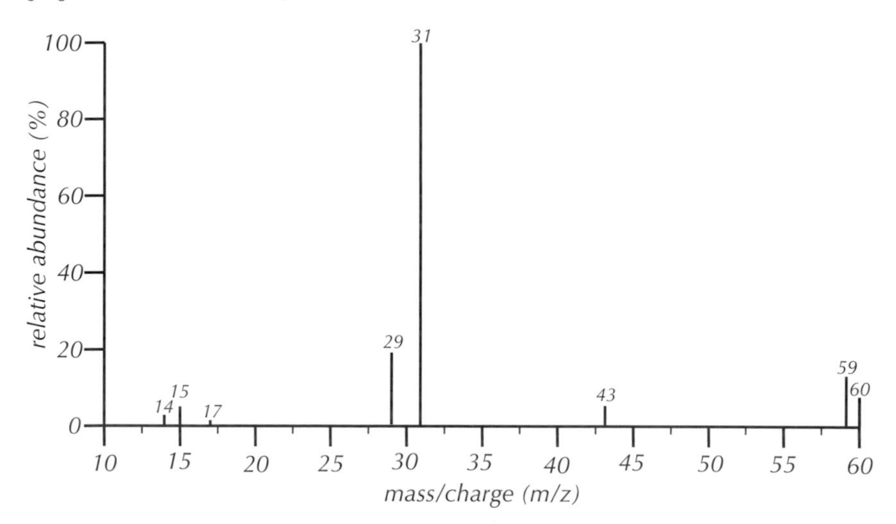

Tip: The numbers above the peaks in mass spectrums like this one are telling you the exact m/z value of each peak.

Fragment	m/z
CH_3^+	15
$CH_2CH_3^+$	29
$CH_2CH_2CH_3^+$	43
OH^+	17
$C{=}O^+$	28

***Figure 1:** Common fragment ions.*

First you need to identify the fragments — you can use Figure 1 to help you identify some common ions. This molecule's got a peak at 15 m/z, so it's likely to have a CH_3 group. It's also got a peak at 29 m/z which could be a $CH_2CH_3^+$ ion and a peak at 43 m/z which could be $CH_2CH_2CH_3^+$. It has another peak at 17 m/z, so it probably contains an OH group.

To find the other fragment ions you just have to add combinations of 12 (the mass of carbon), 1 (the mass of hydrogen) and 16 (the mass of oxygen) until you come up with sensible fragment ions. Other ions are matched to the peaks here:

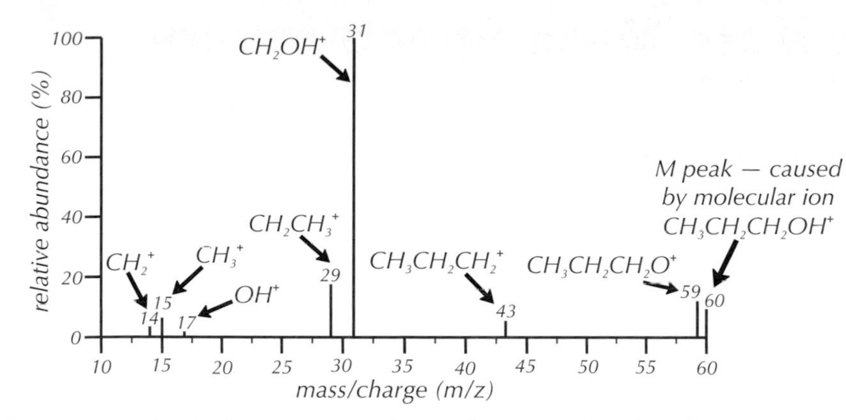

The next step is piecing them together to form a molecule with the correct molecular formula. Propan-1-ol has all the fragments on this spectrum.

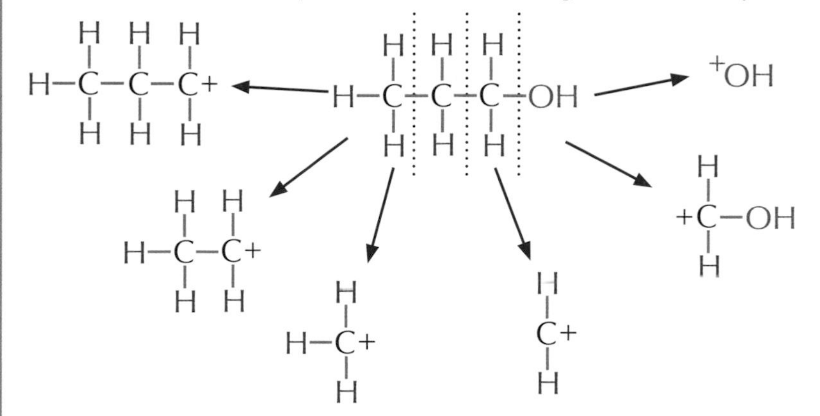

Propan-1-ol's molecular mass is 60. This should be the same as the m/z value of the M peak — it is. So, this is the mass spectrum of propanol.

Exam Tip
The only way to get good at interpreting mass spectrum is to practise. Beware... This is not a topic to try and learn the night before an exam — it just won't make sense.

Exam Tip
A diagram like this is always really useful to help you assign fragments to peaks in an exam — it makes it really easy to see what fragments are possible.

Fragment stability

Some fragment ions are more stable than others, so they're more likely to form. That means they'll be more abundant, and will have higher peaks on the mass spectrum.

Example

The mass spectrum of ethanol, below, shows that the most abundant peak has a mass of 31 — this represents the fragment ion CH_2OH^+. As this fragment ion has the highest abundance it must be the most stable fragment ion formed in the mass spectrometer.

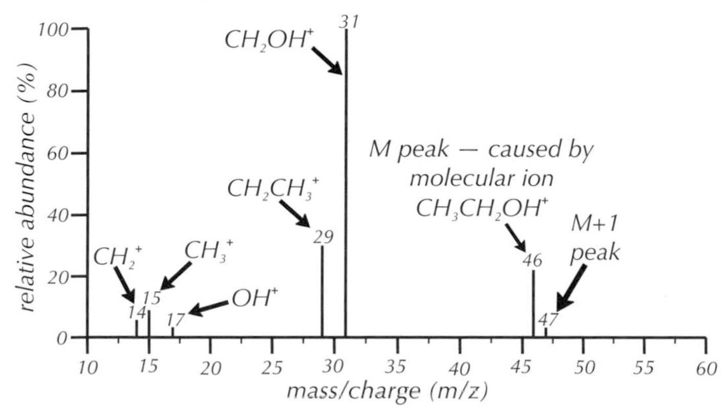

Tip: The most abundant ion is always given a relative abundance of 100%. The other ion abundances are then measured relative to this peak.

Two very stable fragment ions are carbocations and acylium ions — you'd expect high peaks for them.

Carbocation stability

A **carbocation** is an ion with a positively charged carbon. Carbocations are relatively stable ions because alkyl groups feed electrons towards the positive charge (see Figure 2). You can show that an alkyl group is donating electrons by drawing an arrow on the bond that points to where the electrons are donated.

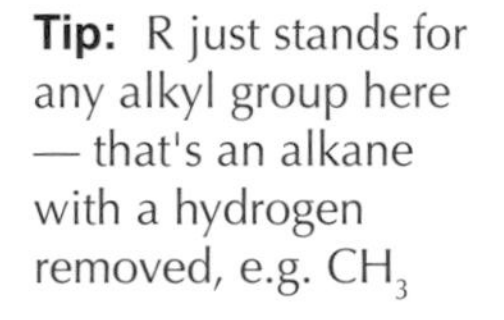

Tip: R just stands for any alkyl group here — that's an alkane with a hydrogen removed, e.g. CH_3

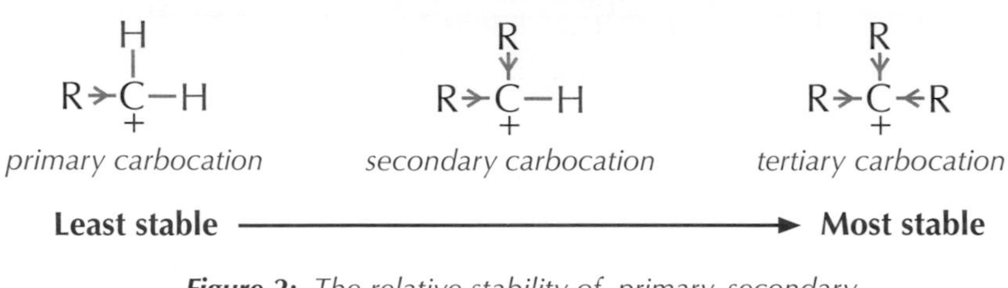

Figure 2: *The relative stability of primary, secondary and tertiary carbocations*

Carbocations with more alkyl groups are more stable because more electrons are being donated to stabilise the carbocation.

Acylium ion stability

Tip: An aliphatic compound is an organic compound that is not aromatic. For example, any straight chain hydrocarbon will be aliphatic.

The acylium ion (RCO^+) is often formed from aliphatic ketones. There are two possible structures of this ion which are called **resonance forms** (see Figure 3).

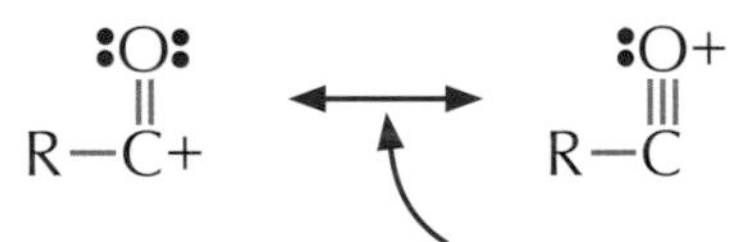

This double headed arrow is used to show resonance between two structures.

Figure 3: *The two resonance forms of an acylium ion.*

The actual structure of the ion is somewhere in the middle of these resonance forms but it makes it easier to understand if you draw out one or the other. Resonance in an ion helps to stabilise what would otherwise be an unstable structure.

As you saw on the previous page, more stable ions have higher abundance peaks on a spectrum. This means that ions stabilised by resonance, like acylium ions, will have a higher abundance. So there's a pretty good chance that a tall peak at m/z = 43 will be CH_3CO^+, and one that's at m/z = 57 will be $CH_3CH_2CO^+$ (as long as you could get such fragments from the molecule).

Exam Tip
Watch out for peaks that could be one of a few ions — a peak at 43 m/z could be CH_3CO^+ but it could also be $C_3H_7^+$.

Predicting structures from a mass spectrum

So, a mass spectrum can give you loads of information.
Have a look at the one on the next page.

Example

The mass spectrum below is for an oxygen-containing compound. Use the spectrum to find the structure of the compound.

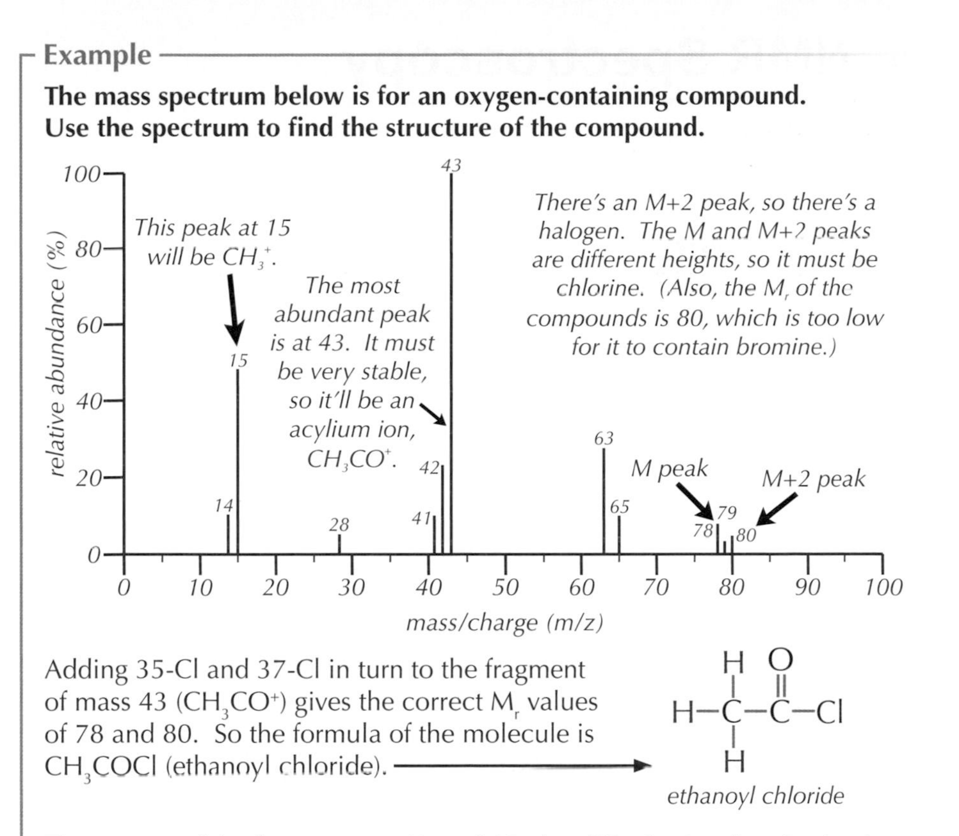

Adding 35-Cl and 37-Cl in turn to the fragment of mass 43 (CH_3CO^+) gives the correct M_r values of 78 and 80. So the formula of the molecule is CH_3COCl (ethanoyl chloride).

The masses of the fragments at 63 and 65 also differ by 2 units. So they're likely to contain the 35-Cl and 37-Cl isotopes. They're due to the fragments $CO^{35}Cl^+$ and $CO^{37}Cl^+$.

Tip: A big peak at 43 m/z could also be down to a stable $C_3H_7^+$ carbocation. You know it's not that here though, because the M peak is at 78 m/z — there isn't enough room in the molecule for a $C_3H_7^+$ ion, an oxygen atom and a chlorine atom (which must be there because of the M+2 peak).

Practice Questions — Application

Q1 The mass spectrum of hexan-3-one has a major peak in its spectrum at 57 m/z. Identify the fragment ion that caused this peak.

Q2 The spectrum below is for a molecule with the molecular formula C_3H_6O. Use the spectrum to find the structure of the compound.

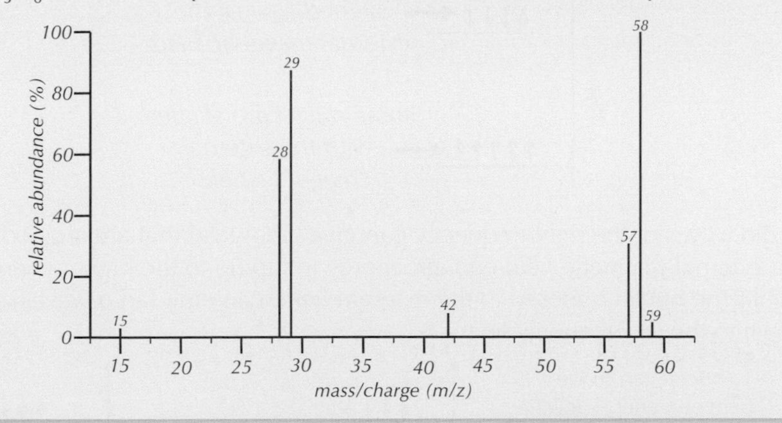

Exam Tip
Make sure you write down as much information as you can if they ask you to identify the structure of a compound from a spectrum in the exam. Even if you get the structure wrong you could still get marks for how you worked it out.

Practice Questions — Fact Recall

Q1 What fragment ion is most likely to have caused a peak at 15 m/z?

Q2 Explain why a tertiary carbocation is the most stable carbocation.

Q3 Explain why the acylium ion has a very high stability.

4. NMR Spectroscopy

Learning Objectives:

- Know the use of the δ scale for recording chemical shift.
- Understand that chemical shift depends on the molecular environment.
- Understand why tetramethylsilane (TMS) is used as a standard.
- Understand that nuclear magnetic resonance gives information about the position of ^{13}C atoms in a molecule.

Specification Reference 3.4.11

Here's a lovely new analytical technique for you to sink your teeth into. NMR (nuclear magnetic resonance) spectroscopy provides information on the different environments of atoms in molecules.

Nuclear spin

There are two types of nuclear magnetic resonance (NMR) spectroscopy that you need to know about — ^{13}C NMR, which gives you information about how the carbon atoms in a molecule are arranged, and ^{1}H (or proton) NMR, which tells you how the hydrogen atoms in a molecule are arranged.

Any atomic nucleus with an odd number of nucleons (protons and neutrons) in its nucleus has a **nuclear spin**. This causes it to have a weak magnetic field — a bit like a bar magnet. NMR spectroscopy looks at how this tiny magnetic field reacts when you put in a much larger external magnetic field.

Hydrogen nuclei are single protons (1 nucleon), so they have spin. Carbon usually has six protons and six neutrons (12 nucleons), so it doesn't have spin. But about 1% of carbon atoms are the isotope ^{13}C (six protons and seven neutrons), which does have spin.

The effect of an external magnetic field

Normally the nuclei are spinning in random directions — so their magnetic fields cancel out.

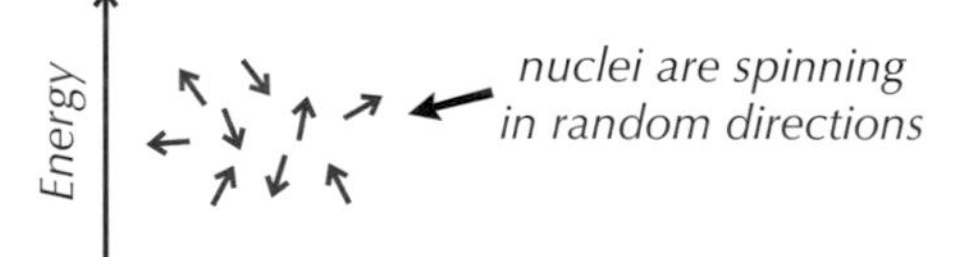

When a strong external magnetic field is applied, the nuclei will all align either with the field or opposed to it. The nuclei aligned with the external field are at a slightly lower energy level than the opposed nuclei.

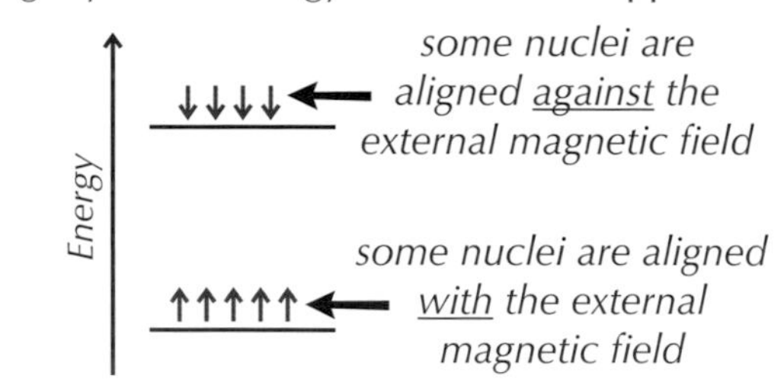

Exam Tip

You won't be asked to recall any of this stuff in the exam but if you understand it all it'll make learning the rest of it an awful lot easier.

Radio waves of the right frequency can give the nuclei that are aligned with the external magnetic field enough energy to flip up to the higher energy level. The nuclei opposed to the external field, can emit radio waves and flip down to the lower energy level.

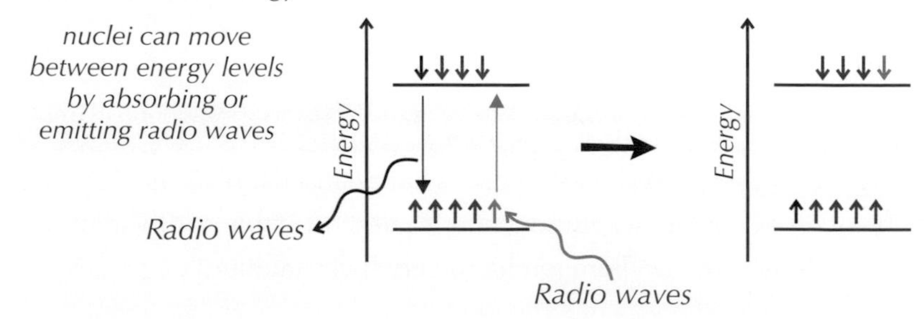

To start with, there are more nuclei aligned with the external field, so there will be an overall absorption of energy. NMR spectroscopy measures this absorption.

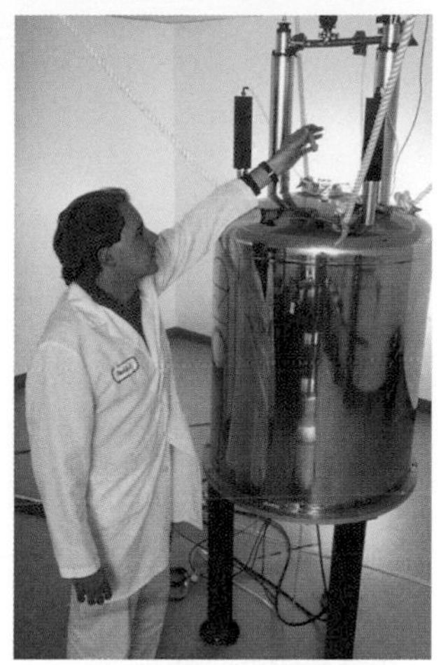

Figure 1: An NMR spectrometer.

Nuclear environments

A nucleus is partly **shielded** from the effects of an external magnetic field by its surrounding electrons. Any other atoms and groups of atoms that are around a nucleus will also affect the amount of electron shielding. So the nuclei in a molecule feel different magnetic fields depending on their environments. This means that they absorb different amounts of energy at different frequencies.

Example

If a carbon atom bonds to a more electronegative atom (like oxygen) the amount of electron shielding around its nucleus will decrease.

C:C*1* O:C*2*

These electrons provide the carbon atoms with shielding from a magnetic field.

These electrons are pulled further away from the carbon atom by the electronegative oxygen atom. The carbon atom is less shielded.

This means that carbon 1 and carbon 2 are in different environments.

Tip: Here's the ^{13}C NMR spectrum for TMS:

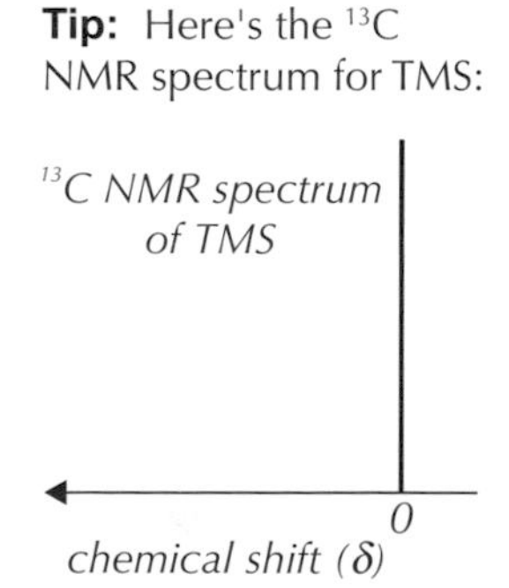

Chemical shift

Nuclei in different environments absorb energy of different frequencies. NMR spectroscopy measures these differences relative to a standard substance — the difference is called the **chemical shift** (δ). The standard substance is tetramethylsilane (TMS), $Si(CH_3)_4$.

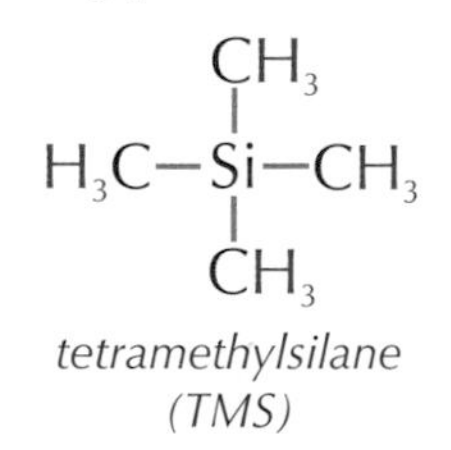

tetramethylsilane (TMS)

This molecule has 12 hydrogen atoms all in identical environments and 4 carbon atoms all in identical environments. This means that, in both ^1H NMR and ^{13}C NMR, it will produce a single absorption peak, well away from most other absorption peaks. Chemical shift is measured in parts per million (or ppm) relative to TMS. So the single peak produced by TMS is given a chemical shift value of 0. You'll often see a peak at δ = 0 on spectra because TMS is added to the test compound for calibration purposes. Tetramethylsilane is inert (so it doesn't react with the sample), non-toxic, and volatile (so it's easy to remove from the sample).

Type of carbon	δ (ppm)
C–C	5 – 40
C–Cl	10 – 70
$-\overset{\overset{O}{\|}}{C}-C-$ (arrow to second C)	20 – 50
C–N	25 – 60
C–O	50 – 90
C=C	90 – 150
C≡N	110 – 125
$-\overset{\overset{O}{\|}}{C}-$	160 – 220

Figure 2: Chemical shifts of different carbon environments.

^{13}C NMR

If you have a sample of a chemical that contains carbon atoms, you can use a ^{13}C NMR spectrum of the molecule to help work out what it is. The spectrum will have one peak on it for each carbon environment in the molecule. The carbon atoms which are attached to more electronegative atoms (for example, oxygen, nitrogen or chlorine) will be less shielded and so have a higher chemical shift, see Figure 2.

Example

There are two carbon atoms in a molecule of ethanol:

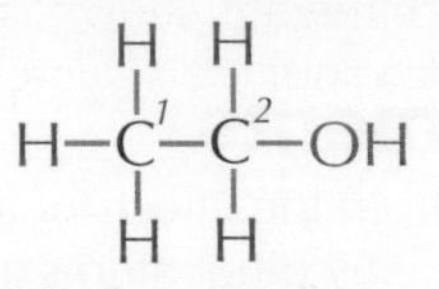

Because they are bonded to different atoms, each has a different amount of electron shielding — so there are two carbon environments in the ethanol molecule and two peaks on its ^{13}C NMR spectrum.

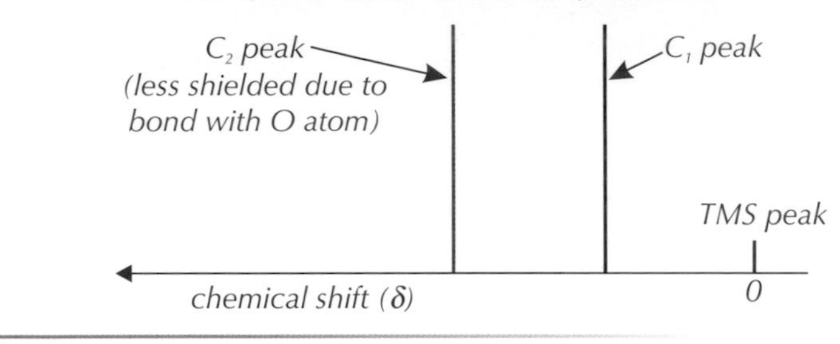

Exam Tip
Watch out for the scale on ^{13}C spectra in the exam — the chemical shift increases from right to left.

Here are some more examples:

Examples

Ethane

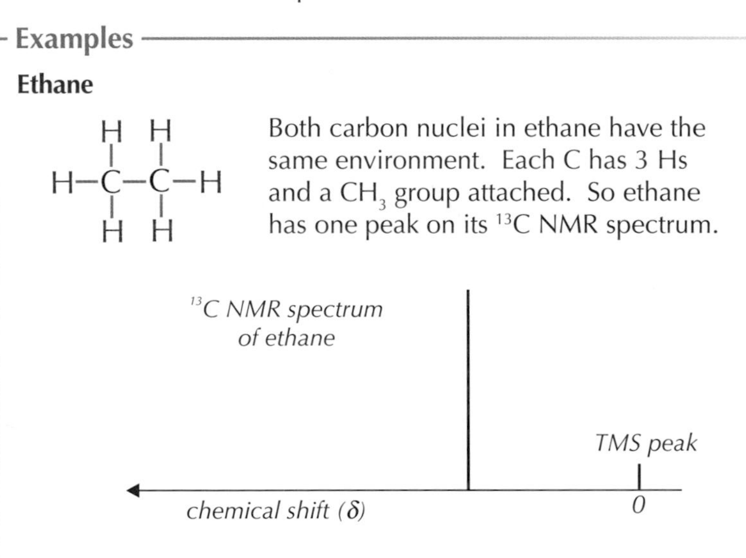

Both carbon nuclei in ethane have the same environment. Each C has 3 Hs and a CH_3 group attached. So ethane has one peak on its ^{13}C NMR spectrum.

Propanone

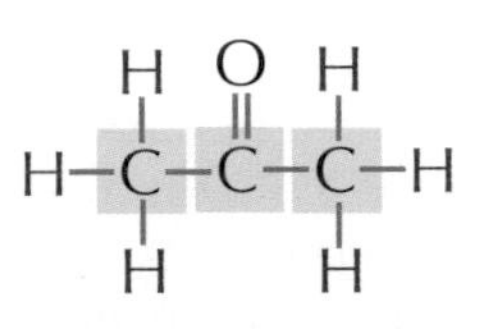

In propanone there are two different carbon environments. The end carbons both have the same environment — they each have 3 Hs and a $COCH_3$ attached. The centre carbon has 2 CH_3 groups and an O attached by a double bond. So propanone's ^{13}C NMR spectrum has 2 peaks.

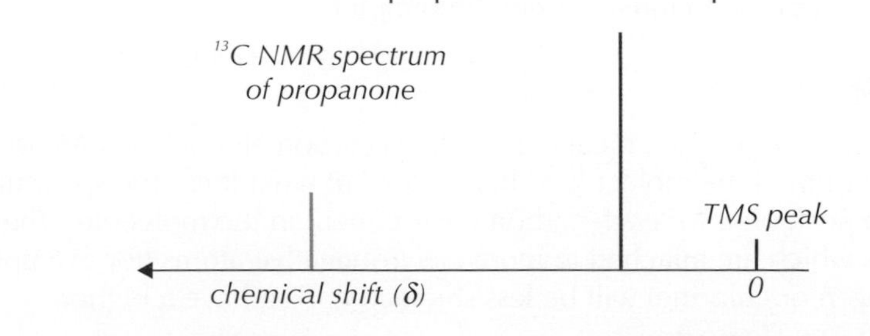

Tip: Remember, carbons next to more electronegative atoms will have a higher chemical shift and will be further to the left on the spectrum.

Cyclohexane-1,3-diol

In cyclohexane-1,3-diol there are four different carbon environments — each different carbon environment is shown in a different colour on the diagram below. If you think about the symmetry of the molecule you can see why this is.

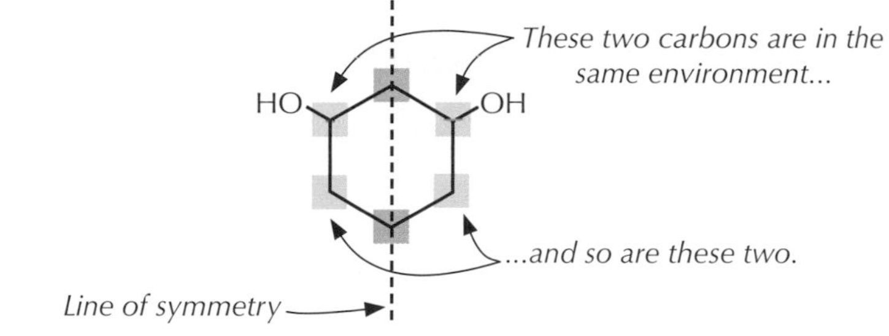

So cyclohexane-1,3-diol's ^{13}C NMR spectrum will have 4 peaks.

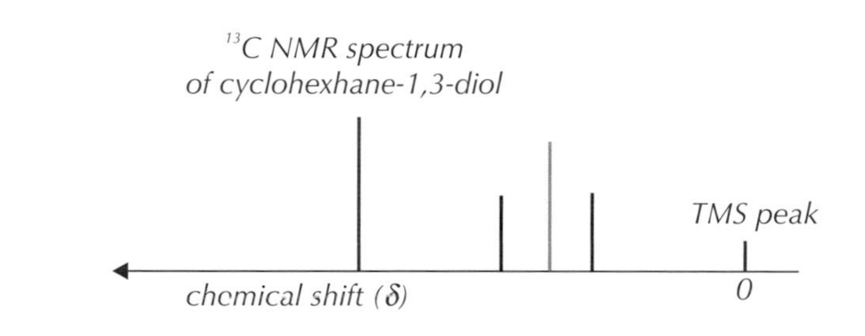

Tip: When you're thinking about the chemical shift of different carbon atoms you have to take into account all the atoms they're near — not just the ones right next to them.
For example, in 1-chlorobutane all of the carbons are in different environments:

```
  H  H  H  H
  |4 |3 |2 |1
H-C--C--C--C-Cl
  |  |  |  |
  H  H  H  H
```

Carbon-2 and carbon-3 look like they might be in the same environment. But carbon-2 is much closer to the electronegative chlorine atom — so it will have a higher chemical shift.

Practice Questions — Application

Q1 Which of the carbon atoms in the molecule below will have the highest chemical shift on a ^{13}C NMR spectrum?

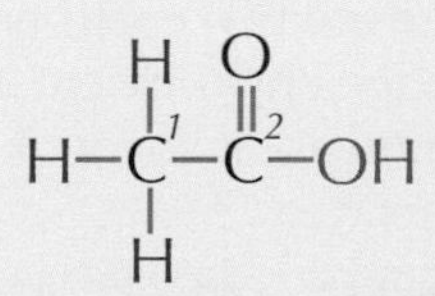

Q2 How many peaks would you see on a ^{13}C NMR spectrum of butanone?

Q3 How many peaks would you see on a ^{13}C NMR spectrum of the molecule shown below.

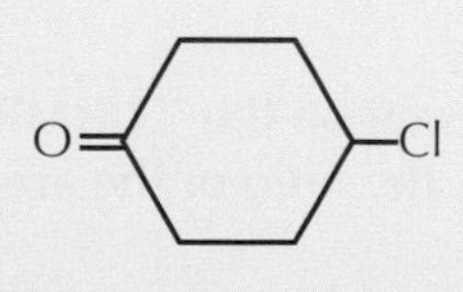

Exam Tip

In the exam you'll get a table showing you the chemical shifts of different carbon environments (like the one on page 129).

Tip: For questions like these it helps to number the carbon atoms and then write down what groups each carbon atom is attached to. Then you can see which carbons are in the same environment.

Practice Questions — Fact Recall

Q1 Explain why carbon atoms in different environments in a molecule have different chemical shifts on a ^{13}C NMR spectrum.

Q2 What is chemical shift (δ) measured in?

Q3 a) What is the standard substance used in NMR?

b) Give one reason why this substance is used.

5. More About NMR

This topic contains loads of interesting stuff about ^1H NMR. It works in pretty much the same way as ^{13}C NMR except this time the spectra tell you about the different hydrogen environments in a molecule.

Learning Objectives:

- Understand that nuclear magnetic resonance gives information about the position of ^1H atoms in a molecule.
- Understand how integrated spectra indicate the relative numbers of ^1H atoms in different environments.
- Understand that chemical shift depends on the molecular environment.
- Be able to use the n + 1 rule to deduce the spin–spin splitting patterns of adjacent, non-equivalent protons, limited to doublet, triplet and quartet formation in simple aliphatic compounds.
- Understand that ^{13}C NMR gives a simpler spectrum than ^1H NMR.
- Understand that ^1H NMR spectra are obtained using samples dissolved in proton-free solvents (e.g. deuterated solvents and CCl_4).

Specification Reference 3.4.11

Hydrogen environments

Each peak on a ^1H NMR spectrum is due to one or more hydrogen nuclei (protons) in a particular environment — this is similar to a ^{13}C NMR spectrum (which tells you the number of different carbon environments). But, with ^1H NMR, the relative area under each peak also tells you the relative number of H atoms in each environment.

Examples

The spectrum below is the ^1H NMR spectrum of ethanoic acid (CH_3COOH).

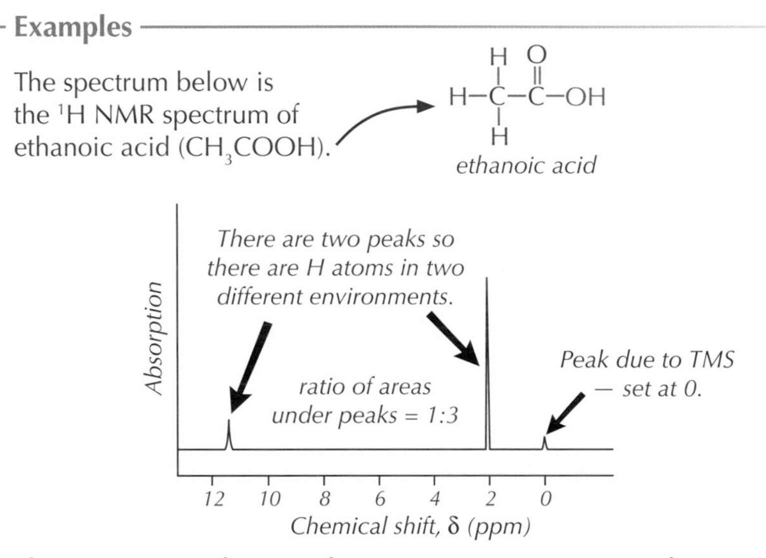

There are two peaks — so there are two environments. The area ratio is 1 : 3 — so there's 1 H atom in the environment at δ = 11.5 ppm to every 3 H atoms in the other environment. If you look at the structure of ethanoic acid, this makes sense:

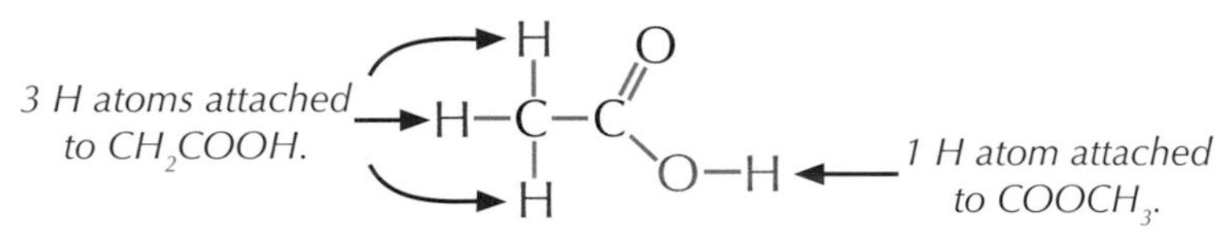

How many peaks will be present on the ^1H NMR spectrum of 1-chloropropanone? Predict the ratio of the areas of these peaks.

By looking at the structure of 1-chloropropanone we can see that there are two different hydrogen environments, which means there will be 2 peaks on the ^1H NMR spectrum.

There are 2 hydrogens in one environment and 3 hydrogens in the other so the ratio of the peak areas will be 2 : 3.

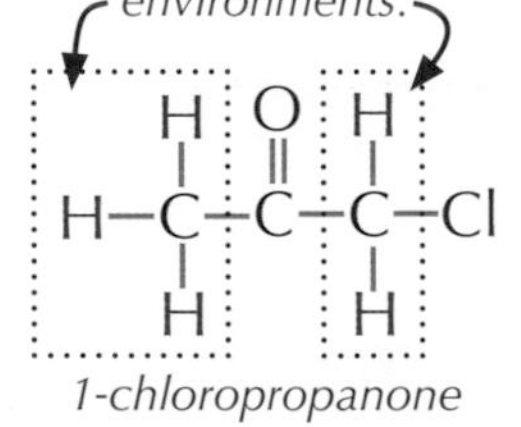

1-chloropropanone

Exam Tip

It can be difficult to work out how many hydrogen environments you have in a molecule. Sometimes it helps if you grab a highlighter and highlight all the hydrogens that are in the same environment the same colour — then you can go back and count up how many environments there are.

Integration traces

^{1}H NMR spectra can get quite cramped and sometimes it's not easy to see the ratio of the areas — so an **integration trace** is often shown. The height increases shown on the integration trace are proportional to the areas of the peaks.

Example

Here's the spectrum for ethanoic acid again:

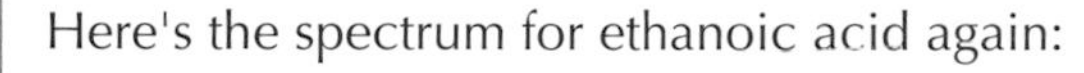

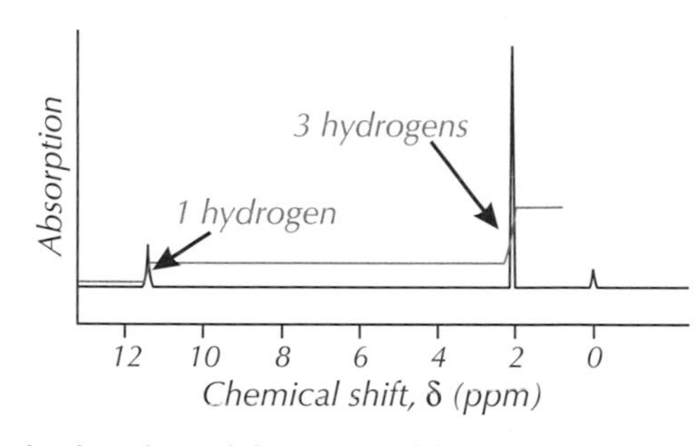

The integration trace (shown in green on the diagram) has a peak around 11.5 ppm and one around 2 ppm.

The heights of the vertical lines are in the ratio 1 : 3 — this means that for every one hydrogen in the first environment there are three in the second environment.

Tip: If the ratio of areas isn't given to you, you can use a ruler to measure the ratios off the integration trace. Measure the heights of the trace peaks and divide the measurements by the smallest peak height, et voilà — you've got your area ratio.

Chemical shift

You use a table like the one shown in Figure 1 to identify which functional group each peak in a ^{1}H NMR spectrum is due to. Don't worry — you don't need to learn it. You'll be given one in your exam, so use it. The copy you get in your exam may look a little different, and have different values — they depend on the solvent, temperature and concentration.

Tip: The nucleus of a hydrogen atom is a single proton. So ^{1}H NMR is also known as 'proton NMR' — and you might see the hydrogen atoms involved being called 'protons'.

The hydrogen atoms that cause the shift are highlighted in red.

This empty bond just means that there are other things attached to this carbon too. (So this group could be $COCH_3$, $COCH_2R$, or $COCHR_2$.)

R stands for any alkyl group.

Type of H atom	Chemical shift, δ (ppm)
$R-CH_3$	0.8 – 1.3
$R-CH_2-R$	1.2 – 1.4
$R-COCH-$	2.0 – 2.9
$halogen-CH_3$	3.2 – 3.7
$R-CH_2-Cl$	3.6 – 3.8
$R-OCH_2-R$	3.3 – 3.9
$R-CH_2OH$	3.3 – 4.0
R−OH	3.5 – 5.5
⌬	6.0 – 8.0
R−CHO	9.5 – 10
R−COOH	11.0 – 11.7

Figure 1: *Chemical shifts of different hydrogen environments.*

Exam Tip

Try and get your hands on a copy of the data sheet that you'll get in the exam before the day (you can download one from AQA's website). That way you'll know exactly what's given to you and what you'll be expected to know.

Example

According to the table, ethanoic acid (CH_3COOH) should have a peak at 11 – 11.7 ppm due to R-COOH, and a peak at 2.0 – 2.9 ppm due to R-COCH–. You can see these peaks on ethanoic acid's spectrum below.

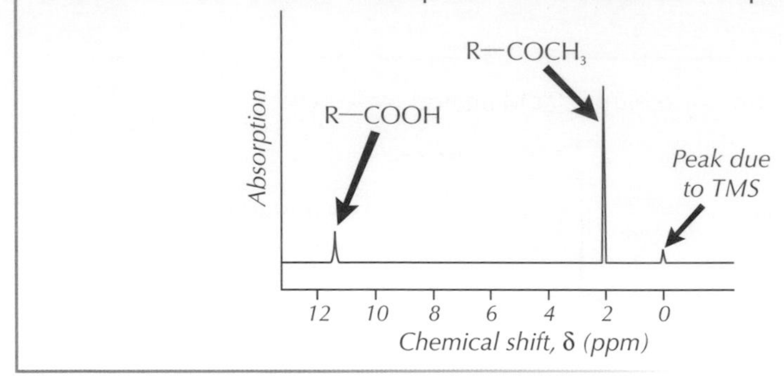

Splitting patterns

Tip: You don't need to know at A-level why ^1H NMR peaks split. It's all down to how the tiny magnetic fields of the hydrogen nuclei interact — it's pretty tricky stuff...

The peaks on a ^1H NMR spectrum may be split into smaller peaks (this is called spin-spin splitting). Peaks always split into the number of hydrogens on the neighbouring carbon, plus one. It's called the **n+1 rule**. Some of the different **splitting patterns** you'll find in ^1H spectra are shown in Figure 2.

Type of peak	Structure of peak	Number of hydrogens on adjacent carbon
Singlet		0
Doublet		1
Triplet		2
Quartet		3

Figure 2: *Splitting patterns in ^1H NMR.*

Tip: If you want to work out the number of hydrogens on an adjacent carbon from a peak you have to take 1 away from the number of peaks. For example, a doublet (two peaks) on a spectrum means there's 1 hydrogen on the adjacent carbon.

Example

Here's the ^1H NMR spectrum for 1,1,2-trichloroethane:

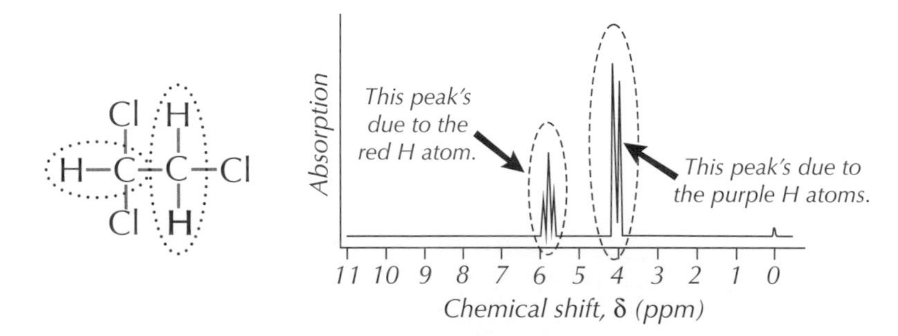

The peak due to the purple hydrogens is split into two because there's one hydrogen on the adjacent carbon atom. The peak due to the red hydrogen is split into three because there are two hydrogens on the adjacent carbon atom.

^1H NMR spectra are usually more complicated than ^{13}C NMR spectra because they have more, unclear split peaks to worry about.

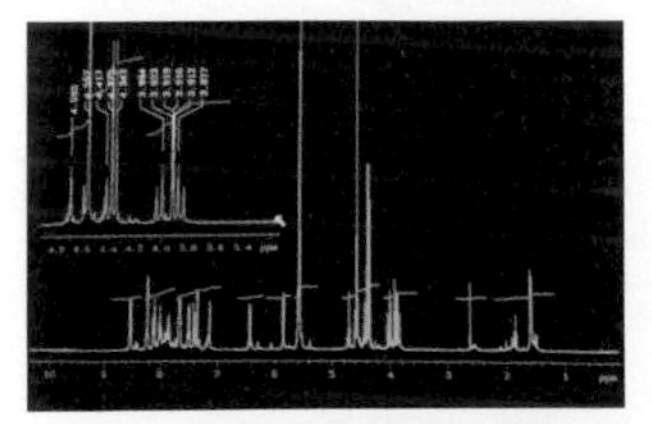

Figure 3: *^1H NMR spectrum. In the ^1H NMR spectra of large organic molecules the splitting patterns can be very complicated. Thankfully you'll never have to deal with one like this.*

Proton-free solvents

If a sample has to be dissolved, then a solvent is needed that doesn't contain any ^1H atoms — because these would show up on the spectrum and confuse things. **Deuterated solvents** are often used — their hydrogen atoms have been replaced by deuterium (D or ^2H) (see Figure 4). Deuterium's an isotope of hydrogen that's got two nucleons (a proton and a neutron). Because deuterium has an even number of nucleons, it doesn't have a nuclear spin (see page 128) so it doesn't create a magnetic field. Here are some examples of deuterated solvents:

CCl_4 can also be used — it doesn't contain any ^1H atoms either.

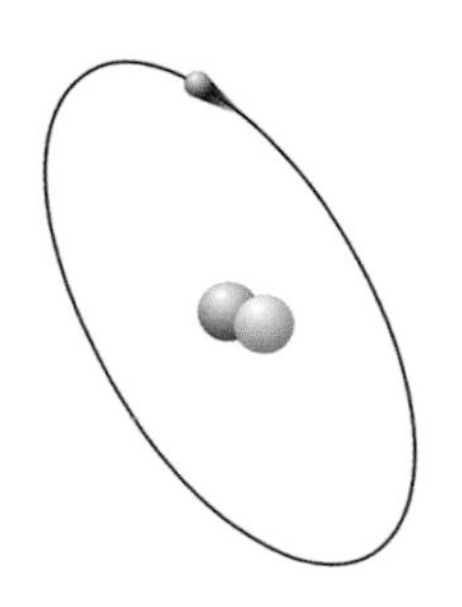

Figure 4: *Atomic model of deuterium. Deuterium has one neutron and one proton in its nucleus, whereas hydrogen has no neutrons. The atom also has one electron orbiting the nucleus.*

Predicting structure from ^1H NMR spectra

^1H NMR spectra provide you with an awful lot of information to analyse. Here's a run down of the things to look out for:

- The number of peaks tells you how many different hydrogen environments there are in your compound.
- The ratio of the peak areas tells you about the relative number of hydrogens in each environment. Sometimes these ratios are written above the peaks on the spectrum for you, other times you may have to use the integration traces.
- You can use the chemical shift of each peak to work out what type of environment the hydrogen is in. You can use a table like the one in Figure 1 to help you.
- The splitting pattern of each peak tells you the number of hydrogens on the adjacent carbon. You can use the n+1 rule to work this out.

And here's one last example to help you on your way...

Example

Using the spectrum below, and the table of chemical shift data on page 133, predict the structure of the compound.

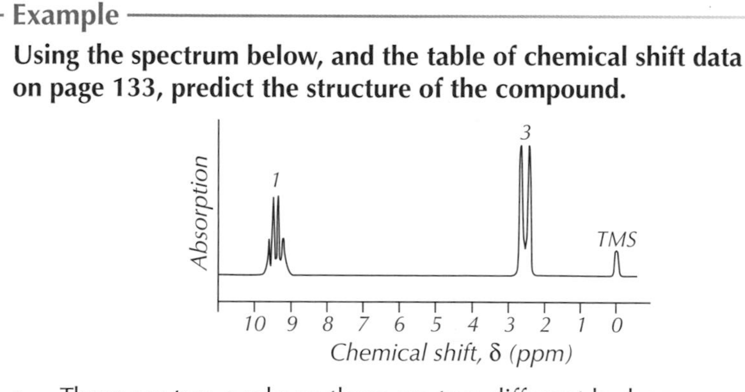

- There are two peaks so there are two different hydrogen environments.
- From the area ratios, there's one proton in the environment at $\delta = 9.5$ ppm for every three in the environment at $\delta = 2.5$ ppm.
- Now using the chemical shift data, the peak at $\delta = 2.5$ ppm is likely to be due to an R–COCH– group, and the peak at $\delta = 9.5$ ppm is likely to be due to an R–CHO group. This fits nicely with the area ratio data.
- The peak at $\delta = 9.5$ ppm is a quartet so this proton has got three neighbouring hydrogens. The peak at $\delta = 2.5$ ppm is a doublet so these protons have got one neighbouring hydrogen. So, it's likely these two groups are next to each other.

Exam Tip

When you're analysing a spectrum in an exam write down all the information you're given and can work out first. Then try and work out the structure — that way you're less likely to miss out an important detail.

Now you know the molecule has to contain these groups:

All you have to do is fit them together:

H O
| ||
H–C–C–H
|
H

So this is the ^{1}H NMR spectrum for ethanal.

Exam Tip
Always go back and check to see if your structure matches the spectrum — you need to make sure you haven't overlooked an important piece of information.

Practice Questions — Application

Q1 The spectrum below is the ^{1}H NMR spectrum for propanoic acid.

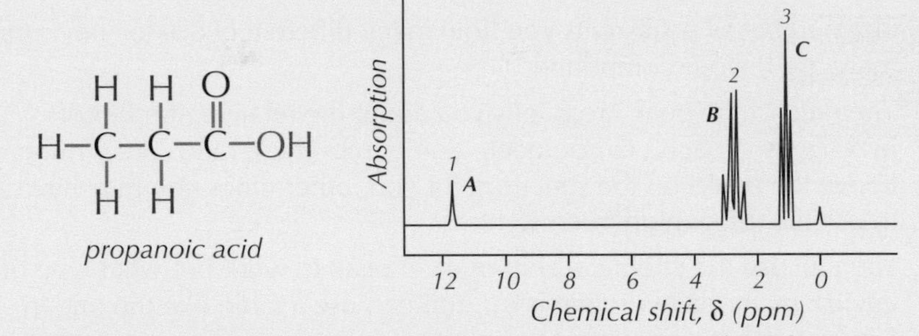

Assign the peaks **A** – **C** to the hydrogen environments found in propanoic acid.

Q2 Use the ^{1}H spectrum of compound **X** below, along with the chemical shift data on page 133, to work out the structure of compound **X**.
HINT: Compound **X** has the molecular formula C_4H_8O.

Tip: Remember to use all the different types of information that the spectrum gives you...

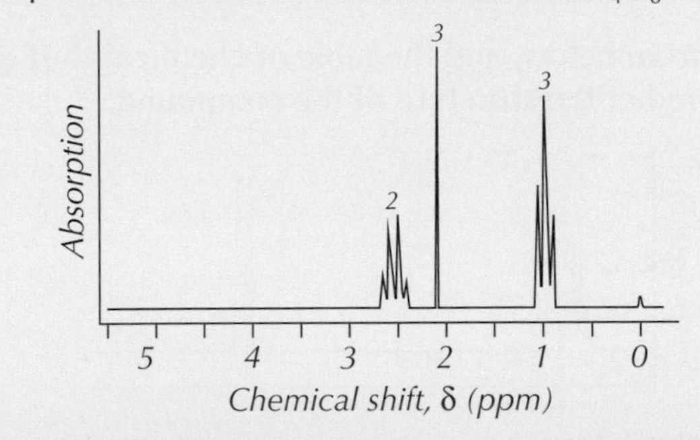

Practice Questions — Fact Recall

Q1 What does the number of peaks on the ^{1}H NMR spectrum of a compound correspond to?

Q2 What does the area under the peaks on an ^{1}H NMR spectrum of a compound correspond to?

Q3 What data from an ^{1}H NMR spectrum can you use to work out the type of hydrogen environment a peak corresponds to?

Q4 Suggest one solvent that could be used to dissolve a sample for analysis by ^{1}H NMR.

6. Infrared Spectroscopy

Here's another analytical technique — you'll probably remember it from AS-Level. Infrared spectroscopy uses the different absorbencies of the bonds in functional groups to produce a spectrum which we can analyse to find out about a compound's structure.

Learning Objectives:

- Be able to use infrared spectra to identify the functional groups that are covered in the AS- and A2-Level Chemistry course.
- Be able to use data from infrared spectroscopy to determine the structure of specified compounds.

Specification Reference 3.4.11

The basics

In **infrared (IR) spectroscopy**, a beam of IR radiation is passed through a sample of a chemical. The IR radiation is absorbed by the covalent bonds in the molecules, increasing their vibrational energy. Bonds between different atoms absorb different frequencies of IR radiation. Bonds in different places in a molecule absorb different frequencies too — so the O–H group in an alcohol and the O–H in a carboxylic acid absorb different frequencies. Figure 1 shows what frequencies different bonds absorb — you don't need to learn this data, but you do need to understand how to use it. Wavenumber is the measure used for the frequency (it's just 1/wavelength).

Functional group	Where it's found	Frequency / Wavenumber (cm^{-1})	Type of absorption
C–H	most organic molecules	2800 – 3100	strong, sharp
O–H	alcohols	3200 – 3750	strong, broad
O–H	carboxylic acids	2500 – 3300	medium, broad
C–O	alcohols, carboxylic acids and esters	1100 – 1310	strong, sharp
C=O	aldehydes, ketones, carboxylic acids and esters	1680 – 1800	strong, sharp
C=O	amides	1630 – 1700	medium
C=C	alkenes	1620 – 1680	medium, sharp
N–H	primary amines	3300 – 3500	medium to strong
N–H	amides	about 3500	medium

***Figure 1:** Bond absorption for different functional groups.*

Exam Tip
Don't worry about learning all this data — you'll be given a handy table with all of the groups and wavenumbers on it in the exam.

Tip: O–H groups tend to have broad absorptions because they take part in hydrogen bonding. All the O–H groups are hydrogen bonded to different extents so they all have slightly different absorptions. This results in the broad peak seen on the spectrum.

Infrared spectra

An infrared spectrometer produces a graph that shows you what frequencies of radiation the molecules are absorbing. So you can use it to identify the functional groups in a molecule. The peaks show you where radiation is being absorbed — the 'peaks' on IR spectra are upside-down.

Ethyl ethanoate is an ester.
Here's its structure:

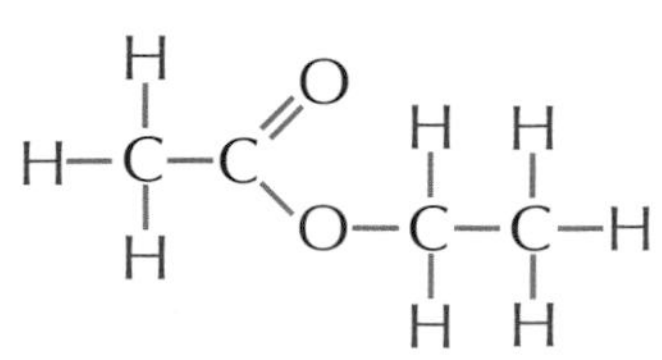

The infrared spectrum of ethyl ethanoate is shown on the next page.
There's a strong, sharp absorption at 1740 cm^{-1} because of the C=O bond.

Tip: The 'type of absorption' column tells you what the peak is going to look like. A strong peak is a big, easy-to-see peak, a medium peak is smaller. A sharp peak is quite narrow and a broad peak is really wide.

Tip: The peaks on an IR spectrum show you the wavelengths of radiation that have been absorbed.

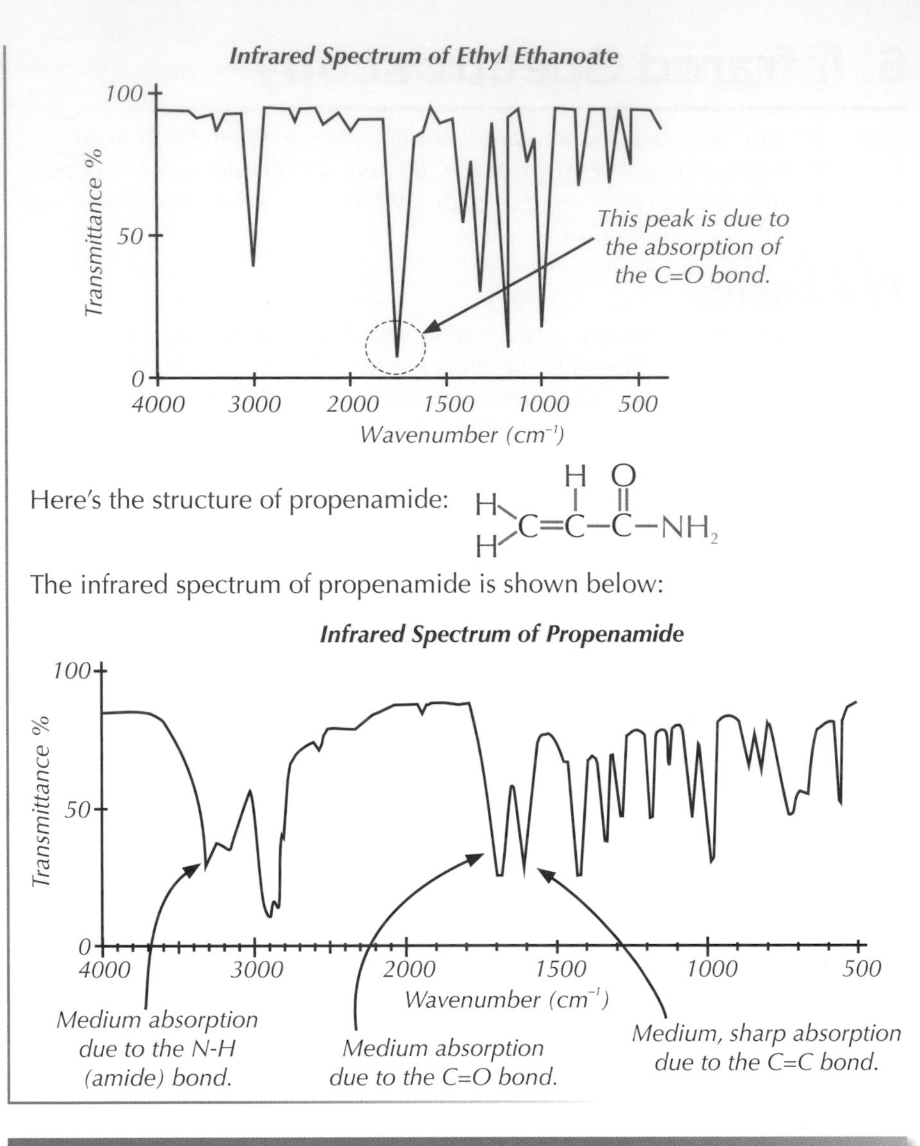

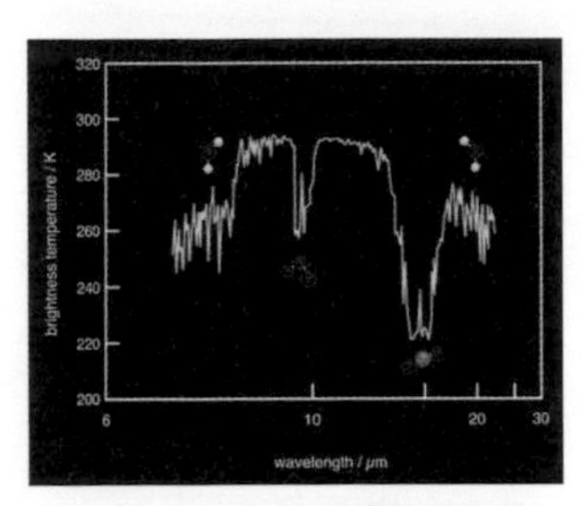

Figure 2: Infrared spectrum of gases in the Earth's atmosphere. The big peak on the right of the spectrum is caused by the C=O bonds in CO_2.

Exam Tip
Sometimes it can be quite difficult to spot the important peaks on IR spectrums but don't worry — the ones you'll have to analyse in the exam will be really obvious.

Practice Questions — Application

Q1 Identify the peak(s) on the IR spectrum below which indicate the presence of an amide group.

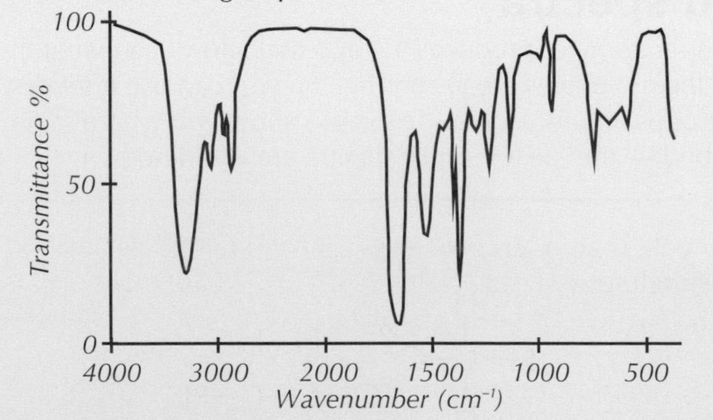

Q2 Compound **Y** has the molecular formula $C_3H_7NO_2$. Its IR spectrum has a strong, sharp peak at 1680 cm^{-1}, a broad peak at 2800 cm^{-1} and a medium peak at 3300 cm^{-1}. Give a possible structure for compound **Y**.

Tip: Use Figure 1 to help you with these questions.

7. Chromatography

Chromatography is used for separating and identifying mixtures. There are two different types of chromatography you need to know about — column chromatography and gas-liquid chromatography.

Learning Objectives:

- Know that separation by column chromatography depends on the balance between solubility in the moving phase and retention in the stationary phase.
- Know that gas-liquid chromatography can be used to separate mixtures of volatile liquids.
- Be able to use data from chromatography to determine the structure of specified compounds.

Specification Reference 3.4.11

The basics

Chromatography is used to separate stuff in a mixture — once it's separated out, you can often identify the components. There are quite a few different types of chromatography — but the ones you need to know about are column chromatography and gas-liquid chromatography (GLC). All types of chromatography have two phases:

- A **mobile phase** — where the molecules can move. This is always a liquid or a gas.
- A **stationary phase** — where the molecules can't move. This must be a solid, or a liquid held in a solid.

The components in the mixture separate out as the mobile phase moves through the stationary phase.

Column chromatography

Column chromatography is mostly used for purifying an organic product. This needs to be done to separate it from unreacted chemicals or side products. It involves packing a glass column with a solid, absorbent material such as aluminium oxide coated with water — this is called a slurry. This is the stationary phase. The mixture to be separated is added to the top of the column and allowed to drain down into the slurry. A solvent is then run slowly and continually through the column. This solvent is the mobile phase.

Figure 1: *Column chromatography equipment.*

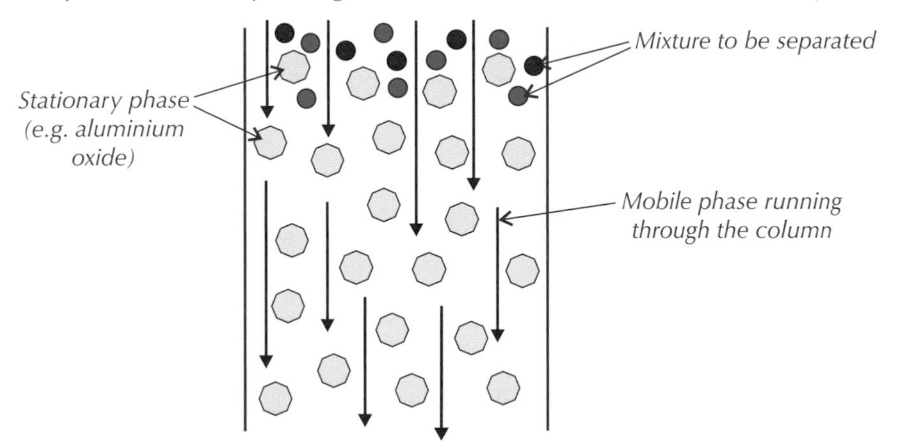

Figure 2: *The initial set-up of a column for column chromatography.*

As the mixture is washed through the column, its components separate out according to how soluble they are in the mobile phase and how strongly they are adsorbed onto the stationary phase (**retention**). Each different component will spend some time adsorbed onto (stuck to) the stationary phase and some time dissolved in the mobile phase.

The longer a component spends dissolved in the mobile phase, the quicker it travels down the column. If a component spends a long time adsorbed onto the stationary phase, it will take a long time to travel down the column. So, the more soluble a component is in the mobile phase, the quicker it'll pass through the column (see Figure 3).

Tip: This chromatography stuff isn't as difficult as it first seems. You just have to remember that the mixture separates depending on how soluble components are in the mobile phase. Components that are most soluble will travel through the column quickest.

Exam Tip
If you're asked to explain how column chromatography works in the exam, don't forget to say both that some components are more soluble in the mobile phase and that some are more strongly adsorbed by the stationary phase.

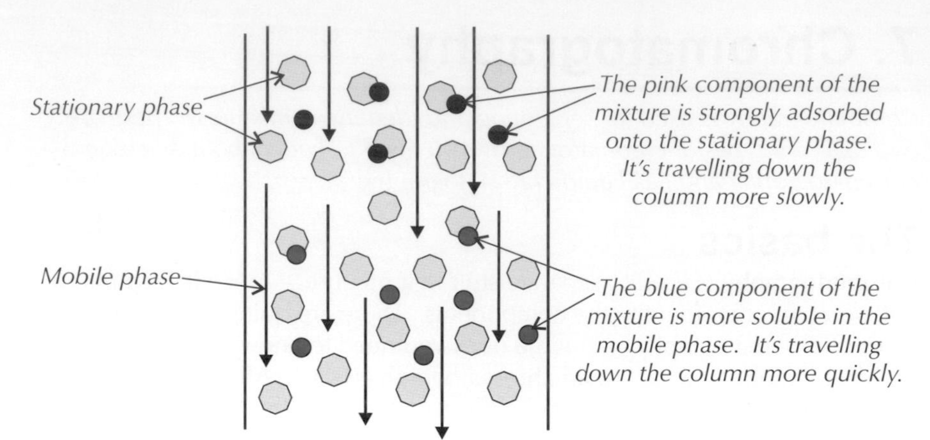

Figure 3: *The passage of a two component mixture through a chromatography column.*

As a component of the mixture reaches the end of the column it is collected. It can then be identified using the time taken to pass through the column (**retention time**) or another technique (e.g. mass spectrometry).

Gas-liquid chromatography

If you've got a mixture of volatile liquids (ones that turn into gases easily), then gas-liquid chromatography (GLC) is the way to separate them out so that you can identify them. The stationary phase is a viscous liquid, such as an oil, which coats the inside of a long tube. This tube is coiled to save space, and built into an oven. The mobile phase is an unreactive carrier gas such as nitrogen. The sample is vaporised and passes through the oven as a gas.

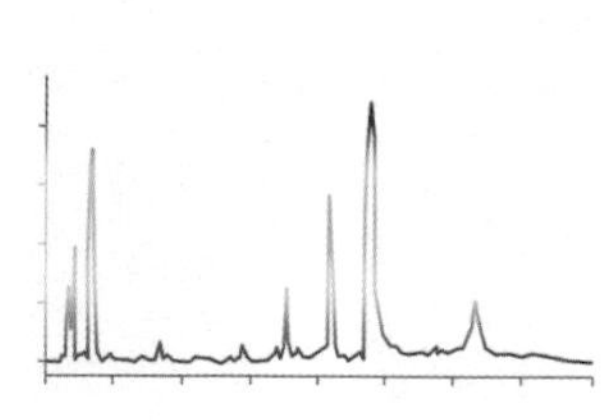

Figure 4: *Chromatogram. The horizontal axis shows the retention time of each component in the mixture.*

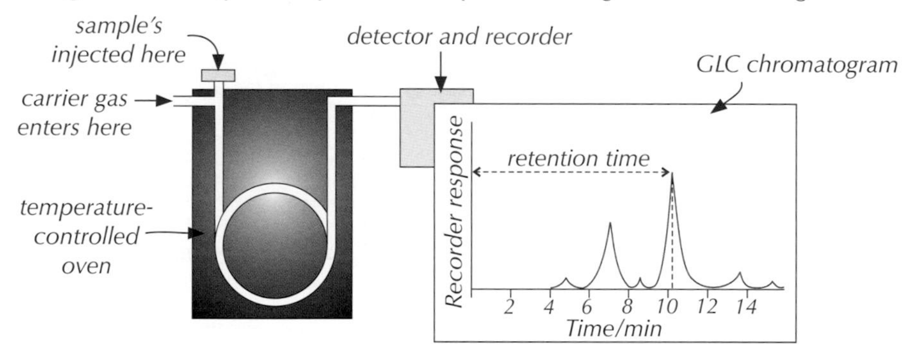

Figure 5: *GLC equipment and chromatogram.*

Each component takes a different amount of time from being injected into the tube to being recorded at the other end. This is the retention time. The retention times for the components in a mixture are shown on a chromatogram (see Figure 5). The retention time depends on how much time the component spends moving along with the carrier gas, and how much time it spends stuck to the viscous liquid. Each separate substance will have a unique retention time — so you can use the retention time to identify the components of the mixture. (You have to run a known sample under the same conditions for comparison).

Tip: You have to run the known sample under the same conditions as the unknown to ensure the variables of the experiment are kept the same.

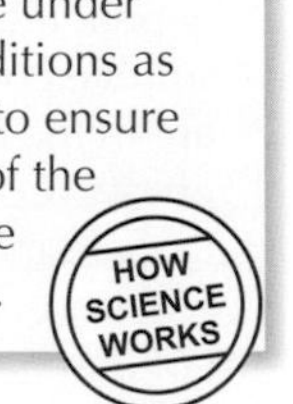

Example

If you wanted to know if a mixture contained octane, you could run a sample of the mixture through the system, then run a sample of pure octane through, and see if there's a peak at the same retention time on both spectra.

The area under each peak tells you the relative amount of each component that's present in the mixture (see Figure 6).

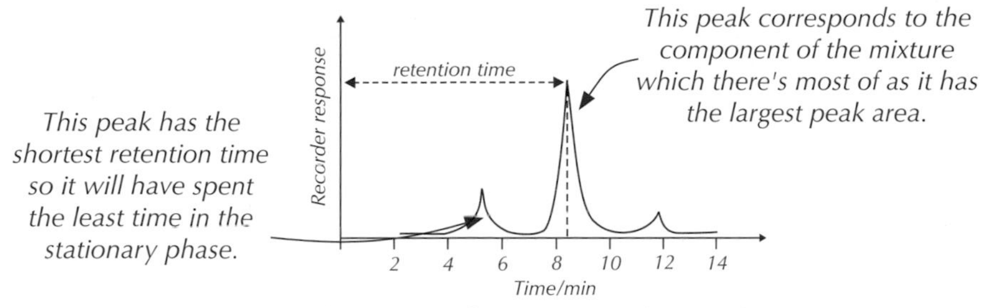

Figure 6: *A chromatogram showing the separation of three components in a mixture.*

GLC can be used to find the level of alcohol in blood or urine — the results are accurate enough to be used as evidence in court. It's also used to find the proportions of various esters in oils used in paints — this lets picture restorers know exactly what paint was originally used.

Tip: Column chromatography and gas-liquid chromatography work in pretty much the same way — their mobile and stationary phases are just in different states.

Practice Questions — Application

Q1 A scientist is using column chromatography to purify an organic product. She knows that the pure product is more strongly adsorbed to the stationary phase than the impurities. Will the pure product leave the column before or after the impurities? Explain your answer.

Q2 The GLC chromatogram below shows the retention times of three components in a mixture.

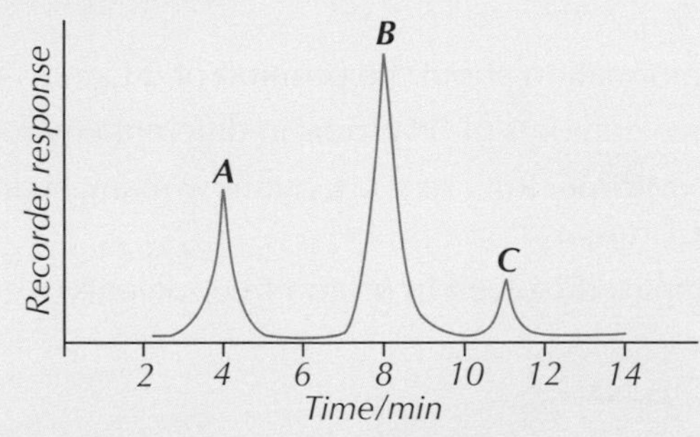

a) State which peak corresponds to the component that spends the highest proportion of its time in the tube in the mobile phase.

b) One component of the mixture is hexene. When pure hexene is run through the machine it has a retention time of 8 minutes. Which of the components, A, B or C, is hexene?

Figure 7: *Chromatography being used by a police lab to analyse evidence found at a crime scene. GLC is so accurate that the evidence it provides can be used in court.*

Practice Questions — Fact Recall

Q1 What is chromatography used for?

Q2 Give an example of a stationary phase used in column chromatography.

Q3 Briefly explain why the components in a mixture separate out during column chromatography.

Q4 Give an example of a mobile phase used in gas-liquid chromatography.

Q5 What is retention time?

Q6 Give one use of chromatography.

Section Summary

Make sure you know...

- How to identify organic functional groups, including using tests for primary, secondary and tertiary alcohols, the test for unsaturation and the test for distinguishing between haloalkanes.
- All of the functional groups of molecules found in the AS- and A2-Level Chemistry courses.
- How to deduce the synthesis routes of organic compounds using the reactions covered in the AS- and A2-Level Chemistry course.
- How to find the relative molecular mass of a molecule from its mass spectrum.
- What the molecular ion peaks (M peak, plus M+1, M+2 and M+4 peaks) are on a mass spectrum.
- What information molecular ion peaks can give you about the structure of a compound.
- What the molecular ion peaks are on a mass spectrum and what information they can give you about the structure of a compound.
- That the fragmentation of the molecular ion gives rise to a characteristic mass spectrum that may give information about the structure of the molecule.
- That more stable positive ions give higher peaks in mass spectrum.
- That tertiary carbocations are more stable that primary carbocations.
- That the acylium ion (RCO^+) is stabilised by resonance.
- How to predict the structure of an organic compound from its mass spectrum.
- How NMR spectroscopy works including the use of the δ scale for recording chemical shift.
- That chemical shift depends on the molecular environment of a nucleus.
- Why tetramethylsilane (TMS) is used as a standard in NMR.
- That ^{13}C nuclear magnetic resonance (NMR) spectroscopy gives information about the position of ^{13}C atoms in a molecule.
- That ^{1}H nuclear magnetic resonance gives information about the position of ^{1}H atoms in a molecule.
- That integration traces can tell you the relative numbers of ^{1}H atoms in different environments.
- How to use peak splitting patterns on a ^{1}H NMR spectrum to work out how many hydrogens there are on two next door carbons (using the $n + 1$ rule).
- That ^{1}H NMR spectra are obtained using samples dissolved in proton-free solvents (e.g. deuterated solvents and CCl_4).
- That ^{13}C NMR gives a simpler spectrum that ^{1}H NMR.
- How to use data from NMR to determine the structure of specified compounds.
- How to use data from infrared spectroscopy to determine the structure of specified compounds.
- What chromatography is.
- What the mobile and stationary phases are in chromatography.
- That separation by column chromatography depends on the balance between solubility in the moving phase and retention in the stationary phase.
- Know that gas-liquid chromatography can be used to separate mixtures of volatile liquids.
- What a retention time is.
- How to interpret a chromatogram.
- How to use data from chromatography to determine the structure of specified compounds.

Exam-style Questions

1 A scientist is trying to synthesise phenylethanone.
The structure of phenylethanone is shown below.

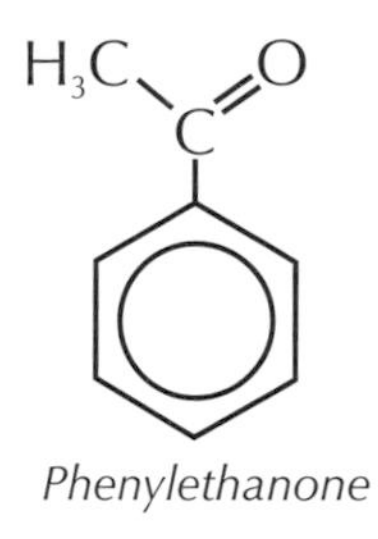

Phenylethanone

1 (a) Give a one step synthesis of this molecule from benzene.

(3 marks)

1 (b) The scientist wants to check that he has made a ketone and not an aldehyde.
Describe a test that could be used to distinguish between an aldehyde and a ketone.

(2 marks)

1 (c) The table below gives details of the δ values of the peaks seen on the ^{13}C NMR spectra of three different compounds. Which compound, **A, B** or **C**, is phenylethanone? Explain your answer.

Peak number	Spectrum A — δ (ppm)	Spectrum B — δ (ppm)	Spectrum C — δ (ppm)
1	26.5	26.5	26.5
2	128.3	128.3	128.3
3	137.2	128.6	128.6
4	197.9	133.0	133.0
5		137.2	137.2
6			197.9

(3 marks)

1 (d) The scientist purifies his compound using column chromatography.
Briefly explain why the pure phenylethanone separates out from the impurities as the mixture passes through the column. Include in your answer a suggestion of a stationary phase that the scientist could use in the column.

(4 marks)

2 Use the data given below, along with your knowledge of chemical tests, to deduce the structures of the unknown compounds **X**–**Z**. Explain your answers. You can use the tables on pages 129, 133 and 137 to help you.

2 (a) Compound **X** contains an aromatic ring.

The infrared spectrum of compound **X** has a medium strength absorption peak at 3350 cm^{-1}.

The mass spectrum of compound **X** has an M peak at 93 m/z and an M+1 peak at 94 m/z. These peaks have a relative abundance of 100% and 6% respectively.

(5 marks)

2 (b) Compound **Y** has the molecular formula $C_2H_4Br_2$.

The ^{1}H NMR spectrum for compound **Y** is shown below.

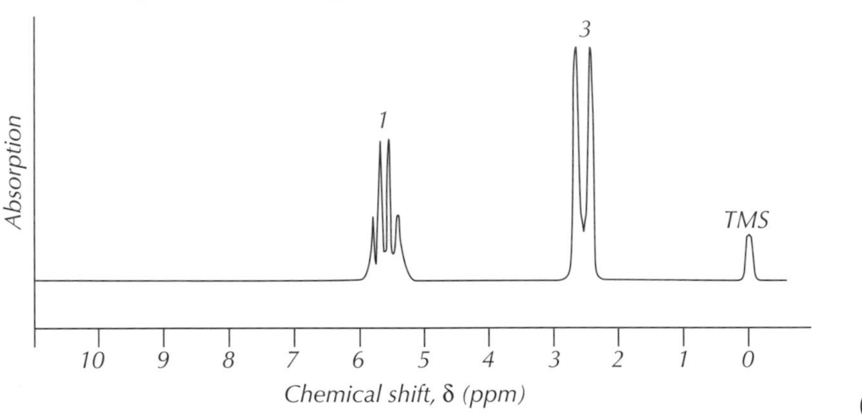

(5 marks)

2 (c) Compound **Z** has an M_r = 74 and contains only carbon, hydrogen and oxygen atoms.

The ^{1}H NMR has two singlet peaks with a ratio of the areas under the peaks of 1 : 1.
The ^{13}C NMR spectrum for compound Z is shown below.

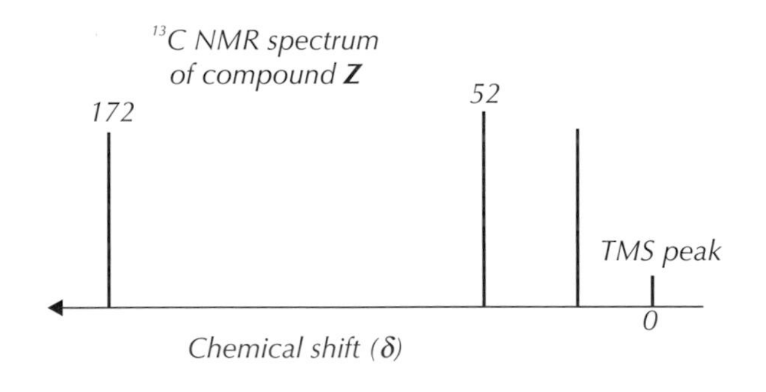

(8 marks)

3 The equations below and on the next page show the steps for the synthesis of a ketone.

Step 1

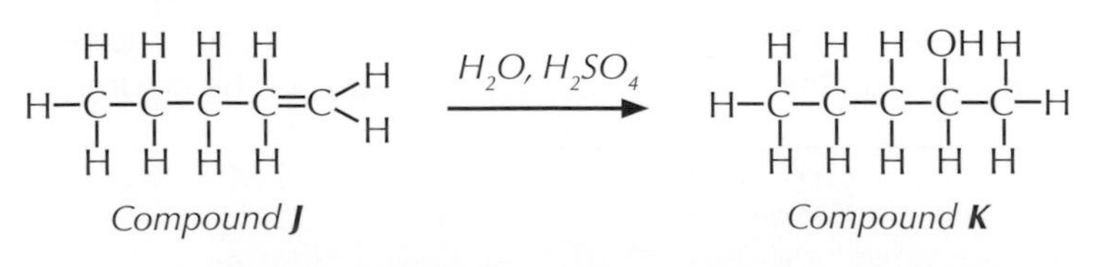

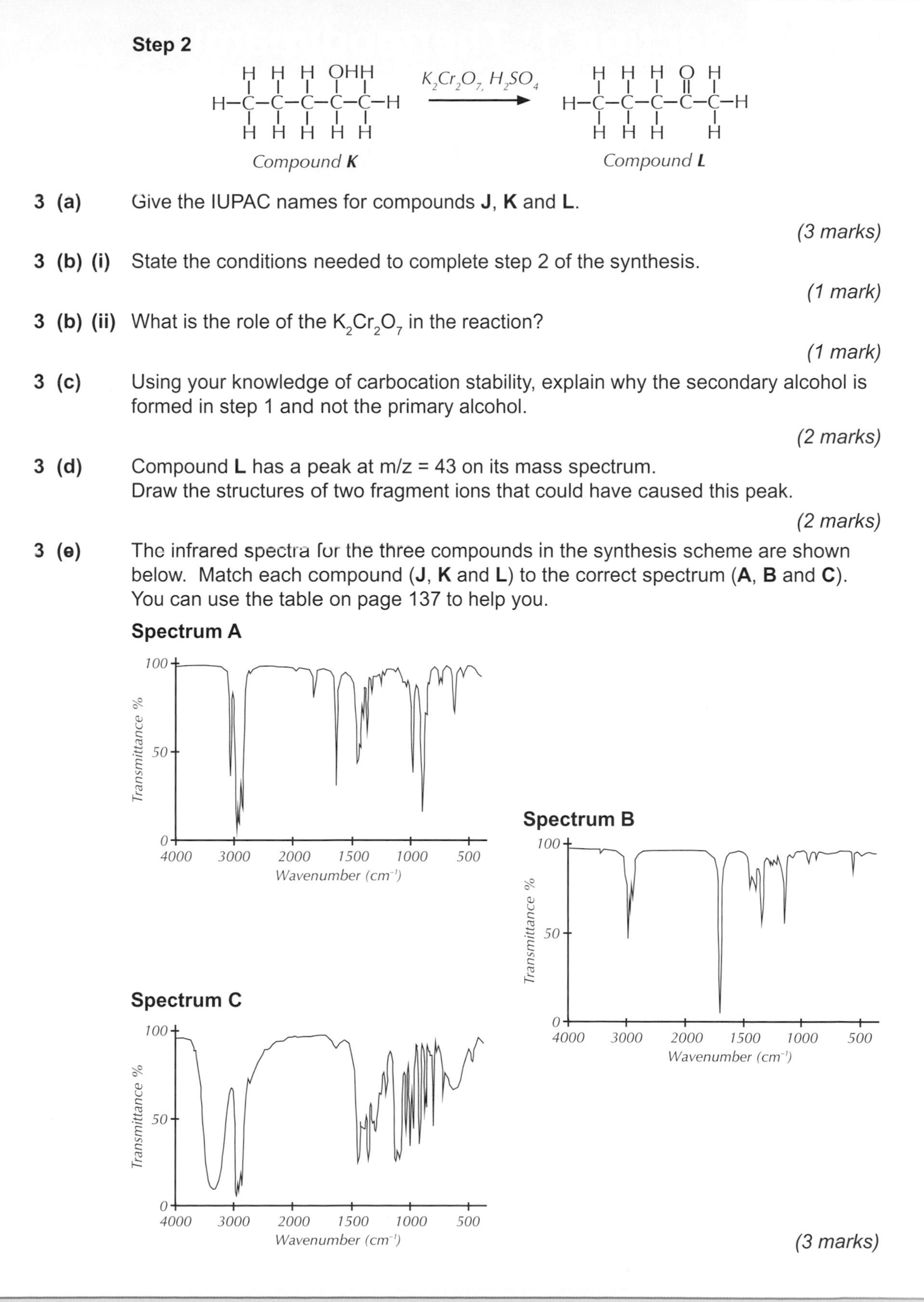

Step 2

Compound **K** (pentan-2-ol structure) $\xrightarrow{K_2Cr_2O_7,\ H_2SO_4}$ Compound **L**

3 (a) Give the IUPAC names for compounds **J**, **K** and **L**.

(3 marks)

3 (b) (i) State the conditions needed to complete step 2 of the synthesis.

(1 mark)

3 (b) (ii) What is the role of the $K_2Cr_2O_7$ in the reaction?

(1 mark)

3 (c) Using your knowledge of carbocation stability, explain why the secondary alcohol is formed in step 1 and not the primary alcohol.

(2 marks)

3 (d) Compound **L** has a peak at m/z = 43 on its mass spectrum.
Draw the structures of two fragment ions that could have caused this peak.

(2 marks)

3 (e) The infrared spectra for the three compounds in the synthesis scheme are shown below. Match each compound (**J**, **K** and **L**) to the correct spectrum (**A**, **B** and **C**).
You can use the table on page 137 to help you.

(3 marks)

Unit 5 Section 1: Thermodynamics

Learning Objective:

- Be able to define and apply the terms enthalpy of formation, ionisation enthalpy, enthalpy of atomisation of an element and of a compound, bond dissociation enthalpy, electron affinity, lattice enthalpy (defined as either lattice dissociation or lattice formation), enthalpy of hydration and enthalpy of solution.

Specification Reference 3.5.1

1. Lattice Enthalpies

Some of this stuff may ring a few bells from AS. Make sure you understand all the definitions in this topic because they're really important for the rest of the section.

The basics

Enthalpy notation

Enthalpy change, ΔH (delta H), is the heat energy transferred in a reaction at constant pressure. The units of ΔH are kJ mol^{-1}. You write $\Delta H^{\ominus}$ to show that the substances were in their standard states and that the measurements were made under **standard conditions**. Standard conditions are 100 kPa (about 1 atm) pressure and a stated temperature (e.g. $\Delta H^{\ominus}_{298}$). In this book, all the enthalpy changes are measured at 298 K (25 °C). Sometimes the notation will also include a letter to signify whether the enthalpy change is for a reaction (r), for combustion (c), or for the formation of a new compound (f).

Exothermic and endothermic reactions

Exothermic reactions have a negative ΔH value, because heat energy is given out (the chemicals lose energy). **Endothermic reactions** have a positive ΔH value, because heat energy is absorbed (the chemicals gain energy).

Tip: You covered enthalpy notation at AS level so if you need a reminder, get your old AS notes out.

What is lattice enthalpy?

Ions in lattices are held together by ionic bonds. It takes energy to break apart the bonds, and energy is given out when new bonds form. The energy needed to break a bond between two ions is the same amount of energy that is given out when that bond is formed. These 'lattice enthalpies' have specific values that differ depending on the ions involved (see Figure 1). So, lattice enthalpy is a measure of ionic bond strength. It can be defined in two ways.

Compound	*Lattice formation enthalpy (kJmol^{-1})*
LiCl	*–826*
NaCl	*–787*
KCl	*–701*
RbCl	*–692*

Figure 1: *Lattice formation enthalpies of chloride compounds.*

Lattice formation enthalpy: the enthalpy change when 1 mole of a solid ionic compound is formed from its gaseous ions under standard conditions.

Example

Formation of sodium chloride:

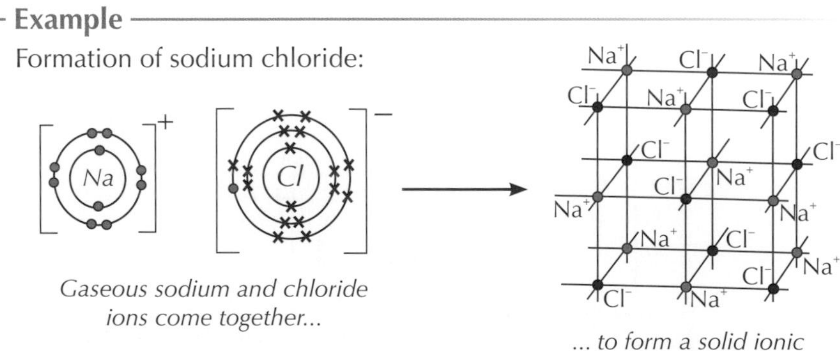

Gaseous sodium and chloride ions come together...

... to form a solid ionic lattice of sodium chloride.

Lattice formation enthalpy, $\Delta H^{\ominus}$, for this reaction is –787 kJ mol^{-1}.
The negative ΔH value shows that lattice formation is an exothermic process.

Lattice dissociation enthalpy: the enthalpy change when 1 mole of a solid ionic compound is completely dissociated into its gaseous ions under standard conditions.

Example

Dissociation of sodium chloride:

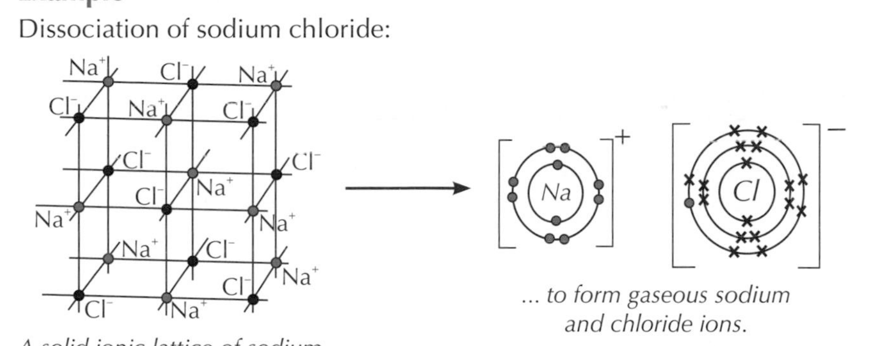

Lattice dissociation enthalpy, $\Delta H^{\ominus}$, for this reaction is +787 kJ mol^{-1}. The positive ΔH value shows that the reaction is endothermic.

Exam Tip
In the exam, make sure you use the term 'enthalpy' and not 'energy' otherwise you'll lose a mark.

Exam Tip
If you're asked to define the lattice formation enthalpy or the lattice dissociation enthalpy in the exam, don't forget to mention that it's measured under standard conditions.

Tip: Notice that the lattice formation enthalpy and the lattice dissociation enthalpy are exactly the same size — the only difference is that one's negative and the other one's positive.

Measuring lattice enthalpy

Lattice enthalpy can't be measured directly. Instead, you have to combine the enthalpies from a number of other processes to work out the lattice enthalpy — see Figure 2.

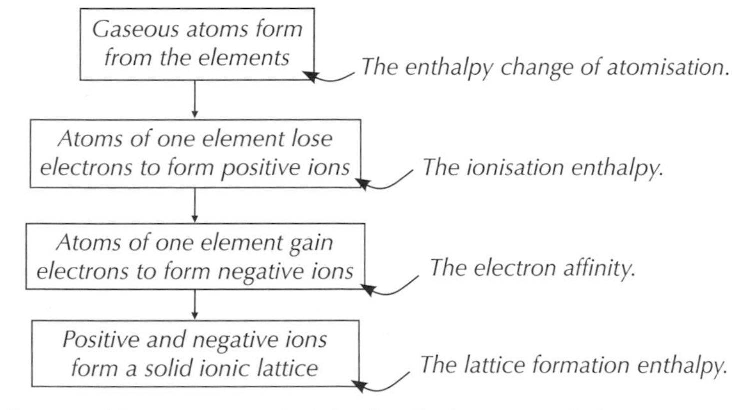

Figure 2: *The processes which lead to the formation of a lattice.*

Tip: Although lattice enthalpy can't be measured directly, it can be calculated using a Born-Haber cycle — all will be revealed on page 149.

Example

The processes that lead to the formation of sodium chloride:

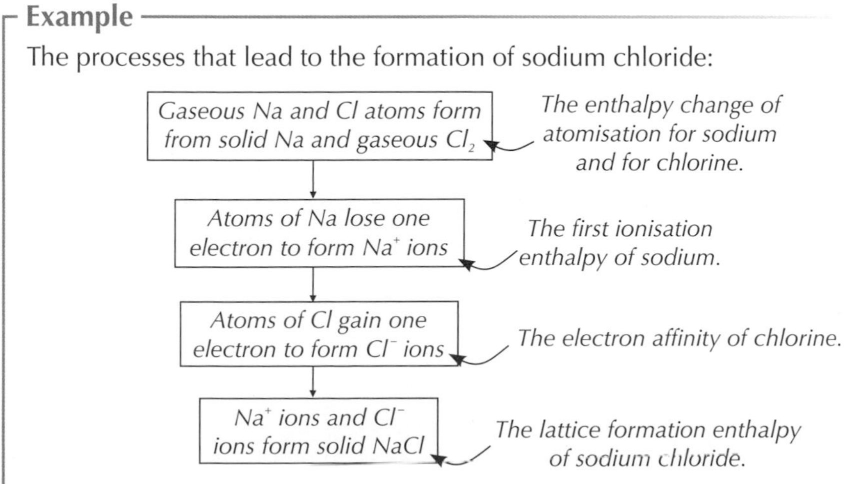

Figure 3: *A 3D model of a sodium chloride lattice.*

Unfortunately, each specific type of enthalpy change has its own definition and you need to learn them all.

- **Enthalpy change of formation**, $\Delta H^{\ominus}_f$, is the enthalpy change when 1 mole of a compound is formed from its elements in their standard states under standard conditions, e.g. $Ca_{(s)} + Cl_{2(g)} \rightarrow CaCl_{2(s)}$
- The **bond dissociation enthalpy**, $\Delta H^{\ominus}_{diss}$, is the enthalpy change when all the bonds of the same type in 1 mole of gaseous molecules are broken, e.g. $Cl_{2(g)} \rightarrow 2Cl_{(g)}$
- **Enthalpy change of atomisation of an element**, $\Delta H^{\ominus}_{at}$, is the enthalpy change when 1 mole of gaseous atoms is formed from an element in its standard state, e.g. $\frac{1}{2}Cl_{2(g)} \rightarrow Cl_{(g)}$
- **Enthalpy change of atomisation of a compound**, $\Delta H^{\ominus}_{at}$, is the enthalpy change when 1 mole of a compound in its standard state is converted to gaseous atoms, e.g. $NaCl_{(s)} \rightarrow Na_{(g)} + Cl_{(g)}$
- The **first ionisation enthalpy**, $\Delta H^{\ominus}_{ie1}$, is the enthalpy change when 1 mole of gaseous 1+ ions is formed from 1 mole of gaseous atoms, e.g. $Mg_{(g)} \rightarrow Mg^{+}_{(g)} + e^{-}$
- The **second ionisation enthalpy**, $\Delta H^{\ominus}_{ie2}$, is the enthalpy change when 1 mole of gaseous 2+ ions is formed from 1 mole of gaseous 1+ ions, e.g. $Mg^{+}_{(g)} \rightarrow Mg^{2+}_{(g)} + e^{-}$
- **First electron affinity**, $\Delta H^{\ominus}_{ea1}$, is the enthalpy change when 1 mole of gaseous 1– ions is made from 1 mole of gaseous atoms, e.g. $O_{(g)} + e^{-} \rightarrow O^{-}_{(g)}$
- **Second electron affinity**, $\Delta H^{\ominus}_{ea2}$, is the enthalpy change when 1 mole of gaseous 2– ions is made from 1 mole of gaseous 1– ions, e.g. $O^{-}_{(g)} + e^{-} \rightarrow O^{2-}_{(g)}$
- The **enthalpy change of hydration**, $\Delta H^{\ominus}_{hyd}$, is the enthalpy change when 1 mole of aqueous ions is formed from gaseous ions, e.g. $Na^{+}_{(g)} \rightarrow Na^{+}_{(aq)}$
- The **enthalpy change of solution**, $\Delta H^{\ominus}_{solution}$, is the enthalpy change when 1 mole of solute is dissolved in sufficient solvent that no further enthalpy change occurs on further dilution, e.g. $NaCl_{(s)} \rightarrow NaCl_{(aq)}$

Exam Tip
You could be asked to give any of these definitions in the exam, so make sure you've learned them all word for word.

Tip: These terms will crop up a lot in this section so don't move on until you understand what each one means — you might want to fold this page over so you can find it again if you need to.

Practice Questions — Fact Recall

Q1 What is meant by the term enthalpy change?

Q2 Give the symbol for enthalpy change.

Q3 Give two different definitions for lattice enthalpy.

Q4 Define the following:
  a) enthalpy change of formation.
  b) second electron affinity.
  c) enthalpy change of solution.

Q5 Name the changes in enthalpy defined below:
  a) The enthalpy change when 1 mole of gaseous atoms is formed from an element in its standard state.
  b) The enthalpy change when 1 mole of gaseous 1+ ions is formed from 1 mole of gaseous atoms.

Q6 Write the symbol for the following enthalpy changes:
  a) The enthalpy change of hydration.
  b) The bond dissociation enthalpy.

2. Calculating Lattice Enthalpies

Get those rulers and pencils out — it's time to draw some Born-Haber cycles.

Born-Haber cycles

You can't calculate a lattice enthalpy directly, so you have to use a **Born-Haber cycle** to figure out what the enthalpy change would be if you took another, less direct, route. There are two routes you can follow to get from the elements in their standard states to the ionic lattice. On the diagram below, the blue arrow shows the direct route and the red arrows show the indirect route.

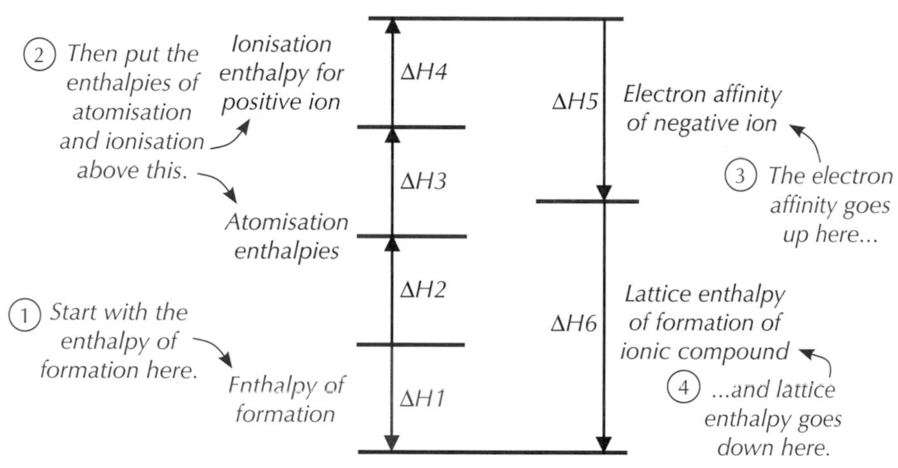

The enthalpy change for each route is the same. This is **Hess's law**:

> The total enthalpy change of a reaction is always the same, no matter which route is taken.

So, to calculate the lattice enthalpy change of formation (ΔH6), you use an alternative route around the diagram:

$$\Delta H6 = -\Delta H5 - \Delta H4 - \Delta H3 - \Delta H2 + \Delta H1$$

Notice that you add in a minus sign if you go the wrong way along an arrow.

Example

To calculate the lattice enthalpy of NaCl:

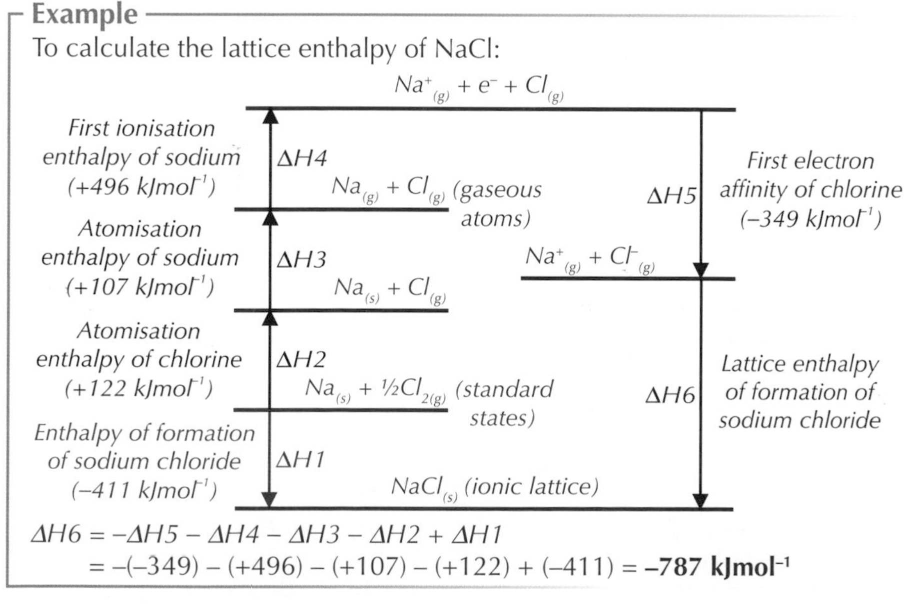

$\Delta H6 = -\Delta H5 - \Delta H4 - \Delta H3 - \Delta H2 + \Delta H1$

$= -(-349) - (+496) - (+107) - (+122) + (-411) =$ **-787 kJmol^{-1}**

Learning Objectives:

- Be able to construct Born–Haber cycles to calculate lattice enthalpies from experimental data.
- Be able to compare lattice enthalpies from Born–Haber cycles with those from calculations based on a perfect ionic model to provide evidence for covalent character in ionic compounds.

Specification Reference 3.5.1

Figure 1: *German physicist Max Born who, along with Fritz Haber, developed Born-Haber cycles.*

Tip: You can also get the equation above by re-arranging this equation:
$\Delta H1 = \Delta H2 + \Delta H3 + \Delta H4 + \Delta H5 + \Delta H6$.

Tip: The Haber who helped develop Born-Haber cycles is the same Haber who invented the Haber process for synthesising ammonia.

Exam Tip
Make sure you understand what's going on with these Group 2 elements so you can handle whatever compound they throw at you in the exam.

Born-Haber cycles for compounds containing Group 2 elements have a few changes from the one on the previous page. Here's a Born-Haber cycle for a compound containing a Group 2 element:

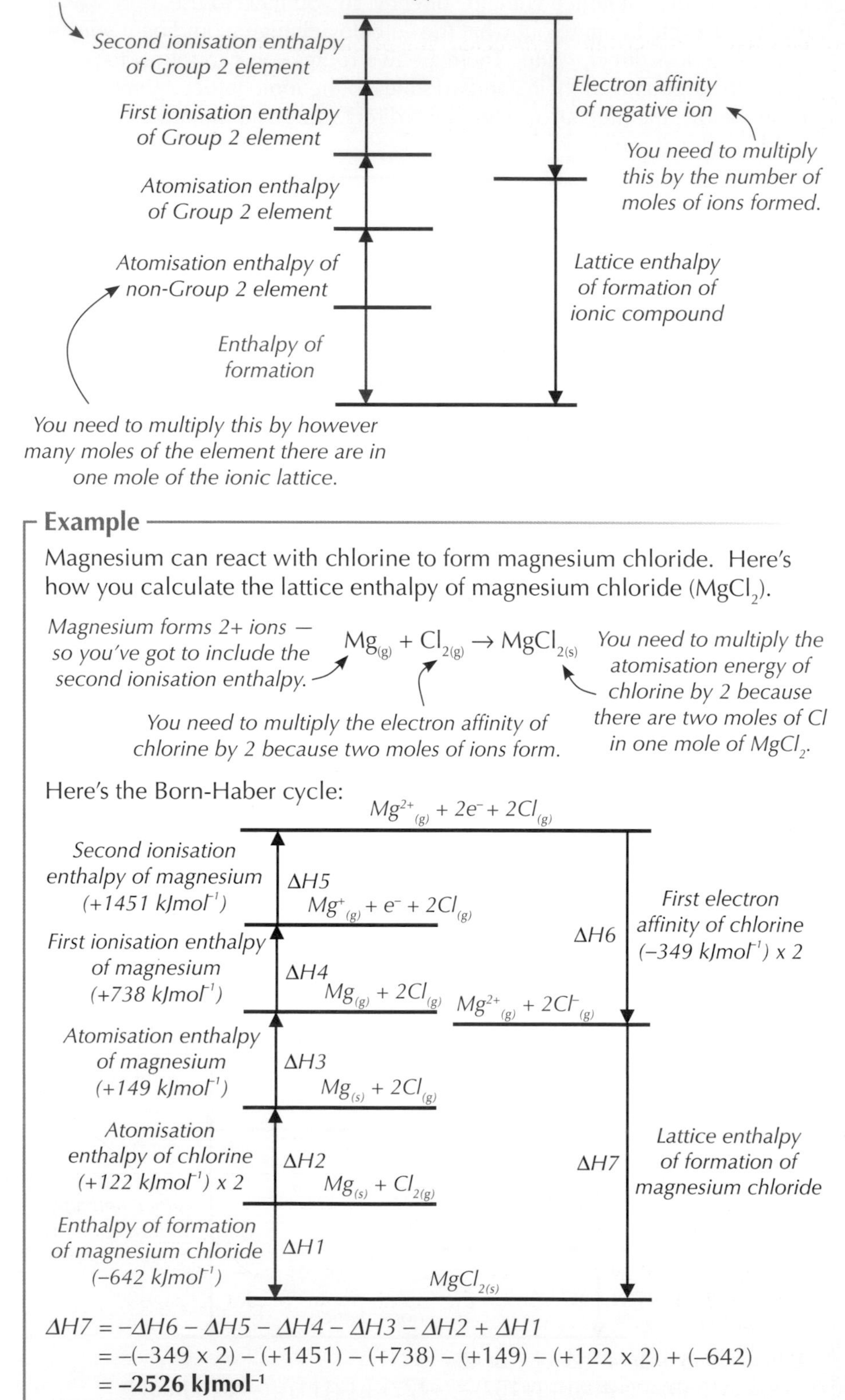

Tip: Remember, enthalpy change of formation, ΔH°_{f}, is the enthalpy change when one mole of a compound is formed from its elements in their standard states under standard conditions.

Example

Magnesium can react with chlorine to form magnesium chloride. Here's how you calculate the lattice enthalpy of magnesium chloride ($MgCl_2$).

$$Mg_{(g)} + Cl_{2(g)} \rightarrow MgCl_{2(s)}$$

Magnesium forms 2+ ions — so you've got to include the second ionisation enthalpy.

You need to multiply the electron affinity of chlorine by 2 because two moles of ions form.

You need to multiply the atomisation energy of chlorine by 2 because there are two moles of Cl in one mole of $MgCl_2$.

Here's the Born-Haber cycle:

$Mg^{2+}_{(g)} + 2e^- + 2Cl_{(g)}$

Second ionisation enthalpy of magnesium (+1451 kJmol⁻¹) — $\Delta H5$ — $Mg^{+}_{(g)} + e^- + 2Cl_{(g)}$

First ionisation enthalpy of magnesium (+738 kJmol⁻¹) — $\Delta H4$ — $Mg_{(g)} + 2Cl_{(g)}$

Atomisation enthalpy of magnesium (+149 kJmol⁻¹) — $\Delta H3$ — $Mg_{(s)} + 2Cl_{(g)}$

Atomisation enthalpy of chlorine (+122 kJmol⁻¹) x 2 — $\Delta H2$ — $Mg_{(s)} + Cl_{2(g)}$

Enthalpy of formation of magnesium chloride (−642 kJmol⁻¹) — $\Delta H1$ — $MgCl_{2(s)}$

First electron affinity of chlorine (−349 kJmol⁻¹) x 2 — $\Delta H6$ — $Mg^{2+}_{(g)} + 2Cl^-_{(g)}$

Lattice enthalpy of formation of magnesium chloride — $\Delta H7$

$$\Delta H7 = -\Delta H6 - \Delta H5 - \Delta H4 - \Delta H3 - \Delta H2 + \Delta H1$$
$$= -(-349 \times 2) - (+1451) - (+738) - (+149) - (+122 \times 2) + (-642)$$
$$= \mathbf{-2526\ kJmol^{-1}}$$

Figure 2: Dry magnesium chloride.

Tip: State symbols are really important here. If you're not sure what symbols should go where, double-check the definitions on page 148.

Theoretical and experimental enthalpies

You can work out a theoretical lattice enthalpy by doing some calculations based on the purely ionic model of a lattice. The **purely ionic model of a lattice** assumes that all the ions are spherical, and have their charge evenly distributed around them. But the experimental lattice enthalpy from the Born-Haber cycle is usually different. This is evidence that ionic compounds usually have some covalent character. The positive and negative ions in a lattice aren't usually exactly spherical (see Figure 3). Positive ions polarise neighbouring negative ions to different extents, and the more polarisation there is, the more covalent the bonding will be.

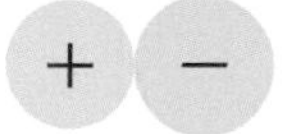

Purely ionic bonding — the ions are spherical and unpolarised.

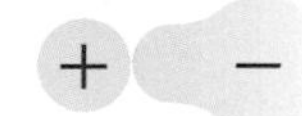

Partial covalent bonding — the electrons in the negative ion are pulled towards the positive ion.

Figure 3: *Purely ionic and partial covalent bonding.*

If the experimental and theoretical lattice enthalpies for a compound are very different, it shows that the compound has a lot of covalent character.

Example

Here are both lattice enthalpy values for some magnesium halides.

Compound	Lattice Enthalpy of Formation ($kJmol^{-1}$)	
	From experimental values in Born-Haber cycle	From theory
Magnesium chloride	*−2526*	*−2326*
Magnesium bromide	*−2440*	*−2079*
Magnesium iodide	*−2327*	*−1944*

The experimental lattice energies are more exothermic than the theoretical values by a fair bit. This tells you that the bonding is stronger than the calculations from the ionic model predict. The difference shows that the ionic bonds in the magnesium halides are quite strongly polarised and so they have quite a lot of covalent character.

If the experimental and theoretical lattice enthalpies for a compound are very similar, it shows that the compound has very little covalent character.

Example

Here are some more lattice energies, for sodium halides this time:

Compound	Lattice Enthalpy of Formation ($kJmol^{-1}$)	
	From experimental values in Born-Haber cycle	From theory
Sodium chloride	*−787*	*−766*
Sodium bromide	*−742*	*−731*
Sodium iodide	*−698*	*−686*

The experimental and theoretical values are a pretty close match — so you can say that these compounds fit the 'purely ionic' model very well. This indicates that the structure of the lattice for these compounds is quite close to being purely ionic. There's almost no polarisation so they don't have much covalent character.

Tip: The purely ionic model of a lattice is also known as the perfect ionic model.

Tip: Although lattice enthalpy cannot be directly measured, the value obtained from the Born–Haber cycle is the actual, true value of the lattice enthalpy because all of the other values which have been used to calculate it are real experimental values for that substance.

Exam Tip
Don't worry — you don't have to memorise any of these enthalpy values. You'll always be given them in the question if you need them.

Tip: If you're struggling to remember which way round it goes, just think — lots of difference means lots of covalent character, little difference means little covalent character.

Practice Questions — Application

Q1 Look at the following Born-Haber cycle.

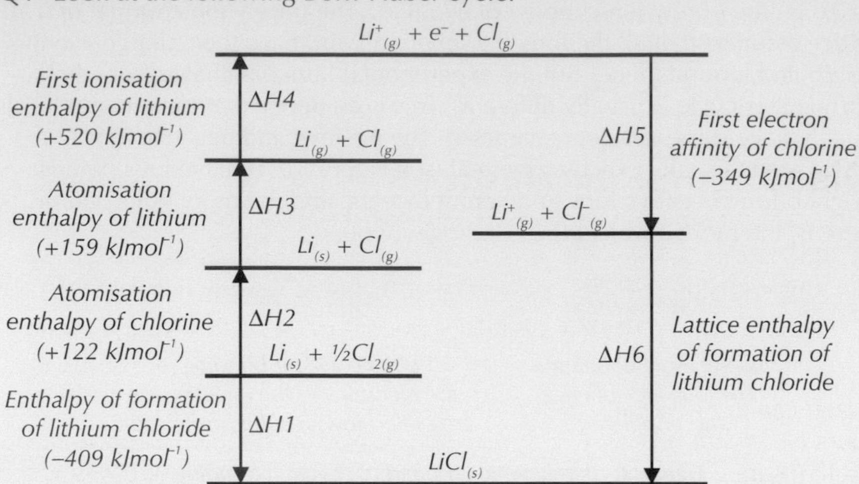

Use Hess's law to calculate the lattice enthalpy change of formation of lithium chloride.

Q2 Complete the following Born-Haber cycle for the formation of $CaBr_2$.

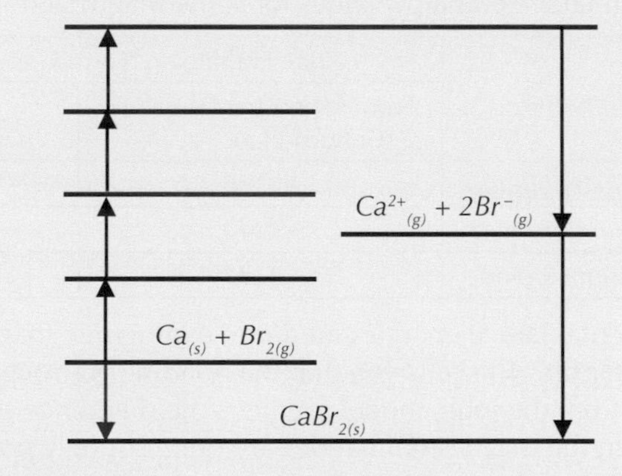

Q3 Look at the table below.

Enthalpy change	ΔH°/ kJmol^{-1}
Enthalpy change of atomisation of potassium	+89
Enthalpy change of atomisation of fluorine	+79
First ionisation enthalpy of potassium	+419
Electron affinity of fluorine	–328
Enthalpy of formation of potassium fluoride	–563

a) Draw the Born-Haber cycle for the formation of KF.

b) Use Hess's law to calculate the lattice enthalpy change of formation of KF.

Practice Questions — Fact Recall

Q1 What does Hess's law state?

Q2 Explain why theoretical lattice enthalpies are often different from experimental values.

Exam Tip
Always double-check that you've got the plus and minus signs right when you're doing calculations using a Born-Haber cycle. It's really easy to make a mistake and get it wrong in the exam — and you will lose precious marks.

Tip: Calcium is a Group 2 element.

Exam Tip
If you're asked to complete a Born-Haber cycle, it just means fill in the black bits on the diagram — you don't have to write out what each stage is unless it specifically asks you to.

Exam Tip
When completing Born-Haber cycles in the exam, make sure you get the enthalpy changes in the right order. Atomisation always comes before ionisation, and they always come before electron affinity.

3. Enthalpies of Solution

Lattice enthalpies aren't the only enthalpies you can calculate using Hess's law. You can work out enthalpies of solution too. You'll need to remind yourself of the definitions for lattice dissociation enthalpy (page 147) and enthalpy changes of solution and hydration (page 148) before you start.

Learning Objectives:

- Be able to calculate enthalpies of solution for ionic compounds from lattice enthalpies and enthalpies of hydration.
- Be able to use mean bond enthalpies to calculate an approximate value of ΔH for other reactions.
- Be able to explain why values from mean bond enthalpy calculations differ from those determined from enthalpy cycles.

Specification Reference 3.5.1

Dissolving ionic lattices

When a solid ionic lattice dissolves in water these two things happen:

- The bonds between the ions break — this is endothermic. This enthalpy change is the **lattice enthalpy of dissociation**.
- Bonds between the ions and the water are made — this is exothermic. The enthalpy change here is called the **enthalpy change of hydration**.

Water can form bonds with the ions because it is a polar molecule. Oxygen is more electronegative than hydrogen, so it draws the bonding electrons toward itself, creating a dipole. Consequently, positive ions form weak bonds with the partial negative charge on the oxygen atom and negative ions form weak bonds with the partial positive charge on the hydrogen atoms (see Figure 1).

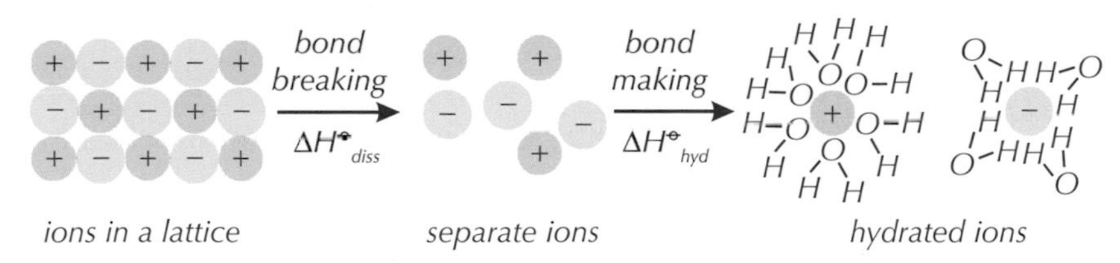

***Figure 1:** A solid ionic lattice dissolving in water.*

Tip: Take a look back at your AS notes if you need a reminder about electronegativity and the δ+ and δ– charges on polar molecules such as water: $H\delta+$ $\delta-O-H\delta+$

The enthalpy change of solution is the overall effect on the enthalpy of bond breaking and bond making.

Calculating enthalpy change of solution

You can work out the enthalpy change of solution using an enthalpy cycle. You just need to know the lattice dissociation enthalpy of the compound and the enthalpies of hydration of the ions. Here's how to draw an enthalpy cycle for calculating the enthalpy change of solution:

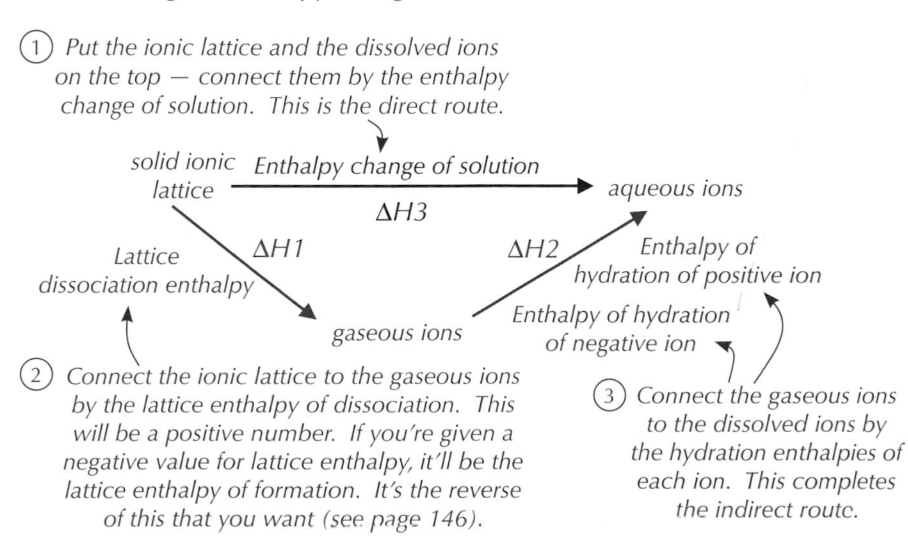

***Figure 2:** Copper(II) sulfate ($CuSO_4$) dissolved in water.*

Tip: A negative enthalpy value means that a reaction is exothermic.

Tip: Take a look back at page 149 for more on Hess's law.

Tip: The enthalpy change of solution for silver chloride is much more endothermic than the enthalpy change of solution for sodium chloride. Take a look at page 157 to see why changes in entropy mean that sodium chloride is soluble in water but silver chloride isn't.

Tip: Another way to think of this is:

enthalpy change for a reaction = sum of enthalpies of bonds broken – sum of enthalpies of bonds formed.

Examples

Here's the enthalpy cycle for working out the enthalpy change of solution for sodium chloride.

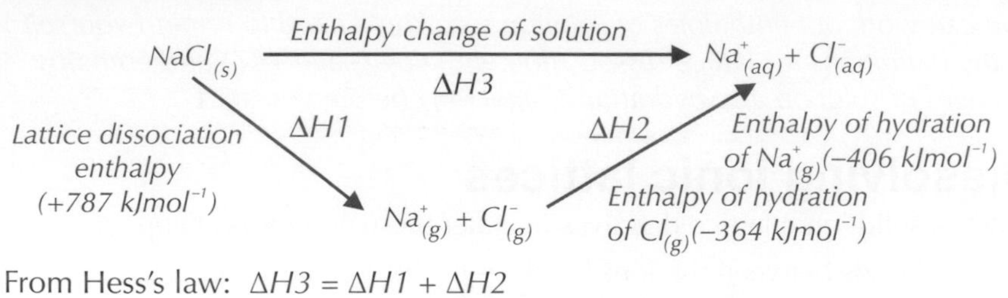

From Hess's law: $\Delta H3 = \Delta H1 + \Delta H2$
$= +787 + (-406 + -364) = \mathbf{+17\ kJmol^{-1}}$

And here's another example. This enthalpy cycle is for working out the enthalpy change of solution for silver chloride.

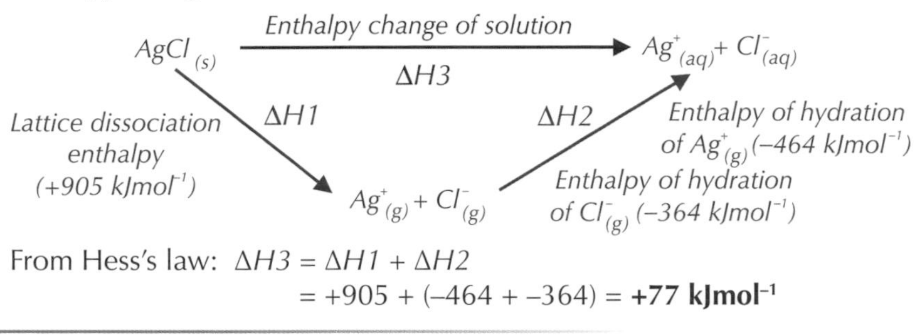

From Hess's law: $\Delta H3 = \Delta H1 + \Delta H2$
$= +905 + (-464 + -364) = \mathbf{+77\ kJmol^{-1}}$

Calculating enthalpy changes

In any chemical reaction, energy is absorbed to break bonds and given out during bond formation. The difference between the energy absorbed and released is the overall enthalpy change of reaction:

Enthalpy change of reaction = Total energy absorbed – Total energy released

- To calculate the overall enthalpy change for a reaction, first calculate the total energy needed to break the bonds in the reactants. You'll usually be given the average bond enthalpies for each type of bond, so just multiply each value by the number of each bond present. This total will be the total energy absorbed in the reaction.
- To find the total energy released by the reaction, calculate the total energy needed to form all the new bonds in the products. Use the average bond enthalpies to do this.
- The overall enthalpy change for the reaction can then be found by subtracting the total energy released from the total energy absorbed.

Bond	Bond Enthalpy (Mean value except where stated)
N≡N	945 kJmol⁻¹
H–H	436 kJmol⁻¹
N–H	391 kJmol⁻¹
O=O	498 kJmol⁻¹
O–H	460 kJmol⁻¹
C–H	413 kJmol⁻¹
C–C	347 kJmol⁻¹
C=O (in CO_2)	805 kJmol⁻¹

Figure 3: *Bond enthalpies.*

Example

Calculate the overall enthalpy change for the following reaction:

$$CH_{4\,(g)} + 2O_{2\,(g)} \rightarrow CO_{2\,(g)} + 2H_2O_{(g)}$$

Use the bond enthalpy values shown in Figure 3.

Bonds broken: 4 × C–H bonds broken + 2 × O=O bonds broken
Total energy absorbed = (4 × 413) + (2 × 498) = 2648 kJmol⁻¹

Bonds formed: 2 × C=O bonds formed + 4 x O–H bonds formed
Total energy released = (2 × 805) + (4 x 460) = 3450 kJmol⁻¹

Enthalpy change of reaction = 2648 – 3450 = **–802 kJmol⁻¹**.

The bond enthalpy given in Figure 3 for C–H bonds is not exactly right for every C–H bond. A given type of bond will vary in strength from compound to compound and can even vary within a compound. **Mean bond enthalpies** are the averages of these bond enthalpies. Only the bond enthalpies of diatomic molecules, such as H_2 and HCl, will always be the same. So calculations done using mean bond enthalpies will never be perfectly accurate. You get much more exact results from experimental data obtained from the specific compounds.

Tip: This is why mean bond enthalpy calculations differ from those determined from enthalpy cycles.

Practice Questions — Application

Q1 The cycle below shows the enthalpy change of solution for LiCl.

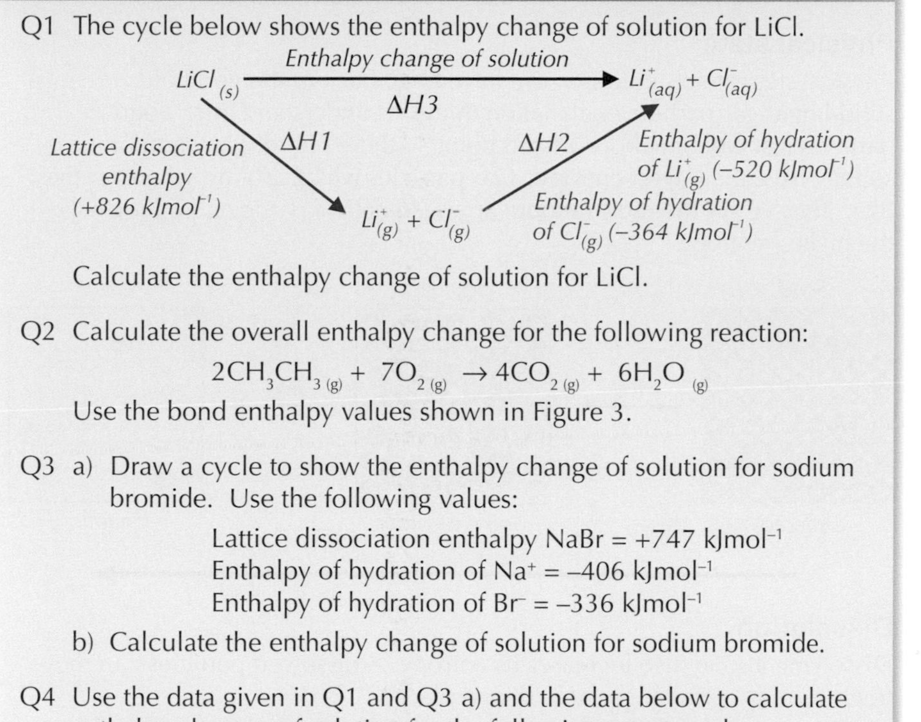

Calculate the enthalpy change of solution for LiCl.

Q2 Calculate the overall enthalpy change for the following reaction:

$$2CH_3CH_{3\,(g)} + 7O_{2\,(g)} \rightarrow 4CO_{2\,(g)} + 6H_2O_{(g)}$$

Use the bond enthalpy values shown in Figure 3.

Q3 a) Draw a cycle to show the enthalpy change of solution for sodium bromide. Use the following values:

Lattice dissociation enthalpy NaBr = +747 $kJmol^{-1}$
Enthalpy of hydration of Na^+ = −406 $kJmol^{-1}$
Enthalpy of hydration of Br^- = −336 $kJmol^{-1}$

b) Calculate the enthalpy change of solution for sodium bromide.

Exam Tip
In the exam, there's no need to draw the cycle out unless the question specifically asks for it. However, if you find it easier to calculate values from a cycle, it's a good idea to draw one out anyway.

Q4 Use the data given in Q1 and Q3 a) and the data below to calculate enthalpy changes of solution for the following compounds:

a) lithium bromide.
b) potassium chloride.
c) magnesium bromide.

Lattice dissociation enthalpy LiBr = +807 $kJmol^{-1}$
Lattice dissociation enthalpy KCl = +701 $kJmol^{-1}$
Lattice dissociation enthalpy $MgBr_2$ = +2440 $kJmol^{-1}$
Enthalpy of hydration of K^+ = −322 $kJmol^{-1}$
Enthalpy of hydration of Mg^{2+} = −1921 $kJmol^{-1}$

Tip: Don't forget that if your compound includes a Group 2 element, it may contain two moles of a 1– ion, and you'll need to double the enthalpy values for that ion.

Practice Questions — Fact Recall

Q1 a) What two things happen when a solid ionic lattice dissolves in water?

b) State whether each of these things is exothermic or endothermic.

Q2 The enthalpy change of solution is the combined effect of two enthalpy changes. Name them.

Q3 Give the formula you'd use to calculate the overall enthalpy change of a reaction.

Q4 Explain why mean bond enthalpy calculations give you different enthalpy values from experimental data.

4. Entropy

Some reactions can happen spontaneously — that's where entropy comes in.

Learning Objectives:

- Understand that ΔH, whilst important, is not sufficient to explain spontaneous change (e.g. spontaneous endothermic reactions).
- Understand that the concept of increasing disorder (entropy change ΔS) accounts for the above deficiency, illustrated by physical change (e.g. melting, evaporation) and chemical change (e.g. dissolution, evolution of CO_2 from hydrogencarbonates with acid).
- Be able to calculate entropy changes from absolute entropy values.

Specification Reference 3.5.1

What is entropy?

Entropy tells you how much disorder there is. It's a measure of the number of ways that particles can be arranged and the number of ways that the energy can be shared out between the particles. Substances really like disorder, so the particles move to try to increase the entropy. Entropy is represented by the symbol *S*. There are a few things that affect entropy, such as:

Physical state

Physical state affects entropy. You have to go back to the good old solid-liquid-gas particle explanation thingy to understand this. Solid particles just wobble about a fixed point — there's hardly any randomness, so they have the lowest entropy. Gas particles whizz around wherever they like. They've got the most random arrangements of particles, so they have the highest entropy.

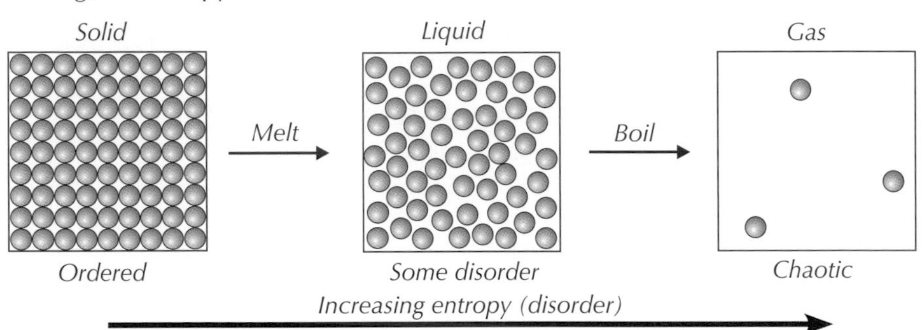

Dissolution

Dissolving a solid also increases its entropy — dissolved particles can move freely as they're no longer held in one place:

Solid Solution

Dissolution in water

Increasing entropy

Figure 1: *Melting ice. When ice melts its entropy increases.*

Number of particles

More particles means more entropy. It makes sense — the more particles you've got, the more ways they and their energy can be arranged. So in a reaction like $N_2O_{4(g)} \rightarrow 2NO_{2(g)}$, entropy increases because the number of moles increases:

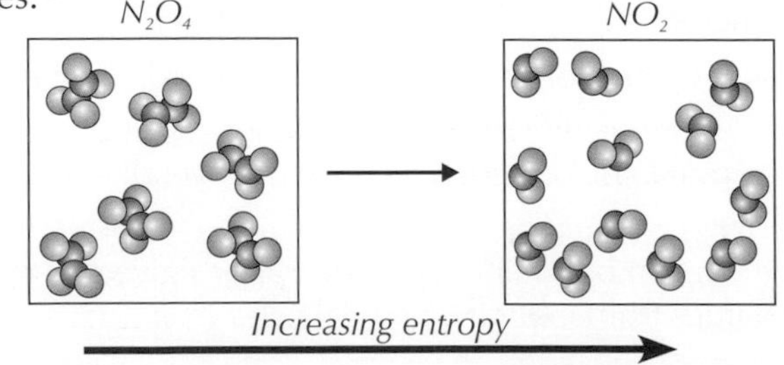

Spontaneous endothermic reactions

A **spontaneous** (or feasible) change is one that'll just happen by itself — you don't need to give it energy. You might think that only exothermic reactions could be spontaneous because you need to supply energy to endothermic reactions. But the weird thing is, some endothermic reactions are spontaneous. You normally do have to supply energy to make an endothermic reaction happen, but in some reactions the entropy increases such a lot that the reaction will happen by itself, without you supplying any energy.

Figure 2: *Water evaporates spontaneously and then condenses to form clouds even though the evaporation process is endothermic.*

Examples

Evaporation of water

Water evaporates at room temperature. This change needs energy to break the bonds between the molecules (i.e. it's endothermic) — but because it's changing state from a liquid to a gas, the entropy increases.

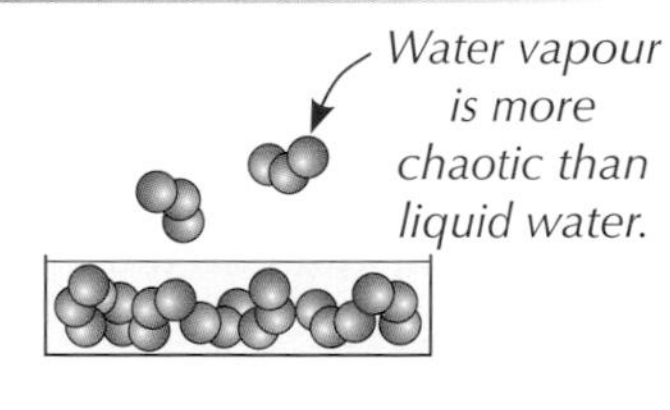

Reaction of $NaHCO_3$ and HCl

The reaction of sodium hydrogencarbonate with hydrochloric acid is a spontaneous endothermic reaction. Again there's an increase in entropy.

$$NaHCO_{3(s)} + H^+_{(aq)} \rightarrow Na^+_{(aq)} + CO_{2(g)} + H_2O_{(l)}$$

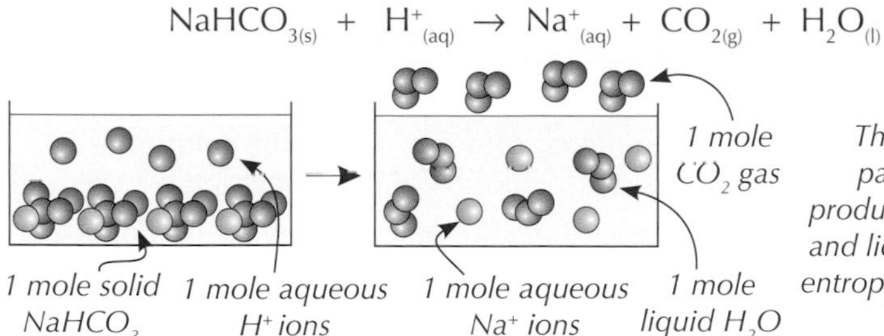

Tip: These reactions are both feasible, even though they are endothermic, because they involve an overall increase in entropy.

Effect of entropy change

Reactions won't happen unless the total entropy change is positive. During a reaction, there's an entropy change (ΔS) between the reactants and products — the entropy change of the system. The entropy of the surroundings changes too (because energy is transferred to or from the system). The total entropy change is the sum of the entropy changes of the system and the surroundings.

$$\Delta S_{total} = \Delta S_{system} + \Delta S_{surroundings}$$

The units of entropy are $JK^{-1}mol^{-1}$

This equation isn't much use unless you know ΔS_{system} and $\Delta S_{surroundings}$. Luckily, there are formulas for them too:

This is just the difference between the entropies of the reactants and products.

$$\Delta S_{system} = S_{products} - S_{reactants}$$

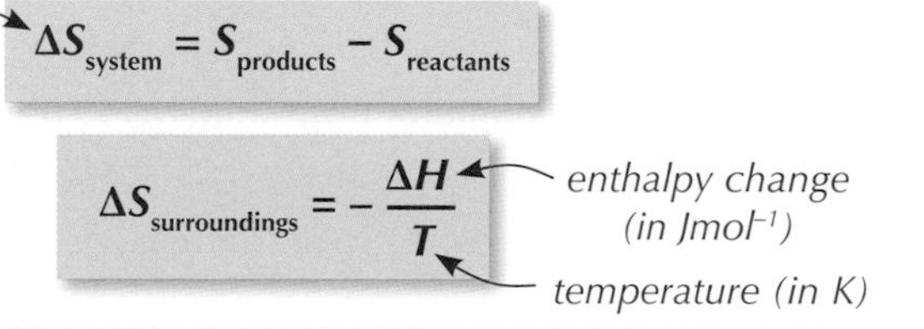

$$\Delta S_{surroundings} = -\frac{\Delta H}{T}$$

ΔH: enthalpy change (in $Jmol^{-1}$); T: temperature (in K)

Exam Tip
You need to be able to calculate entropy changes in your exam so make sure you learn these equations.

Example

Calculate the total entropy change for the reaction of ammonia and hydrogen chloride under standard conditions.

$$NH_{3(g)} + HCl_{(g)} \rightarrow NH_4Cl_{(s)}$$

$\Delta H^\ominus = -315\ kJmol^{-1}$ (at 298 K)

$S^\ominus[NH_{3(g)}] = 192.3\ JK^{-1}mol^{-1}$
$S^\ominus[HCl_{(g)}] = 186.8\ JK^{-1}mol^{-1}$
$S^\ominus[NH_4Cl_{(s)}] = 94.6\ JK^{-1}mol^{-1}$

Exam Tip
If there is more than one mole of a reactant in an equation you need to multiply the $S^\ominus$ value by the number of moles.

First find the entropy change of the system:

$\Delta S_{system} = S_{products} - S_{reactants} = 94.6 - (192.3 + 186.8)$
$= -284.5\ JK^{-1}mol^{-1}$

This reaction has a negative change in entropy. It's not surprising, as 2 moles of gas have combined to form 1 mole of solid.

Now find the entropy change of the surroundings:

$\Delta H^{\ominus} = -315\ kJmol^{-1} = -315 \times 10^3\ Jmol^{-1}$

Put $\Delta H^{\ominus}$ in the right units.

$$\Delta S_{surroundings} = -\frac{\Delta H}{T} = \frac{-(-315 \times 10^3)}{298} = +1057.0\ JK^{-1}mol^{-1}$$

Finally you can find the total entropy change:

$\Delta S^{\ominus}_{total} = \Delta S^{\ominus}_{system} + \Delta S^{\ominus}_{surroundings} = -284.5 + (+1057.0)$
$= \mathbf{+772.5\ JK^{-1}mol^{-1}}$

The total entropy has increased so the reaction will happen spontaneously.

Tip: When you calculate an entropy change, don't forget to give the units — they're always $JK^{-1}mol^{-1}$.

Tip: If the total entropy change was negative the reaction wouldn't happen spontaneously.

Practice Questions — Application

Q1 Solid sodium hydroxide is added to aqueous hydrogen chloride. The reaction produces sodium chloride solution. The solution is heated to produce solid sodium chloride and water vapour.

Describe the entropy changes that take place during these processes.

Q2 Using the data from Figure 3 for this reaction under standard conditions: $CH_{4(g)} + 2O_{2(g)} \rightarrow CO_{2(g)} + 2H_2O_{(l)}$ $\Delta H^{\ominus} = -730\ kJmol^{-1}$

a) calculate ΔS_{system}.

b) calculate $\Delta S^{\ominus}_{surroundings}$.

c) calculate $\Delta S^{\ominus}_{total}$.

d) explain whether the reaction will happen spontaneously.

Q3 Using the data in Figure 3 work out the total entropy change for this reaction under standard conditions:

$SO_{2(g)} + 2H_2S_{(g)} \rightarrow 3S_{(s)} + 2H_2O_{(l)}$ $\Delta H^{\ominus} = -235\ kJmol^{-1}$

Substance	*Standard entropy of substance, $S^{\ominus}$ ($JK^{-1}mol^{-1}$)*
$CH_{4(g)}$	186
$O_{2(g)}$	205
$CO_{2(g)}$	214
$H_2O_{(l)}$	69.9
$SO_{2(g)}$	248
$H_2S_{(g)}$	206
$S_{(s)}$	31.6

***Figure 3:** Standard entropy values for different substances.*

Practice Questions — Fact Recall

Q1 a) What is entropy?

b) Give the symbol for entropy change.

Q2 Explain how the following affect the entropy of a system:

a) a substance changing from a liquid to a gas.

b) a solid dissolving in water.

c) a reaction that results in an increased number of particles.

Q3 Explain why entropy changes mean that an endothermic reaction can happen spontaneously.

Q4 Give the formulas you'd use to work out the following:

a) total entropy change.

b) entropy change of the system.

c) entropy change of the surroundings.

5. Free-Energy Change

Everyone likes free things, so I can almost guarantee you'll like free energy.

Learning Objectives:

- Understand that the balance between entropy and enthalpy determines the feasibility of a reaction; know that this is given by the relationship $\Delta G = \Delta H - T\Delta S$. Be able to use this equation to determine how ΔG varies with temperature.
- Be able to use this relationship to determine the temperature at which a reaction is feasible.

Specification Reference 3.5.1

What is free-energy change?

Free energy change, ΔG, is a measure used to predict whether a reaction is **feasible**. If ΔG is negative or equal to zero, then the reaction might happen by itself. Free energy change takes into account the changes in enthalpy and entropy in the system. And of course, there's a formula for it:

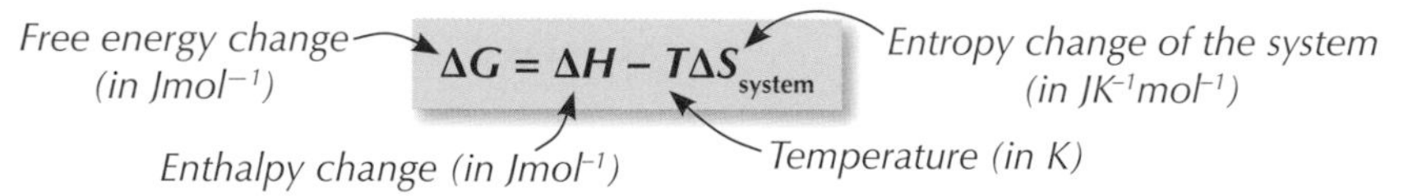

A negative ΔG doesn't guarantee a reaction will happen or tell you about its rate. Even if ΔG shows that a reaction is theoretically feasible, it might have a really high activation energy or be so slow that you wouldn't notice it happening at all. Here's an example of calculating free energy change.

Example

Calculate the free energy change for the following reaction at 298 K.

$MgCO_{3(s)} \rightarrow MgO_{(s)} + CO_{2(g)}$ $\quad \Delta H^{\ominus} = +117 \text{ kJmol}^{-1}$

$\Delta S^{\ominus}_{system} = +175 \text{ JK}^{-1}\text{mol}^{-1}$

$\Delta G = \Delta H - T\Delta S_{system} = +117 \times 10^3 - [(298 \times (+175)]$

$= \mathbf{+64\ 850\ Jmol^{-1}}$

ΔG is positive — so the reaction isn't feasible at this temperature.

Tip: The units of ΔH and ΔS must be the same. So, if you're given a value for ΔH in kJ, multiply it by 10^3 to get it in J (alternatively you could change the ΔS from J into kJ).

Effect of temperature

If a reaction is exothermic (negative ΔH) and has a positive entropy change, then ΔG is always negative since $\Delta G = \Delta H - T\Delta S_{system}$. These reactions are feasible at any temperature.

If a reaction is endothermic (positive ΔH) and has a negative entropy change, then ΔG is always positive. These reactions are not feasible at any temperature. But for other combinations, temperature has an effect.

If ΔH is positive (endothermic) and ΔS_{system} is positive then the reaction won't be feasible at some temperatures but will be at a higher temperature.

Example

The decomposition of calcium carbonate is endothermic but results in an increase in entropy (the number of molecules increases and CO_2 is a gas).

$$CaCO_{3(s)} \rightarrow CaO_{(s)} + CO_{2(g)}$$

The reaction will only occur when $CaCO_3$ is heated — it isn't feasible at 298 K.

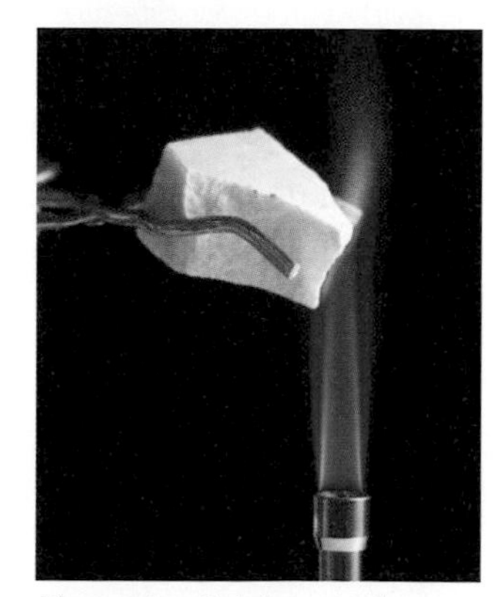

Figure 1: Calcium carbonate ($CaCO_3$) being heated to produce CaO and CO_2.

If ΔH is negative (exothermic) and ΔS_{system} is negative then the reaction will be feasible at some temperatures but won't be feasible at a higher temperature.

Example

The process of turning water from a liquid to a solid is exothermic but results in a decrease in entropy (a solid is more ordered than a liquid), which means it will only occur at certain temperatures (i.e. at 0 °C or below).

You need to know how to decide if a reaction is feasible at different temperatures, so there are some more examples on the next page.

Examples

Reaction 1: $\Delta H = +10$ kJmol^{-1}, $\Delta S_{system} = +10$ JK^{-1}mol^{-1}

At 300 K:

$$\Delta G = \Delta H - T\Delta S_{system}$$
$$= +10 \times 10^3 - (300 \times +10)$$
$$= \mathbf{+7000\ Jmol^{-1}}$$

At 1500 K:

$$\Delta G = \Delta H - T\Delta S_{system}$$
$$= +10 \times 10^3 - (1500 \times +10)$$
$$= \mathbf{-5000\ Jmol^{-1}}$$

So this reaction is feasible at 1500 K, but not at 300 K.

Reaction 2: $\Delta H = -10$ kJmol^{-1}, $\Delta S_{system} = -10$ JK^{-1}mol^{-1}

At 300 K:

$$\Delta G = \Delta H - T\Delta S_{system}$$
$$= -10 \times 10^3 - (300 \times -10)$$
$$= \mathbf{-7000\ Jmol^{-1}}$$

At 1500 K:

$$\Delta G = \Delta H - T\Delta S_{system}$$
$$= -10 \times 10^3 - (1500 \times -10)$$
$$= \mathbf{+5000\ Jmol^{-1}}$$

So this reaction is feasible at 300 K, but not at 1500 K.

Tip: Don't forget — the value of ΔG has to be less than or equal to zero for a reaction to be feasible.

When ΔG is zero, a reaction is just feasible. You can find the temperature when ΔG is zero by rearranging the free energy equation.

$\Delta G = \Delta H - T\Delta S_{system}$, so when $\Delta G = 0$, $T\Delta S_{system} = \Delta H$. So:

$$T = \frac{\Delta H}{\Delta S_{system}}$$

temperature at which a reaction becomes feasible (in K) → T

ΔH ← *enthalpy change (in Jmol^{-1})*

ΔS_{system} ← *entropy change of the system (in JK^{-1}mol^{-1})*

Example

Tungsten, W, can be extracted from its ore, WO_3, by reduction using hydrogen.

$$WO_{3(s)} + 3H_{2(g)} \rightarrow W_{(s)} + 3H_2O_{(g)} \qquad \Delta H^{\ominus} = +117\ \text{kJmol}^{-1}$$

Use the data in Figure 2 to find the minimum temperature at which the reaction becomes feasible.

First, convert the enthalpy change, ΔH, to joules per mole:

$\Delta H = 117 \times 10^3 = 117\ 000$ Jmol^{-1}

Then find the entropy change, ΔS_{system}:

$$\Delta S_{system} = S_{products} - S_{reactants} = [33 + (3 \times 189)] - [76 + (3 \times 65)]$$
$$= +329\ \text{JK}^{-1}\text{mol}^{-1}$$

Then divide ΔH by ΔS_{system} to find the temperature at which the reaction just becomes feasible:

$$T = \frac{\Delta H}{\Delta S_{system}} = \frac{117\ 000}{329} = \mathbf{\mathit{356\ K}}$$

Substance	Standard entropy of substance, $S^{\ominus}$ (JK^{-1}mol^{-1})
$WO_{3(s)}$	76
$H_{2(g)}$	65
$W_{(s)}$	33
$H_2O_{(g)}$	189

Figure 2: *Standard entropy values for different substances.*

Tip: For more on the ΔS_{system} formula, see page 157.

Substance	Standard entropy of substance, $S^{\ominus}$ (JK^{-1}mol^{-1})
$Al_2O_{3(s)}$	51.0
$Mg_{(s)}$	32.5
$Al_{(s)}$	28.3
$MgO_{(s)}$	27.0

Figure 3: *Standard entropy values for different substances.*

Practice Questions — Application

Q1 Using the data from Figure 3 for this reaction under standard conditions: $Al_2O_{3(s)} + 3Mg_{(s)} \rightarrow 2Al_{(s)} + 3MgO_{(s)}$ $\quad \Delta H^{\ominus} = -130$ kJmol^{-1}

a) calculate ΔS_{system}.

b) calculate ΔG.

c) explain whether the reaction is feasible at 298K.

Q2 Calculate the temperature at which this reaction becomes feasible:

$$CaCO_{3(s)} \rightarrow CaO_{(s)} + CO_{2(g)}$$

$\Delta H^{\circ} = +178 \text{ kJmol}^{-1}$ $\Delta S_{system} = +165 \text{ JK}^{-1}\text{mol}^{-1}$

Practice Questions — Fact Recall

Q1 a) What is free energy change?

b) Give the symbol for free energy change.

c) What are the units of free energy change?

Q2 Give the formula needed to work out free energy.

Q3 A reaction is endothermic, has a negative entropy change and so has a positive value for free energy. Is this reaction feasible?

Q4 Give the formula that you'd use to calculate the temperature at which a reaction becomes feasible.

Section Summary

Make sure you know...

- That enthalpy change is the heat energy transferred in a reaction at constant pressure, and the symbol for it is ΔH.
- That exothermic reactions have negative ΔH values and endothermic reactions have positive ΔH values.
- What lattice enthalpy is and the two different ways that it can be defined.
- The definitions of enthalpy change of formation, bond dissociation enthalpy, enthalpy change of atomisation for elements and for compounds, ionisation enthalpy, electron affinity, enthalpy change of hydration and enthalpy change of solution.
- What a Born-Haber cycle is and how to use one to calculate lattice enthalpies from experimental data.
- Why theoretical lattice enthalpies are often different from experimental values.
- How to determine the amount of covalent character in an ionic lattice by comparing its theoretical and experimental lattice enthalpy values.
- The different enthalpy changes that take place when a solid ionic lattice dissolves.
- How to calculate the enthalpy change of solution for an ionic compound from lattice dissociation enthalpy and enthalpy of hydration values.
- How mean bond enthalpies can be used to calculate enthalpy changes, and why they sometimes differ from experimental values.
- That some endothermic reactions occur spontaneously so enthalpy changes alone can't explain why some reactions are spontaneous and some aren't.
- That entropy, S, is a measure of disorder.
- How entropy is affected by physical state, dissolution and number of particles.
- Why an increase in entropy may (or may not) mean a reaction occurs spontaneously.
- How to calculate the total entropy change for a reaction.
- That it's the balance between entropy and enthalpy that determines the feasibility of a reaction.
- What free energy change is and how to calculate it using $\Delta G = \Delta H - T\Delta S_{system}$.
- That the feasibility of some reactions depends on temperature, and how to calculate the temperature at which a reaction becomes feasible.

Exam-style Questions

1 Rubidium chloride is an ionic compound that dissolves easily in water and can be used as a cell marker in laboratories. The table below shows thermodynamic data for rubidium chloride.

Enthalpy change	ΔH° / kJmol^{-1}
Enthalpy change of atomisation of rubidium	+81
First ionisation enthalpy of rubidium	+403
Enthalpy change of hydration of Rb^+ ions	−296
Enthalpy change of atomisation of chlorine	+122
Electron affinity of chlorine	−349
Enthalpy change of hydration of Cl^- ions	−364
Enthalpy of change formation of rubidium chloride	−435

1 (a) Define the term enthalpy change of atomisation of an element.

(2 marks)

1 (b) Complete the Born-Haber cycle for the formation of rubidium chloride by filling in the blank lines. You should include chemical symbols and state symbols.

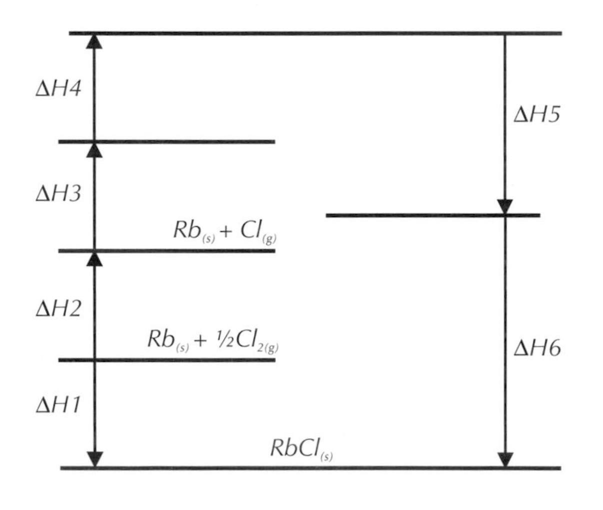

(3 marks)

1 (c) Use the data in the table to calculate the lattice enthalpy change of formation of rubidium chloride.

(3 marks)

1 (d) The theoretical value for the lattice enthalpy change of formation of rubidium chloride is very close to the experimental value calculated using a Born-Haber cycle. What does this tell you about the bonding character of rubidium chloride?

(2 marks)

1 (e) (i) State the value of the lattice dissociation enthalpy of rubidium chloride.

(1 mark)

1 (e) (ii) Name the enthalpy change for rubidium chloride which is equal to the sum of its lattice dissociation enthalpy, the enthalpy change of hydration of Rb^+ ions and the enthalpy change of hydration of Cl^- ions.

(1 mark)

1 (e) (iii) Calculate the enthalpy change you named in **(e) (ii)**.
(If you have not been able to answer **(e) (i)** use the value of +300 $kJmol^{-1}$. This value is incorrect.)

(1 mark)

2 When methane undergoes incomplete combustion, carbon monoxide and water are produced as shown:

$$2CH_{4\,(g)} + 3O_{2\,(g)} \rightarrow 2CO_{(g)} + 4H_2O_{(g)}$$

The standard enthalpies of formation and the standard entropies for the products and reactants are given in the table below.

	$CH_{4\,(g)}$	$O_{2\,(g)}$	$CO_{(g)}$	$H_2O_{(g)}$
$\Delta H^{\ominus}$ / $kJmol^{-1}$	–78	0	–111	–242
$S^{\ominus}$ / $J\,K^{-1}mol^{-1}$	+186	+205	+198	+189

2 (a) (i) Use the balanced equation to explain whether you would expect entropy to decrease or increase during this reaction.

(2 marks)

2 (a) (ii) The water vapour produced in the reaction condenses to form liquid water. Explain how the entropy of the system would change during this process.

(2 marks)

2 (b) Calculate the enthalpy change of reaction for the incomplete combustion of methane.

(3 marks)

2 (c) Calculate the entropy change for this reaction.

(3 marks)

2 (d) (i) Give the equation for calculating the free energy change ΔG.

(1 mark)

(ii) Use your answers to **(b)** and **(c)** to explain why this reaction is feasible at any temperature. (If you have not been able to answer (b) or (c) use –900 $kJmol^{-1}$ for the enthalpy change and +611 $kJmol^{-1}$ for the entropy change. These values are incorrect.)

(2 marks)

3 Manganese can be extracted from its ore manganese(IV) oxide, MnO_2, by reduction using carbon at 1473 K. The reaction is shown in the equation below.

$$MnO_{2\,(s)} + C_{(s)} \rightarrow Mn_{(s)} + CO_{2\,(g)} \qquad \Delta H^{\circ} = +127\ \text{kJmol}^{-1}$$

	$MnO_{2\,(s)}$	$C_{(s)}$	$Mn_{(s)}$	$CO_{2\,(g)}$
S° / J $K^{-1}mol^{-1}$	53	5.7	32	214

3 (a) (i) Calculate the free energy change for the extraction of manganese from its ore.

(4 marks)

3 (a) (ii) Explain how the free energy change of a reaction relates to the feasibility of that reaction.

(2 marks)

3 (b) (i) Give the equation which links the temperature at which a reaction becomes feasible, T, the enthalpy change for the reaction, ΔH, and the entropy change of the system, ΔS_{system}.

(1 mark)

3 (b) (ii) Calculate the temperature at which the reduction of manganese oxide using carbon becomes feasible.

(2 marks)

3 (c) The standard enthalpy of change formation of MnO_2 is –521 $kJmol^{-1}$.

3 (c) (i) Define the term standard enthalpy change of formation.

(2 marks)

3 (c) (ii) State whether you would expect the formation of manganese(IV) oxide from manganese and oxygen to be endothermic or exothermic.

(1 mark)

3 (c) (iii) Suggest why the standard enthalpy change of formation of manganese(II) oxide, MnO, is less exothermic than the standard enthalpy change of formation of MnO_2.

(2 marks)

Unit 5 Section 2: Period 3 and Redox Equilibria

1. Period 3 Elements

Periodicity means the trends that occur across a period of the periodic table. You did a little bit about periodicity at AS, but at A2 you need to know a bit more about the trends which occur across Period 3.

Learning Objectives:
- Be able to describe trends in the reactions of the elements with water, limited to Na and Mg.
- Be able to describe the trends in the reactions of the elements Na, Mg, Al, Si, P and S with oxygen, limited to the formation of Na_2O, MgO, Al_2O_3, SiO_2, P_4O_{10} and SO_2.

Specification Reference 3.5.2

Period 3

Period 3 is the third row in the periodic table. The elements of Period 3 are sodium (Na), magnesium (Mg), aluminium (Al), silicon (Si), phosphorus (P), sulfur (S), chlorine (Cl) and argon (Ar) — see Figure 1.

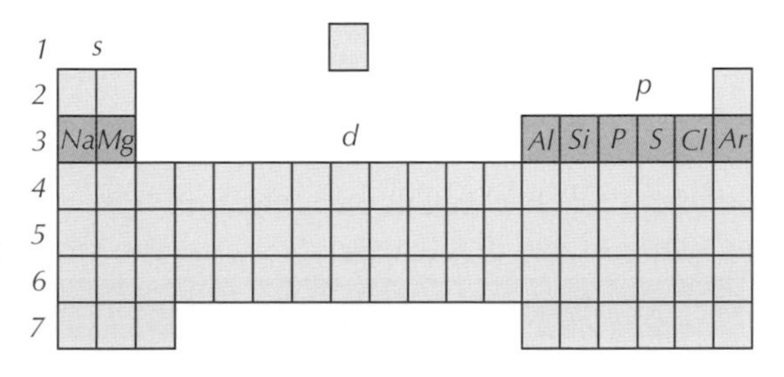

***Figure 1:** Period 3 of the periodic table.*

Reactions with water

You need to know how two of the Period 3 elements — sodium and magnesium — react with water. Sodium and magnesium are the first two elements in Period 3. Sodium is in Group 1, and magnesium is in Group 2. When they react, sodium loses one electron to form an Na^+ ion, while magnesium loses two electrons to form Mg^{2+}. Sodium is more reactive than magnesium because it takes less energy to lose one electron than it does to lose two. So more energy (usually heat) is needed for magnesium to react. This is shown in their reactions with water.

Sodium

Sodium reacts vigorously with cold water, forming a molten ball on the surface, fizzing and producing H_2 gas:

$$2Na_{(s)} + 2H_2O_{(l)} \rightarrow 2NaOH_{(aq)} + H_{2(g)}$$

The reaction produces sodium hydroxide, so forms a strongly alkaline solution (pH 12 – 14).

***Figure 2:** The reaction of sodium with water.*

Magnesium

Magnesium reacts very slowly with cold water. You can't see any reaction, but it forms a weakly alkaline solution (pH 9 – 10), which shows that a reaction has occurred:

$$Mg_{(s)} + 2H_2O_{(l)} \rightarrow Mg(OH)_{2(aq)} + H_{2(g)}$$

The solution is only weakly alkaline because magnesium hydroxide is not very soluble in water, so relatively few hydroxide ions are produced. Magnesium reacts much faster with steam (i.e. when there is more energy), to form magnesium oxide.

Tip: Don't worry about the reactions of the other Period 3 elements with water. You only need to know about sodium and magnesium.

Reactions with oxygen

Tip: See page 169 for more on oxidation states.

Period 3 elements form oxides when they react with oxygen. They're usually oxidised to their highest oxidation states — the same as their group numbers. So sodium, which is in Group 1, has an oxidation state of +1 in sodium oxide. Magnesium (Group 2) has an oxidation state of +2 in magnesium oxide. Sulfur is the exception to this — it forms SO_2, in which it's only got a +4 oxidation state (a high temperature and a catalyst are needed to make SO_3).

The equations are all really similar — element + oxygen → oxide:

$2Na_{(s)} + \frac{1}{2}O_{2(g)} \rightarrow Na_2O_{(s)}$ sodium oxide

$Mg_{(s)} + \frac{1}{2}O_{2(g)} \rightarrow MgO_{(s)}$ magnesium oxide

$2Al_{(s)} + 1\frac{1}{2}O_{2(g)} \rightarrow Al_2O_{3(s)}$ aluminium oxide

$Si_{(s)} + O_{2(g)} \rightarrow SiO_{2(s)}$ silicon dioxide

$P_{4(s)} + 5O_{2(g)} \rightarrow P_4O_{10(s)}$ phosphorus(V) oxide

$S_{(s)} + O_{2(g)} \rightarrow SO_{2(g)}$ sulfur dioxide

Tip: All of these oxides are white solids except for sulfur dioxide, which is a colourless gas.

The more reactive metals (Na, Mg) and the non-metals (P, S) react readily in air, while Al and Si react slowly — see the table below:

Element	Oxide	Reaction in air	Flame
Na	Na_2O	Vigorous	Yellow
Mg	MgO	Vigorous	Brilliant white
Al	Al_2O_3	Slow	N/A
Si	SiO_2	Slow	N/A
P	P_4O_{10}	Spontaneously combusts	Brilliant white
S	SO_2	Burns steadily	Blue

Figure 3: *The yellow flame produced when sodium burns.*

Figure 4: *The blue flame produced when sulfur burns.*

You can use the colours of the flames produced when the Period 3 elements react with air to identify them (e.g. if you burn a Period 3 element and it produces a blue flame, you know it's sulfur). This is known as a flame test.

Practice Question — Application

Q1 The reactions of three Period 3 elements with oxygen are summarised in the table below:

Element	Reaction in air	Flame
A	Vigorous	Yellow
B	Vigorous	Brilliant white
C	Burns steadily	Blue

a) Identify the three elements A, B and C.

b) Write an equation for each of these reactions.

Exam Tip
For the exam, you'll also need to know the trends in the properties of the Period 3 elements which you learnt at AS (e.g. melting point, electronegativity, ionisation energy) — so remember to brush up on those too.

Practice Questions — Fact Recall

Q1 a) Write an equation to show the reaction of water with:
(i) Sodium (ii) Magnesium

b) Which of these elements reacts more vigorously with water? Why?

Q2 Write an equation to show the reaction of:
a) aluminium with oxygen. b) phosphorus with oxygen.

2. Period 3 Oxides

Knowing the trends in the Period 3 elements isn't enough at A2. You also need to know about the trends in the properties of the Period 3 oxides.

Melting points

The differences in the melting points of the Period 3 oxides are all down to differences in their structure and bonding. The trend in melting points across Period 3 is shown in Figure 1.

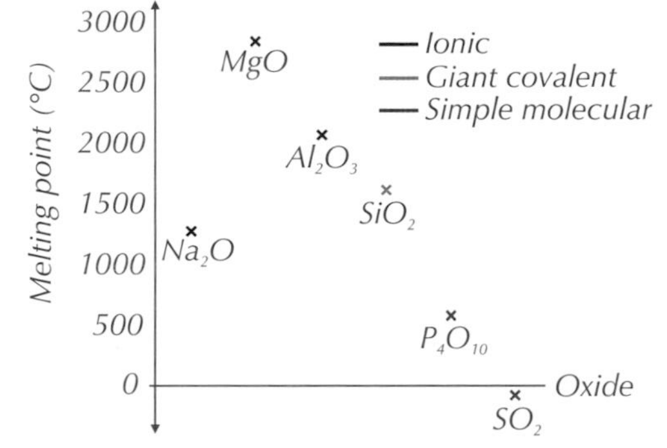

***Figure 1:** The trend in melting points of the Period 3 oxides as you move across Period 3*

Na_2O, MgO and Al_2O_3 — the metal oxides — all have high melting points because they form **giant ionic lattices**. The strong forces of attraction between each ion mean it takes a lot of heat energy to break the bonds and melt them. MgO has a higher melting point than Na_2O because magnesium forms 2+ ions, which attract O^{2-} ions more strongly than the 1+ sodium ions in Na_2O. Al_2O_3 has a lower melting point than you might expect because the 3+ ions distort the oxygen's electron cloud making the bonds partially covalent.

SiO_2 has a higher melting point than the other non-metal oxides because it has a giant **macromolecular** structure. Strong covalent bonds hold the structure together so lots of energy is needed to break the bonds and the melting temperature is high.

P_4O_{10} and SO_2 are covalent molecules. They have relatively low melting points because they form simple molecular structures. The molecules are held together by weak intermolecular forces (dipole-dipole and van der Waals), which take little energy to overcome.

Reactions with water

The ionic oxides of the metals Na and Mg dissolve in water to form hydroxides. The solutions are both alkaline, but sodium hydroxide is more soluble in water, so it forms a more alkaline solution than magnesium hydroxide:

$Na_2O_{(s)} + H_2O_{(l)} \rightarrow 2NaOH_{(aq)}$ pH 12 - 14

$MgO_{(s)} + H_2O_{(l)} \rightarrow Mg(OH)_{2(aq)}$ pH 9 - 10

The simple covalent oxides of the non-metals phosphorus and sulfur form acidic solutions. All of the acids are strong and so the pH of their solutions is about 0-2.

Examples

$P_4O_{10(s)} + 6H_2O_{(l)} \rightarrow 4H_3PO_{4(aq)}$ phosphoric(V) acid

$SO_{2(g)} + H_2O_{(l)} \rightarrow H_2SO_{3(aq)}$ sulfurous acid (or sulfuric(IV) acid)

$SO_{3(l)} + H_2O_{(l)} \rightarrow H_2SO_{4(aq)}$ sulfuric(VI) acid

Learning Objectives:

- Be able to explain the link between the physical properties of the highest oxides of the elements Na – S in terms of their structure and bonding.
- Be able to describe the reactions of the oxides of the elements Na – S with water, limited to Na_2O, MgO, Al_2O_3, SiO_2, P_4O_{10}, SO_2 and SO_3.
- Know the change in pH of the resulting solutions across the Period.
- Be able to explain the trends in these properties in terms of the type of bonding present.
- Be able to write equations for the reactions which occur between these oxides and given simple acids and bases.

Specification Reference 3.5.2

Exam Tip

If you're asked to explain the trend in melting points of the Period 3 oxides, make sure you mention their structure <u>and</u> the type of bonding — otherwise you might lose marks.

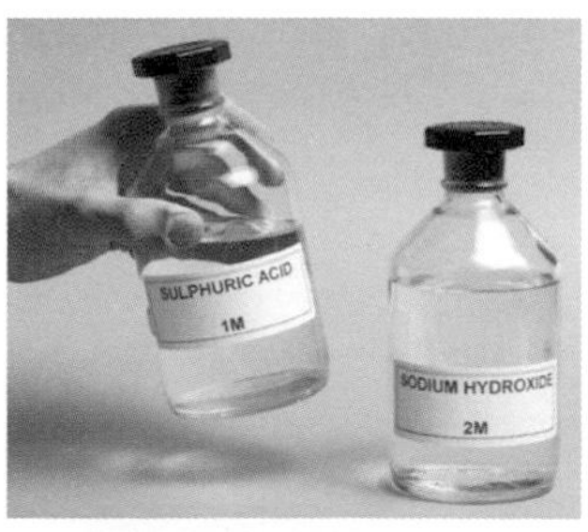

***Figure 2:** NaOH and H_2SO_4 can both be made by reacting Period 3 oxides with water.*

Tip: If you're struggling to remember this, just think — SiO_2 is the main component of sand and sand definitely doesn't dissolve in water.

Tip: Amphoteric means it has the properties of an acid and a base.

Exam Tip
In your exam you could be asked to write an equation for any Period 3 oxide with any simple acid or base, so make sure you understand these reactions — just learning the examples won't be enough.

The giant covalent structure of silicon dioxide means that it is insoluble in water. However, it will react with bases to form salts so it's classed as acidic.

Aluminium oxide is also insoluble in water. But, it will react with acids and bases to form salts — i.e. it can act as an acid or a base, so it is classed as **amphoteric**.

Reactions with acids and bases

The equation for neutralising an acid with a base is a classic:

Acid + Base → Salt + Water

And it's no different for reactions of the Period 3 oxides. You may be asked to write equations for these reactions. Here are some examples:

Sodium and magnesium oxides are basic so will neutralise acids:

Examples

$$Na_2O_{(s)} + 2HCl_{(aq)} \rightarrow 2NaCl_{(aq)} + H_2O_{(l)}$$
$$MgO_{(s)} + H_2SO_{4(aq)} \rightarrow MgSO_{4(aq)} + H_2O_{(l)}$$

Silicon, phosphorus and sulfur oxides are acidic so will neutralise bases:

Examples

$$SiO_{2(s)} + 2NaOH_{(aq)} \rightarrow Na_2SiO_{3(aq)} + H_2O_{(l)}$$
$$P_4O_{10(s)} + 12NaOH_{(aq)} \rightarrow 4Na_3PO_{4(aq)} + 6H_2O_{(l)}$$
$$SO_{2(g)} + 2NaOH_{(aq)} \rightarrow Na_2SO_{3(aq)} + H_2O_{(l)}$$
$$SO_{3(g)} + 2NaOH_{(aq)} \rightarrow Na_2SO_{4(aq)} + H_2O_{(l)}$$

Aluminium oxides are amphoteric so can neutralise acids or bases:

Examples

$$Al_2O_{3(s)} + 3H_2SO_{4(aq)} \rightarrow Al_2(SO_4)_{3(aq)} + 3H_2O_{(l)}$$
$$Al_2O_{3(s)} + 2NaOH_{(aq)} + 3H_2O_{(l)} \rightarrow 2NaAl(OH)_{4(aq)}$$

Practice Question — Application

Q1 The properties of three Period 3 oxides are shown in the table below:

Oxide	Structure	Melting point (°C)	Acidic/basic
A	Giant ionic lattice	3125	Basic
B	Giant ionic lattice	2345	Amphoteric
C	Macromolecular	1883	Acidic

a) Identify the three oxides A, B and C.
b) Explain why A has a higher melting point than B.

Practice Questions — Fact Recall

Q1 a) Describe the structure and bonding of:
i) MgO ii) Al_2O_3 iii) SiO_2 iv) P_4O_{10}
b) Write equations for the reactions of oxides (i) and (iv) with water.
c) State whether the oxides (i) – (iv) are acidic, basic or amphoteric.

Q2 a) Write an equation to show the neutralisation of HCl by MgO.
b) Write an equation to show the neutralisation of NaOH by SO_2.

3. Redox Equations

You did quite a lot about redox reactions and half-equations at AS level but you need to know it at A2-level as well — so here's a reminder.

Learning Objective:
- Be able to apply the electron transfer model of redox, including oxidation states and half-equations, to d block elements.

Specification Reference 3.5.3

What is a redox reaction?

A loss of electrons is called **oxidation**. A gain of electrons is called **reduction**. Reduction and oxidation happen simultaneously — hence the term 'redox' reaction. An oxidising agent accepts electrons and gets reduced. A reducing agent donates electrons and gets oxidised.

Example

In the reaction between sodium and chlorine:

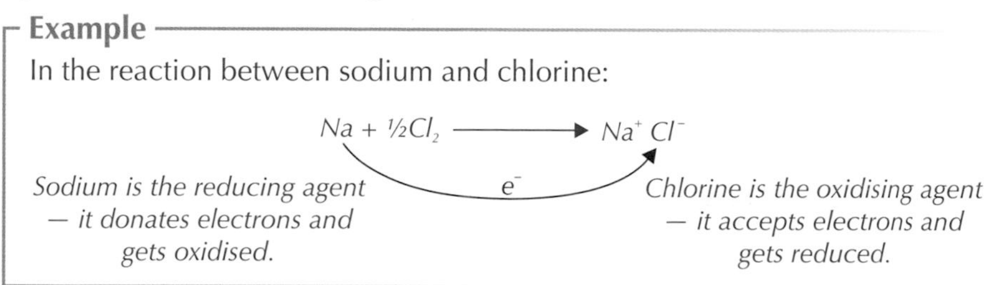

Tip: Don't forget:
OIL RIG
Oxidation Is Loss
Reduction Is Gain
(...of electrons)

Oxidation states

The **oxidation state** of an element tells you the total number of electrons it has donated or accepted. There is a set of rules for assigning oxidation states:

- Uncombined elements have an oxidation state of 0.
- Elements just bonded to identical atoms also have an oxidation state of 0. E.g. oxygen in O_2 has an oxidation state of 0.
- The oxidation state of a simple monatomic ion is the same as its charge. E.g. Na^+ has an oxidation state of +1.
- In compound ions, the overall oxidation state is just the ion charge. E.g. SO_4^{2-} has an overall oxidation state of –2.
- The sum of the oxidation states for a neutral compound is 0. E.g. the sum of the oxidation states of the atoms in Fe_2O_3 is 0.
- Combined oxygen is almost always –2.
- Combined hydrogen is +1 (except in metal hydrides where it is –1 and H_2 where it's 0).

You can use all these rules to work out the oxidation state of an element in a compound.

Tip: Oxidation states are also known as oxidation numbers.

Tip: The only times oxygen doesn't have an oxidation state of –2 are in peroxides (where it's –1), fluorides (where it can be +1 or +2) and O_2 (where it's 0).

Example

What is the oxidation state of chromium in Cr_2O_3?

The sum of oxidation states for a neutral compound is 0 — so the overall oxidation state of Cr_2O_3 is 0.

Combined oxygen has an oxidation state of –2.

There are three oxygen atoms and two chromium atoms in the compound. So the oxidation state of the chromium atoms must be:

$(0 - (3 \times -2)) \div 2 =$ **+3**

> **Tip:** You covered oxidation states and how they change in redox reactions at AS-level, so if you need a more detailed reminder dig out the old AS notes and you should be fine.

Changes in oxidation state

Oxidation states go up or down as electrons are lost or gained. To work out which atoms are oxidised and which are reduced in a reaction, you need to look at the oxidation states. The oxidation state for an atom will increase by one for each electron lost. The oxidation state will decrease by one for each electron gained.

Example

The reaction between vanadium(V) oxide and sulfur dioxide is shown below:

	V_2O_5	+	SO_2	$\rightarrow$	V_2O_4	+	SO_3	
Oxidation state of V:	*+5*			$\rightarrow$	*+4*			*reduction*
Oxidation state of S:			*+4*	$\rightarrow$			*+6*	*oxidation*

In this reaction, V is reduced from +5 to +4 (it gains 1 electron) and S is oxidised from +4 to +6 (it loses two electrons).

Half-equations

Ionic half-equations show oxidation or reduction — see Figure 1.

> **Tip:** Electrons are shown in half-equations so that the charges balance.

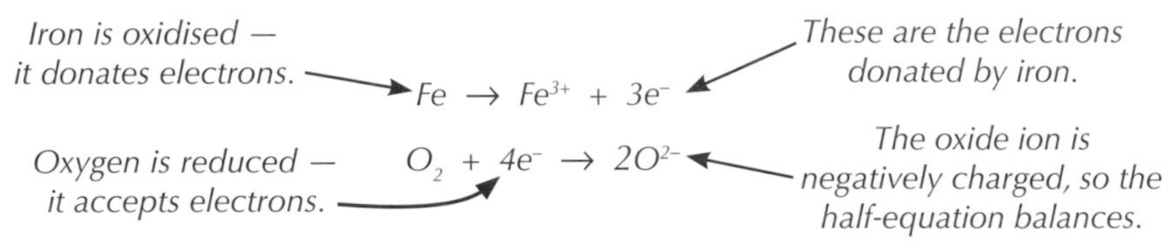

***Figure 1:** Half-equations for the oxidation of iron and the reduction of oxygen.*

An oxidation half-equation can be combined with a reduction half-equation to make a full equation.

Example

Zinc metal displaces silver ions from silver nitrate solution to form a solution of zinc ions and a deposit of silver metal.

The zinc atoms each lose 2 electrons (oxidation): $Zn_{(s)} \rightarrow Zn^{2+}_{(aq)} + 2e^-$
The silver ions each gain 1 electron (reduction): $Ag^+_{(aq)} + e^- \rightarrow Ag_{(s)}$

Two silver ions are needed to accept the two electrons released by each zinc atom. So you need to double the silver half-equation before the two half-equations can be combined: $2Ag^+_{(aq)} + 2e^- \rightarrow 2Ag_{(s)}$

Now the number of electrons lost and gained balance, so the half-equations can be combined:
$$Zn_{(s)} + 2Ag^+_{(aq)} \rightarrow Zn^{2+}_{(aq)} + 2Ag_{(s)}$$

> **Tip:** Electrons aren't included in overall equations because they cancel out. If yours don't, go back and check your half-equations are right.

If one of the ions in your half-equations contains oxygen or hydrogen, you may need to add H_2O and H^+ ions to balance the half-equation.

> **Tip:** If you see Roman numerals in a chemical name, it's an oxidation number. For example, in manganate(VII) ions, manganese has an oxidation state of +7.

Example

Acidified manganate(VII) ions (MnO_4^-) can be reduced to Mn^{2+} by Fe^{2+} ions. The Fe^{2+} ions are oxidised to Fe^{3+}. Write an equation for this reaction.

To tackle this type of question you need to start by writing out the half-equations. The half-equation for the oxidation of Fe^{2+} to Fe^{3+} is simple:
$$Fe^{2+} \rightarrow Fe^{3+} + e^-$$
The half-equation for the reduction of MnO_4^- ions is a bit more complicated.
Start with the basic reaction:
$$MnO_4^- \rightarrow Mn^{2+}$$

Now add some H_2O to the right side to balance the oxygen in MnO_4^-:

$$MnO_4^- \rightarrow Mn^{2+} + 4H_2O$$

Next, add H^+ ions to the left side to balance the hydrogen:

$$MnO_4^- + 8H^+ \rightarrow Mn^{2+} + 4H_2O$$

Finally, add electrons in to balance the charges:

$$MnO_4^- + 8H^+ + 5e^- \rightarrow Mn^{2+} + 4H_2O$$

Once you have the two half-equations, you're ready to construct the full redox equation. To balance the electrons you need to multiply the first half-equation by 5 (as there are 5 electrons in the reduction half-equation):

$$5Fe^{2+}_{(aq)} \rightarrow 5Fe^{3+}_{(aq)} + 5e^-$$

Now you can combine the half-equations:

$$MnO^-_{4\,(aq)} + 8H^+_{(aq)} + 5Fe^{2+}_{(aq)} \rightarrow Mn^{2+}_{(aq)} + 4H_2O_{(l)} + 5Fe^{3+}_{(aq)}$$

Finish by checking that the charges balance:

$$MnO^-_{4\,(aq)} + 8H^+_{(aq)} + 5Fe^{2+}_{(aq)} \rightarrow Mn^{2+}_{(aq)} + 4H_2O_{(l)} + 5Fe^{3+}_{(aq)}$$

Charges: $(-1) \quad (+1 \times 8) \quad (+2 \times 5) \rightarrow (+2) \quad 0 \quad (+3 \times 5)$

$$+17 \rightarrow +17$$

Exam Tip
If a question tells you that a solution is acidifed, it's a big clue that you'll need to add some H^+ ions into one of the half-equations.

Tip: Electrons, H^+ ions and water are the only things you can add in to balance a redox equation — so don't go adding in anything else.

Exam Tip
You should always finish by checking that the charges balance — that way you know you haven't made a mistake.

Practice Questions — Application

Q1 Give the oxidation states of:

a) Na in NaOH b) Cr in CrO_4^- c) O in H_2O_2

Q2 Copper metal can displace silver(I) ions in solution to form a solution of copper(II) ions and a deposit of silver metal.

a) Write the oxidation and reduction half-equations for this reaction.

b) Combine these half-equations to give the full redox equation for this reaction.

Q3 When a solution containing iron(II) ions is mixed with chlorine gas the iron(II) ions are oxidised to iron(III) and the chlorine is reduced to chloride ions. Write the full redox equation for this reaction.

Q4 Acidified manganate(VII) ions (MnO_4^-) oxidise hydrogen peroxide (H_2O_2) to oxygen gas.

a) Write a half-equation for the oxidation of H_2O_2 to O_2.

b) Write a half-equation for the reduction of MnO_4^- to Mn^{2+}.

c) Give the full redox equation for this reaction.

Practice Questions — Fact Recall

Q1 a) What is oxidation?

b) What is an oxidising agent?

Q2 a) What is the oxidation state of an uncombined element?

b) What is the oxidation state of a simple monatomic ion?

c) Hydrogen has an oxidation state of –1 in metal hydrides, but what is the usual oxidation state of hydrogen?

Q3 What happens to the oxidation state of elements that gain an electron?

Q4 What do ionic half-equations show?

4. Electrode Potentials

Learning Objectives:

- Know and be able to use the conventional representation of cells.
- Know the IUPAC convention for writing half-equations for electrode reactions.
- Be able to use electrode potentials to calculate the e.m.f. of a cell.

Specification Reference 3.5.3

In redox reactions, electrons move from one atom to another. When electrons move, you get electricity. So redox reactions can be used to make electricity.

Electrochemical Cells

Electrochemical cells can be made from two different metals dipped in salt solutions of their own ions and connected by a wire (the external circuit). There are always two reactions within an electrochemical cell — one's an oxidation and one's a reduction — so it's a **redox** process.

Tip: See page 169 for more on redox reactions

Example

The diagram below shows an electrochemical cell made using copper and zinc.

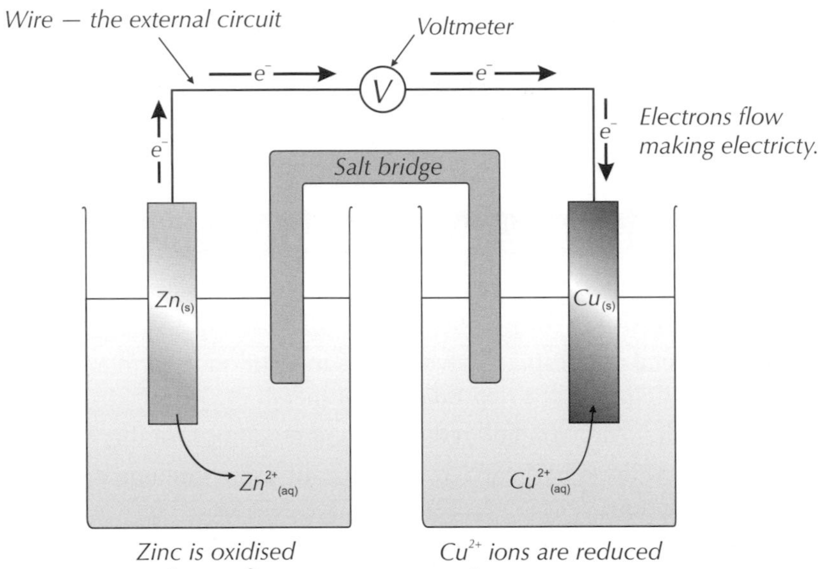

Figure 1: *A zinc/copper electrochemical cell.*

A copper electrode is dipped in a solution of Cu^{2+} ions and a zinc electrode is dipped in a solution of Zn^{2+} ions. Zinc loses electrons more easily than copper. So in the half-cell on the left, zinc (from the zinc electrode) is oxidised to form $Zn^{2+}_{(aq)}$ ions. This releases electrons into the external circuit. In the other half-cell, the same number of electrons are taken from the external circuit, reducing the Cu^{2+} ions to copper atoms.

The solutions are connected by a **salt bridge**, e.g. a strip of filter paper soaked in $KNO_{3(aq)}$. This allows ions to flow through and balance out the charges — it completes the circuit.

Tip: The two different sides of the electrochemical cell are called half-cells — two half-cells make a whole.

Electrons flow through the wire from the most reactive metal to the least. A voltmeter in the external circuit shows the voltage between the two half-cells. This is the **cell potential** or e.m.f., E_{cell}.

You can also have half-cells involving solutions of two aqueous ions of the same element.

Tip: e.m.f. stands for electromotive force.

Example

You can make an electrochemical half-cell using solutions of Fe^{2+} and Fe^{3+} ions. A platinum electrode is dipped into the solution (as shown on the next page).

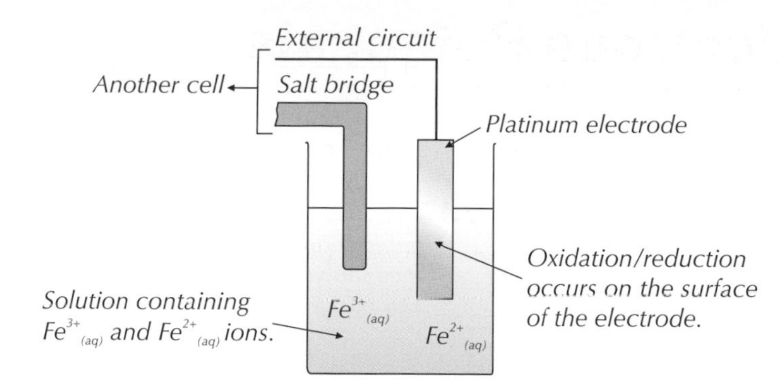

Platinum is used as the electrode because it is inert and conducts electricity. The conversion from Fe^{2+} to Fe^{3+}, or vice versa, happens on the surface of the electrode.

The direction of the conversion depends on the other half-cell in the circuit. If the other cell contains a metal that is **less reactive** than iron then Fe^{2+} will be oxidised to Fe^{3+} at the electrode. But if the other cell contains a **more reactive** metal, Fe^{3+} will be reduced to Fe^{2+} at the electrode.

Tip: An electrode has to be a solid that conducts electricity. If a half-cell doesn't contain anything like this, you can use something else (like platinum) as an electrode.

Tip: Inert means it won't react with anything. (The electrode has to be inert or it could react with the solution it's in.)

Electrode potentials

The reactions that occur at each electrode in a cell are reversible.

Example

The reactions that occur at each electrode in the zinc/copper cell are:

$$Zn^{2+}_{(aq)} + 2e^- \rightleftharpoons Zn_{(s)}$$

$$Cu^{2+}_{(aq)} + 2e^- \rightleftharpoons Cu_{(s)}$$

The reversible arrows show that both reactions can go in either direction.

Tip: These are half-equations for the reactions occurring in the electrochemical cell. See page 170 for more on half-equations and how to write them.

Which direction each reaction goes in depends on how easily each metal loses electrons (i.e. how easily it's oxidised). How easily a metal is oxidised is measured using **electrode potentials**. A metal that's easily oxidised has a very negative electrode potential, while one that's harder to oxidise has a less negative (or positive) electrode potential.

Example

The table below shows the electrode potentials for the copper and zinc half-cells:

Half-cell	Electrode potential (V)
$Zn^{2+}_{(aq)}/Zn_{(s)}$	−0.76
$Cu^{2+}_{(aq)}/Cu_{(s)}$	+0.34

The zinc half-cell has a more negative electrode potential, so in a zinc/copper cell, zinc is oxidised (the reaction goes backwards), while copper is reduced (the reaction goes forwards).

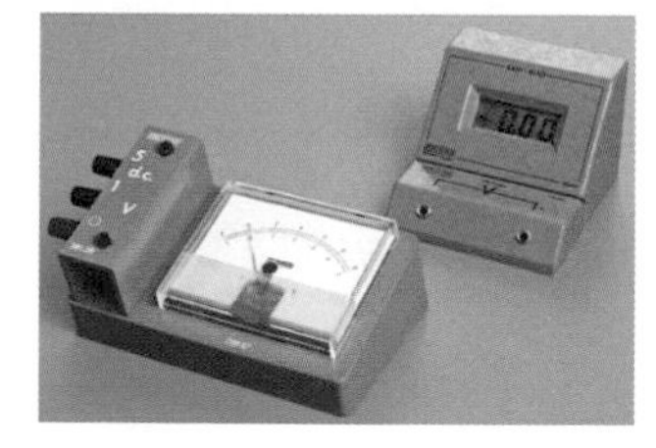

Figure 2: Analogue or digital voltmeters can be used to measure electrode potentials.

Tip: There's more on how electrode potentials are measured coming up.

Drawing electrochemical cells

It's a bit of a faff drawing pictures of electrochemical cells. There's a shorthand way of representing them though. You just take the oxidised and reduced species from each of the half-cells and arrange them in a row (see figure 3).

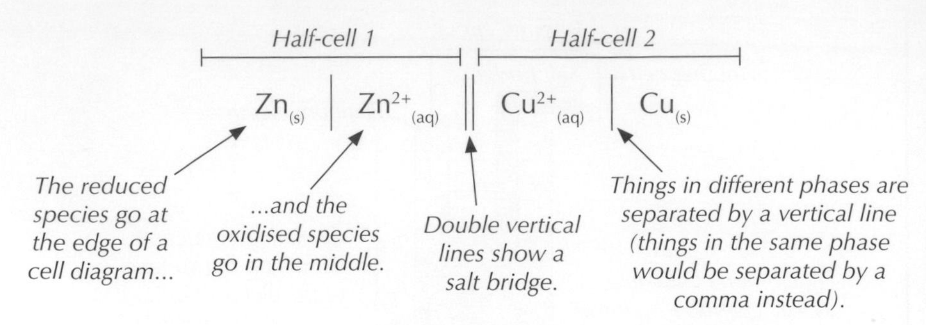

Figure 3: *The standard representation of a zinc/copper cell.*

Tip: The term 'phase' just means whether it's a solid, a liquid, an aqueous solution or a gas.

You always put the half-cell that has the more negative electrode potential on the left. In figure 3 the zinc half-cell is on the left because it has an electrode potential of –0.76 V, while the potential of the copper half-cell is +0.34 V.

The zinc/copper electrochemical cell is quite simple. Some cells are a bit trickier to draw, e.g. they might have platinum electrodes or involve more reagents. If you need to draw a cell diagram for any cell, just follow these steps and you'll be fine:

Tip: Remember, the one with the more negative electrode potential goes on the left.

Tip: If you write out the half-equations like this, you'll always end up with the reduced forms on the outside and the oxidised forms in the middle.

1. Use the electrode potentials to work out which half-equation goes on the left and which goes on the right.
2. Write out the left-hand half-equation as an oxidation reaction. Then write out the right-hand half-equation as a reduction reaction.
3. Write out the reactants and products of the oxidation reaction, followed by the reactants and products of the reduction reaction
4. Add in a salt bridge by drawing two vertical lines between the half-cells.
5. Draw a vertical line between any reagents that are in different phases. Put a comma between any reagents that are in the same phase.
6. If either of your half-cells has a separate electrode (like a platinum electrode, Pt) put that on the outside and separate it from the half-cell with a vertical line.

Example

The two half-equations below show the reactions at the positive and negative electrodes of a lithium cell:

$$Li^{+}_{(aq)} + e^{-} \rightarrow Li_{(s)} \qquad E^{\ominus} = -3.04$$
$$Li^{+}_{(aq)} + MnO_{2(s)} + e^{-} \rightarrow LiMnO_{2(s)} \qquad E^{\ominus} = -0.13$$

A platinum rod is used as the positive electrode. Draw the conventional representation of this cell.

Tip: The positive electrode is the one on the right of the cell diagram. The negative electrode is on the left.

1. The Li^{+}/Li reaction has a more negative electrode potential so it will go on the left. The $Li^{+},MnO_2/LiMnO_2$ reaction will go on the right.
2. Oxidation: $Li_{(s)} \rightarrow Li^{+}_{(aq)} + e^{-}$ *(left)*
   Reduction: $Li^{+}_{(aq)} + MnO_{2(s)} + e^{-} \rightarrow LiMnO_{2(s)}$ *(right)*
3. Write out the reactants and products of the oxidation equation, followed by the reactants and products of the reduction equation:

$$Li_{(s)} \quad Li^{+}_{(aq)} \quad Li^{+}_{(aq)} \quad MnO_{2(s)} \quad LiMnO_{2(s)}$$

4. Put in the salt bridge between the half-cells:

Half-cell 1 — *Half-cell 2*

$$Li_{(s)} \quad Li^{+}_{(aq)} \; \| \; Li^{+}_{(aq)} \quad MnO_{2(s)} \quad LiMnO_{2(s)}$$

5. Add in the phase boundaries:

$$Li_{(s)} \, | \, Li^{+}_{(aq)} \, \| \, Li^{+}_{(aq)} \, | \, MnO_{2(s)}, \, LiMnO_{2(s)}$$

Vertical lines for different phases. *Comma for same phase.*

6. Finally, add in the platinum electrode that's part of the right-hand cell:

$$Li_{(s)} \, | \, Li^{+}_{(aq)} \, \| \, Li^{+}_{(aq)} \, | \, MnO_{2(s)}, \, LiMnO_{2(s)} \, | \, Pt$$

Tip: The platinum electrode goes on the left if it's for the half-cell on the left. It goes on the right if it's for the half-cell on the right.

Writing half-equations from cell diagrams

You won't always be asked to draw a cell diagram from the half-equations. Sometimes, you might be given a cell diagram and asked to write half-equations for one or both of the electrodes.

Example

A conventional representation of an aluminium/lead cell is given below:

$$Al_{(s)} \, | \, Al^{3+}_{(aq)} \, \| \, Pb^{2+}_{(aq)} \, | \, Pb_{(s)}$$

Write half-equations for the reactions occurring at the positive and negative electrodes of this cell.

The positive electrode is the one on the right-hand side (Pb^{2+}/Pb) and the negative electrode is the one on the left-hand side (Al/Al^{3+}).

Reduction always happens at the positive electrode, so the half-equation for the reaction occurring at the positive electrode is:

$$Pb^{2+}_{(aq)} + 2e^{-} \rightleftharpoons Pb_{(s)}$$

Oxidation always happens at the negative electrode, so the half-equation for the reaction occurring at the negative electrode will be:

$$Al_{(s)} \rightleftharpoons Al^{3+}_{(aq)} + 3e^{-}$$

Tip: Each half-equation should just look like one half of the cell diagram (with the arrow and the electrons put back in).

Calculating the cell potential

$E^{\ominus}$ is the symbol for standard electrode potential. If you follow the conventions for drawing electrochemical cells, you can calculate the standard cell potential ($E^{\ominus}_{cell}$) (see page 172) using this formula:

$$E^{\ominus}_{cell} = (E^{\ominus}_{right\text{-}hand\ side} - E^{\ominus}_{left\text{-}hand\ side})$$

The cell potential will always be a positive voltage, because the more negative $E^{\ominus}$ value is being subtracted from the more positive $E^{\ominus}$ value.

Tip: If you don't have a cell diagram you can still use this formula. You just work out which half-cell would go on the left — it's always the one with the more negative electrode potential.

Example

For the Zn/Cu cell:

$$E^{\ominus}_{cell} = (E^{\ominus}_{right\text{-}hand\ side} - E^{\ominus}_{left\text{-}hand\ side})$$
$$= +0.34 - (-0.76)$$
$$= +1.10\ V$$

You can also use this formula to calculate an unknown electrode potential if you know the other electrode potential and the cell potential.

Tip: See page 177 for more on how electrode potentials for half-cells are measured.

Exam Tip
Because the Al/Al^{3+} half-cell is on the left-hand side, you know it should have a more negative electrode potential than the Cu^{2+}/Cu half-cell.
You can use this idea to check your answers in the exam.

Example

The cell below has an e.m.f. of +2.00 V:

$$Al_{(s)} \mid Al^{3+}_{(aq)} \parallel Cu^{2+}_{(aq)} \mid Cu_{(s)}$$

The standard electrode potential of the copper half-cell is +0.34 V. Calculate the standard electrode potential of the aluminium half-cell.

$$E^{\ominus}_{cell} = \left(E^{\ominus}_{right\text{-}hand\ side} - E^{\ominus}_{left\text{-}hand\ side}\right)$$
$$E^{\ominus}_{left\text{-}hand\ side} = E^{\ominus}_{right\text{-}hand\ side} - E^{\ominus}_{cell}$$
$$= 0.34 - 2.00$$
$$= -1.66\ V$$

Exam Tip
You don't have to memorise values for electrode potentials. You'll always be told them in the question.

Exam Tip
If you're drawing a cell diagram in the exam, use the state symbols you're given in the question to work out whether things should be separated by vertical lines or commas.

Tip: You don't need to include the platinum electrode in the half-equations because it's not actually involved in the redox reaction.

Practice Questions — Application

Q1 An electrochemical cell containing a calcium half-cell and a silver half-cell was set up using a salt bridge.

Half-cell	Electrode potential (V)
$Ca^{2+}_{(aq)}/Ca_{(s)}$	–2.87
$Ag^{+}_{(aq)}/Ag_{(s)}$	+0.80

a) Draw a conventional representation of this cell.
b) (i) Write a half-equation for the reaction at the positive electrode.
(ii) Write a half-equation for the reaction at the negative electrode.
c) Calculate the cell potential.

Q2 The conventional representation of an iron/thallium electrochemical cell is shown below:

$$Pt \mid Fe^{2+}_{(aq)},\ Fe^{3+}_{(aq)} \parallel Tl^{3+}_{(aq)},\ Tl^{+}_{(aq)} \mid Pt$$

a) Write half-equations for the reactions occurring at the positive and negative electrodes.
b) Calculate the electrode potential of the Tl^{3+}/Tl^{+} electrode given that the overall cell potential is +0.48 V and the Fe^{3+}/Fe^{2+} electrode potential is +0.77 V.

Q3 In an electrochemical cell with Mg^{2+}/Mg and Fe^{3+}/Fe^{2+} half-cells, oxidation occurs in the Mg^{2+}/Mg half-cell and reduction occurs in the Fe^{3+}/Fe^{2+} half-cell.
a) Which half-cell has the more negative electrode potential?
b) Draw a conventional representation of this cell.

Practice Questions — Fact Recall

Q1 a) What type of electrode is used for half-cells involving solutions of two aqueous ions of the same element?
b) Why is this type of electrode suitable?

Q2 Does oxidation or reduction occur in the half-cell with the more positive electrode potential?

Q3 Give two important conventions that you have to follow when you're drawing electrochemical cells.

5. Standard Electrode Potentials

Electrode potentials are influenced by things like temperature and pressure. So if you want to compare electrode potentials they need to be standardised. This is done using a standard hydrogen electrode.

Learning Objectives:

- Understand how cells are used to measure electrode potentials by reference to the standard hydrogen electrode.
- Know the importance of the conditions when measuring the electrode potential, E.
- Know that standard electrode potential, $E^{\ominus}$, refers to conditions of 298 K, 100 kPa and 1.00 $moldm^{-3}$ solution of ions.

Specification Reference 3.5.3

Factors affecting the electrode potential

Half-cell reactions are reversible. So just like any other reversible reaction, the equilibrium position is affected by changes in temperature, pressure and concentration. Changing the equilibrium position changes the cell potential. To get around this, **standard conditions** are used to measure electrode potentials — using these conditions means you always get the same value for the electrode potential and you can compare values for different cells.

Tip: See page 17 for more on how changes in temperature, pressure and concentration affect the position of equilibria.

The standard hydrogen electrode

You measure the electrode potential of a half-cell against a **standard hydrogen electrode**. In the standard hydrogen electrode, hydrogen gas is bubbled into a solution of aqueous H^+ ions. A platinum electrode is used as a platform for the oxidation/reduction reactions — see Figure 1.

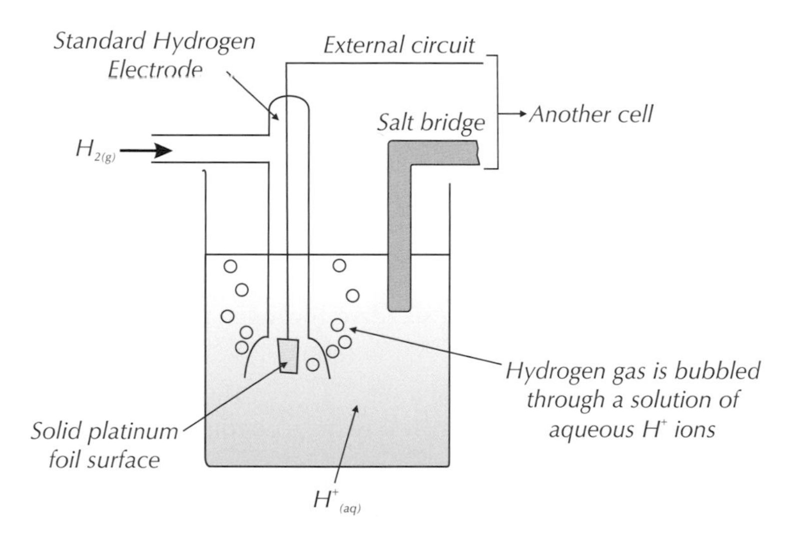

Figure 1: *The standard hydrogen electrode*

Tip: A platinum electrode is needed because you can't have a gas electrode.

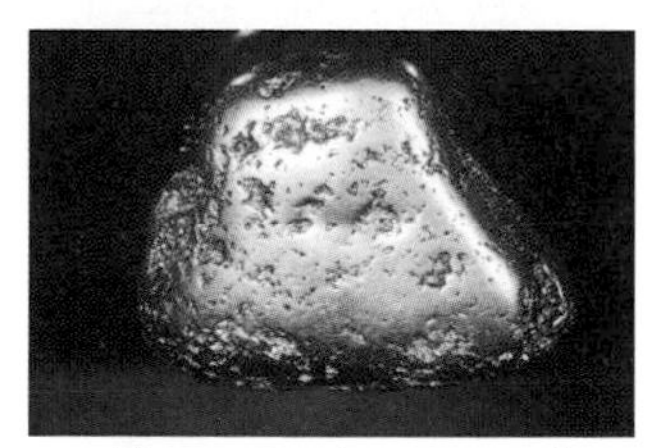

Figure 2: *A nugget of platinum. Platinum is used as the electrode in the standard hydrogen electrode.*

When measuring electrode potentials using the standard hydrogen electrode it is important that everything is done under standard conditions:

1. Any solutions of ions must have a concentration of 1.00 $moldm^{-3}$.
2. The temperature must be 298 K (25 °C).
3. The pressure must be 100 kPa.

Exam Tip
Make sure you learn the standard conditions — you might well be asked about them in the exam.

Measuring standard electrode potentials

The standard electrode potential of a half-cell is the voltage measured under standard conditions when the half-cell is connected to a standard hydrogen electrode — see Figure 3 (next page).

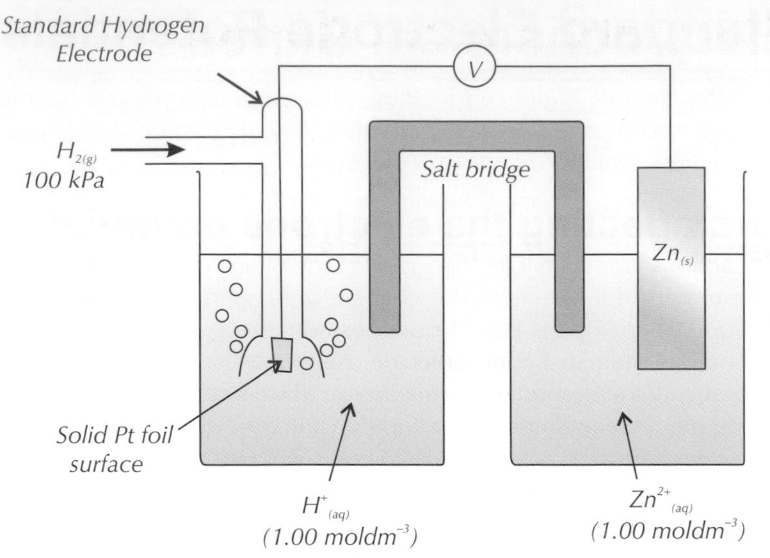

Figure 3: *A zinc electrode connected to a standard hydrogen electrode. This system could be used to measure the standard electrode potential of the zinc electrode.*

Tip: Notice how the H_2 gas is at a pressure of 100 kPa and the H^+ and Zn^{2+} solutions both have concentrations of 1.00 moldm^{-3}. These are the standard conditions.

The electrochemical cell in Figure 3 can be written as:

$$Pt \mid H_{2(g)} \mid H^+_{(aq)} \mid\mid Zn^{2+}_{(aq)} \mid Zn_{(s)}$$

The standard hydrogen electrode is always shown on the left — it doesn't matter whether or not the other half-cell has a more positive value.

Standard hydrogen electrodes can be used to calculate standard electrode potentials because the standard hydrogen electrode half-cell has an electrode potential of 0.00 V. The whole cell potential is:

$$E^{\ominus}_{cell} = \left(E^{\ominus}_{\text{right-hand side}} - E^{\ominus}_{\text{left-hand side}}\right)$$

The cell on the left-hand side is the standard hydrogen electrode so:

$$E^{\ominus}_{\text{left-hand side}} = 0.00\text{ V}$$

So the voltage reading will be equal to $E^{\ominus}_{\text{right-hand side}}$. This reading could be positive or negative, depending which way the electrons flow.

Tip: If you've forgotten what cell potential is, have a read of page 172.

Tip: The standard hydrogen electrode has an electrode potential of 0.00 V by definition — it's that because scientists say it is.

Practice Question — Application

Q1 When a $Pb^{2+}_{(aq)}/Pb_{(s)}$ half-cell was connected to a standard hydrogen electrode via a voltmeter, the reading on the voltmeter was –0.13 V.

a) Draw the conventional representation of this cell.

b) What is the standard electrode potential of the Pb^{2+}/Pb half-cell?

c) Is oxidation or reduction occurring in the Pb^{2+}/Pb half-cell?

Tip: Remember, oxidation happens in the half-cell with the more negative electrode potential — see page 173 for more on this.

Practice Questions — Fact Recall

Q1 Give three factors that can influence electrode potentials.

Q2 Describe how a standard hydrogen electrode is set up and give the standard conditions used when measuring electrode potentials.

Q3 a) What is the electrode potential of the standard hydrogen electrode?

b) Why is it this value?

Q4 Define the term "standard electrode potential".

6. Electrochemical Series

The standard electrode potentials of different reactions are different (unsurprisingly). If you write a big long list of electrode potentials in order, you get an electrochemical series. These are very useful for predicting the outcomes of reactions. But first a bit of how science works....

Learning Objectives:

- Know that standard electrode potentials can be listed as an electrochemical series.
- Be able to use $E^\ominus$ values to predict the direction of simple redox reactions and to calculate the e.m.f. of a cell.

Specification Reference 3.5.3

Evidence for electron transfer

Redox reactions involve the transfer of electrons from one substance to another — or so the theory goes. But you might wonder how anyone knows this — you can't see the electrons move.

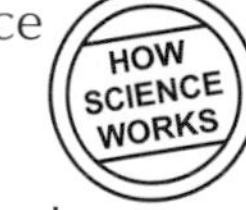

What you can do is use the theory to make a prediction, and then test the prediction with an experiment. For example, you could predict that a current will flow between the electrodes of an electrochemical cell if an oxidation reaction happens at one electrode and a reduction at the other electrode. And a current does flow — you can even stick an ammeter in the circuit and measure it. So, the electrochemical cell provides evidence that electrons are transferred in redox reactions.

Don't forget that an experiment doesn't prove a theory — someone, someday might do an experiment that shows electrons aren't transferred in chemical reactions. That seems unlikely at the moment because all the evidence we have fits the theory that electrons are transferred. So for now that's the theory that chemists are sticking to.

Tip: See page 1 for more on how scientists use theories, models and ideas to develop and modify scientific explanations.

What is an electrochemical series?

An **electrochemical series** is basically a big long list of electrode potentials for different electrochemical half-cells. They look something like this:

Half-reaction	$E^\ominus$ (V)
$Mg^{2+}_{(aq)} + 2e^- \rightleftharpoons Mg_{(s)}$	–2.38
$Al^{3+}_{(aq)} + 3e^- \rightleftharpoons Al_{(s)}$	–1.66
$Zn^{2+}_{(aq)} + 2e^- \rightleftharpoons Zn_{(s)}$	–0.76
$Ni^{2+}_{(aq)} + 2e^- \rightleftharpoons Ni_{(s)}$	–0.25
$2H^+_{(aq)} + 2e^- \rightleftharpoons H_{2(g)}$	0.00
$Sn^{4+}_{(aq)} + 2e^- \rightleftharpoons Sn^{2+}_{(aq)}$	+0.15
$Cu^{2+}_{(aq)} + 2e^- \rightleftharpoons Cu_{(s)}$	+0.34
$Fe^{3+}_{(aq)} + e^- \rightleftharpoons Fe^{2+}_{(aq)}$	+0.77
$Ag^+_{(aq)} + e^- \rightleftharpoons Ag_{(s)}$	+0.80
$Br_{2(aq)} + 2e^- \rightleftharpoons 2Br^-_{(aq)}$	+1.09
$Cr_2O_7^{2-}{}_{(aq)} + 14H^+_{(aq)} + 6e^- \rightleftharpoons 2Cr^{3+}_{(aq)} + 7H_2O_{(l)}$	+1.33
$Cl_{2(aq)} + 2e^- \rightleftharpoons 2Cl^-_{(aq)}$	+1.36
$MnO_4^-{}_{(aq)} + 8H^+_{(aq)} + 5e^- \rightleftharpoons Mn^{2+}_{(aq)} + 4H_2O_{(l)}$	+1.52

Exam Tip
Don't panic — you don't have to memorise any of these values. You'll always be told them in the question if you need to use them.

The electrode potentials are written in order, starting from the most negative and going down to the most positive. The half-equations are always written as reduction reactions — but the reactions are reversible and can go the opposite way. When two half-equations are put together in an electrochemical cell, the one with the more negative electrode potential goes in the direction of oxidation (backwards) and the one with the more positive electrode potential goes in the direction of reduction (forwards).

Tip: If you can't remember which half-reaction in a cell goes backwards and which goes forwards, think NO P.R. — the more Negative electrode potential will go in the Oxidation direction and the more Positive electrode potential will go in the Reduction direction.

Electrochemical series and reactivity

An electrochemical series shows you what's reactive and what's not.
The more reactive a metal is, the more it wants to lose electrons to form a positive ion. More reactive metals have more negative standard electrode potentials.

> **Example**
>
> Magnesium is more reactive than zinc — so it's more eager to form 2+ ions than zinc is. The list of standard electrode potentials shows that Mg^{2+}/Mg has a more negative value than Zn^{2+}/Zn — its –2.38 V for Mg^{2+}/Mg and –0.76 V for Zn^{2+}/Zn. In terms of oxidation and reduction, magnesium would reduce Zn^{2+} (or Zn^{2+} would oxidise magnesium).

Exam Tip
If you're given the electrode potential of a half-cell and asked to say how reactive something is, make sure you identify whether it's a metal or a non-metal first — they're very different.

The more reactive a non-metal the more it wants to gain electrons to form a negative ion. More reactive non-metals have more positive standard electrode potentials.

> **Example**
>
> Chlorine is more reactive than bromine — so it's more eager to form a negative ion than bromine is. The list of standard electrode potentials shows that $Cl_2/2Cl^-$ is more positive than $Br_2/2Br^-$ — it's +1.36 V for $Cl_2/2Cl^-$ and +1.09 V for $Br_2/2Br^-$. In terms of oxidation and reduction, chlorine would oxidise Br^- (or Br^- would reduce chlorine).

Figure 1: Chlorine will displace bromide ions — this confirms that chlorine is more reactive.

Predicting the outcome of reactions

You can use the anticlockwise rule to predict whether a redox reaction will happen and to show which direction it will go in. Just follow these steps:

1. Find the two half-equations for the redox reaction, and write them both out as reduction reactions.
2. Use an electrochemical series to work out which half-equation has the more negative electrode potential.
3. Put the half-equation with the more negative electrode potential on top of the other one.
4. Draw on two anticlockwise arrows — one going from the products of the top equation to the reactants of the top equation and one going from the reactants of the bottom equation to the products of the bottom equation.
5. If you mix the substances at the non-pointy ends of the arrows a redox reaction will occur — the arrows show the direction that the half-equations will go. But if you use any other combination of reactants there will be no reaction.

Tip: Once you know these steps, you can apply them to predict the outcome of any redox reaction.

> **Examples**
>
> **Will zinc react with aqueous copper ions?**
>
> 1. Write down the two half-equations for the redox reaction as reduction reactions:
>
> $$Zn^{2+}_{(aq)} + 2e^- \rightleftharpoons Zn_{(s)} \quad \text{and} \quad Cu^{2+}_{(aq)} + 2e^- \rightleftharpoons Cu_{(s)}$$
>
> 2. Find out the electrode potentials for the two half-equations:
>
> $$Zn^{2+}/Zn = -0.76\ V$$
> $$Cu^{2+}/Cu = +0.34\ V$$

Tip: These values for the electrode potentials came from the electrochemical series on page 179.

3. Put the half-equation with the more negative electrode potential on top:

$$Zn^{2+}_{(aq)} + 2e^- \rightleftharpoons Zn_{(s)}$$
$$Cu^{2+}_{(aq)} + 2e^- \rightleftharpoons Cu_{(s)}$$

4. Draw on the anticlockwise arrows:

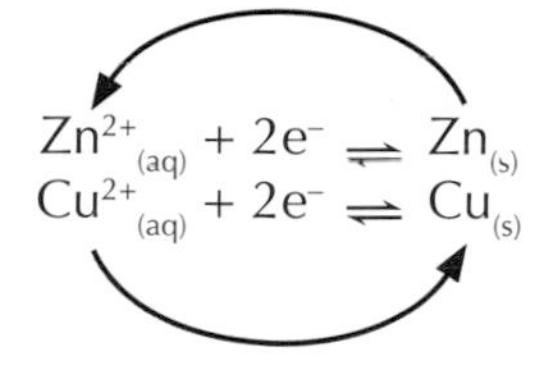

5. Look at the non-pointy ends of the arrows to work out if the reaction would happen:

   The substances at the ends of the arrows are $Zn_{(s)}$ and $Cu^{2+}_{(aq)}$. So zinc will react with aqueous copper(II) ions. (The arrows show that the zinc half-reaction goes backwards and the copper half-reaction goes forwards, so the overall equation is: $Zn_{(s)} + Cu^{2+}_{(aq)} \rightarrow Zn^{2+}_{(aq)} + Cu_{(s)}$)

Will silver react with aqueous magnesium ions?

Following the same steps as before, you get:

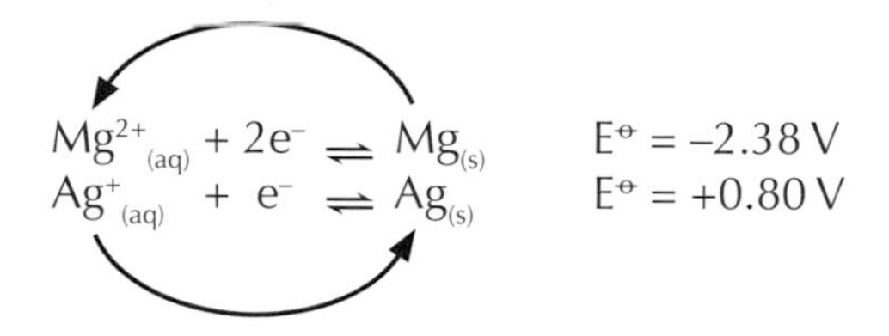

Here, the substances at the non-pointy ends of the arrows are $Mg_{(s)}$ and $Ag^{+}_{(aq)}$. So, magnesium will react with aqueous silver ions, but silver and aqueous magnesium ions will not react.

Exam Tip
Remember — the arrows must go anticlockwise. If your arrows are clockwise you'll get the answer wrong. Look at the clock in the exam room if you can't picture which way is clockwise and which way is anticlockwise.

Exam Tip
In the exam, don't assume you'll always be given a reaction that will happen — you're just as likely to get given one that won't.

You can use the rule to work out whether any two substances will react — just remember to put the half-cell with the more negative standard electrode potential on the top.

Finding the cell potential

You can also use the anticlockwise rule to find cell potentials.
To find the cell potential you use this formula:

$$E^{\ominus}_{cell} = (E^{\ominus}_{bottom} - E^{\ominus}_{top})$$

Just put in the values for $E^{\ominus}_{bottom}$ and $E^{\ominus}_{top}$ and you'll have your value for $E^{\ominus}_{cell}$.

Examples

For the Zn/Cu electrochemical cell:

$$E^{\ominus}_{cell} = (E^{\ominus}_{bottom} - E^{\ominus}_{top}) = 0.34 - (-0.76) = +1.10\ V$$

For the Mg/Ag electrochemical cell:

$$E^{\ominus}_{cell} = (E^{\ominus}_{bottom} - E^{\ominus}_{top}) = 0.80 - (-2.38) = +3.18\ V$$

Tip: The cell potential is also known as the cell e.m.f. or electromotive force.

Tip: You can calculate cell potentials using cell diagrams too. See page 175 for more on this.

Tip: This makes sense because the one with the more negative electrode potential goes backwards (see page 179).

Tip: It's easier to explain how you know that two things will react using this method, because you can talk about their electrode potentials. But it's easier to make mistakes with too — so stick with the anticlockwise rule if you're finding it tricky.

Making predictions without using the anticlockwise rule

For any two reduction half-equations, things on the right side of the one with the more negative electrode potential will react with things on the left side of the other one. That's why the anticlockwise rule works. But once you know that, you can make predictions just by looking at electrode potentials.

Example

Will aluminium metal react with aqueous nickel ions? Explain your answer.

Here are the half-equations and their electrode potentials:

$$Al^{3+}_{(aq)} + 3e^- \rightleftharpoons Al_{(s)} \qquad E^\ominus = -1.66\ V$$
$$Ni^{2+}_{(aq)} + 2e^- \rightleftharpoons Ni_{(s)} \qquad E^\ominus = -0.25\ V$$

$E^\ominus$ is more negative for the Al^{3+}/Al half-equation than for the Ni^{2+}/Ni half-equation. So aluminium will react with Ni^{2+} ions.

Practice Questions — Application

For these questions use the electrochemical series on page 179.

Q1 For each of the combinations below state which species is more reactive and explain how you know.

a) Aluminium and nickel.

b) Bromine and chlorine.

c) Silver and copper.

Q2 Magnesium is more reactive than zinc. Use electrode potentials to explain why.

Q3 Use the anticlockwise rule to say whether these reactions will happen:

a) $Mg_{(s)} + Ni^{2+}_{(aq)} \rightarrow Mg^{2+}_{(aq)} + Ni_{(s)}$

b) $2Br^-_{(aq)} + Fe^{3+}_{(aq)} \rightarrow Fe^{2+}_{(aq)} + Br_{2(aq)}$

c) $Sn^{2+}_{(aq)} + Cu^{2+}_{(aq)} \rightarrow Sn^{4+}_{(aq)} + Cu_{(s)}$

Q4 Calculate the e.m.f. for the following reactions:

a) $Al_{(s)} + Ag^+_{(aq)} \rightarrow Al^{3+}_{(aq)} + Ag_{(s)}$

b) $Cu_{(s)} + Cl_{2(aq)} \rightarrow Cu^{2+}_{(aq)} + 2Cl^-_{(aq)}$

c) $Sn^{2+}_{(aq)} + Fe^{3+}_{(aq)} \rightarrow Sn^{4+}_{(aq)} + Fe^{2+}_{(aq)}$

Q5 Will Ag^+ ions react with Sn^{2+} ions in solution? Explain your answer.

Practice Questions — Fact Recall

Q1 What is an electrochemical series?

Q2 In what direction are half-equations written in electrochemical series?

Q3 A half-reaction has a very positive electrode potential. Is it more likely to go in the direction of oxidation or reduction?

Q4 a) Do very reactive metals generally have very negative or very positive electrode potentials?

b) Do very reactive non-metals generally have very negative or very positive electrode potentials?

Q5 a) Name the rule that can be used to predict whether a reaction will happen or not.

b) Write the formula for calculating cell potential using this rule.

7. Electrochemical Cells

The last few topics told you all about electrochemical cells. This one's all about what electrochemical cells are actually used for.

Learning Objectives:

- Appreciate that electrochemical cells can be used as a commercial source of electrical energy.
- Appreciate that cells can be non-rechargeable (irreversible), rechargeable and fuel cells.
- Be able to use given electrode data to deduce the reactions occurring in non-rechargeable and rechargeable cells and to deduce the e.m.f. of a cell.
- Understand the electrode reactions of a hydrogen-oxygen fuel cell and appreciate that a fuel cell does not need to be electrically recharged.
- Appreciate the benefits and risks to society associated with the use of these cells.

Specification Reference 3.5.3

Batteries

The batteries that we use to power everything from watches to digital cameras and mobile phones are all types of electrochemical cell. Some types of cell are rechargeable while others can only be used until they run out.

Non-rechargeable cells

Non-rechargeable cells use irreversible reactions. A common type of non-rechargeable cell is a dry cell alkaline battery. You'll probably find some of these in the TV remote control, torch or smoke alarms in your house. They're useful for gadgets that don't use a lot of power or are only used for short periods of time.

Example

Zinc-carbon dry cell batteries have a zinc anode and a mixture of manganese dioxide and carbon for a cathode. In between the electrodes is a paste of ammonium chloride, which acts as an electrolyte.

The half-equations are:

$Zn_{(s)} \rightarrow Zn^{2+}_{(aq)} + 2e^-$ $\quad E^\ominus = -0.76\ V$

$2MnO_{2(s)} + 2NH_4{}^+_{(aq)} + 2e^- \rightarrow Mn_2O_{3(s)} + 2NH_{3(aq)} + H_2O_{(l)}$ $\quad E^\ominus = +0.75\ V$

So the cell is drawn as: $Zn_{(s)} \mid Zn^{2+}_{(aq)} \parallel MnO_{2(s)} \mid Mn_2O_{3(s)}$

The e.m.f. of this type of cell is:

$$E^\ominus_{cell} = (E^\ominus_{right\text{-}hand\ side} - E^\ominus_{left\text{-}hand\ side}) = +0.75 - (-0.76) = +1.51\ V$$

The half-equations have non-reversible arrows because it is not practical to reverse them in a battery. They can be made to run backwards under the right conditions, but trying to do this in a battery can make it leak or explode. This is because the zinc anode forms the casing of the battery, so becomes thinner as the zinc is oxidised.

Another reason why these batteries cannot be recharged is that the ammonium ions would produce hydrogen gas, which would escape from the battery. Without the hydrogen, the ammonium ions couldn't be reformed by reversing the reactions.

Rechargeable cells

Rechargeable cells use reversible reactions. Rechargeable batteries are found in loads of devices, such as mobile phones, laptops and cars.

Examples

Lead-acid cells are used in car batteries. They normally consist of 6 cells connected in series. Each cell is made up of a lead anode and a lead(IV) dioxide cathode immersed in a sulfuric acid electrolyte. Both electrodes end up coated in lead(II) sulfate. The half-equations are:

$Pb_{(s)} + SO_4{}^{2-}_{(aq)} \rightleftharpoons PbSO_{4(s)} + 2e^-$ $\quad E^\ominus = -0.36\ V$

$PbO_{2(s)} + SO_4{}^{2-}_{(aq)} + 4H^+_{(aq)} + 2e^- \rightleftharpoons PbSO_{4(s)} + 2H_2O_{(l)}$ $\quad E^\ominus = +1.69\ V$

So the cell is drawn as: $Pb_{(s)} \mid PbSO_{4(s)} \parallel PbO_{2(s)} \mid PbSO_{4(s)}$

The e.m.f. of this type of cell is:

$$E^\ominus_{cell} = (E^\ominus_{right\ hand\ side} - E^\ominus_{left\text{-}hand\ side}) = +1.69 - (-0.36) = +2.05\ V$$

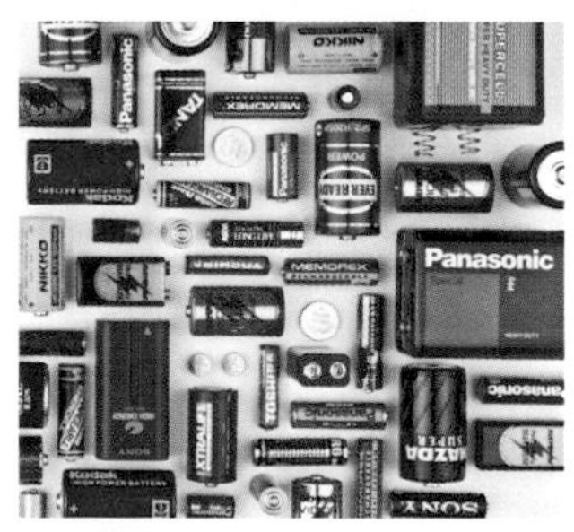

Figure 1: An assortment of batteries — these are all electrochemical cells.

Tip: For batteries, you draw the cell and work out the e.m.f. in exactly the same way as for any electrochemical cell — see pages 173-176.

Two other types of rechargeable battery are NiCad (nickel-cadmium) and L ion (lithium ion). To recharge these batteries, a current is supplied to force electrons to flow in the opposite direction around the circuit and reverse the reactions. This is possible because none of the substances in a rechargeable battery escape or are used up.

Figure 2: A lithium ion battery being recharged.

Pros and cons of non-rechargeable cells

Using non-rechargeable batteries instead of rechargeable batteries has it's advantages and disadvantages:

- **Cost:** non-rechargeable batteries are cheaper than rechargeables to buy. However, non-rechargeable batteries have to be replaced every time they run out, so rechargeables are cheaper in the long run.
- **Lifetime:** a non-rechargeable battery will usually work for longer than a rechargeable battery. But once a rechargeable battery has run out, you can recharge it and use it again whereas non-rechargeables have to be disposed of.
- **Power:** non-rechargeable batteries can't supply as much power as rechargeables, so are no use in devices that use a lot of power — like a mobile phone or a laptop.
- **Use of resources and waste:** more non-rechargeable batteries are produced because they can only be used once, which uses more resources and means they create more waste than rechargeables. Both types of battery can be recycled and the metals in them recovered to use again, but often we just chuck them in the bin and they end up in landfill.
- **Toxicity:** non-rechargeable batteries are less likely to contain the toxic metals lead and cadmium (although they may contain mercury), so they're less hazardous in landfill if the contents leak out and pollute water sources.

Fuel cells

In most cells the chemicals that generate the electricity are contained in the electrodes and the electrolyte that form the cell. In a **fuel cell** the chemicals are stored separately outside the cell and fed in when electricity is required. One example of this is the hydrogen-oxygen fuel cell, which can be used to power electric vehicles. Figure 3 shows how a hydrogen fuel cell works:

Tip: An electrolyte is a substance that contains free ions and can conduct electricity.

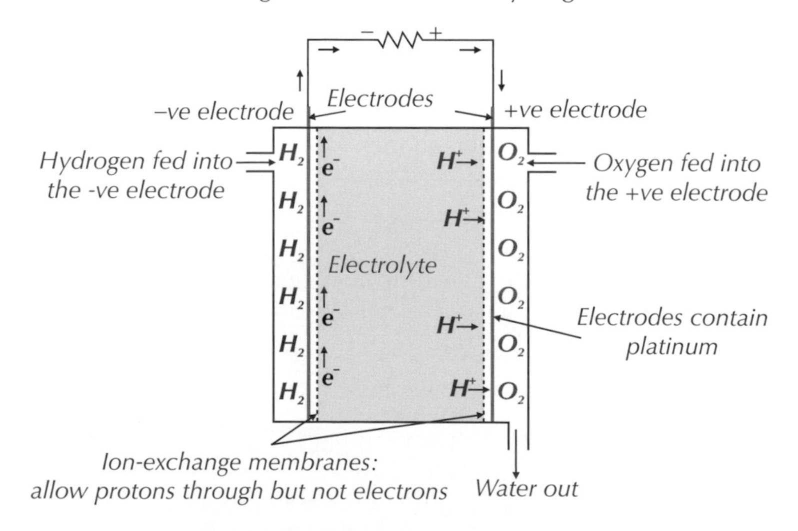

Figure 3: A hydrogen-oxygen fuel cell

Figure 4: A bus powered by a hydrogen-oxygen fuel cell.

Hydrogen and oxygen gases are fed into two separate platinum-containing electrodes. These electrodes are usually made by coating a porous ceramic material with a thin layer of platinum, rather than using solid platinum rods. This is cheaper and it provides a larger surface area so the reactions go faster.

The electrodes are separated by an ion-exchange membrane that allows protons (H^+ ions) to pass through it, but stops electrons going through it. Hydrogen is fed to the negative electrode. The reaction that occurs is: $H_2 \rightarrow 2H^+ + 2e^-$.

The electrons flow from the negative electrode through an external circuit to the positive electrode. The H^+ ions pass through the ion-exchange membrane towards the positive electrode. Oxygen is fed to the positive electrode. The reaction here is: $O_2 + 4H^+ + 4e^- \rightarrow 2H_2O$.

The overall effect is that H_2 and O_2 react to make water: $2H_2 + O_2 \rightarrow 2H_2O$.

Tip: These equations are for fuel cells working in acidic conditions. That means the electrolyte is an acid (e.g. H_3PO_4).

You can make fuel cells with alkaline electrolytes (e.g. KOH) too. Then the electrode reactions look like this instead —
Negative electrode:
$O_2 + 4e^- + 2H_2O \rightarrow 4OH^-$
Positive electrode:
$H_2 + 2OH^- \rightarrow 2H_2O + 2e^-$

Pros and cons of fuel cells

The major advantage of fuel cells over batteries is that they don't need electrical recharging. As long as hydrogen and oxygen are supplied, the cell will continue to produce electricity. Another benefit is that the only waste product is water, so there are no nasty toxic chemicals to dispose of and no CO_2 emissions from the cell itself.

The downside is that you need energy to produce a supply of hydrogen and oxygen. They can be produced from the electrolysis of water — i.e. by reusing the waste product from the fuel cell — but this requires electricity, and this electricity is normally generated by burning fossil fuels. So the whole process isn't usually carbon neutral. Hydrogen is also highly flammable so it needs to be handled carefully when it is stored or transported.

Figure 5: Electrolysis of water being used to make hydrogen and oxygen.

Practice Questions — Application

Q1 Nickel/cadmium batteries are a common type of rechargeable battery. The two half-equations for the reactions happening in this type of battery are shown below:

$Cd(OH)_{2(s)} + 2e^- \rightleftharpoons Cd_{(s)} + 2OH^-_{(aq)}$ $\quad E^\ominus = -0.88$

$NiO(OH)_{(s)} + H_2O + e^- \rightleftharpoons Ni(OH)_{2(s)} + OH^-$ $\quad E^\ominus = +0.52$

a) Calculate the e.m.f. of this cell.

b) Write an equation for the overall reaction occurring in this cell.

Q2 An electric car is being powered by a hydrogen-oxygen fuel cell. The half-equations for the reactions occurring inside this cell are:

$$H_2 \rightarrow 2H^+ + 2e^-.$$
$$O_2 + 4H^+ + 4e^- \rightarrow 2H_2O.$$

a) Write an equation for the overall reaction occurring in this cell.

b) Draw the conventional representation of this cell.

Tip: See pages 173-176 for a recap on how to draw cell diagrams and calculate e.m.f.

Tip: Don't forget that platinum electrodes need to be included in cell diagrams too.

Practice Questions — Fact Recall

Q1 Why can you recharge a rechargeable battery?

Q2 Give an advantage and a disadvantage of non-rechargeable batteries.

Q3 Describe how an acidic oxygen-hydrogen fuel cell works.

Q4 Explain why oxygen-hydrogen fuel cells are not carbon neutral.

Q5 Give an advantage and a disadvantage of using fuel cells.

Section Summary

Make sure you know...

- That sodium is more reactive than magnesium because it takes less energy for sodium to lose one electron than it does for magnesium to lose two.
- How sodium and magnesium react with water (including equations and pH of the resulting solutions).
- How each of the elements in Period 3 reacts with oxygen to produce an oxide.
- The trend in melting points of the Period 3 oxides and that the differences in the melting points are due to differences in their structure and bonding.
- That the ionic Period 3 oxides (Na_2O/MgO) react with water to form basic hydroxides.
- That the simple covalent oxides (P_4O_{10}/SO_2/SO_3) react with water to form strong acids.
- That SiO_2 is insoluble in water but will react with bases — so is classified as acidic.
- That Al_2O_3 is insoluble in water but will react with acids and bases — so is classified as amphoteric.
- How to write equations for the reactions between Period 3 oxides and simple acids and bases.
- That a redox reaction is when oxidation and reduction occur simultaneously.
- How to determine the oxidation state of an element in different compounds.
- What half-equations are and how to write them for redox reactions.
- That electrochemical cells can be made by dipping two different metals in salt solutions of their own ions and connecting them by a wire and a salt bridge.
- That the direction of the reaction in each half-cell depends on their relative electrode potentials.
- That the reaction with the more negative electrode potential goes in the direction of oxidation and the reaction with the more positive electrode potential goes in the direction of reduction.
- The conventions for drawing simplified diagrams of electrochemical cells.
- That the half-cell on the left of a cell diagram has the more negative electrode potential and undergoes oxidation — the one on the right is more positive and is reduced.
- How to write oxidation and reduction half-equations from cell diagrams.
- How to calculate standard cell potentials using the equation $E^{\ominus}_{cell} = (E^{\ominus}_{right\text{-}hand\ side} - E^{\ominus}_{left\text{-}hand\ side})$.
- That temperature, pressure and concentration can all influence the cell potential.
- That standard electrode potentials are measured against the standard hydrogen electrode.
- That in the standard hydrogen electrode, hydrogen gas is bubbled into a solution of aqueous H^+ ions and platinum is used as the electrode.
- That standard conditions are 298 K (25 °C), 100 kPa and 1.00 $mol dm^{-3}$.
- What an electrochemical series is and how it can be used to predict the outcome of a reaction.
- That batteries are electrochemical cells.
- How to draw cell diagrams and calculate the e.m.f. for the electrochemical cells in batteries.
- That non-rechargeable batteries use non-reversible reactions and rechargeable batteries use reversible reactions.
- The advantages and disadvantages of using non-rechargeable batteries.
- How a hydrogen-oxygen fuel cell works.
- The advantages and disadvantages of using fuel cells instead of conventional batteries.

Exam-style Questions

1 Sodium and magnesium are both elements in Period 3 of the periodic table.

1 (a) Sodium reacts vigorously with water but the reaction of magnesium with water is very slow.

1 (a) (i) Write an equation to show the reaction of magnesium with water.

(1 mark)

1 (a) (ii) Explain why magnesium reacts less vigorously with water than sodium.

(3 marks)

1 (b) Sodium and magnesium both react vigorously with oxygen to produce oxides. These oxides are structurally similar but they have very different melting temperatures.

1 (b) (i) Write an equation to show the reaction of sodium with oxygen.

(1 mark)

1 (b) (ii) What colour is the flame that is produced when sodium is burnt in air?

(1 mark)

1 (b) (iii) Describe the structure of sodium oxide and magnesium oxide.

(2 marks)

1 (b) (iv) State which oxide has the higher melting point and explain why their melting temperatures are different.

(3 marks)

1 (c) Non-metal Period 3 elements such as silicon, phosphorus and sulfur also react with oxygen to produce oxides.

1 (c) (i) Explain why sulfur dioxide has a relatively low melting point.

(3 marks)

1 (c) (ii) Explain why the melting point of silicon dioxide is unusually high.

(3 marks)

1 (d) The Period 3 oxides react differently with water.

1 (d) (i) Write equations showing the reactions of magnesium oxide and sulfur dioxide with water. Give the approximate pHs of the solutions formed.

(4 marks)

1 (d) (ii) Name one Period 3 oxide that is insoluble in water.

(1 mark)

1 (e) (i) State which Period 3 oxide is amphoteric.

(1 mark)

1 (e) (ii) Write two equations showing the reaction of this oxide with an acid and a base.

(2 marks)

2 The table below shows a short electrochemical series:

Half-reaction	$E^{\ominus}$ (V)
$Mg^{2+}_{(aq)} + 2e^- \rightleftharpoons Mg_{(s)}$	–2.38
$V^{2+}_{(aq)} + 2e^- \rightleftharpoons V_{(s)}$	–1.18
$V^{3+}_{(aq)} + e^- \rightleftharpoons V^{2+}_{(aq)}$	–0.26
$Sn^{4+}_{(aq)} + 2e^- \rightleftharpoons Sn^{2+}_{(aq)}$	+0.15
$VO^{2+}_{(aq)} + 2H^+_{(aq)} + e^- \rightleftharpoons V^{3+}_{(aq)} + H_2O_{(l)}$	+0.34
$Fe^{3+}_{(aq)} + e^- \rightleftharpoons Fe^{2+}_{(aq)}$	+0.77
$VO_2^+{}_{(aq)} + 2H^+_{(aq)} + e^- \rightleftharpoons VO^{2+}_{(aq)} + H_2O_{(l)}$	+1.00

2 (a) Using the information in the table, determine what reactions, if any, occur when aqueous Sn^{2+} ions are mixed with an acidified solution of VO_2^+ ions. Explain your answer.

(4 marks)

2 (b) An electrochemical cell can be made by connecting an Mg^{2+}/Mg half-cell to an Fe^{2+}/Fe^{3+} half-cell with a platinum electrode.

2 (b) (i) Draw a cell diagram for this cell using the conventional representation.

(2 marks)

2 (b) (ii) Calculate the e.m.f. of this cell.

(1 mark)

2 (b) (iii) Write half-equations for the oxidation and reduction reactions occurring in this cell.

(1 mark)

2 (c) Standard electrode potentials are measured relative to the standard hydrogen electrode.

2 (c) (i) Explain what is meant by 'standard conditions'.

(3 marks)

2 (c) (ii) The electrode potential of the standard hydrogen electrode is 0.00 V. Explain why.

(1 mark)

2 (c) (iii) The electrode itself is made of platinum. Suggest why platinum is a suitable metal to use for this purpose.

(1 mark)

2 (d) When a standard hydrogen electrode was connected to an Ag^+/Ag half-cell, the reading on the voltmeter was +0.80 V.

2 (d) (i) What is the standard electrode potential for the reaction $Ag^+_{(aq)} + e^- \rightleftharpoons Ag_{(s)}$?

(1 mark)

2 (d) (ii) What does this electrode potential tell you about the reactivity of silver compared to vanadium? Explain your answer.

(2 mark)

3 Lead-acid batteries are a type of rechargeable battery commonly used to operate the starter motors of cars. The half-equations for the reactions that occur in a lead-acid battery are shown below:

$$PbO_{2(s)} + SO_4{}^{2-}{}_{(aq)} + 4H^+ + 2e^- \rightarrow PbSO_{4(s)} + 2H_2O_{(l)}$$

$$Pb_{(s)} + SO_4{}^{2-}{}_{(aq)} \rightarrow PbSO_{4(s)} + 2e^-$$

3 (a) Explain why rechargeable batteries can be recharged.

(1 mark)

3 (b) Combine the two half-equations to give the equation for the overall reaction occurring in this cell.

(1 mark)

3 (c) Discuss the advantages and disadvantages of using rechargeable batteries instead of standard non-rechargeable batteries.

(4 marks)

3 (d) Hydrogen-oxygen fuel cells can be used as an alternative source of commercially available electrical energy. They are commonly used to power electric vehicles.

3 (d) (i) Explain why the electrodes of a hydrogen-oxygen fuel cell are typically made by coating a ceramic material with a thin layer of platinum, rather than using solid platinum rods.

(2 marks)

3 (d) (ii) Give two advantages of using hydrogen-oxygen fuel cells over conventional batteries.

(2 marks)

4 The conventional representation of an electrochemical cell is shown below.

$$Pt \mid SO_3{}^{2-}{}_{(aq)}, SO_4{}^{2-}{}_{(aq)} \parallel Cr_2O_7{}^{2-}{}_{(aq)}, Cr^{3+}{}_{(aq)} \mid Pt$$

All the reactions in this cell are taking place in an acidic environment.

4 (a) Write a half-equation for the reaction occurring at the positive electrode of this electrochemical cell.

(2 marks)

4 (b) Calculate the electrode potential of the $Cr_2O_7{}^{2-}{}_{(aq)}/Cr^{3+}$ half-cell given that the overall cell potential is +1.16 V and the electrode potential of the $SO_4{}^{2-}{}_{(aq)}/SO_3{}^{2-}{}_{(aq)}$ half-cell is +0.17 V.

(1 mark)

4 (c) Draw the conventional representation of an electrochemical cell that could be used to measure the standard electrode potential of the $Cr_2O_7{}^{2-}{}_{(aq)}/Cr^{3+}{}_{(aq)}$ half-cell.

(1 mark)

Unit 5 Section 3: Transition Metals

Learning Objectives:
- Know that transition metal characteristics of elements Ti – Cu arise from an incomplete d sub-level in atoms or ions.
- Know that these characteristics include complex formation, formation of coloured ions, catalytic activity and variable oxidation state.

Specification Reference 3.5.4

1. Transition Metals — The Basics

You've already learnt about the halogens and the alkaline earth metals at AS. This section is about another important set of elements — the transition metals.

The d-block

The **d-block** is the block of elements in the middle of the periodic table. Most of the elements in the d-block are **transition elements** (or transition metals). You mainly need to know about the ones in the first row of the d-block. These are the elements from titanium to copper — see Figure 1.

	Group I	Group II											Group III	Group IV	Group V	Group VI	Group VII	Group 0
1								1 H Hydrogen 1										4 He 2
2	7 Li 3	9 Be 4											11 B 5	12 C 6	14 N 7	16 O 8	19 F 9	20 Ne 10
3	23 Na 11	24 Mg 12											27 Al 13	28 Si 14	31 P 15	32 S 16	35.5 Cl 17	40 Ar 18
4	39 K 19	40 Ca 20	45 Sc 21	48 Ti 22	51 V 23	52 Cr 24	55 Mn 25	56 Fe 26	59 Co 27	59 Ni 28	64 Cu 29	65 Zn 30	70 Ga 31	73 Ge 32	75 As 33	79 Se 34	80 Br 35	84 Kr 36
5	86 Rb 37	88 Sr 38	89 Y 39	91 Zr 40	93 Nb 41	96 Mo 42	98 Tc 43	101 Ru 44	103 Rh 45	106 Pd 46	108 Ag 47	112 Cd 48	115 In 49	119 Sn 50	122 Sb 51	128 Te 52	127 I 53	131 Xe 54
6	133 Cs 55	137 Ba 56	57-71 Lanthanides	179 Hf 72	181 Ta 73	184 W 74	186 Re 75	190 Os 76	192 Ir 77	195 Pt 78	197 Au 79	201 Hg 80	204 Tl 81	207 Pb 82	209 Bi 83	210 Po 84	210 At 85	222 Rn 86
7	223 Fr 87	226 Ra 88	89-103 Actinides															
	s-block						d-block								p-block			

Figure 1: *The three main blocks of the periodic table. The transition elements are in the d-block.*

Figure 2: *A variety of transition metals.*

What is a transition metal?

Here's the definition of a transition metal:

> A transition metal is a metal that can form one or more stable ions with a partially filled d-subshell.

A **d-subshell** can fit 10 electrons in. So transition metals must form at least one ion that has between 1 and 9 electrons in the d-subshell. All the Period 4 d-block elements are transition metals apart from scandium and zinc (p. 191).

Exam Tip
Make sure you learn the definition of a transition metal — there's a good chance you'll be asked for it in your exam.

Electronic configurations

At AS level you saw that the electronic configurations of elements can be figured out by following a few simple rules:

- Electrons fill up the lowest energy **subshells** first.
- Electrons fill **orbitals** singly before they start sharing.

The transition metals generally follow the same rules — see Figure 3. The 4s subshell usually fills up first because it has lower energy than the 3d subshell. Once the 4s subshell is full, the 3d subshell starts to fill up. The 3d orbitals are occupied singly at first. They only double up when they have to. But, there are a couple of exceptions...

Tip: Electron orbitals were covered at AS level so if you've forgotten what a d-orbital is — have a quick skim over your AS notes.

- Chromium prefers to have one electron in each orbital of the 3d subshell and just one in the 4s subshell — this gives it more stability.
- Copper prefers to have a full 3d subshell and just one electron in the 4s subshell — it's more stable that way.

		3d					4s	
Ti	[Ar]	↑	↑				↑↓	[Ar] $3d^2 4s^2$
V	[Ar]	↑	↑	↑			↑↓	[Ar] $3d^3 4s^2$
Cr	[Ar]	↑	↑	↑	↑	↑	↑	[Ar] $3d^5 4s^1$
Mn	[Ar]	↑	↑	↑	↑	↑	↑↓	[Ar] $3d^5 4s^2$
Fe	[Ar]	↑↓	↑	↑	↑	↑	↑↓	[Ar] $3d^6 4s^2$
Co	[Ar]	↑↓	↑↓	↑	↑	↑	↑↓	[Ar] $3d^7 4s^2$
Ni	[Ar]	↑↓	↑↓	↑↓	↑	↑	↑↓	[Ar] $3d^8 4s^2$
Cu	[Ar]	↑↓	↑↓	↑↓	↑↓	↑↓	↑	[Ar] $3d^{10} 4s^1$

Figure 3: *The electronic configurations of the Period 4 d-block transition metals.*

Scandium and zinc

Sc and Zn aren't transition metals as their stable ions don't have partially filled d-subshells. Scandium only forms one ion, Sc^{3+}, which has an empty d-subshell. Scandium has the electronic configuration $[Ar]3d^1 4s^2$, so when it loses three electrons to form Sc^{3+}, it ends up with the electronic configuration [Ar]. Zinc only forms one ion, Zn^{2+}, which has a full d-subshell. Zinc has the electronic configuration $[Ar]3d^{10} 4s^2$. When it forms Zn^{2+} it loses two electrons, both from the 4s subshell. This means it keeps its full 3d subshell.

Transition metal ions

Transition metal atoms form positive ions. When this happens, the s electrons are removed first, then the d electrons.

Example

Iron forms Fe^{2+} ions and Fe^{3+} ions.

When it forms 2^+ ions, it loses both its 4s electrons:

$$Fe = [Ar]3d^6 4s^2 \rightarrow Fe^{2+} = [Ar]3d^6$$

Only once the 4s electrons are removed can a 3d electron be removed.

$$\text{E.g. } Fe^{2+} = [Ar]3d^6 \rightarrow Fe^{3+} = [Ar]3d^5$$

You might be asked to write the electronic configuration of a transition metal ion in the exam. To do this, just follow these steps:

- Write down the electronic configuration of the element.
- Work out how many electrons have been removed to make the ion.
- Remove that number of electrons from the electronic configuration taking them out of the s-orbital first and then the d-orbitals.

Example

Write out the electronic configuration of Mn^{2+} ions.

- The electronic configuration of Mn atoms is $[Ar]3d^5 4s^2$.
- Two electrons are removed to convert Mn atoms into Mn^{2+} ions.
- Removing the electrons starting from the s-orbitals gives $[Ar]3d^5 4s^0$.
- So the electronic configuration of Mn^{2+} ions is $[Ar]3d^5$.

Tip: Subshells are made of orbitals — for example, s-subshells contain one orbital, p-subshells contain three orbitals and d-subshells contain five orbitals. Each orbital can hold two electrons.

Tip: The electronic configurations of all the transition metals start in the same way — $1s^2 2s^2 2p^6 3s^2 3p^6$. This is the same as the electronic configuration of the element argon, so [Ar] is used as a short way of writing it.

Exam Tip
The atomic number in the periodic table tells you how many electrons each atom has — you should be able to work the electronic configuration out from there.

Tip: You can work out how many electrons have been lost using oxidation states — see page 170.

Properties of the transition metals

Physical properties

The properties of the transition elements don't gradually change across the periodic table like you might expect. They're all typical metals and have similar physical properties.

- They all have a high density.
- They all have high melting and high boiling points.
- Their ionic radii are more or less the same.

Tip: See page 165 for more on periodicity.

Chemical properties

The chemical properties of the transition metals are much more interesting. They have a few special chemical properties that you need to know about:

- They can form **complex ions** — see pages 194-197.
  E.g. iron forms a complex ion with water — $[Fe(H_2O)_6]^{2+}$.
- They form coloured ions — see pages 198-201.
  E.g. Fe^{2+} ions are pale green and Fe^{3+} ions are yellow.
- They're good **catalysts** — see pages 208-211.
  E.g. iron is the catalyst used in the Haber process.
- They can exist in variable **oxidation states** — see pages 202-204.
  E.g. iron can exist in the +2 oxidation state as Fe^{2+} ions and in the +3 oxidation state as Fe^{3+} ions.

Tip: All of the chemical properties of the transition elements are covered in more detail later in the section.

Some common coloured ions and oxidation states are shown below. The colours refer to the aqueous ions.

Element	Ion	Oxidation state	Colour
V	V^{2+}	+2	violet
	V^{3+}	+3	green
	VO^{2+}	+4	blue
	VO_2^{+}	+5	yellow
Cr	Cr^{3+}	+3	green/violet
	$Cr_2O_7^{2-}$	+6	orange
Mn	Mn^{2+}	+2	pale pink
	MnO_4^{-}	+7	purple
Fe	Fe^{2+}	+2	pale green
	Fe^{3+}	+3	yellow
Co	Co^{2+}	+2	pink
Ni	Ni^{2+}	+2	green
Cu	Cu^{2+}	+2	blue

Figure 4: The different colours of the aqueous transition metal ions.

These elements show variable oxidation states because the energy levels of the 4s and the 3d subshells are very close to one another. So different numbers of electrons can be gained or lost using fairly similar amounts of energy.

Tip: See page 169 for more on oxidation states and how to find them.

The incomplete d-subshell

It's the incomplete d-subshell that causes the special chemical properties of transition metals. d-block elements without an incomplete d-subshell don't have these properties.

Example

Scandium and zinc don't form ions with incomplete d-subshells. As a result they don't have the same chemical properties as transition metals.

For example, they can't form complex ions, they don't form coloured ions and they can't exist in variable oxidation states.

Practice Questions — Application

Q1 Write out the electronic configurations for the following transition metal elements:

a) V b) Co c) Cu d) Ni

Q2 Write out the electronic configurations for the following transition metal ions:

a) V^{3+} b) Co^{2+} c) Cu^{2+} d) Ni^{2+}

Q3 Using electronic configurations, explain why zinc is not a transition metal, despite being in the d-block of the periodic table.

Exam Tip

If you're asked for an electronic configuration it's fine to use shorthand and start them with [Ar], but if you're asked for a full electronic configuration you need to write it all out starting from $1s^2$.

Practice Questions — Fact Recall

Q1 Where in the periodic table are transition elements found?

Q2 What is the definition of a transition metal?

Q3 How many electrons can a d-subshell hold?

Q4 Give two rules that are usually followed when working out electronic configurations.

Q5 a) Explain why chromium has the electronic configuration $[Ar]3d^5 4s^1$ and not $[Ar]3d^4 4s^2$ as you would expect.

b) Explain why copper has the electronic configuration $[Ar]3d^{10} 4s^1$ and not $[Ar]3d^9 4s^2$ as you would expect.

Q6 Explain why zinc and scandium aren't transition metals.

Q7 a) Give three physical properties that all of the transition metals have in common.

b) Give four chemical properties that all of the transition metals have in common.

Q8 What feature of transition metals causes their chemical properties?

2. Complex Ions

Learning Objectives:

- Understand that a complex is a central metal ion surrounded by ligands.
- Know that co-ordinate bonding is involved in complex formation.
- Be able to define the term ligand.
- Understand that ligands can be unidentate (e.g. H_2O, NH_3 and Cl^-), bidentate (e.g. $NH_2CH_2CH_2NH_2$ and $C_2O_4^{2-}$) or multidentate (e.g. $EDTA^{4-}$).
- Know the meaning of co-ordination number.
- Know that transition metal ions commonly form octahedral complexes with small ligands (e.g. H_2O and NH_3).
- Know that transition metal ions commonly form tetrahedral complexes with larger ligands (e.g. Cl^-).
- Know that square planar complexes are also formed, e.g. cisplatin.
- Know that Ag^+ commonly forms the linear complex $[Ag(NH_3)_2]^+$ as used in Tollens' reagent.
- Know that haem is an iron(II) complex with a multidentate ligand.

Specification Reference 3.5.4

Tip: EDTA stands for ethylenediaminetetra-acetic acid.

The ability to form complex ions is an important property of transition metals. You probably haven't come across complex ions before but the next few pages should tell you everything you need to know.

What are complex ions?

A **complex ion** is a metal ion surrounded by coordinately bonded ligands. A **coordinate bond** (or dative covalent bond) is a covalent bond in which both electrons in the shared pair come from the same atom. In a complex, they come from the ligands. So, a **ligand** is an atom, ion or molecule that donates a pair of electrons to a central metal ion.

Example

$[Cu(H_2O)_6]^{2+}$

The central metal ion is a Cu^{2+} ion and water molecules are acting as ligands. There are six water molecules that each form a coordinate bond with the Cu^{2+} ion:

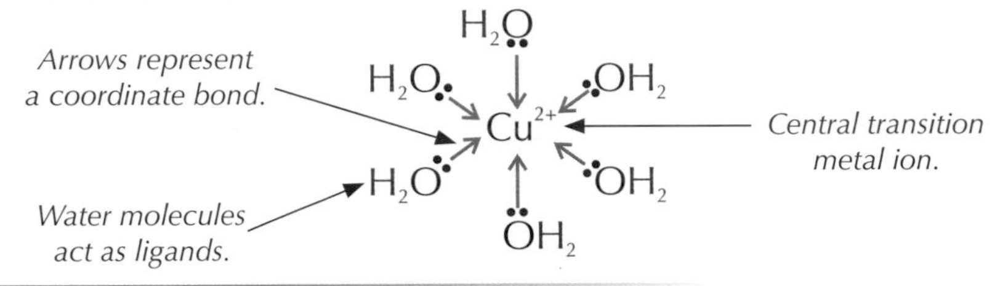

The different types of ligand

A ligand must have at least one lone pair of electrons, or it won't have anything to use to form a coordinate bond. But, different ligands can have different numbers of lone pairs and can form different numbers of coordinate bonds. Ligands that can only form one coordinate bond are called **unidentate**.

Examples

Here are some examples of unidentate ligands:

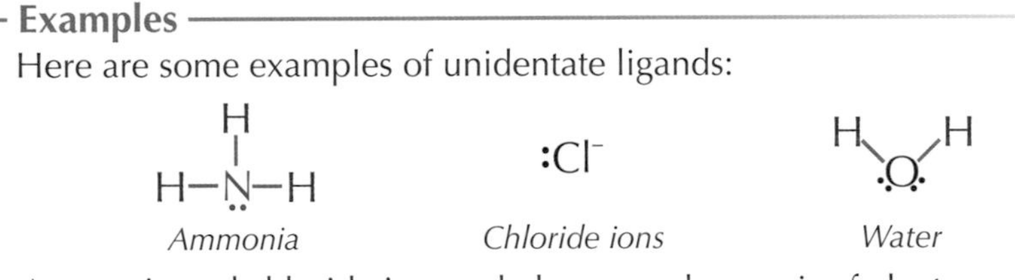

Ammonia and chloride ions only have one lone pair of electrons to donate to form a coordinate bond. Water has two lone pairs of electrons but because they are so close together, it can only form one coordinate bond at a time.

Ligands that can form more than one coordinate bond are called **multidentate**.

Example

$EDTA^{4-}$ is a multidentate ligand:

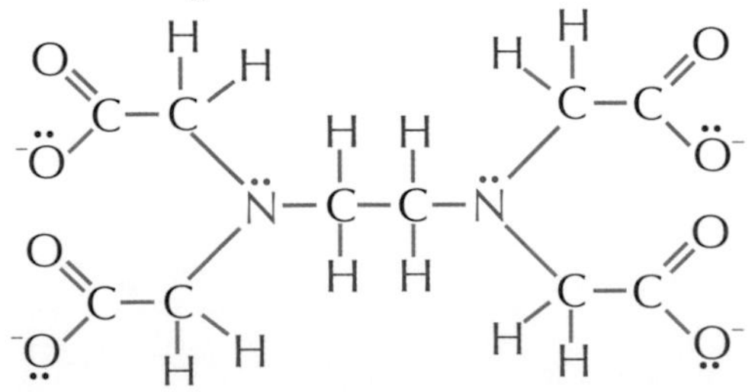

$EDTA^{4-}$ has six lone pairs (two on nitrogen atoms and four on oxygen atoms) so it can form six coordinate bonds with a metal ion.

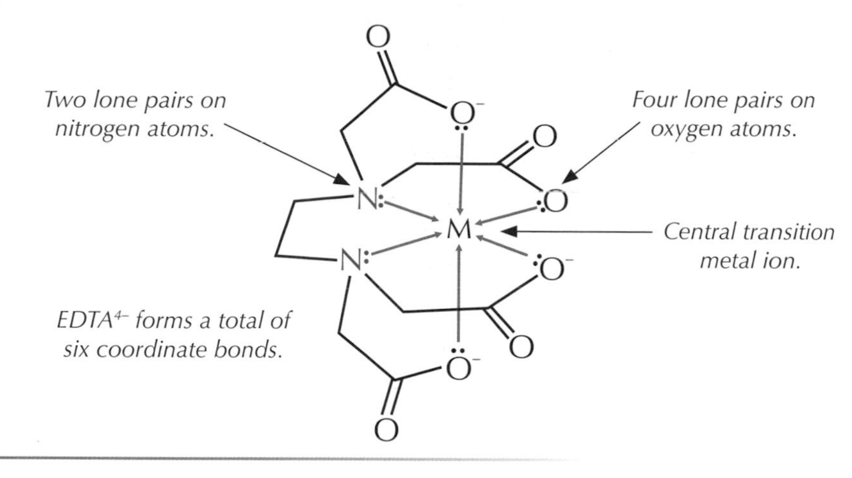

Tip: $EDTA^{4-}$ is hexadentate — hexa meaning six.

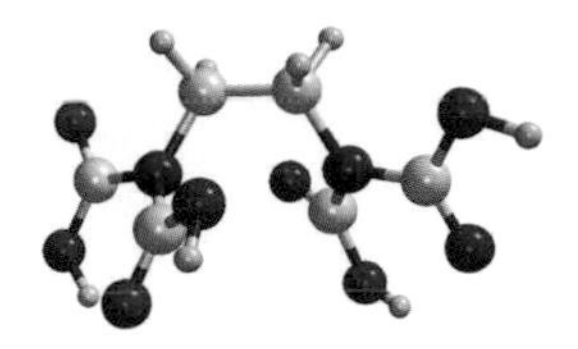

Figure 1: Molecular model of EDTA.

Multidentate ligands that can form two coordinate bonds are called **bidentate**.

Example

Ethane-1,2-diamine ($\ddot{N}H_2CH_2CH_2\ddot{N}H_2$) is a bidentate ligand. It has two amine groups, each of which has a lone pair of electrons that it can donate to form a coordinate bond. In complex ions, each ethane-1,2-diamine molecule forms two coordinate bonds with the metal ion. In the complex ion below, there are three ethane-1,2-diamine molecules forming six coordinate bonds:

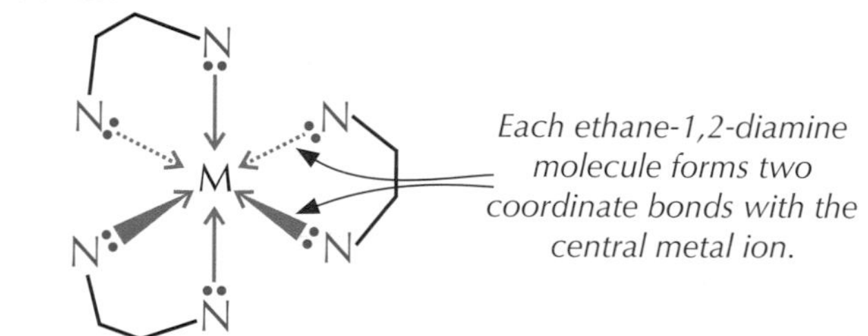

Exam Tip
Don't worry, you'll never be expected to draw the shape of EDTA or complex ions containing EDTA in the exam.

Oxidation states of complex ions

The overall charge on a complex ion is its total oxidation state. It's put outside the square brackets. For example, $[Cu(H_2O)_6]^{2+}$ has a total oxidation state of +2. You can work out the oxidation state of the metal ion within a complex using this equation:

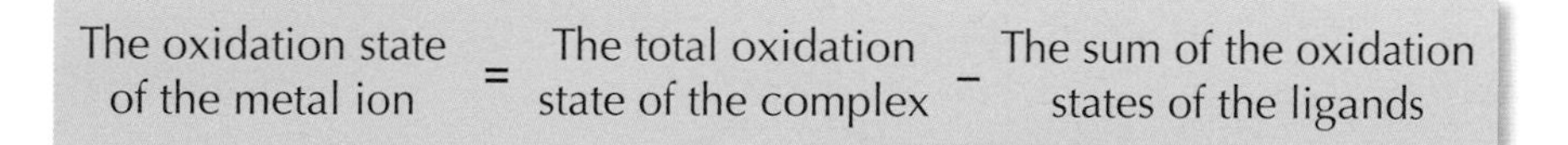

The oxidation state of the metal ion = The total oxidation state of the complex – The sum of the oxidation states of the ligands

Tip: You should be familiar with oxidation states by now — but if not, have a look back at pages 169 and 170.

Example

What is the oxidation state of Co in $[CoCl_4]^{2-}_{(aq)}$?

The total oxidation state of $[CoCl_4]^{2-}_{(aq)}$ is –2 (since it has an overall charge of 2–) and each Cl^- ligand has an oxidation state of –1. So in this complex:

$$\begin{aligned}\text{cobalt's oxidation state} &= \text{total ox. state} - \text{sum of } Cl^- \text{ ox. states}\\ &= (-2) - (4 \times -1)\\ &= \mathbf{+2}\end{aligned}$$

Exam Tip
You might have to work out the oxidation state of a transition metal in a complex ion in the exam, so make sure you know this equation.

Shapes of complex ions

Tip: You learnt a lot about the shapes of molecules at AS, so have a look over your AS notes if you get stuck.

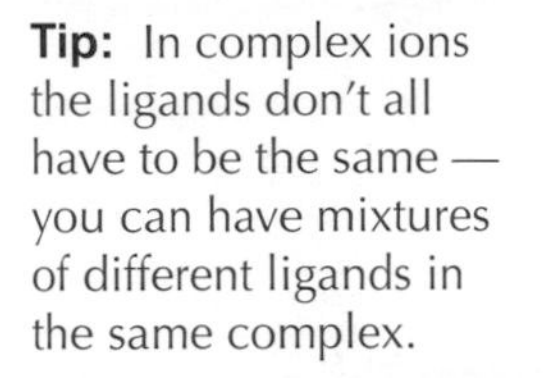

Tip: In complex ions the ligands don't all have to be the same — you can have mixtures of different ligands in the same complex.

The shape of a complex ion depends on its **coordination number**. This is the number of coordinate bonds that are formed with the central metal ion. The usual coordination numbers are 6 and 4. If the ligands are small, like H_2O or NH_3, 6 can fit around the central metal ion. But if the ligands are larger, like Cl^-, only 4 can fit around the central metal ion.

Six coordinate bonds

Complex ions that contain six coordinate bonds have an octahedral shape.

Examples

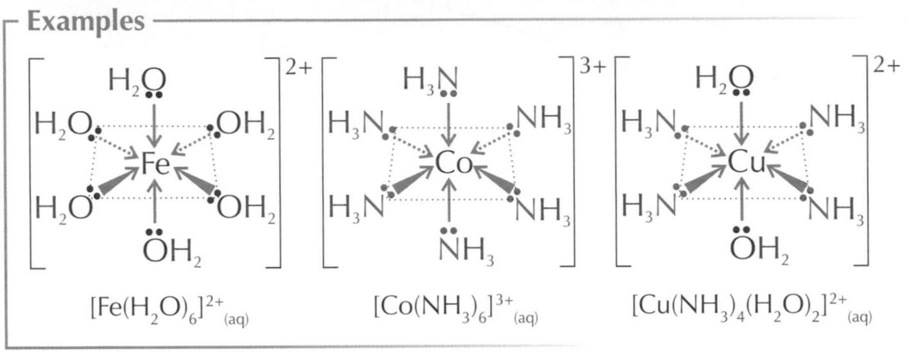

$[Fe(H_2O)_6]^{2+}_{(aq)}$ $[Co(NH_3)_6]^{3+}_{(aq)}$ $[Cu(NH_3)_4(H_2O)_2]^{2+}_{(aq)}$

The different types of bond arrow show that the complex is 3-D. The wedge-shaped arrows represent bonds coming towards you and the dashed arrows represent bonds sticking out behind the molecule.

Four coordinate bonds

Complex ions with four coordinate bonds usually have a tetrahedral shape.

Examples

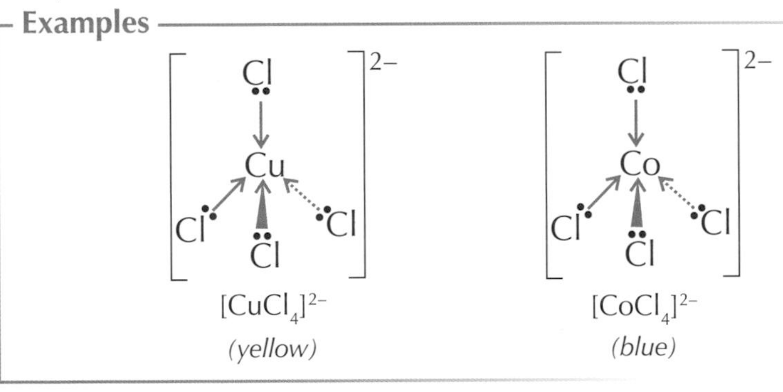

$[CuCl_4]^{2-}$ *(yellow)* $[CoCl_4]^{2-}$ *(blue)*

Figure 2: The flask on the left shows the pink colour of hexaaqua cobalt(II) ions. The flask on the right shows the blue colour of cobalt(II) ions complexed as $[CoCl_4]^{2-}$.

But in a few complexes four coordinate bonds form a square planar shape.

Example

Cisplatin ($Pt(NH_3)_2Cl_2$) has a square planar shape:

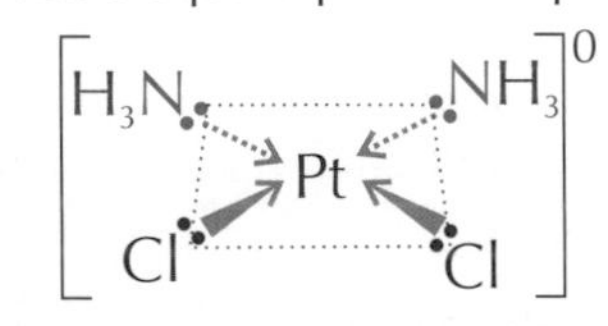

Tip: Cisplatin is used as an anti-cancer drug. See page 213 for more information on this.

Two coordinate bonds

Some silver complexes have 2 coordinate bonds and form a linear shape.

Example

$[Ag(NH_3)_2]^+$ forms a linear shape, as shown:

$$[H_3N{:}\rightarrow Ag \leftarrow{:}NH_3]^+$$

Tip: $[Ag(NH_3)_2]^+$ is used in Tollens' reagent. See pages 66 and 213 for more.

Haem and haemoglobin

Haemoglobin is a protein found in blood that helps to transport oxygen around the body. It contains Fe^{2+} ions, which are hexa-coordinated — six lone pairs are donated to them to form six coordinate bonds. Four of the lone pairs come from nitrogen atoms, which form a circle around the Fe^{2+}. This part of the molecule is called haem. The molecule that the four nitrogen atoms are part of is a multidentate ligand called a **porphyrin**. A protein called a globin and either an oxygen or a water molecule also bind to the Fe^{2+} ion to form an octahedral structure — see Figure 3.

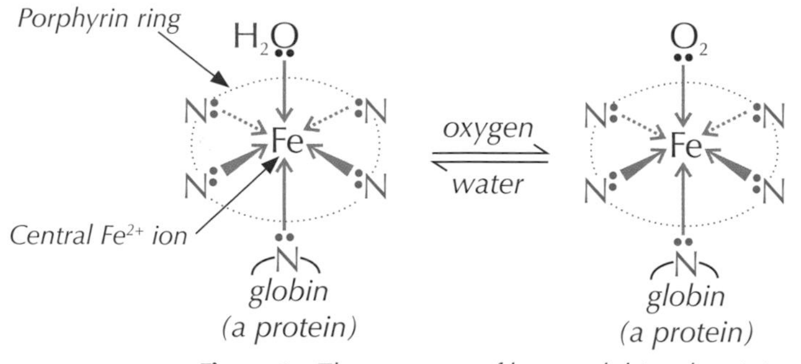

Figure 3: The structure of haemoglobin when it is bound to oxygen or water.

Tip: There's more on how haemoglobin works on page 212.

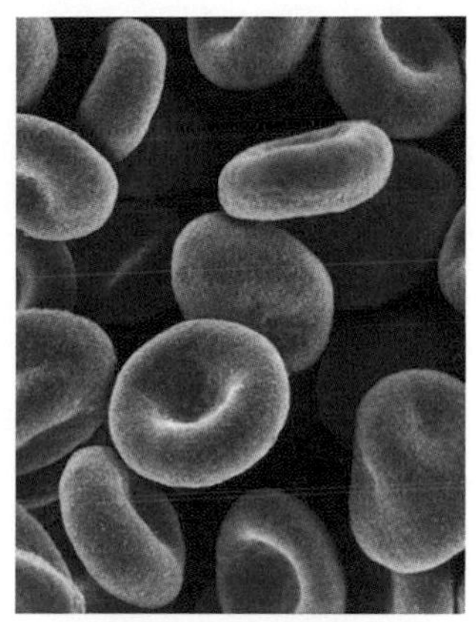

Figure 4: Red blood cells are packed full of haemoglobin.

Practice Questions — Application

Q1 Describe and draw the shapes of the following complex ions:

a) $[AlF_6]^{3-}$ b) $[Ag(S_2O_3)_2]^{3-}$ c) $[CuCl_4]^{2-}$

Q2 Deduce the oxidation state of the transition metal in each of the complex ions in Q1.

Q3 What is the coordination number of the transition metal in each of the complex ions in Q1?

Q4 $C_2O_4^{2-}$ is a bidentate ligand. Its structure is shown below:

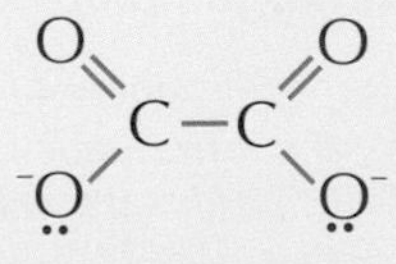

a) Copy the diagram and circle the atoms that could form a coordinate bond with a metal ion.

b) How many $C_2O_4^{2-}$ ligands would bind to a single ion?

Q5 $[Ni(CN)_4]^{2-}$ is a complex ion. It does not have a tetrahedral shape. What shape could it have instead? Draw the structure of $[Ni(CN)_4]^{2-}$.

Practice Questions — Fact Recall

Q1 Define the following terms:

a) Ligand b) Coordinate bond c) Complex ion

Q2 a) Explain what is meant by the terms unidentate, bidentate and multidentate.

b) Give an example of each type of ligand mentioned in a).

Q3 What is meant by the term coordination number?

Q4 a) What is the role of haemoglobin in the body?

b) Where do the six coordinate bonds come from in haemoglobin?

3. Formation of Coloured Ions

Learning Objectives:

- Know that colour arises from electronic transitions from the ground state to excited states: $\Delta E = h\nu$.
- Know that transition metal ions can be identified by their colour, limited to the complexes in this unit.
- Know that colour changes arise from changes in oxidation state, co-ordination number and ligand.
- Appreciate that the absorption of visible light is used in spectrometry to determine the concentration of coloured ions.

Specification Reference 3.5.4

This section explains why different complex ions are different colours and how this can be used to identify them.

Subshell energy levels

Normally the 3d orbitals of transition element ions all have the same energy. But when ligands come along and bond to the ions, some of the orbitals are given more energy than others. This splits the 3d orbitals into two different energy levels — see Figure 1.

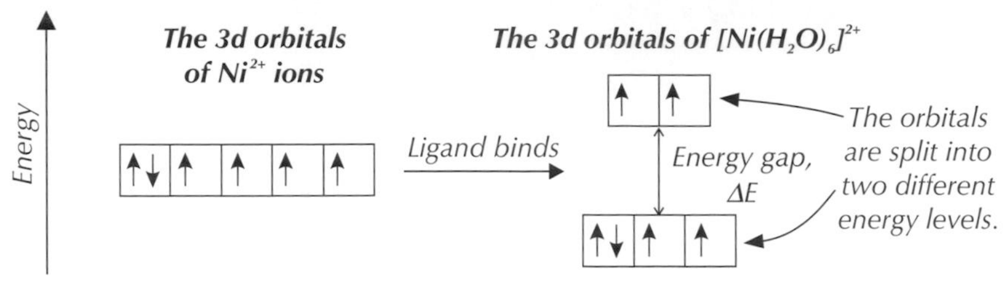

Figure 1: *The different subshell energy levels in Ni complex ions.*

Electrons tend to occupy the lower orbitals (the ground state). To jump up to the higher orbitals (excited states) they need energy equal to the **energy gap, ΔE**. They get this energy from visible light — see Figure 2.

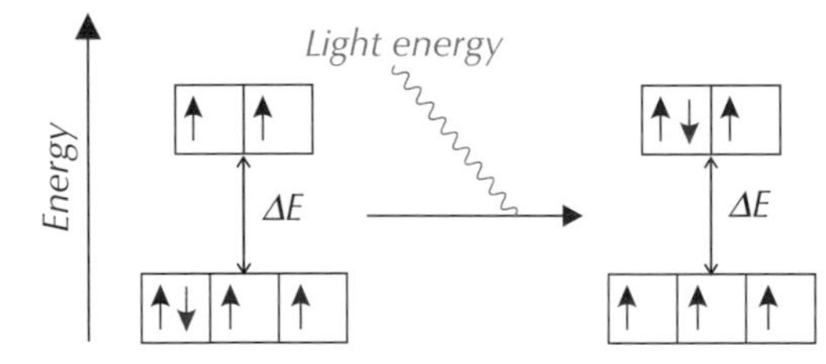

Figure 2: *The transition of an electron from the ground state to the excited state.*

Tip: When an electron jumps to a different orbital it's called an electronic transition.

The energy absorbed when electrons jump up can be worked out using this equation:

$$\Delta E = h\nu$$

Where ΔE is the energy absorbed, ν = frequency of light absorbed (hertz/Hz) and h = Planck's constant (6.63×10^{-34} Js).

Tip: It's the incomplete d-subshell that means transition metals can absorb light. If it were empty/full there would be no electrons to jump between energy levels.

The amount of energy needed to make electrons jump depends upon the central metal ion and its oxidation state, the ligands and the coordination number, as these affect the size of the energy gap.

The colours of compounds

When visible light hits a transition metal ion, some frequencies are absorbed as electrons jump up to the higher orbitals. The frequencies absorbed depend on the size of the energy gap. The rest of the frequencies are reflected. These reflected frequencies combine to make the complement of the colour of the absorbed frequencies — this is the colour you see.

Tip: It's not just visible light that can cause electronic transitions — any electromagnetic radiation can excite electrons if it's the right frequency.

Example

$[Cu(H_2O)_6]^{2+}$ ions absorb yellow light. The remaining frequencies combine to produce the complementary colour — in this case that's blue.
So $[Cu(H_2O)_6]^{2+}$ solution appears blue.

If there are no 3d electrons or the 3d subshell is full, then no electrons will jump, so no energy will be absorbed. If there's no energy absorbed, the compound will look white or colourless because all the light will be reflected.

Identifying transition metal ions

It'd be nice if each transition metal formed ions or complexes with just one colour, but sadly it's not that simple. The colour of a complex can be altered by any of the factors that can affect the size of the energy gap.

Changes in oxidation state

If the oxidation state of a transition metal in a complex ion changes, then the colour of the complex ion may also change.

Examples

Complex ions containing iron change colour when the oxidation state of iron increases from +2 to +3.

Complex:	$[Fe(H_2O)_6]^{2+}_{(aq)}$	→	$[Fe(H_2O)_6]^{3+}_{(aq)}$
Oxidation state:	+2	→	+3
Colour:	pale green	→	yellow

Complex ions containing vanadium change colour when the oxidation state of vanadium increases from +2 to +3.

Complex:	$[V(H_2O)_6]^{2+}_{(aq)}$	→	$[V(H_2O)_6]^{3+}_{(aq)}$
Oxidation state:	+2	→	+3
Colour:	violet	→	green

Tip: See page 202 for more examples of transition metals with multiple oxidation states.

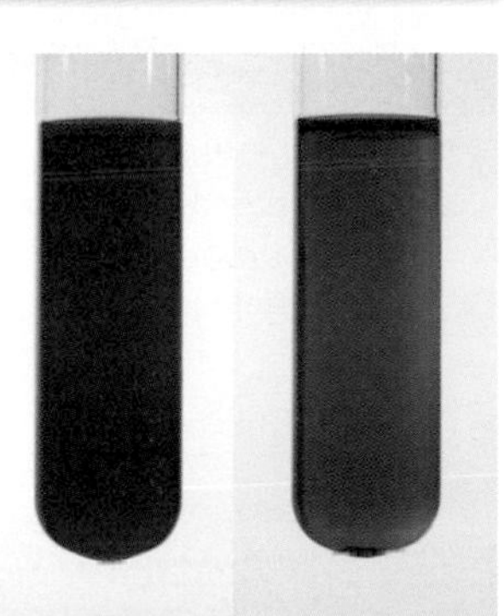

Figure 3: The test tube on the left shows the violet colour of a V(II) solution. The test tube on the right shows the green colour of a V(III) solution.

Changes in coordination number

Changes in coordination number may also result in a colour change. This always involves a change of ligand too.

Example

Complex ions containing Cu change colour when the coordination number of Cu decreases from 6 to 4.

Complex:	$[Cu(H_2O)_6]^{2+} + 4Cl^-$	→	$[CuCl_4]^{2-} + 6H_2O$
Coordination number:	6	→	4
Colour:	blue	→	yellow

Changes in ligand

Changing the ligand can cause a colour change even if the oxidation state and coordination number remain the same.

Example

If $[Co(H_2O)_6]^{2+}$ is converted to $[Co(NH_3)_6]^{2+}$ the colour will change from pink to straw coloured.

Complex:	$[Co(H_2O)_6]^{2+} + 6NH_3$	→	$[Co(NH_3)_6]^{2+} + 6H_2O$
Oxidation state:	+2	→	+2
Colour:	pink	→	straw coloured

Exam Tip
You might be asked to identify a complex ion from its colour in your exam — all the complex ions and colour changes that you need to learn are covered on page 223.

Spectrometry

Spectrometry can be used to determine the concentration of a solution by measuring how much light it absorbs. White light is shone through a filter, which is chosen to only let the colour of light through that is absorbed by the sample. The light then passes through the sample to a **colorimeter**, which shows how much light was absorbed by the sample. The more concentrated a coloured solution is, the more light it will absorb.

Tip: Spectrometry is the study of what happens when radiation interacts with matter. There are loads of different types — mass spectrometry and NMR spectrometry are covered on pages 121-136.

So you can use this measurement to work out the concentration of a solution of transition metal ions — see Figure 5.

Figure 4: *A student using a colorimeter to measure the absorbance of a solution of Cu^{2+} ions.*

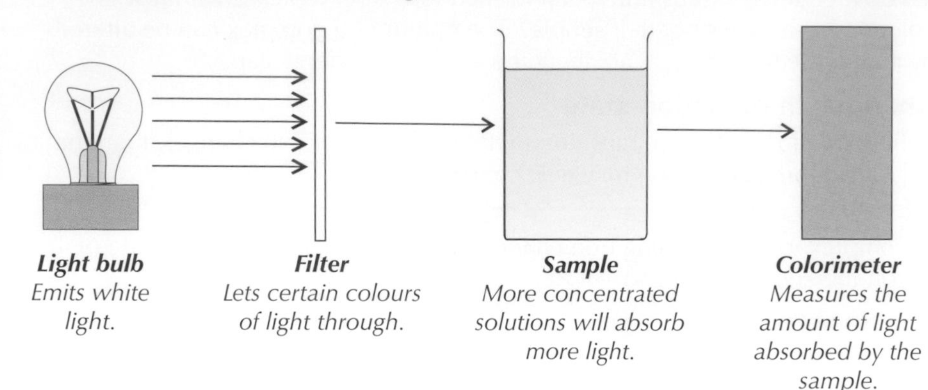

Figure 5: *Measuring the concentration of a solution using spectrometry.*

Before you can find the unknown concentration of a sample, you have to produce a **calibration graph** — like the lovely one below.

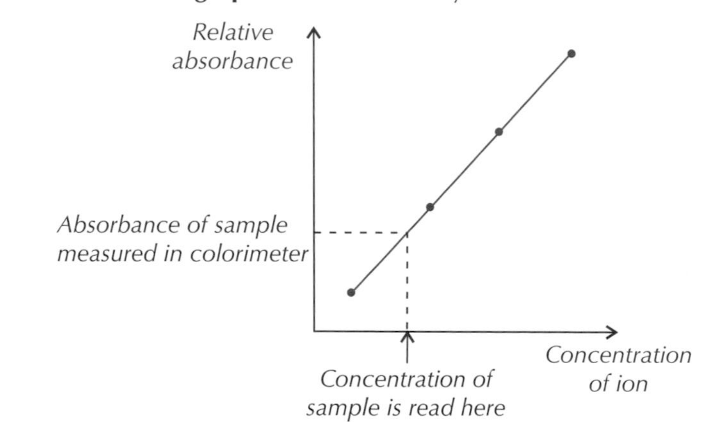

Tip: Calibration graphs like this one are usually a straight line because, at low concentrations, the amount of light absorbed is directly proportional to the number of complex ions in the solution.

This involves measuring the absorbances of known concentrations of solutions and plotting the results on a graph. Once you've done this, you can measure the absorbance of your sample and read its concentration off the graph.

Example

Say you want to find the concentration of a solution of $[Cu(H_2O)_6]^{2+}$ ions. These ions absorb yellow light so you'll need a filter that only lets yellow light through. You then need to measure the absorbance of some $[Cu(H_2O)_6]^{2+}$ ion solutions that you know the concentration of. Your results will look something like this:

Concentration ($moldm^{-3}$)	Relative Absorbance
0.2	0.050
0.3	0.055
0.4	0.100
0.6	0.150
1.0	0.250
1.6	0.400

Plotting these results on a graph gives you a calibration graph. Once you have your calibration graph you measure the absorbance of the unknown solution, then read its concentration off the graph.

Tip: Different complex ions absorb different wavelengths of light so you'll need a different filter to measure the absorbance of each one.

For example, if its relative absorbance is 0.225, its concentration is around 0.9 $moldm^{-3}$.

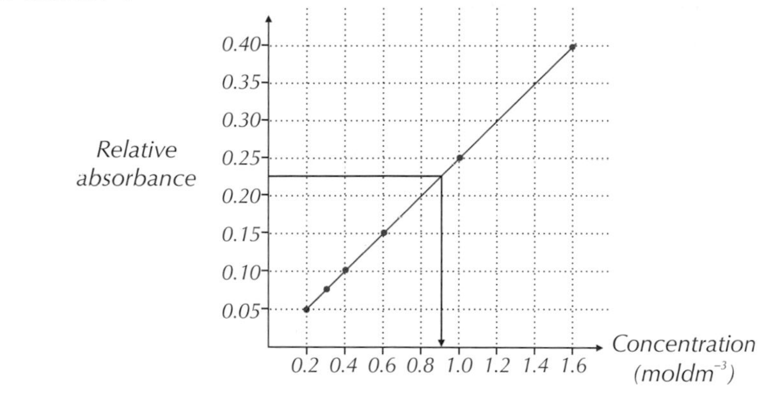

Tip: When you plot a calibration curve, concentration goes on the *x*-axis and absorbance goes on the *y*-axis.

Spectrometry is a useful method for measuring the concentration of coloured ions because it's easy to get loads of readings and you can work out the concentration quite quickly. Plus, you can measure very low concentrations and it doesn't use up any of the substance or interfere with any reactions.

Exam Tip
For the exam you'll need to know how concentrations are determined using spectrometry and why spectrometry is a good method to use, so read these pages carefully.

Practice Questions — Application

Q1 When the following reaction occurs, the colour of the solution changes from violet to green.

$$[Cr(H_2O)_6]^{3+} + 6NH_3 \rightarrow [Cr(NH_3)_6]^{3+} + 6H_2O$$

What causes the change in colour of the solution?

Q2 This reaction is accompanied by a green to yellow colour change:

$$[Fe(H_2O)_6]^{2+} \rightarrow [Fe(H_2O)_6]^{3+} + e^-$$

What has caused the change in colour of the solution?

Practice Questions — Fact Recall

Q1 What happens to the 3d orbitals of a transition metal when a ligand binds to it?

Q2 a) What type of energy is needed for an electron to jump from a lower energy orbital to a higher energy orbital?

b) Write the equation for calculating the energy absorbed (ΔE) when an electron jumps between orbitals.

Q3 Explain why transition metal ions have colour.

Q4 List three things that could cause the colour of a complex ion to change.

Q5 What colour change would you expect to see if the following reactions took place:

a) $[Cu(H_2O)_6]^{2+} + 4Cl^- \rightarrow [CuCl_4]^{2-} + 6H_2O$

b) $[Co(H_2O)_6]^{2+} + 6NH_3 \rightarrow [Co(NH_3)_6]^{2+} + 6H_2O$

Q6 a) Describe how spectrometry can be used to measure the amount of light absorbed by a solution of complex ions.

b) Explain how you would produce a calibration curve to measure the concentration of a solution of complex ions.

4. Variable Oxidation States

Learning Objectives:

- Know that transition elements show variable oxidation states.
- Know the equilibrium reaction: $2CrO_4^{2-}{}_{(aq)} + 2H^+{}_{(aq)} \rightleftharpoons Cr_2O_7^{2-}{}_{(aq)} + H_2O_{(l)}$
- Know that Cr^{3+} and Cr^{2+} are formed by reduction of $Cr_2O_7^{2-}$ by zinc in acid solution.
- Know the oxidation in alkaline solution of Co^{2+} and Cr^{3+} by H_2O_2.
- Know the oxidation of Co^{2+} by air in ammoniacal solution.

Specification Reference 3.5.4, 3.5.5

Transition metals can usually form more than one type of ion and in different ions, transition metals can have different oxidation states. These variable oxidation states are another important feature of the transition metals.

Oxidation states of chromium

Chromium most commonly exists in the +3 or +6 oxidation state. It can exist in the +2 oxidation state as well, but it's much less stable. Here are the main ions that chromium forms and their oxidation states:

Oxidation state	Formula of ion	Colour of ion
+6	$Cr_2O_7^{2-}{}_{(aq)}$	Orange
+6	$CrO_4^{2-}{}_{(aq)}$	Yellow
+3	$Cr^{3+}{}_{(aq)}$	Green / Violet
+2	$Cr^{2+}{}_{(aq)}$	Blue

In the +6 oxidation state, chromium can form chromate(VI) ions (CrO_4^{2-}) and dichromate(VI) ions ($Cr_2O_7^{2-}$). Both these ions are good **oxidising agents** because they can easily be reduced to Cr^{3+}. When Cr^{3+} ions are surrounded by 6 water ligands they're violet. But the water ligands are often substituted, so this solution usually looks green instead.

Figure 1: *Orange and yellow solutions of dichromate(VI) and chromate(VI) ions.*

Chromate(VI) and dichromate(VI) ions in equilibrium

When an alkali (OH^- ions) is added to aqueous dichromate(VI) ions ($Cr_2O_7^{2-}$), the orange colour turns yellow, because aqueous chromate(VI) (CrO_4^{2-}) ions are formed.

$$Cr_2O_7^{2-}{}_{(aq)} + OH^-{}_{(aq)} \rightarrow 2CrO_4^{2-}{}_{(aq)} + H^+{}_{(aq)}$$

orange *yellow*

When an acid (H^+ ions) is added to aqueous chromate(VI) ions, the yellow colour turns orange, because aqueous dichromate(VI) ions form.

$$2CrO_4^{2-}{}_{(aq)} + H^+{}_{(aq)} \rightarrow Cr_2O_7^{2-}{}_{(aq)} + OH^-{}_{(aq)}$$

yellow *orange*

These are opposite processes and the two ions exist in equilibrium.

$$Cr_2O_7^{2-}{}_{(aq)} + H_2O_{(l)} \rightleftharpoons 2CrO_4^{2-}{}_{(aq)} + 2H^+{}_{(aq)}$$

The position of equilibrium depends on the pH — yep, it's good ol' **Le Chatelier's principle** again. If H^+ ions are added, the equilibrium shifts to the left so orange $Cr_2O_7^{2-}$ ions are formed. If OH^- ions are added, H^+ ions are removed and the equilibrium shifts to the right, forming yellow CrO_4^{2-} ions.

Tip: The conversion of chromate(VI) ions to dichromate(VI) ions and back again isn't a redox process because chromium stays in the +6 oxidation state.

Tip: See page 17 for a recap of Le Chatelier's principle.

Oxidation and reduction of chromium ions

Dichromate(VI) ions can be reduced using a good reducing agent, such as zinc and dilute acid.

Equation:	$Cr_2O_7^{2-}{}_{(aq)}$	$+ 14H^+{}_{(aq)}$	$+ 3Zn_{(s)} \rightarrow$	$3Zn^{2+}{}_{(aq)}$	$+ 2Cr^{3+}{}_{(aq)}$	$+ 7H_2O_{(l)}$
Colour:	orange				green	
Oxidation state:	+6		0	+2	+3	

Zinc will reduce Cr^{3+} further to Cr^{2+}:

Equation:	$2Cr^{3+}_{(aq)}$ + $Zn_{(s)}$ → $Zn^{2+}_{(aq)}$ + $2Cr^{2+}_{(aq)}$
Colour:	green ... blue
Oxidation state:	+3, 0, +2, +2

$$2Cr^{3+}_{(aq)} + Zn_{(s)} \rightarrow Zn^{2+}_{(aq)} + 2Cr^{2+}_{(aq)}$$

Colour: green → blue

Oxidation state: +3, 0 → +2, +2

But unless you use an **inert atmosphere**, you're wasting your time — Cr^{2+} is so unstable that it oxidises straight back to Cr^{3+} in air.

You can oxidise Cr^{3+} to chromate(VI) ions with hydrogen peroxide, H_2O_2, in an alkaline solution.

$$2Cr^{3+}_{(aq)} + 10OH^-_{(aq)} + 3H_2O_{2(aq)} \rightarrow 2CrO_4^{2-}{}_{(aq)} + 8H_2O_{(l)}$$

Colour: green → yellow

Oxidation state: +3 → +6

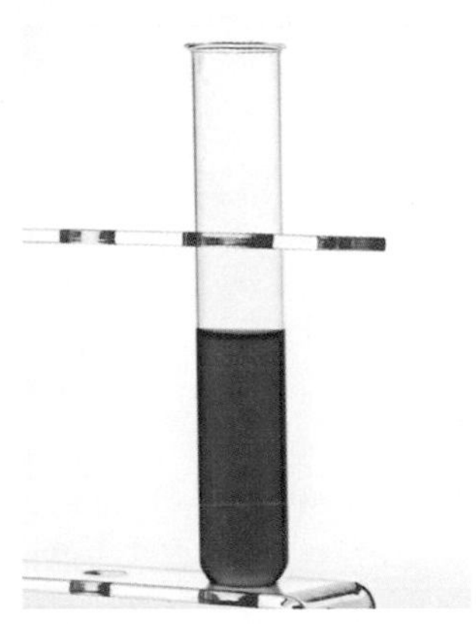

Figure 2: Green Cr^{3+} ions.

Tip: The term 'inert atmosphere' just means that the reactions are done in a non-reactive gas like nitrogen (N_2) or helium (He).

Here's a summary of all the chromium reactions you need to know:

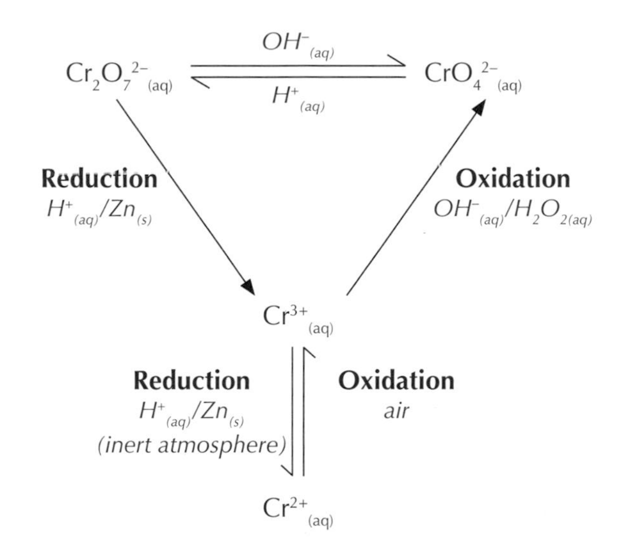

Exam Tip
You need to know all the reduction and oxidation reactions of the different chromium ions for the exam. This summary diagram covers the main things you need to know, but make sure you learn all the colours and oxidation states too.

Oxidation states of cobalt

Cobalt can exist in two oxidation states — +2 as Co^{2+}, and +3 as Co^{3+}. It much prefers to be in the +2 state though. There are two ways of oxidising Co^{2+} ions to Co^{3+} ions. Firstly, Co^{3+} can be made by oxidising $Co^{2+}_{(aq)}$ with hydrogen peroxide in alkaline conditions:

$$2Co^{2+}_{(aq)} + H_2O_{2(aq)} \rightarrow 2Co^{3+}_{(aq)} + 2OH^-_{(aq)}$$

Secondly, you can oxidise Co^{2+} with air in an **ammoniacal solution**. You start with a pink solution of $[Co(H_2O)_6]^{2+}$ ions. If you add a small amount of $NH_{3(aq)}$ to this solution, the following reaction occurs:

$$[Co(H_2O)_6]^{2+}_{(aq)} + 2NH_{3\,(aq)} \rightarrow [Co(H_2O)_4(OH)_2]_{(s)} + 2NH_4^+{}_{(aq)}$$

$[Co(H_2O)_4(OH)_2]_{(s)}$ is a blue precipitate and can also be written as $Co(OH)_2$. If you add an excess of ammonia to the solution then $[Co(NH_3)_6]^{2+}$ ions form, producing a straw coloured solution. If these complex ions are left to stand in air, oxygen oxidises them to $[Co(NH_3)_6]^{3+}$ which is dark brown in colour. This is summarised in Figure 3 (next page).

Tip: 'Ammoniacal' is just a fancy word for something that contains ammonia (NH_3).

Tip: See page 198 for info. on why complex ions are different colours.

Figure 4: *A blue precipitate of $[Co(H_2O)_4(OH)_2]_{(s)}$ forming in a pink solution of $[Co(H_2O)_6]^{2+}_{(aq)}$ ions.*

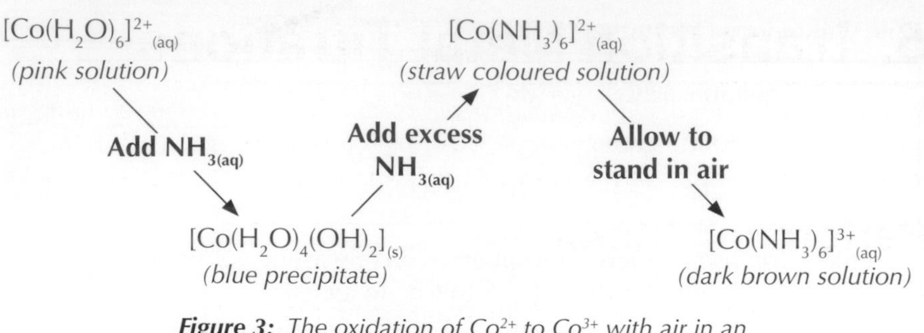

Figure 3: *The oxidation of Co^{2+} to Co^{3+} with air in an ammoniacal solution.*

The reaction is done this way because $[Co(NH_3)_6]^{2+}_{(aq)}$ ions are far easier to oxidise than $[Co(H_2O)_6]^{2+}_{(aq)}$ ions.

Tip: There's more on the variable oxidation states of transition metals on page 192.

Practice Questions — Application

Q1 When Cr^{3+} ions are added to H_2O_2 in an alkaline solution an oxidation reaction occurs.

a) Write an equation for this oxidation reaction.

b) What colour change would you expect to see?

c) Suggest how the Cr^{3+} ions could be produced from $Cr_2O_7^{2-}$.

Q2 When NH_3 is added to $[Co(H_2O)_6]^{2+}_{(aq)}$, a blue precipitate is formed.

a) Identify the blue precipitate.

b) How could you convert this blue precipitate to a straw coloured solution?

c) What colour would you expect this straw coloured solution to go if it was left to stand in air?

d) Why is this a better method for producing Co^{3+} ions than oxidation with hydrogen peroxide?

Practice Questions — Fact Recall

Q1 a) Which three oxidation states can chromium exist in?

b) Give an example of a chromium ion in which chromium has each of these oxidation states.

c) Give the colour of each of these ions.

Q2 a) Write an equation for the reversible reaction involving chromate(VI) (CrO_4^{2-}) and dichromate(VI) ($Cr_2O_7^{2-}$) ions.

b) Suggest how you could increase production of CrO_4^{2-} ions in this reaction.

Q3 a) Name a reducing agent that could be used to reduce $Cr_2O_7^{2-}$ ions.

b) Explain why an inert atmosphere is needed to produce Cr^{2+} ions.

Q4 a) Write an equation for the oxidation of Co^{2+} to Co^{3+} using H_2O_2.

b) Suggest an alternative method for oxidising Co^{2+} to Co^{3+}.

5. Transition Metal Titrations

You might remember covering titrations in Unit 4. Well... you can do titrations with transition metals too. And the best bit is, you don't even need an indicator because the transition metal ions change colour all on their own.

Learning Objectives:

- Know the redox titration of Fe^{2+} with MnO_4^- and $Cr_2O_7^{2-}$ in acid solution.
- Be able to perform calculations for this titration and for others when the reductant and its oxidation product are given.

Specification Reference 3.5.4

Performing titrations

Titrations using transition element ions let you find out how much oxidising agent is needed to exactly react with a quantity of reducing agent — they're **redox titrations**. If you know the concentration of either the oxidising agent or the reducing agent, you can use the titration results to work out the concentration of the other.

- First you measure out a quantity of reducing agent, e.g. aqueous Fe^{2+} ions, using a pipette, and put it in a conical flask.
- Using a measuring cylinder, you add about 20 cm^3 of dilute sulfuric acid to the flask — this is an excess, so you don't have to be too exact. The acid is added to make sure there are plenty of H^+ ions to allow the oxidising agent to be reduced.
- Now you add the oxidising agent, e.g. aqueous potassium manganate(VII), to the reducing agent using a burette, swirling the conical flask as you go.
- The oxidising agent that you add reacts with the reducing agent. This reaction will continue until all of the reducing agent is used up.
- The very next drop you add to the flask will give the mixture the colour of the oxidising agent. (You could use a coloured reducing agent and a colourless oxidising agent instead — then you'd be watching for the moment that the colour in the flask disappears.)
- Stop when the mixture in the flask just becomes tainted with the colour of the oxidising agent (the end point) and record the volume of the oxidising agent added. This is the rough titration.
- Now you do some accurate titrations. You need to do a few until you get two or more readings that are within 0.10 cm^3 of each other.

Tip: Titrations are covered in loads more detail on page 28.

Tip: You can also do titrations the other way round — adding the reducing agent to the oxidising agent.

The equipment you'll need to do a titration is shown in Figure 1.

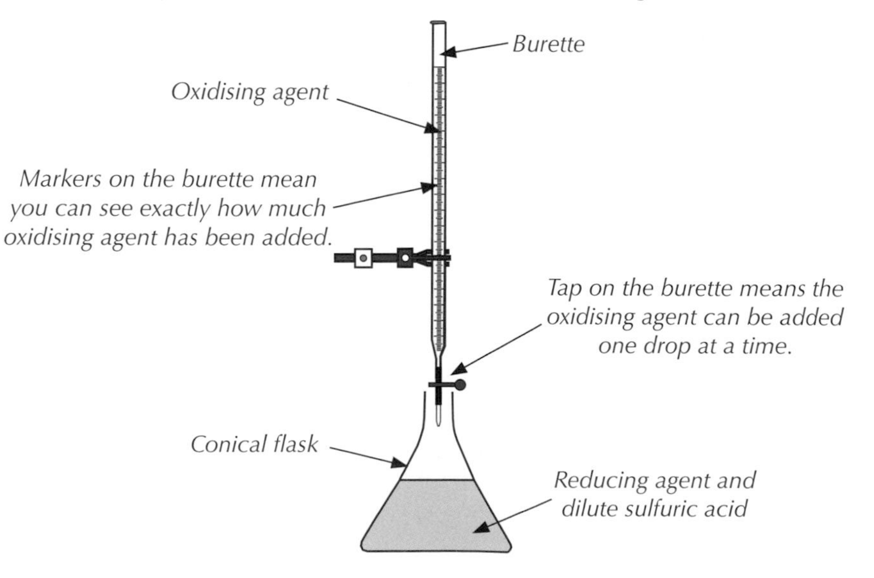

Figure 1: *The equipment needed to perform a titration.*

Figure 2: *A student reading a burette during a titration experiment.*

You need to know the titration reactions of Fe^{2+} ions with two different oxidising agents:

- Manganate(VII) ions (MnO_4^-) in aqueous potassium manganate(VII) ($KMnO_4$). The solution turns purple at the end point (see Figure 3) and the equation for the reaction is:

$$MnO_4^-{}_{(aq)} + 8H^+{}_{(aq)} + 5Fe^{2+}{}_{(aq)} \rightarrow Mn^{2+}{}_{(aq)} + 4H_2O_{(l)} + 5Fe^{3+}{}_{(aq)}$$

- Dichromate(VI) ions ($Cr_2O_7^{2-}$) in aqueous potassium dichromate(VI) ($K_2Cr_2O_7$). The solution turns orange at the end point (see Figure 4) and the equation for the reaction is.

$$Cr_2O_7^{2-}{}_{(aq)} + 14H^+{}_{(aq)} + 6Fe^{2+}{}_{(aq)} \rightarrow 2Cr^{3+}{}_{(aq)} + 7H_2O_{(l)} + 6Fe^{3+}{}_{(aq)}$$

Figure 3: *$KMnO_4$ being added to Fe^{2+} ions. The solution turns purple at the end point.*

Figure 4: *$K_2Cr_2O_7$ being added to Fe^{2+} ions. The solution turns orange at the end point.*

Calculating the concentration of a reagent

Once you've done a titration you can use your results to calculate the concentration of either the oxidising agent or the reducing agent. To do this:

Step 1: Write out a balanced equation for the redox reaction that's happening in the conical flask.

Step 2: Decide what you know already and what you need to know — usually you'll know the two volumes and the concentration of one of the reagents and want to find the concentration of the other reagent.

Step 3: For the reagent you know both the concentration and the volume for, calculate the number of moles of this reagent using the equation:

$$\text{moles} = \frac{\text{concentration (moldm}^{-3}) \times \text{volume (cm}^3)}{1000}$$

Step 4: Use the molar ratios in the balanced equation to find out how many moles of the other reagent were present in the solution.

Step 5: Calculate the unknown concentration using the equation:

$$\text{concentration (moldm}^{-3}) = \frac{\text{moles} \times 1000}{\text{volume (cm}^3)}$$

Tip: These calculations are the same as those for acid-base titrations covered on page 32.

Tip: In these calculations the units of concentration should always be $moldm^{-3}$.

Example

27.5 cm^3 of 0.0200 $moldm^{-3}$ aqueous potassium manganate(VII) reacted with 25.0 cm^3 of acidified iron(II) sulfate solution. Calculate the concentration of Fe^{2+} ions in the solution.

1. The balanced equation for this titration reaction is:

$$MnO_4^-{}_{(aq)} + 8H^+{}_{(aq)} + 5Fe^{2+}{}_{(aq)} \rightarrow Mn^{2+}{}_{(aq)} + 4H_2O_{(l)} + 5Fe^{3+}{}_{(aq)}$$

2. You know the concentration and the volume of the MnO_4^- ion solution (0.02 $moldm^{-3}$ and 27.5 cm^3) — and the volume of the Fe^{2+} solution (25 cm^3). You need to know the concentration of the Fe^{2+} solution.

3. Work out the number of moles of MnO_4^- ions added to the flask.

$$\text{moles } MnO_4^- = \frac{\text{conc.} \times \text{volume}}{1000} = \frac{0.02 \times 27.5}{1000} = 5.50 \times 10^{-4} \text{ moles}$$

4. From the molar ratios in the equation, you know 1 mole of MnO_4^- reacts with 5 moles of Fe^{2+}. So 5.50×10^{-4} moles of MnO_4^- must react with $5.50 \times 10^{-4} \times 5 = 2.75 \times 10^{-3}$ moles of Fe^{2+}.

5. Calculate the concentration of Fe^{2+}:

$$\text{conc. } Fe^{2+} = \frac{\text{moles} \times 1000}{\text{volume}} = \frac{(2.75 \times 10^{-3}) \times 1000}{25} = \mathbf{0.11\ moldm^{-3}}$$

Calculating the volume of a reagent

If you know the concentration of both the solutions, you can calculate unknown volumes. You follow the same steps as if you were trying to find the concentration — but at the end, you rearrange the equation to find the volume instead.

Example

Aqueous potassium dichromate(VI) with a concentration of 0.008 moldm^{-3} was used to completely oxidise 25.0 cm^3 of 0.06 moldm^{-3} acidified iron(II) sulfate solution. Calculate the volume of potassium dichromate(VI) solution that was used in the reaction.

1. The balanced equation for this titration reaction is:

$$Cr_2O_7^{2-}{}_{(aq)} + 14H^+{}_{(aq)} + 6Fe^{2+}{}_{(aq)} \rightarrow 2Cr^{3+}{}_{(aq)} + 7H_2O_{(l)} + 6Fe^{3+}{}_{(aq)}$$

2. You know the concentration and the volume of the Fe^{2+} ion solution (0.06 moldm^{-3} and 25 cm^3) — and the concentration of the $Cr_2O_7^{2-}$ ions (0.008 moldm^{-3}). You need to know the volume of the $Cr_2O_7^{2-}$ solution

3. Work out the number of moles of Fe^{2+} ions in the flask.

$$\text{moles } Fe^{2+} = \frac{\text{conc.} \times \text{volume}}{1000} = \frac{0.06 \times 25.0}{1000} = 1.5 \times 10^{-3} \text{ moles}$$

4. From molar ratios in the equation, you know that 6 moles of Fe^{2+} reacts with 1 mole of $Cr_2O_7^{2-}$. So 1.5×10^{-3} moles of Fe^{2+} must react with $1.5 \times 10^{-3} \div 6 = 2.5 \times 10^{-4}$ moles.

5. Calculate the volume of the $Cr_2O_7^{2-}$ ion solution:

$$\text{Volume of } Cr_2O_7^{2-} = \frac{\text{moles} \times 1000}{\text{conc.}} = \frac{(2.5 \times 10^{-4}) \times 1000}{0.008} = 31.3 \text{ cm}^3$$

Exam Tip

In the exam, you may have to recognise the end point of a titration for yourself — so don't forget, when MnO_4^- is used the solution turns purple at the end point and when $Cr_2O_7^{2-}$ is used the solution turns orange at the end point.

Practice Questions — Application

Q1 28.3 cm^3 of a 0.05 moldm^{-3} acidified iron(II) sulfate solution reacted exactly with 30 cm^3 of aqueous potassium manganate(VII). Calculate the concentration of the potassium manganate(VII) solution.

Q2 22.5 cm^3 of 0.15 moldm^{-3} aqueous potassium dichromate(VI) was needed to completely react with 20 cm^3 of an acidified iron(II) sulfate solution. Calculate the concentration of Fe^{2+} ions in the solution.

Q3 Aqueous potassium manganate(VII) with a concentration of 0.075 moldm^{-3} was used to completely react with 28.0 cm^3 of a 0.60 moldm^{-3} solution of acidified iron(II) sulfate. Calculate the volume of potassium manganate(VII) solution used.

Q4 A 0.45 moldm^{-3} solution of acidified iron(II) sulfate completely reacted with 24.0 cm^3 of a 0.055 moldm^{-3} solution of aqueous potassium dichromate(VI). Calculate the volume of iron(II) sulfate solution used.

Exam Tip

These questions are quite wordy. You might find it helpful to highlight the key bits of information in the question that you're going to use.

Practice Questions — Fact Recall

Q1 Why is acid added to the reducing agent in redox titrations?

Q2 a) What are the two main oxidising agents used in redox titrations?

b) What colour are they?

6. Transition Metals as Catalysts

A catalyst is something that speeds up the rate of a reaction by providing an alternative reaction pathway with a lower energy — you learnt all about them at AS-level. Transition metals make really good catalysts.

Learning Objectives:

- Know that transition metals and their compounds can act as heterogeneous and homogeneous catalysts.
- Understand the importance of variable oxidation states in catalysis.
- Understand how V_2O_5 acts as a catalyst in the Contact Process.
- Know that a heterogeneous catalyst is in a different phase from the reactants and that the reaction occurs at the surface.
- Know that Fe is used as a catalyst in the Haber Process.
- Know that a Cr_2O_3 catalyst is used in the manufacture of methanol from carbon monoxide and hydrogen.
- Understand the use of a support medium to maximise the surface area and minimise the cost (e.g. Rh in catalytic converters).
- Know that catalysts can become poisoned by impurities and consequently have reduced efficiency and that this has a cost implication (e.g. poisoning in the Haber Process and in catalytic converters).
- Know that when catalysts and reactants are in the same phase, the reaction proceeds through an intermediate species (e.g. the reaction of I^- and $S_2O_8^{2-}$ and autocatalysis by Mn^{2+}).

Specification Reference 3.5.4

Why transition metals make good catalysts

Transition metals and their compounds make good **catalysts** because they can change oxidation states by gaining or losing electrons within their d orbitals. This means they can transfer electrons to speed up reactions.

Example

The **Contact Process** is used industrially to make sulfuric acid. One of the key steps in this process is:

$$SO_{2(g)} + \tfrac{1}{2}O_{2(g)} \xrightarrow{V_2O_{5(s)}\text{ catalyst}} SO_{3(g)}$$

Vanadium(V) oxide (V_2O_5) catalyses this reaction in two steps.
First, Vanadium(V) oxidises SO_2 to SO_3 and is reduced itself to vanadium(IV):

$$V_2O_5 + SO_2 \rightarrow V_2O_4 + SO_3$$

The reduced catalyst is then oxidised by oxygen gas back to its original state:

$$V_2O_4 + \tfrac{1}{2}O_2 \rightarrow V_2O_5$$

Vanadium(V) oxide is able to oxidise SO_2 to SO_3 because it can be reduced to vanadium(IV) oxide. It's then oxidised back to vanadium(V) oxide by oxygen ready to start all over again. If vanadium didn't have a variable oxidation state, it wouldn't be able to catalyse this reaction.

Elements in the other blocks of the periodic table (e.g. the s-block) generally don't make effective catalysts because they don't have an incomplete 3d-subshell and don't have variable oxidation states.

Heterogeneous catalysts

A **heterogeneous catalyst** is one that is in a different phase from the reactants — i.e. in a different physical state.

Examples

There are three examples of heterogenous catalysts that you need to know about.

1. Iron, which is used in the **Haber Process** for making ammonia:

$$N_{2(g)} + 3H_{2(g)} \xrightarrow{Fe_{(s)}\text{ catalyst}} 2NH_{3(g)}$$

2. Vanadium(V) oxide that's used in the Contact Process (see above):

$$SO_{2(g)} + \tfrac{1}{2}O_{2(g)} \xrightarrow{V_2O_{5(s)}\text{ catalyst}} SO_{3(g)}$$

3. Chromium(III) oxide, which is used in the manufacture of methanol from carbon monoxide (CO) and hydrogen:

$$CO_{(g)} + 2H_{2(g)} \xrightarrow{Cr_2O_{3(s)}\text{ catalyst}} CH_3OH_{(g)}$$

In all of these reactions, the catalyst is a solid and the reactants are gases. The gases are passed over the solid catalyst.

Use of support mediums

When a heterogenous catalyst is used, the reaction happens on the surface of the catalyst. So, increasing the surface area of the catalyst increases the number of molecules that can react at the same time, increasing the rate of the reaction. A support medium is often used to make the area of a catalyst as large as possible.

Example

Catalytic converters (which 'clean up' emissions from car engines) contain a ceramic lattice coated with a thin layer of rhodium. The rhodium acts as a catalyst helping to convert the really nasty waste gases to less harmful products. Here's one of the reactions that occurs in a catalytic converter:

$$2CO_{(g)} + 2NO_{(g)} \xrightarrow{Rh_{(s)} \text{ catalyst}} 2CO_{2(g)} + N_{2(g)}$$

The lattice structure maximises the surface area of the catalyst, making it more effective. And, it minimises the cost of the catalyst because only a thin coating is needed.

Figure 1: *A catalytic converter fitted to a car.*

Catalyst poisoning

During a reaction, reactants are adsorbed onto active sites on the surfaces of heterogeneous catalysts. Impurities in the reaction mixture may also bind to the catalyst's surface and block reactants from being adsorbed. This process is called **catalyst poisoning**. Catalyst poisoning reduces the surface area of the catalyst available to the reactants, slowing down the reaction. It also increases the cost of a chemical process because less product can be made in a certain time or with a certain amount of energy. The catalyst may even need replacing or regenerating, which also costs money.

Tip: Adsorbed means stuck to the surface.

Tip: Catalytic poisoning is only a problem for heterogenous catalysts — homogenous catalysts aren't affected because the reaction doesn't occur on their surface.

Examples

Lead poisons the catalyst in catalytic converters:
Catalytic converters reduce harmful emissions from car engines.
Lead can coat the surface of the catalyst in a catalytic converter, so vehicles that have them fitted must only be run on unleaded petrol.

Sulfur poisons the iron catalyst in the Haber Process:
The hydrogen in the Haber process is produced from methane.
The methane is obtained from natural gas, which contains impurities, including sulfur compounds. Any sulfur that is not removed is adsorbed onto the iron, forming iron sulfide, and stopping the iron from catalysing the reaction efficiently.

Exam Tip
You need to know these examples of catalyst poisoning — they come up a lot in the exam.

Catalyst poisoning can be reduced by purifying the reactants. This removes many of the impurities which would otherwise poison the catalyst.

Homogeneous catalysts

Homogeneous catalysts are in the same physical state as the reactants. Usually a homogeneous catalyst is an aqueous catalyst for a reaction between two aqueous solutions.

A homogeneous catalyst works by forming an intermediate species. The reactants combine with the catalyst to make an intermediate species, which then reacts to form the products and reform the catalyst. This causes the enthalpy profile for a homogeneously catalysed reaction to have two humps in it, corresponding to the two reactions. The activation energy needed

Tip: Don't get confused between homogenous and heterogenous catalysts. Just remember — homo- means 'same' and homogeneous catalysts are in the same phase as the reactants.

to form the intermediates (and to form the products from the intermediates) is lower than that needed to make the products directly from the reactants (see Figure 2).

Tip: You met enthalpy profile diagrams at AS-level so if you need a quick reminder about what it all means — get your old AS notes out.

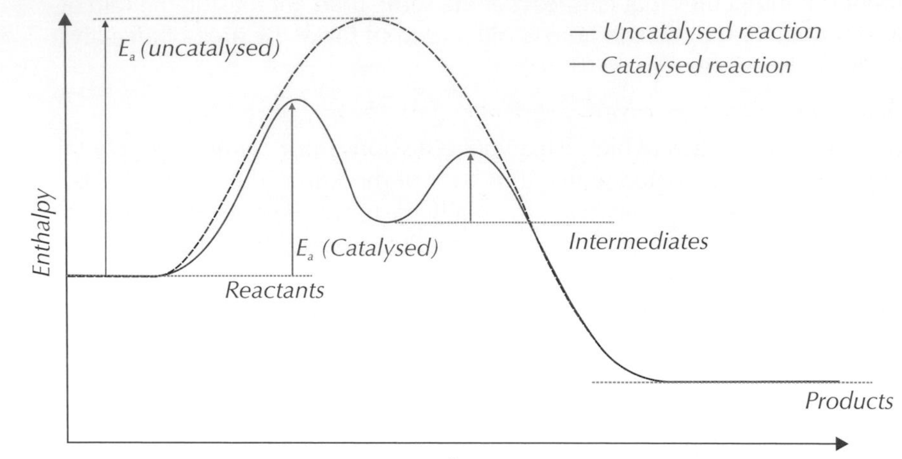

Figure 2: *Enthalpy profile for a reaction with a homogenous catalyst. E_a represents the activation energy.*

The catalyst is always reformed so it can carry on catalysing the reaction. There are two reactions catalysed by homogenous catalysts that you need to know about at A2:

Tip: Fe^{2+}, $S_2O_8^{2-}$ and I^- are all in the aqueous phase so Fe^{2+} is a homogenous catalyst.

Fe^{2+} catalysing the reaction between $S_2O_8^{2-}$ and I^-

The redox reaction between iodide ions and peroxodisulfate ($S_2O_8^{2-}$) ions is shown below:

$$S_2O_8^{2-}{}_{(aq)} + 2I^-{}_{(aq)} \rightarrow I_{2(aq)} + 2SO_4^{2-}{}_{(aq)}$$

Tip: The negative charges of the two ions is one reason why this reaction has high activation energy.

This reaction takes place annoyingly slowly because both ions are negatively charged. The ions repel each other, so it's unlikely they'll collide and react. But if Fe^{2+} ions are added, things are really speeded up because each stage of the reaction involves a positive and a negative ion, so there's no repulsion. First, the Fe^{2+} ions are oxidised to Fe^{3+} ions by the $S_2O_8^{2-}$ ions:

$$S_2O_8^{2-}{}_{(aq)} + 2Fe^{2+}{}_{(aq)} \rightarrow 2Fe^{3+}{}_{(aq)} + 2SO_4^{2-}{}_{(aq)}$$

The newly formed intermediate Fe^{3+} ions now easily oxidise the I^- ions to iodine, and the catalyst is regenerated:

$$2Fe^{3+}{}_{(aq)} + 2I^-{}_{(aq)} \rightarrow I_{2(aq)} + 2Fe^{2+}{}_{(aq)}$$

You can test for iodine by adding starch solution — it'll turn blue-black if iodine is present — see Figure 3.

Figure 3: *A starch test for iodine. Starch solution is added and the solution turns black if iodine is present.*

Mn^{2+} autocatalysing the reaction between MnO_4^- and $C_2O_4^{2-}$

Another example of a homogeneous catalyst is Mn^{2+} in the reaction between $C_2O_4^{2-}$ and MnO_4^-. It's an **autocatalysis** reaction because Mn^{2+} is a product of the reaction and acts as a catalyst for the reaction. This means that as the reaction progresses and the amount of the product increases, the reaction speeds up. The equation for this reaction is shown below:

$$2MnO_4^-{}_{(aq)} + 16H^+{}_{(aq)} + 5C_2O_4^{2-}{}_{(aq)} \rightarrow 2Mn^{2+}{}_{(aq)} + 8H_2O_{(l)} + 10CO_{2(g)}$$

There isn't any Mn^{2+} present at the beginning of the reaction to catalyse it, so at first the rate of reaction is very slow. During this uncatalysed part of the reaction, the activation energy is very high. This is because the reaction proceeds via the collision of negative ions, which requires a lot of energy to achieve. But once a little bit of the Mn^{2+} catalyst has been made it reacts with the MnO_4^- ions to make Mn^{3+} ions:

$$4Mn^{2+}_{(aq)} + MnO^-_{4\,(aq)} + 8H^+_{(aq)} \rightarrow 5Mn^{3+}_{(aq)} + 4H_2O_{(l)}$$

The Mn^{3+} ions are the intermediate. They then react with the $C_2O_4^{2-}$ ions to make CO_2 and reform the Mn^{2+} catalyst:

$$2Mn^{3+}_{(aq)} + C_2O^{2-}_{4\,(aq)} \rightarrow 2Mn^{2+}_{(aq)} + 2CO_{2(g)}$$

Because Mn^{2+} autocatalyses the reaction, the rate of reaction increases with time as more catalyst is made. This means a concentration-time graph for this reaction looks a bit unusual — see Figure 4.

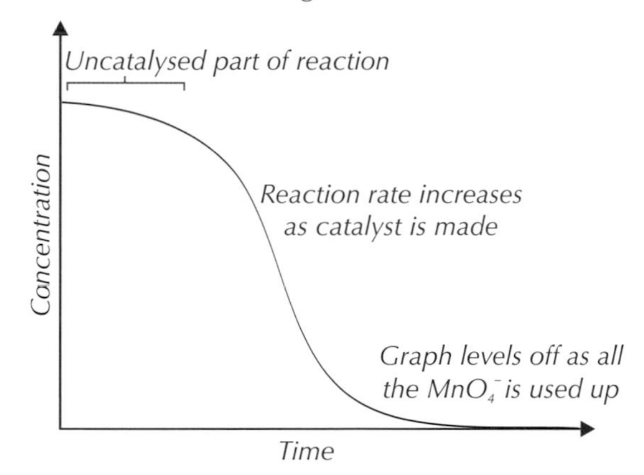

Figure 4: *Concentration-time graph for a reaction where autocatalysis is taking place.*

Tip: $C_2O_4^{2-}$ is called an ethandioate ion. It comes from ethanedioc acid.

Exam Tip
You could be asked to sketch this curve and explain its shape in the exam — so make sure you understand it.

Tip: This concentration-time graph shows the change in concentration of a reactant. If it showed the change in concentration of a product instead the shape of the graph would be reversed.

Practice Question — Application

Q1 Manganese dioxide ($MnO_{2(s)}$) is used as a catalyst for the following reaction: $2H_2O_{2(l)} \rightarrow 2H_2O_{(l)} + O_{2(g)}$

a) What type of catalyst is MnO_2 in this reaction?

b) Explain why MnO_2 can act as a catalyst.

Tip: You can use the state symbols in the equation to work out if a catalyst is heterogenous or homogenous.

Practice Questions — Fact Recall

Q1 Why do transition metals make good catalysts?

Q2 What are heterogenous catalysts and homogenous catalysts?

Q3 Give three examples of processes which use a heterogenous catalyst. For each example name the catalyst and write an equation for the reaction it catalyses.

Q4 Why is a heterogenous catalyst often spread over a support medium?

Q5 a) What is catalytic poisoning and how can it be reduced?

b) Give two examples of processes where catalyst poisoning is a problem.

Q6 Explain how Fe^{2+} speeds up the rate of reaction between $S_2O_8^{2-}$ and I^-.

Q7 What is autocatalysis? Give an example of a reaction where it occurs.

Learning Objectives:

- Understand that Fe(II) in haemoglobin enables oxygen to be transported in the blood.
- Understand why CO is toxic.
- Know that the Pt(II) complex cisplatin is used as an anticancer drug.
- Appreciate the benefits and risks associated with cisplatin.
- Understand that $[Ag(NH_3)_2]^+$ is used in Tollens' reagent to distinguish between aldehydes and ketones.

Specification Reference 3.5.4

7. Other Uses of Transition Metals

Transition metals make good catalysts, but that isn't their only use — it's time to look at some other places they turn up.

Haemoglobin

The blood product, **haemoglobin**, contains complexes formed from Fe^{2+} ions (see page 197 for the structure). Both water and oxygen will bind to the Fe^{2+} ions as ligands, so the complex can transport oxygen to where it's needed, and then swap it for a water molecule — here's how it works:

- In the lungs, where the oxygen concentration is high, water ligands are substituted for oxygen molecules to form oxyhaemoglobin, which is carried around the body in the blood.
- When the oxyhaemoglobin gets to a place where oxygen is needed, the oxygen molecules are exchanged for water molecules. The haemoglobin then returns to the lungs and the whole process starts again.

The process of oxygen transport is summarised in Figure 1.

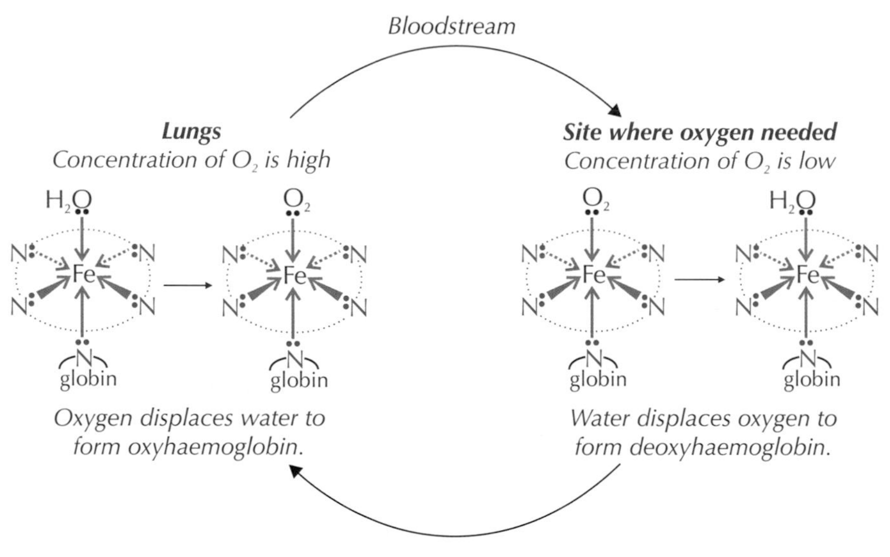

Figure 1: The role of haemoglobin in the transport of oxygen around the body.

Tip: It's the oxyhaemoglobin in red blood cells that makes them red — see page 198 for more on why transition metal complex ions are coloured.

Carbon monoxide poisoning

The process of oxygen transport can be disrupted if carbon monoxide (CO) is inhaled. Carbon monoxide is a colourless, odourless and tasteless gas which is produced by incomplete combustion.

When carbon monoxide is inhaled, the haemoglobin can swap its water ligands for carbon monoxide ligands, forming carboxyhaemoglobin (Figure 2). This is bad news because carbon monoxide is a strong ligand and doesn't readily exchange with oxygen or water ligands, meaning the haemoglobin can't transport oxygen any more. Carbon monoxide poisoning starves the organs of oxygen — it can cause headaches, dizziness, unconsciousness and even death if it's not treated.

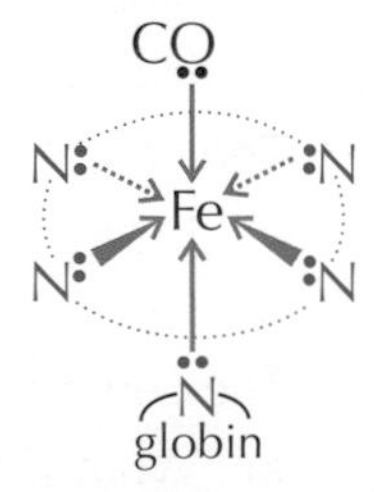

Figure 2: Carboxyhaemoglobin.

Figure 3: Carbon monoxide detectors signal an alarm when carbon monoxide levels get dangerously high.

Cisplatin

Cisplatin is a complex of platinum(II) with two chloride ions and two ammonia molecules in a square planar shape. Note that the two Cl^- ions are next to each other, never opposite, as this would be a different isomer (transplatin) with different biological properties — see Figure 4.

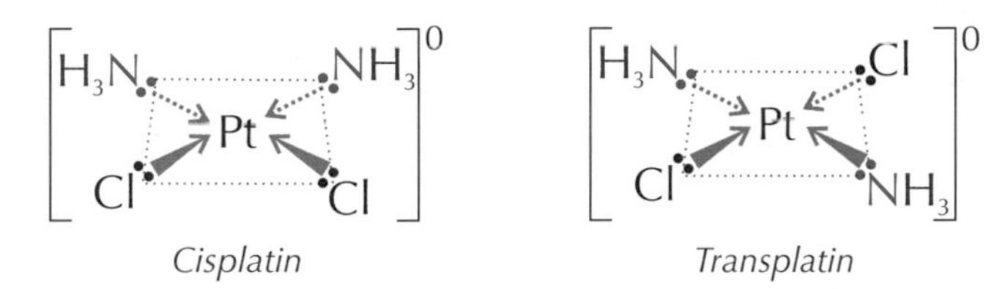

Figure 4: *The structures of cisplatin and transplatin.*

Cisplatin can be used to treat some types of cancer. Cancer is caused by cells in the body dividing uncontrollably and forming tumours. Cisplatin is active against a variety of cancers, including lung and bladder cancer, because it prevents cancer cells from reproducing.

Before a cell can divide it has to replicate its DNA, which involves unwinding the two strands of the DNA double helix so that they can be copied. Cisplatin forms coordinate bonds with nitrogen atoms in the DNA molecule and prevents the two strands from unwinding. So, the cell can no longer replicate its DNA and it can't divide.

The downside is that cisplatin also prevents normal cells from reproducing, including blood and hair cells. This can cause hair loss and suppress the immune system, increasing the risk of infection. Cisplatin may also cause damage to the kidneys.

Tip: The structure of Cisplatin was covered in more detail on page 196.

Tip: Transplatin has no effect on cell division — it can't be used as an anticancer drug.

Tollens' reagent

Tollens' reagent is prepared by adding just enough ammonia solution to silver nitrate solution to form a colourless solution containing the complex ion $[Ag(NH_3)_2]^+$. Tollens' reagent is used to distinguish between aldehydes and ketones. Aldehydes react to give a silver mirror on the inside of the test tube:

$$RCHO + 2[Ag(NH_3)_2]^+ + 3OH^- \rightarrow RCOO^- + 2Ag + 4NH_3 + 2H_2O$$

Ketones don't react with Tollens' reagent.

Tip: $[Ag(NH_3)_2]^+$ is a linear complex. See page 196 for more.

Tip: More on the reactions of aldehydes and ketones with Tollens' reagent can be found on page 66.

Practice Questions — Fact Recall

Q1 Haemoglobin is found in red blood cells.
- a) Describe what happens to haemoglobin in the lungs.
- b) Describe what happens to haemoglobin at sites where oxygen is needed.

Q2 Explain why carbon monoxide is toxic.

Q3 The complex ion cisplatin can be used as an anticancer drug.
- a) Explain why cisplatin is active against cancer cells.
- b) Give a side effect of using cisplatin to treat cancer.

Q4 The complex ion $[Ag(NH_3)_2]^+$ is used in Tollens' reagent.
- a) What is Tollens' reagent used for?
- b) Explain why it can be used for this purpose.

Section Summary

Make sure you know...

- That transition metals are found in the d-block of the periodic table.
- That the definition of a transition metal is a metal that can form one or more stable ions with a partially filled d-subshell.
- How to write out the electronic configurations of transition metals and their ions.
- That all of the transition metals have similar physical properties — high density, high melting point, high boiling point and similar ionic radii.
- That the chemical properties of the transition metals are due to the incomplete d-subshell.
- That transition metals can form complex ions.
- That a complex ion is a metal ion surrounded by coordinately bonded ligands.
- That a ligand is an atom, ion or molecule that donates a pair of electrons to a central metal ion.
- The difference between unidentate (e.g. NH_3, H_2O, Cl^-), bidentate (e.g. $NH_2CH_2CH_2NH_2$) and multidentate (e.g. $EDTA^{4-}$) ligands.
- That the coordination number is the number of coordinate bonds formed by the central metal ion.
- That complex ions with six coordinate bonds usually form octahedral complexes.
- That complex ions with four coordinate bonds can form tetrahedral or square planar complexes.
- That silver complexes can have two coordinate bonds and form linear complexes.
- That haemoglobin is a protein that contains hexa-coordinated Fe^{2+} complex ions.
- That the binding of a ligand causes the 3d subshell to split into two different energy levels.
- That energy from visible light can cause electrons to jump from a lower energy orbital to a higher energy orbital and this is called an electronic transition.
- That the amount of energy absorbed can be calculated using $\Delta E = h\nu$.
- That frequencies of light which aren't absorbed are reflected and this gives complex ions colour.
- That changes in oxidation state, coordination number and ligand can cause changes in colour.
- How the concentration of a solution of complex ions can be determined using spectrometry.
- That transition metals show variable oxidation states.
- The oxidation states of chromium when it forms Cr^{2+}, Cr^{3+}, CrO_4^{2-} and $Cr_2O_7^{2-}$ ions.
- That Cr^{3+} and Cr^{2+} are formed by reducing $Cr_2O_7^{2-}$ with zinc in dilute acid.
- That Cr^{3+} can be oxidised to CrO_4^{2-} by H_2O_2 in alkaline solution.
- That Co^{2+} can be oxidised to Co^{3+} using H_2O_2 or with air in ammoniacal solution.
- That transition metals can be used in titrations — specifically Fe^{2+} with MnO_4^- and $Cr_2O_7^{2-}$.
- How to calculate the concentration or volume of a reagent using titration results.
- That the variable oxidation states of transition metals means they make good catalysts.
- What homogenous and heterogenous catalysts are.
- The examples of heterogenous catalysts — Fe, V_2O_5 and Cr_2O_3, and the reactions they catalyse.
- Why support mediums are used with heterogenous catalysts.
- What catalyst poisoning is and the examples of where it is a problem.
- The examples of homogenous catalysts — Fe^{2+} in the reaction between $S_2O_8^-$ and I^- and autocatalysis by Mn^{2+} in the reaction between MnO_4^- and $C_2O_4^{2-}$.
- How haemoglobin is used to transport oxygen around the body and why CO is toxic.
- That cisplatin can be used as an anticancer drug because it prevents cells from reproducing.
- The benefits and risks of using cisplatin as an anticancer drug.
- That $[Ag(NH_3)_2]^+$ is used in Tollens' reagent to distinguish between aldehydes and ketones.

Exam-style Questions

1 The transition metals are found in the d-block of the periodic table. They have some unusual chemical properties, one of which is the ability to exist in different oxidation states.

1 (a) State the definition of a transition metal.

(1 mark)

1 (b) Explain why transition metals are able to have variable oxidation states.

(2 marks)

An example of a transition metal that can exist in variable oxidation states is chromium (Cr). The scheme below shows some of the main chromium containing ions and their reactions.

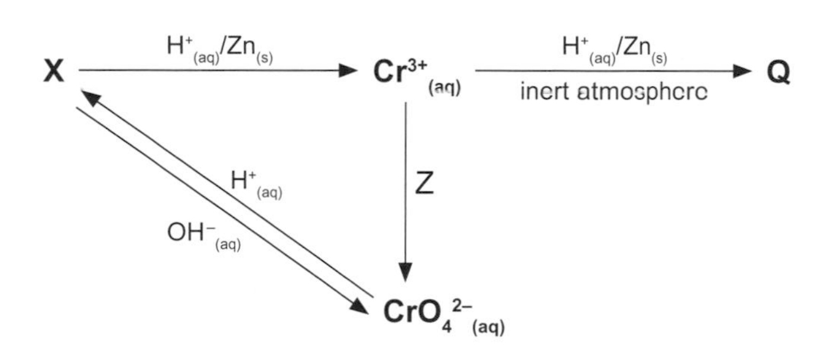

1 (c) (i) Identify ion **X.** Describe its appearance and write an equation for its conversion to Cr^{3+}.

(3 marks)

1 (c) (ii) What is the oxidation state of chromium in ion **X**?

(1 mark)

1 (c) (iii) State the role of Zn in this reaction and explain why dilute acid is added.

(2 marks)

1 (d) Identify ion **Q**. Explain why an inert atmosphere is needed when converting Cr^{3+} to ion **Q**.

(2 marks)

1 (e) (i) Describe the conditions, **Z**, needed to convert Cr^{3+} to CrO_4^{2-}.

(2 marks)

1 (e) (ii) Write an equation for this reaction and state the colour change you would expect to see when this reaction takes place.

(2 marks)

2 The ability to form complex ions is an important property of transition metals. Transition metal complex ions are often brightly coloured.

2 (a) State what is meant by the term complex ion.

(2 marks)

2 (b) (i) Explain why transition metal complex ions have a colour.

(3 marks)

2 (b) (ii) Give two factors which can affect the colour of a complex ion.

(2 marks)

Porphyrin rings act as multidentate ligands in a number of different biological complex ions, including haemoglobin. The structure of a porphyrin ring is shown below:

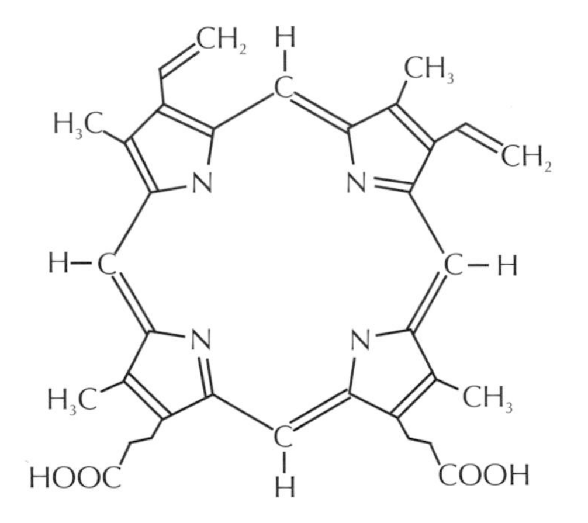

2 (c) (i) Explain what is meant by the term multidentate.

(1 mark)

2 (c) (ii) Identify the atoms in the porphyrin ring which bond with the Fe^{2+} ion in haemoglobin.

(1 mark)

2 (c) (iii) What is meant by the term coordination number?
What is the coordination number of Fe^{2+} in haemoglobin?

(2 marks)

2 (d) (i) What is the role of haemoglobin in the body?

(1 mark)

2 (d) (ii) Explain why carbon monoxide (CO) is extremely toxic to humans.

(2 marks)

3 Transition metals and their oxides make good catalysts. Rhodium (Rh) is used in catalytic converters to catalyse the reaction shown below:

$$2CO_{(g)} + 2NO_{(g)} \rightarrow 2CO_{2(g)} + N_{2(g)}$$

3 (a) (i) Explain why transition metals make good catalysts.

(2 marks)

3 (a) (ii) What type of catalyst is rhodium in this reaction?

(1 mark)

3 (b) Explain why catalytic converters contain a ceramic lattice coated with a thin layer of rhodium rather than a solid rhodium block.

(3 marks)

3 (c) The rhodium used in catalytic converters is vulnerable to catalytic poisoning. Explain what catalytic poisoning is and how it is prevented in catalytic converters.

(4 marks)

3 (d) Fe^{2+} catalyses this reaction between $S_2O_8^{2-}$ and I^-:

$$S_2O_8^{2-}{}_{(aq)} + 2I^-_{(aq)} \rightarrow I_{2(aq)} + 2SO_4^{2-}{}_{(aq)}$$

3 (d) (i) Explain why this reaction is extremely slow in the absence of a catalyst.

(2 marks)

3 (d) (ii) Write two equations to show how Fe^{2+} catalyses this reaction.

(2 marks)

3 (d) (iii) Suggest how you could test for I_2 at the end of the reaction.

(2 marks)

4 This question is all about the uses of transition metals.

4 (a) Cisplatin is a complex ion containing the transition metal platinum. It is used as an anticancer drug.

Explain why cisplatin is an effective treatment for cancer. Give a potential side effect of using this drug.

(4 marks)

4 (b) The key component of Tollens' reagent is a complex ion.

Identify the complex ion present in Tollens' reagent, sketch it and describe its structure.

State what Tollens' reagent is used for and explain why it can be used for this purpose.

(6 marks)

4 (c) Transition metals can also be used in titrations. In one titration, 15.8 cm^3 of acidified potassium manganate(VII) was needed to completely react with 30.0 cm^3 of a 0.15 $moldm^{-3}$ solution of acidified iron(II) sulfate. Calculate the concentration of the potassium manganate solution used. What colour will the solution be at the end point?

(5 marks)

Learning Objective:

- Know the definitions of a Lewis acid and Lewis base.

Specification Reference 3.5.5

1. Lewis Acids and Bases

You've gone through your life thinking that there's only one type of acid and one type of base and then boom... we introduce some more. Make sure you really understand what's what in this topic — you'll need it for the next few.

Acids and bases

The **Brønsted-Lowry** theory of acids and bases says that an acid is a proton donor, and a base is a proton acceptor.

Tip: There's more on Brønsted-Lowry acids and bases on page 19.

Example

Reaction between NH_3 and HCl:

$$NH_{3(aq)} + HCl_{(aq)} \rightarrow NH_4^+{}_{(aq)} + Cl^-{}_{(aq)}$$

HCl is donating a proton, so it's acting as a Brønsted-Lowry acid.
NH_3 is accepting a proton, so it's acting as a Brønsted-Lowry base.

Figure 1: Gilbert Lewis. The chemist who devised Lewis theory.

Some acid-base reactions don't have proton donors or proton acceptors. You'd think this would mean that they weren't acid-base reactions, but a chemist (Mr Lewis) came up with an alternative theory that broadens the definition of acids and bases. The Lewis theory is based on the transfer of electrons, rather than protons:

A **Lewis acid** is an electron pair acceptor.
A **Lewis base** is an electron pair donor.

Example

Reaction between ammonia and boron trifluoride:

$$NH_{3\,(aq)} + BF_{3\,(aq)} \rightarrow NH_3BF_{3\,(aq)}$$

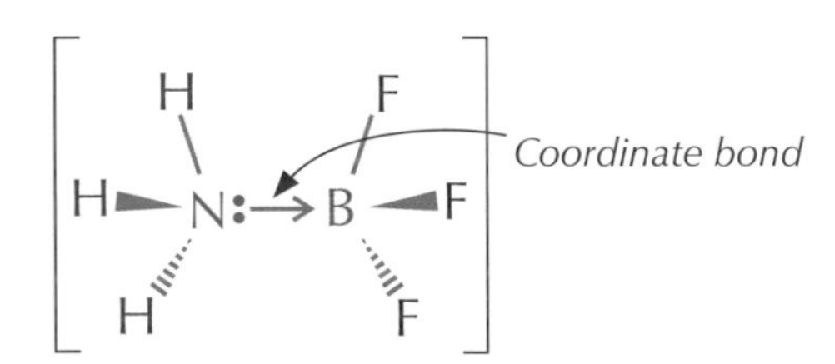

In this reaction, the ammonia molecule donates a pair of electrons to the boron atom, forming a coordinate bond. So NH_3 is acting as a Lewis base, and BF_3 is acting as a Lewis acid.

Exam Tip

Make sure you fully understand the different definitions of acids and bases. You need to be able to work out whether compounds you've never seen before are Lewis acids/bases or Brønsted-Lowry acids/bases.

Some substances fit both the Brønsted-Lowry and the Lewis definitions of an acid or base. Others only fit one. So, if you're describing something as an acid or base, you should say whether it's a Brønsted-Lowry or a Lewis acid or base.

Examples

The hydronium ion

Water can combine with an H^+ ion to form a hydronium ion:

$$H_2O + H^+ \rightarrow H_3O^+$$

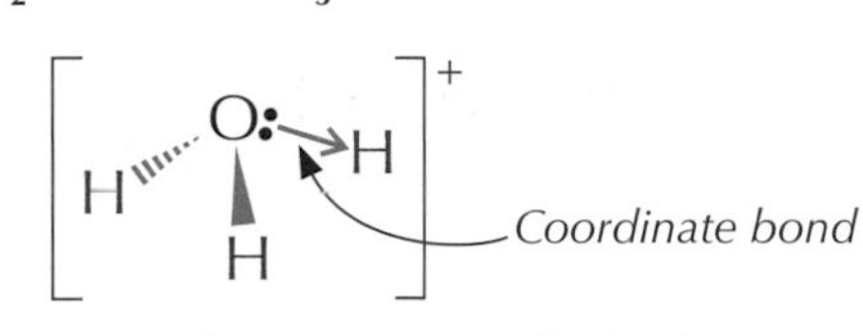

The water molecule's donating an electron pair to the hydrogen ion, and the hydrogen ion is accepting an electron pair from the water. So the water molecule is the Lewis base and the hydrogen ion's the Lewis acid.

Aluminium tetrachloride ion

Aluminium chloride can combine with a chloride anion to form $AlCl_4^-$.

$$AlCl_3 + Cl^- \rightarrow AlCl_4^-$$

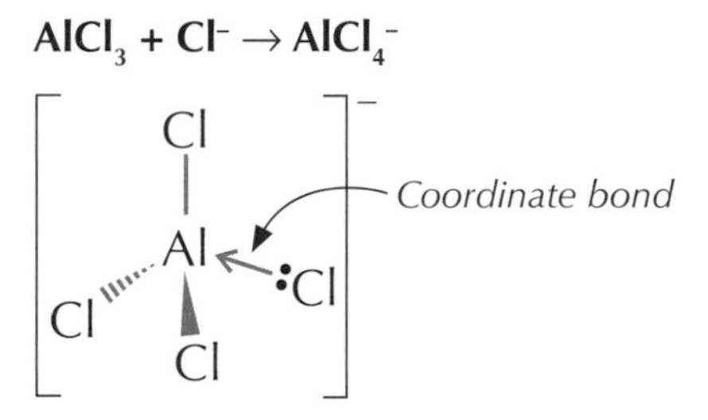

The aluminium chloride is accepting an electron pair — so it's the Lewis acid. The chloride ion is donating an electron pair — so it's the Lewis base.

Tip: The water molecule is also a Brønsted-Lowry base as it is accepting a proton.

Tip: There's more on coordinate bonds on page 194.

Exam Tip
If you're asked to draw a structure like this in the exam don't forget to add the charge to the diagram if it has one — you'll lose easy marks if you don't.

Practice Questions — Application

Q1 State whether the acids below are Brønsted-Lowry acids, Lewis acids or both.

a) HCl in the reaction: $HCl_{(aq)} + NaOH_{(aq)} \rightarrow H_2O_{(l)} + NaCl_{(aq)}$

b) Mg in the reaction: $Mg_{(s)} + 2HCl_{(aq)} \rightarrow MgCl_{2(aq)} + H_{2(g)}$

c) BF_3 in the reaction: $BF_{3(aq)} + F^-_{(aq)} \rightarrow BF^-_{4\,(aq)}$

Q2 State whether the bases below are Brønsted-Lowry bases, Lewis bases or both.

a) NaOH in the reaction: $HCl_{(aq)} + NaOH_{(aq)} \rightarrow H_2O_{(l)} + NaCl_{(aq)}$

b) KOH in the reaction: $H_2SO_{4(aq)} + 2KOH_{(aq)} \rightarrow 2H_2O_{(l)} + K_2SO_{4(aq)}$

c) NH_2CH_3 in the reaction: $NH_2CH_{3(aq)} + BF_{3(aq)} \rightarrow NH_2CH_3BF_{3(aq)}$

Q3 An ammonia molecule can react with an H^+ ion to form NH_4^+.

a) State which reactant is acting as an acid and which reactant is acting as a base in this reaction.

b) Is the acid acting as a Brønsted-Lowry or a Lewis acid? Why?

Practice Questions — Fact Recall

Q1 What is a Brønsted-Lowry acid?

Q2 Give the definition for a Brønsted-Lowry base.

Q3 What is a Lewis acid?

Q4 Define a Lewis base.

2. Metal-Aqua Ions

This topic's all about complex ions and their reactions. If you've forgotten what complex ions are have a quick look back at pages 194-196.

Learning Objectives:

- Understand the importance of lone pair electrons in co-ordinate bond formation.
- Know that metal–aqua ions are formed in aqueous solution: $[M(H_2O)_6]^{2+}$, limited to M = Fe, Co and Cu, $[M(H_2O)_6]^{3+}$, limited to M = Al, Cr and Fe.
- Understand the equilibria $[M(H_2O)_6]^{2+} + H_2O \rightleftharpoons M(H_2O)_5(OH)]^+ + H_3O^+$ and $[M(H_2O)_6]^{3+} + H_2O \rightleftharpoons [M(H_2O)_5(OH)]^{2+} + H_3O^+$ to show generation of acidic solutions with M^{3+}, and very weakly acidic solutions with M^{2+}.
- Understand that the acidity of $[M(H_2O)_6]^{3+}$ is greater than that of $[M(H_2O)_6]^{2+}$ in terms of the (charge/size ratio) of the metal ion.
- Be able to describe and explain the simple test-tube reactions of $M^{2+}_{(aq)}$ ions, limited to M = Fe, Co and Cu, and of $M^{3+}_{(aq)}$ ions, limited to M = Al, Cr and Fe, with the bases OH^-, NH_3 and CO_3^{2-}.
- Know that some metal hydroxides show amphoteric character by dissolving in both acids and bases (e.g. hydroxides of Al^{3+} and Cr^{3+}).
- Know that MCO_3 is formed but that $M_2(CO_3)_3$ is not formed.

Specification Reference 3.5.5

Hydration of metal ions

Coordinate bonds always involve one substance donating an electron pair to another. So if there's a coordinate bond, there are no two ways about it — it must have been formed in a Lewis acid-base reaction (see page 218).

When transition metal compounds dissolve in water, the water molecules form coordinate bonds with the metal ions. This forms **metal-aqua complex ions**. Metal ions act as Lewis acids in aqueous solution because they accept electron pairs from the water molecules that surround them. And the water molecules, like any ligands, are electron pair donors so they must be Lewis bases. In general, six water molecules form coordinate bonds with each metal ion. The water molecules do this by donating a non-bonding pair of electrons from their oxygen.

Examples

Cobalt can form the metal-aqua ion $[Co(H_2O)_6]^{2+}$. In this cobalt complex the H_2O ligands act as Lewis bases (electron pair donors). Each H_2O ligand donates a lone pair of electrons to the cobalt ion, forming a coordinate bond.

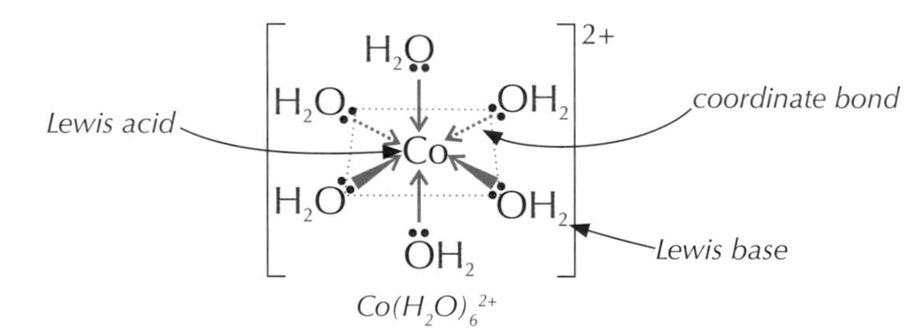

$Co(H_2O)_6^{2+}$

The diagrams show the metal-aqua ions formed by iron — $Fe(H_2O)_6^{2+}$ and by chromium — $Cr(H_2O)_6^{3+}$.

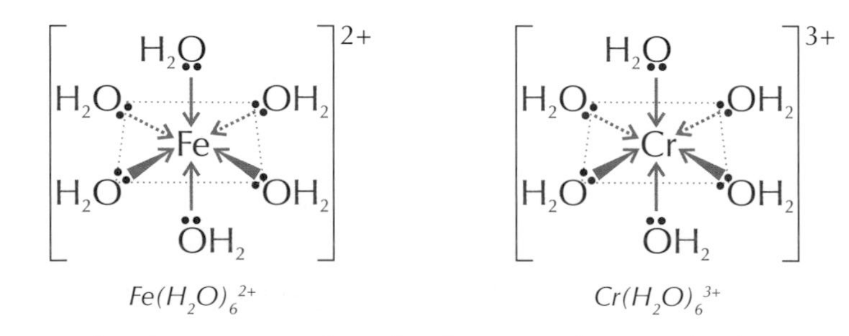

$Fe(H_2O)_6^{2+}$ *$Cr(H_2O)_6^{3+}$*

Water molecules are neutral, so the charge on the complex ion must also be the charge on the metal ion.

The acidity of metal-aqua ion solutions

In a solution containing metal-aqua 2+ ions, there's a reaction between the metal-aqua ion and the water — this is a hydrolysis or acidity reaction. The metal-aqua 2+ ions release H^+ ions, so an acidic solution is formed. There's only slight dissociation though, so the solution is only weakly acidic.

Example

$Fe(H_2O)_6^{2+}$ will dissociate in water to form $[Fe(H_2O)_5(OH)]^+$:

$$Fe(H_2O)_6^{2+}{}_{(aq)} + H_2O_{(l)} \rightleftharpoons [Fe(H_2O)_5(OH)]^+{}_{(aq)} + H_3O^+{}_{(aq)}$$

Tip: In the forward reaction, the metal-aqua ion is acting as a Brønsted-Lowry acid. It donates a proton from one of its water ligands to a free water molecule.

Metal-aqua 3+ ions react in the same way. They form more acidic solutions though.

Example

$Al(H_2O)_6^{3+}$ will dissociate in water to form $[Al(H_2O)_5(OH)]^{2+}$:

$$Al(H_2O)_6^{3+}{}_{(aq)} + H_2O_{(l)} \rightleftharpoons [Al(H_2O)_5(OH)]^{2+}{}_{(aq)} + H_3O^+{}_{(aq)}$$

Relative acidity of 2+ and 3+ metal-aqua ion solutions

Metal 3+ ions are pretty small but have a big charge — so they've got a high charge density (otherwise known as charge/size ratio). The metal 2+ ions have a much lower charge density. This makes the 3+ ions much more polarising than the 2+ ions. More polarising power means that they attract electrons from the oxygen atoms of the coordinated water molecules more strongly, weakening the O–H bond. So it's more likely that a hydrogen ion will be released. And more hydrogen ions means a more acidic solution — so metal 3+ ions are more acidic than metal 2+ ions.

Exam Tip
Make sure you understand why metal 3+ ions are more acidic than metal 2+ ions — it's all because of their polarising power.

Further hydrolysis of metal-aqua ions

Adding OH^- ions to solutions of metal-aqua 3+ ions produces insoluble precipitates of metal hydroxides. Here's why:

- In water, metal-aqua 3+ ions form the equilibrium:

  $$M(H_2O)_6^{3+}{}_{(aq)} + H_2O_{(l)} \rightleftharpoons [M(H_2O)_5(OH)]^{2+}{}_{(aq)} + H_3O^+{}_{(aq)}$$

  If you add OH^- ions to the equilibrium H_3O^+ ions are removed — this shifts the equilibrium to the right.
- Now another equilibrium is set up in the solution:

  $$[M(H_2O)_5(OH)]^{2+}{}_{(aq)} + H_2O_{(l)} \rightleftharpoons [M(H_2O)_4(OH)_2]^+{}_{(aq)} + H_3O^+{}_{(aq)}$$

  Again the OH^- ions remove H_3O^+ ions from the solution, pulling the equilibrium to the right.
- This happens one last time — now you're left with an insoluble uncharged metal hydroxide:

  $$[M(H_2O)_4(OH)_2]^+{}_{(aq)} + H_2O_{(l)} \rightleftharpoons M(H_2O)_3(OH)_{3(s)} + H_3O^+{}_{(aq)}$$
- The overall equation for this reaction is:

  $$M(H_2O)_6^{3+}{}_{(aq)} + 3H_2O_{(l)} \rightleftharpoons M(H_2O)_3(OH)_{3(s)} + 3H_3O^+{}_{(aq)}$$

Tip: You could also write out the equations using OH^- instead of water. This would leave you with $H_2O_{(l)}$ on the right hand side of the equation instead of $H_3O^+{}_{(aq)}$.

Tip: In this reaction M could be Fe, Al or Cr.

The same thing happens with metal-aqua 2+ ions (e.g. Fe, Co or Cu), except this time there are only two steps:

Step 1: $M(H_2O)_6^{2+}{}_{(aq)} + H_2O_{(l)} \rightleftharpoons [M(H_2O)_5(OH)]^+{}_{(aq)} + H_3O^+{}_{(aq)}$

Step 2: $[M(H_2O)_5(OH)]^+{}_{(aq)} + H_2O_{(l)} \rightleftharpoons M(H_2O)_4(OH)_{2(s)} + H_3O^+{}_{(aq)}$

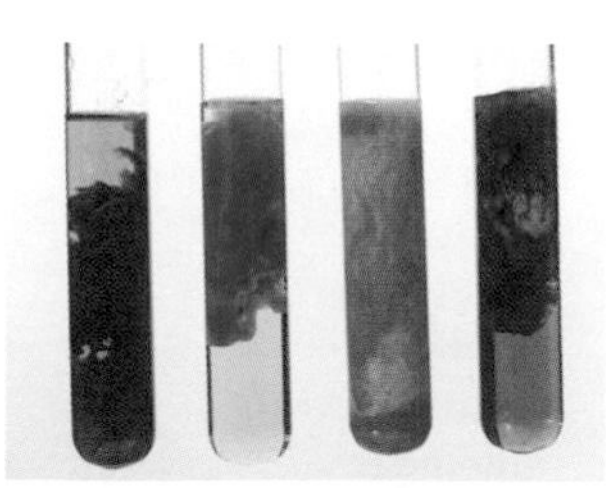

Figure 1: Metal-aqua ion precipitates. From left to right — iron(III) hydroxide, copper(II) hydroxide, chromium(III) hydroxide and cobalt(II) hydroxide.

***Figure 2:** Brown precipitate of iron(III) hydroxide.*

***Figure 3:** Limonitic rocks. The rocks contain a large amount of hydrated iron(III) hydroxide, which gives them their distinctive reddish brown colour.*

Example

Adding NaOH to a solution of iron 3+ ions will produce a brown precipitate.

$$Fe(H_2O)_6{}^{3+}{}_{(aq)} + H_2O_{(l)} \rightleftharpoons [Fe(H_2O)_5(OH)]^{2+}{}_{(aq)} + H_3O^+{}_{(aq)}$$

$$[Fe(H_2O)_5(OH)]^{2+}{}_{(aq)} + H_2O_{(l)} \rightleftharpoons [Fe(H_2O)_4(OH)_2]^+{}_{(aq)} + H_3O^+{}_{(aq)}$$

$$[Fe(H_2O)_4(OH)_2]^+{}_{(aq)} + H_2O_{(l)} \rightleftharpoons Fe(H_2O)_3(OH)_{3(s)} + H_3O^+{}_{(aq)}$$

brown precipitate

All the metal hydroxide precipitates will dissolve in acid. They act as Brønsted-Lowry bases and accept H^+ ions. This reverses the hydrolysis reactions above.

Example

Adding an acid to iron(III) hydroxide will reform the soluble metal-aqua ion.

$$Fe(H_2O)_3(OH)_{3(s)} + H^+{}_{(aq)} \rightleftharpoons [Fe(H_2O)_4(OH)_2]^+{}_{(aq)}$$

$$[Fe(H_2O)_4(OH)_2]^+{}_{(aq)} + H^+{}_{(aq)} \rightleftharpoons [Fe(H_2O)_5(OH)]^{2+}{}_{(aq)}$$

$$[Fe(H_2O)_5(OH)]^{2+}{}_{(aq)} + H^+{}_{(aq)} \rightleftharpoons Fe(H_2O)_6{}^{3+}{}_{(aq)}$$

Some metal hydroxides are **amphoteric** — they can act as both acids and bases. This means they'll dissolve in an excess of base as well as in acids.

Examples

Aluminium hydroxide and chromium(III) hydroxide are amphoteric.
They act as Brønsted-Lowry acids and donate H^+ ions to the OH^- ions:

$$Al(H_2O)_3(OH)_{3(s)} + OH^-{}_{(aq)} \rightleftharpoons [Al(H_2O)_2(OH)_4]^-{}_{(aq)} + H_2O_{(l)}$$

$$Cr(OH)_3(H_2O)_{3(s)} + 3OH^-{}_{(aq)} \rightleftharpoons [Cr(OH)_6]^{3-}{}_{(aq)} + 3H_2O_{(l)}$$

They can also act as Brønsted-Lowry bases and accept H^+ ions:

$$Al(H_2O)_3(OH)_{3(s)} + 3H^+{}_{(aq)} \rightleftharpoons [Al(H_2O)_6]^{3+}{}_{(aq)}$$

$$Cr(OH)_3(H_2O)_{3(s)} + 3H^+{}_{(aq)} \rightleftharpoons [Cr(H_2O)_6]^{3+}{}_{(aq)}$$

Hydrolysis of metal-aqua ions using NH_3

The obvious way of adding hydroxide ions is to use a strong alkali, like sodium hydroxide solution — but you can use ammonia solution too. When ammonia dissolves in water it can accept protons from the water molecules to form $NH_4{}^+$ ions and ^-OH ligands. This gives the same results as adding NaOH.

Example

$[Cr(H_2O)_6]^{3+}{}_{(aq)}$ will react with ammonia to form a $[Cr(H_2O)_3(OH)_3]$ complex.

$$[Cr(H_2O)_6]^{3+}{}_{(aq)} + 3NH_{3(aq)} \rightleftharpoons [Cr(H_2O)_3(OH)_3]_{(s)} + 3NH_4{}^+{}_{(aq)}$$

violet solution *green precipitate*

In some cases, a further reaction happens if you add an excess of ammonia solution — the H_2O and OH^- ligands are displaced by NH_3 ligands. This will happen with Co^{2+}, Cu^{2+} and Cr^{3+} complexes.

Example

Chromium(III) hydroxide will react with excess ammonia to form a $[Cr(NH_3)_6]^{3+}$ complex.

$$[Cr(OH)_6]^{3-}{}_{(aq)} + 6NH_{3(aq)} \rightleftharpoons [Cr(NH_3)_6]^{3+}{}_{(aq)} + 6OH^-{}_{(aq)}$$

green solution *purple solution*

Exam Tip

Make sure you remember which metal ions will react with excess ammonia — some of them won't.

Hydrolysis of metal-aqua ions using Na_2CO_3

Metal 2+ ions react with sodium carbonate to form insoluble metal carbonates, like this:

$$M(H_2O)_6{}^{2+}{}_{(aq)} + CO_3{}^{2-}{}_{(aq)} \rightleftharpoons MCO_{3(s)} + 6H_2O_{(l)}$$

But, metal 3+ ions don't form $M_2(CO_3)_3$ species when you react them with sodium carbonate. They are stronger acids (see page 221) so they always form hydroxide precipitates instead. The carbonate ions react with the H_3O^+ ions, removing them from the solution and forming bubbles of carbon dioxide gas.

$$2M(H_2O)_6{}^{3+}{}_{(aq)} + 3CO_3{}^{2-}{}_{(aq)} \rightleftharpoons 2M(H_2O)_3(OH)_{3(s)} + 3CO_{2(g)} + 3H_2O_{(l)}$$

Figure 4: Copper(II) carbonate. A green-blue precipitate is formed when carbonate ions react with aqueous copper(II) ions.

Complex ion solutions and precipitates

This handy table summarises all the compounds that are formed in the reactions on these pages. You need to know the formulas of all the complex ions, and their colours.

Metal-aqua ion	With $OH^-{}_{(aq)}$ or $NH_{3(aq)}$	With excess $OH^-{}_{(aq)}$	With excess $NH_{3(aq)}$	With $Na_2CO_{3(aq)}$
$[Co(H_2O)_6]^{2+}$ pink solution	$Co(H_2O)_4(OH)_2$ blue-green precipitate	no change	$[Co(NH_3)_6]^{2+}$ straw coloured/pale brown solution	$CoCO_3$ pink precipitate
$[Cu(H_2O)_6]^{2+}$ blue solution	$Cu(H_2O)_4(OH)_2$ blue precipitate	no change	$[Cu(NH_3)_4(H_2O)_2]^{2+}$ deep blue solution	$CuCO_3$ green-blue precipitate
$[Fe(H_2O)_6]^{2+}$ green solution	$Fe(H_2O)_4(OH)_2$ green precipitate	no change	no change	$FeCO_3$ green precipitate
$[Al(H_2O)_6]^{3+}$ colourless solution	$Al(H_2O)_3(OH)_3$ white precipitate	$[Al(H_2O)_2(OH)_4]^-$ colourless solution	no change	$Al(H_2O)_3(OH)_3$ white precipitate
$[Cr(H_2O)_6]^{3+}$ violet solution	$Cr(H_2O)_3(OH)_3$ green precipitate	$[Cr(OH)_6]^{3-}$ green solution	$[Cr(NH_3)_6]^{3+}$ purple solution	$Cr(H_2O)_3(OH)_3$ green precipitate
$[Fe(H_2O)_6]^{3+}$ yellow solution	$Fe(H_2O)_3(OH)_3$ brown precipitate	no change	no change	$Fe(H_2O)_3(OH)_3$ brown precipitate

Practice Questions — Application

Q1 A student has an unknown metal-aqua ion. When she adds sodium carbonate ions to the aqueous metal-aqua ion a pink precipitate forms. What metal ion is present in the solution?

Q2 Write equations to show what happens when OH^- ions are added to aqueous chromium(III) ions.

Practice Questions — Fact Recall

Q1 What type of bonds hold metal-aqua ion complexes together?

Q2 Explain why metal-aqua 3+ ions are more acidic than metal-aqua 2+ ions.

Q3 What would you observe if you added a small amount of OH^- ions to aqueous aluminium(III) ions?

Q4 What would you observe if excess NH_3 was added to aqueous cobalt(II) ions?

Exam Tip
You need to learn the colour of all of these solutions and precipitates for the exam. Gutted. Any of them could come up at any time and they're easy marks if you can remember them.

3. Ligand Substitution

Ligands around a central metal ion can switch places with other ligands in ligand substitution reactions.

Learning Objectives:

- Understand that the ligands NH_3 and H_2O are similar in size and are uncharged, and that ligand exchange occurs without change of co-ordination number (e.g. Co^{2+} and Cr^{3+}).
- Understand that the Cl^- ligand is larger than these uncharged ligands and that ligand exchange can involve a change of co-ordination number (e.g. Co^{2+} and Cu^{2+}).
- Know that substitution may be incomplete (e.g. the formation of $[Cu(NH_3)_4(H_2O)_2]^{2+}$).
- Know that substitution of unidentate ligands with a bidentate or a multidentate ligand leads to a more stable complex.
- Understand this chelate effect in terms of a positive entropy change in these reactions.

Specification Reference 3.5.5

Ligand substitution reactions

One ligand can be swapped for another ligand — this is **ligand exchange**. It pretty much always causes a colour change.

Substitution of similarly sized ligands

If the ligands are of similar size then the coordination number of the complex ion doesn't change, and neither does the shape.

Examples

H_2O and NH_3 ligands are similarly sized and are both uncharged. This means that H_2O ligands can be exchanged with NH_3 ligands without any change in coordination number or shape. There will still be a colour change due to the change of ligand.

$$[Co(H_2O)_6]^{2+}_{(aq)} + 6NH_{3(aq)} \rightarrow [Co(NH_3)_6]^{2+}_{(aq)} + 6H_2O_{(l)}$$

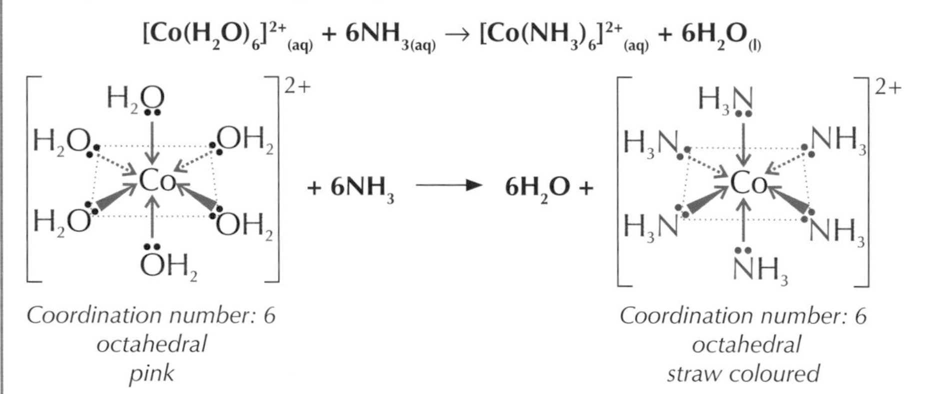

Coordination number: 6
octahedral
pink

Coordination number: 6
octahedral
straw coloured

In a chromium-aqua complex, the H_2O ligands can be exchanged with OH^- ligands without any change in coordination number or shape because the ligands are similar sizes.

$$[Cr(H_2O)_6]^{3+}_{(aq)} + 6OH^-_{(aq)} \rightarrow [Cr(OH)_6]^{3-}_{(aq)} + 6H_2O_{(l)}$$

$[Cr(H_2O)_6]^{3+}$ + $6OH^-$ ⟶ $6H_2O$ + $[Cr(OH)_6]^{3-}$

Coordination number: 6
octahedral
violet

Coordination number: 6
octahedral
green

Substitution of different sized ligands

If the ligands are different sizes there's a change of coordination number and a change of shape.

- Complex ions with a coordination number of two are usually linear.
- Complex ions with a coordination number of four are usually tetrahedral.
- Complex ions with a coordination number of six are usually octahedral.

Exam Tip
You could be asked about any complex metal ion reaction covered in the table on page 223, so don't just learn these examples — make sure you <u>understand</u> them.

Tip: If you've forgotten all this have a look back at page 196 for a reminder.

Examples

In a copper-aqua complex, the H_2O ligands can be exchanged with Cl^- ligands. The shape of the complex changes from octahedral to tetrahedral because fewer of the larger Cl^- ligands can fit around the central metal ion. There is also a colour change during this reaction.

$$[Cu(H_2O)_6]^{2+}_{(aq)} + 4Cl^-_{(aq)} \rightleftharpoons [CuCl_4]^{2-}_{(aq)} + 6H_2O_{(l)}$$

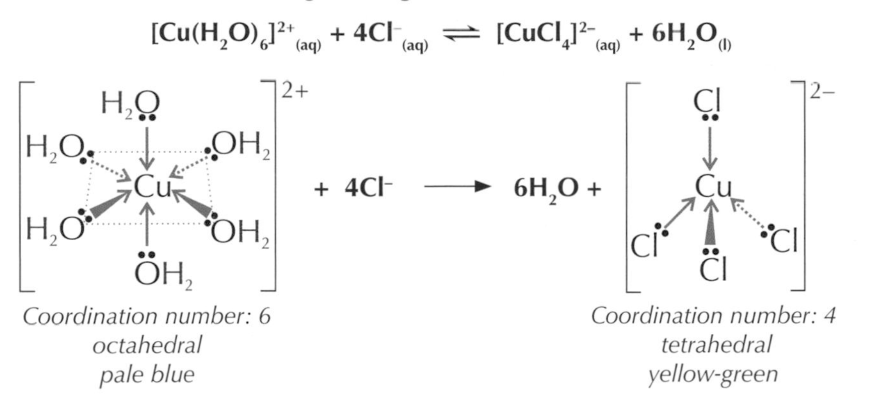

Tip: You can add Cl^- ions to a solution by adding hydrochloric acid (HCl).

Tip: You'll only be asked about a few types of ligand in the exam so try to remember that H_2O, NH_3 and OH^- ligands are about the same size but Cl^- ions are a lot larger.

In a cobalt-aqua complex, the H_2O ligands can be exchanged with the larger Cl^- ligands. The shape of the complex changes from octahedral to tetrahedral and there is also a colour change (see Figure 1).

$$[Co(H_2O)_6]^{2+}_{(aq)} + 4Cl^-_{(aq)} \rightleftharpoons [CoCl_4]^{2}_{(aq)} + 6H_2O_{(l)}$$

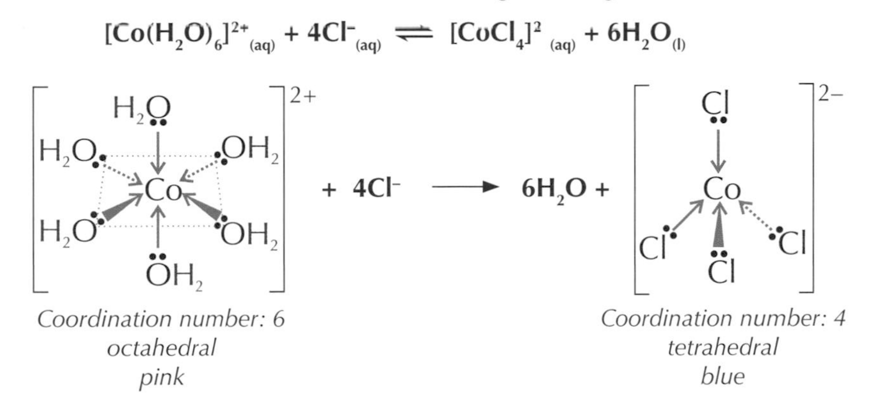

Figure 1: Cobalt chloride equilibrium. The flask on the left contains a low concentration of chloride ions, the flask on the right contains a high concentration.

For this process, the forward reaction is endothermic, so the equilibrium can be shifted to the right-hand side by heating. The equilibrium will also shift to the right if you add more concentrated hydrochloric acid. Adding water to this equilibrium shifts it back to the left.

Partial substitution of ligands

Sometimes the substitution is only partial — not all of the six H_2O ligands are substituted.

Tip: In partial ligand substitution reactions of octahedral complexes either 1, 2, 3, 4 or 5 ligands are substituted during the reaction.

Examples

In a copper-aqua complex, some of the H_2O ligands can be exchanged with NH_3 ligands whilst some H_2O ligands remain where they are.

In this example, four of the H_2O ligands are substituted with NH_3 ligands. The shape of the complex changes from octahedral to elongated octahedral (see Figure 2) and there is also a colour change.

$$[Cu(H_2O)_6]^{2+}_{(aq)} + 4NH_{3(aq)} \rightarrow [Cu(NH_3)_4(H_2O)_2]^{2+}_{(aq)} + 4H_2O_{(l)}$$

octahedral — pale blue; elongated octahedral — deep blue

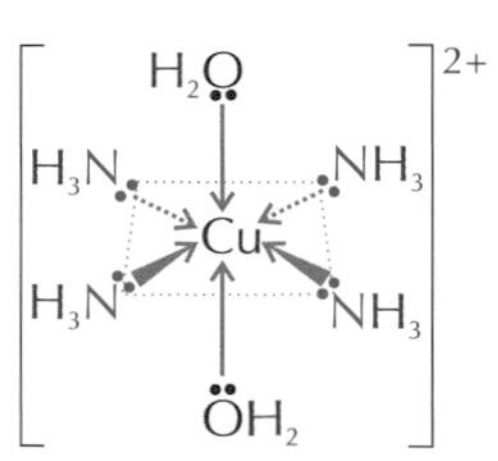

Figure 2: The elongated octahedral structure of $[Cu(NH_3)_4(H_2O)_2]^{2+}$.

Exam Tip
When you're writing ligand substitution reactions in the exam make sure your equations are balanced.

In an iron(III)-aqua complex, some of the H_2O ligands can be exchanged with SCN^- ligands whilst some of them remain where they are.

In this example, one of the H_2O ligands is exchanged with an SCN^- ligand. The shape of the complex changes from octahedral to distorted octahedral and there is also a colour change.

$$[Fe(H_2O)_6]^{3+}_{(aq)} + SCN^-_{(aq)} \rightarrow [Fe(H_2O)_5SCN]^{2+}_{(aq)} + H_2O_{(l)}$$

octahedral *yellow* — *distorted octahedral* *blood red*

Bidentate and multidentate ligands

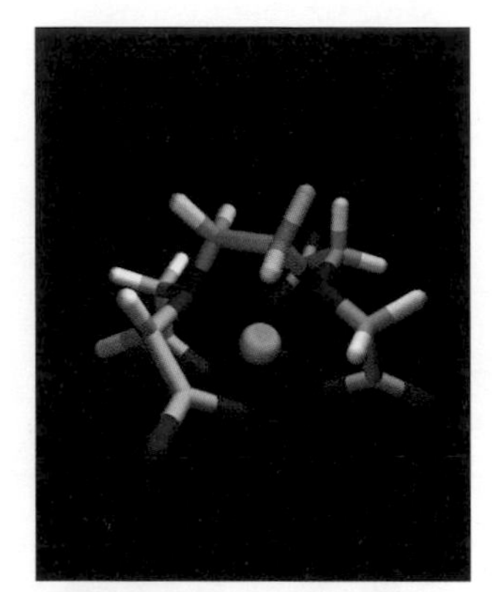

Figure 3: *$EDTA^{4-}$ bonding to a central metal ion. $EDTA^{4-}$ can bind with six bonds to the metal ion via nitrogen and oxygen atoms.*

So far all the ligands in this topic have been **unidentate**, but you'll remember from pages 194-195 that ligands can also be **bidentate** or **multidentate**. Here's a quick recap of what that means:

- Unidentate ligands have one lone pair of electrons to donate to the metal ion to form a dative covalent bond.
- Bidentate ligands have two lone pairs of electrons to donate.
- Multidentate ligands donate more than one lone pair of electrons to form more than one coordinate bond with the metal ion.

Complex ion stability

Ligand exchange reactions can be easily reversed, unless the new complex ion is much more stable than the old one. If the new ligands form stronger bonds with the central metal ion than the old ligands did, the change is less easy to reverse.

Example

CN^- ions form stronger coordinate bonds than H_2O molecules with Fe^{3+} ions. So, the complex formed with CN^- ions will be more stable than the complex formed with H_2O molecules. This means that the substitution of water molecules by CN^- ions in an iron(III) complex is hard to reverse.

$$[Fe(H_2O)_6]^{3+}_{(aq)} + 6CN^-_{(aq)} \rightarrow [Fe(CN)_6]^{3-}_{(aq)} + 6H_2O_{(l)}$$

Multidentate ligands form more stable complexes than unidentate ligands, so ligand exchange reactions involving bidentate and multidentate ligands are hard to reverse.

Example

Complexes that contain the bidentate ligand ethane-1,2-diamine are more stable than those that contain water molecule ligands. So, reactions where water molecules are substituted by ethane-1,2-diamine are hard to reverse.

$$[Cu(H_2O)_6]^{2+}_{(aq)} + 3NH_2CH_2CH_2NH_{2(aq)} \rightarrow [Cu(NH_2CH_2CH_2NH_2)_3]^{2+}_{(aq)} + 6H_2O_{(l)}$$

Enthalpy change

When a ligand exchange reaction occurs, bonds are broken and formed. The strength of the bonds being broken is often very similar to the strength of the new bonds being made. So the enthalpy change for a ligand exchange reaction is usually very small.

Example

Substituting ammonia with ethane-1,2-diamine in a nickel complex

In this reaction, six coordinate bonds break between Ni and N in $[Ni(NH_3)_6]^{2+}$ and six coordinate bonds are formed between Ni and N in $[Ni(NH_2CH_2CH_2NH_2)_3]^{2+}$. This means the enthalpy change for the reaction is very small (only –13 kJmol^{-1}).

$$[Ni(NH_3)_6]^{2+} + 3NH_2CH_2CH_2NH_2 \rightarrow [Ni(NH_2CH_2CH_2NH_2)_3]^{2+} + 6NH_3 \quad \Delta H = -13\ kJmol^{-1}$$

Break 6 coordinate bonds between Ni and N — *Form 6 coordinate bonds between Ni and N*

This is actually a reversible reaction, but the equilibrium lies so far to the right that it is thought of as being irreversible.

Exam Tip
The examiners can ask you about the stability of any metal complex ion in the exam so it's not good enough just to learn these examples — you've got to understand them too.

Entropy change

When unidentate ligands are substituted with bidentate or multidentate ligands, the number of particles increases — the more particles, the greater the entropy. Reactions that result in an increase in entropy are more likely to occur. So that's why multidentate ligands always form much more stable complexes than unidentate ligands. This is known as the **chelate effect**.

Example

In the example above, $[Ni(NH_2CH_2CH_2NH_2)_3]^{2+}$ is much more stable than $[Ni(NH_3)_6]^{2+}$. This isn't accounted for by an enthalpy change, but an increase in entropy can explain it.

The number of particles in the reaction increases from 4 to 7. This means that there is a large increase in entropy for the reaction and therefore the $[Ni(NH_2CH_2CH_2NH_2)_3]^{2+}$ formed in the reaction is more stable than the $[Ni(NH_3)_6]^{2+}$ complex.

$$[Ni(NH_3)_6]^{2+} + 3NH_2CH_2CH_2NH_2 \rightarrow [Ni(NH_2CH_2CH_2NH_2)_3]^{2+} + 6NH_3$$

4 particles — *7 particles*

Exam Tip
When you're asked about the stability of metal ion complexes in an exam make sure you talk about <u>enthalpy</u> and <u>entropy</u> otherwise you could lose out on valuable marks.

Tip: Entropy is covered in more detail on pages 156-158.

When the hexadentate ligand $EDTA^{4-}$ replaces unidentate or bidentate ligands, the complex formed is loads more stable. It's difficult to reverse these reactions, because reversing them would cause a decrease in the system's entropy.

Example

In the reaction below, the $EDTA^{4-}$ ligand is replacing six NH_3 ligands. This increases the number of particles in the reaction from 2 to 7.

$$[Cr(NH_3)_6]^{3+} + EDTA^{4-} \rightarrow [Cr(EDTA)]^{-} + 6NH_3$$

This means that the entropy of the system has greatly increased and so the $[Cr(EDTA)]^{-}$ complex formed will be more stable than the $[Cr(NH_3)_6]^{3+}$ complex.

Tip: There's more information on the $EDTA^{4-}$ ligand on pages 194 and 195.

Free-energy change

You can use the free-energy change formula from page 159 to work out whether a ligand substitution reaction is feasible or not.

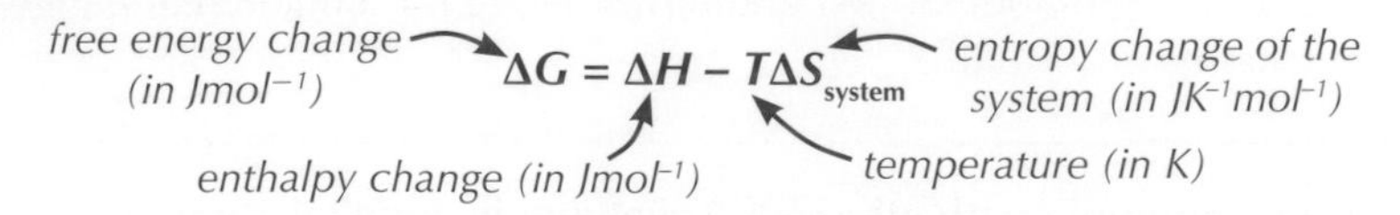

The enthalpy change for a ligand substitution reaction is usually very small so $\Delta H \approx 0\ Jmol^{-1}$. The entropy change of the system will be positive if the number of particles increases during a reaction and negative if the number of particles decreases. So, when unidentate ligands are substituted for bidentate or multidentate ligands, ΔG will usually be negative and the reaction will be feasible.

Tip: Remember that for spontaneous reactions, ΔG must be negative or zero.

Practice Questions — Application

Q1 The H_2O ligands in $[Co(H_2O)_6]^{2+}$ can be exchanged for other ligands. Predict the shape of the complex ions formed after the following substitutions:

a) All the H_2O ligands exchanged for NH_3 ligands.

b) The six H_2O ligands exchanged for four Cl^- ligands.

Q2 The metal-aqua ion, $[Cu(H_2O)_6]^{2+}$ will undergo a ligand substitution reaction with excess ammonia to form $[Cu(NH_3)_4(H_2O)_2]^{2+}$.

a) Write an equation for this reaction.

b) State the shape of $[Cu(NH_3)_4(H_2O)_2]^{2+}$.

c) Explain why the enthalpy change for this reaction is small.

Q3 Ethane-1,2-diamine is a bidentate ligand.

a) Write an equation for the substitution of all the ammonia ligands in $[Cr(NH_3)_6]^{3+}$ with ethane-1,2-diamine ($NH_2CH_2CH_2NH_2$) ligands.

b) Explain why the free-energy change for this reaction is negative.

Practice Questions — Fact Recall

Q1 State whether the colour, coordination number and/or the shape of the complex ion changes in the following situations.

a) Ligand exchange of similarly sized ligands.

b) Ligand exchange of differently sized ligands.

Q2 What is a bidentate ligand?

Q3 What is a multidentate ligand?

Q4 What is the chelate effect?

Section Summary

Make sure you know...

- What a Lewis acid and a Lewis base are, and how they're different from Brønsted-Lowry acids and bases.
- That metal-aqua ions are formed in aqueous solution and are bonded to ligands by coordinate bonds.
- That Fe(II), Co and Cu ions form $[M(H_2O)_6]^{2+}$ in solution.
- That Al, Cr and Fe(III) ions form $[M(H_2O)_6]^{3+}$ in solution.
- The importance of a lone pair of electrons in forming coordinate bonds.
- That the equilibrium $[M(H_2O)_6]^{2+} + H_2O \rightleftharpoons M(H_2O)_5(OH)]^{+} + H_3O^{+}$ generates very weakly acidic solutions with M^{2+}.
- That the equilibrium $[M(H_2O)_6]^{3+} + H_2O \rightleftharpoons [M(H_2O)_5(OH)]^{2+} + H_3O^{+}$ generates acidic solutions with M^{3+}.
- That $[M(H_2O)_6]^{3+}$ is more acidic than $[M(H_2O)_6]^{2+}$ due to the difference in the charge/size ratio of the metal ions.
- The reactions of $M^{2+}_{(aq)}$ ions, where M = Fe, Co or Cu, with the bases OH^-, NH_3 and CO_3^{2-} and be able to explain them.
- The reactions of $M^{3+}_{(aq)}$ ions, where M = Al, Cr and Fe, with the bases OH^-, NH_3 or CO_3^{2-} and be able to explain them.
- That some metal hydroxides (e.g. hydroxides of Al^{3+} and Cr^{3+}) show amphoteric character by dissolving in both acids and bases.
- That MCO_3 is formed when complex M^{2+} ions react with carbonates and what is formed when M^{3+} ions react with carbonates.
- All the colours of the solutions and precipitates of Co^{2+}, Cu^{2+}, Fe^{2+}, Al^{3+}, Cr^{3+} and Fe^{3+} ions with OH^-, NH_3 and CO_3^{2-}.
- That ligand exchange between NH_3 and H_2O occurs without change of coordination number (e.g. in Co^{2+} and Cr^{3+} complexes) because the ligands are similar in size and are uncharged.
- That ligand substitution may be incomplete (e.g. the formation of $[Cu(NH_3)_4(H_2O)_2]^{2+}$).
- That the Cl^- ligand is larger than H_2O and NH_3 ligands so if ligand exchange occurs it can involve a change of coordination number (e.g. in Co^{2+} and Cu^{2+} complexes).
- That substitution of unidentate ligands with a bidentate or a multidentate ligand leads to a more stable complex. That this is called the chelate effect, and it can be explained in terms of a positive entropy change in ligand substitution reactions.

Exam-style Questions

1 Aqueous chromium(III) sulfate contains a chromium-aqua complex ion. The ligands in the complex ion can undergo partial and then complete substitution when ammonia is added to the solution.

For each stage of the process below, describe what you would observe and write the relevant equation(s) for the reactions that take place. Predict the shape of the final complex ion product of each stage.

1 (a) Dry reddish-brown crystals of chromium(III) sulfate are dissolved in water to give an acidic solution.

(4 marks)

1 (b) Ammonia is added dropwise to the reaction until the ion $Cr(H_2O)_3(OH)_3$ is formed.

(4 marks)

1 (c) Ammonia was then added dropwise to the reaction mixture until it was in excess.

(3 marks)

2 The diagram below shows the structure of the transition metal complex ion $[Cr(EDTA)]^-$.

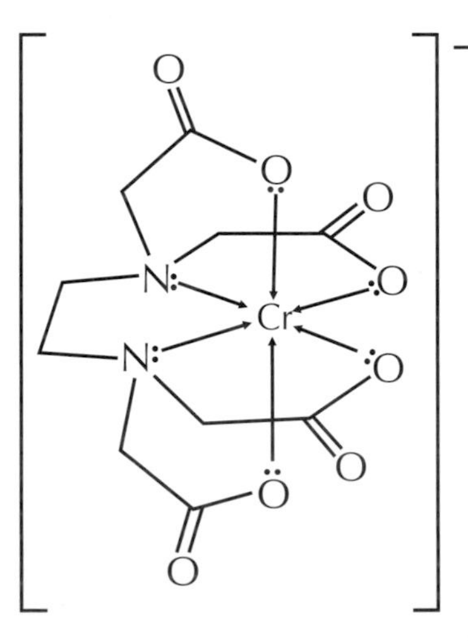

2 (a) $EDTA^{4-}$ is a multidentate ligand. What is a multidentate ligand?

(2 marks)

2 (b) $[Cr(EDTA)]^-$ is formed when $EDTA^{4-}$ is substituted for H_2O ligands in $[Cr(H_2O)_6]^{3+}$. Explain why $[Cr(EDTA)]^-$ is more stable than $[Cr(H_2O)_6]^{3+}$.

(3 marks)

3 Metal-aqua complex ions form when transition metal compounds dissolve in water.

3 (a) Describe the bonding in a metal-aqua complex ion.

(2 marks)

3 (b) (i) Give the formula of the species formed when Co^{2+} ions dissolve in water.

(1 mark)

3 (b) (ii) Write an equation for the reaction of the cobalt-aqua complex ion and water.

(1 mark)

3 (b) (iii) Explain why this solution will be less acidic than a solution of Al^{3+} ions dissolved in water.

(4 marks)

3 (b) (iv) Describe the colour change of the reaction when a small amount of NaOH is added to the solution of Co^{2+} ions and water.

(2 marks)

3 (c) (i) Identify the species formed when Fe^{3+} ions dissolve in water.

(1 mark)

3 (c) (ii) Write an equation for the addition of carbonate ions to this species.

(1 mark)

3 (c) (iii) Describe what you would observe when this reaction takes place.

(2 marks)

3 (d) When aluminium dissolves in water, $[Al(H_2O)_6]^{3+}$ is formed.

3 (d) (i) Write an equation for the ligand substitution reaction between this species and an excess of ethane-1,2-diamine ($NH_2CH_2CH_2NH_2$).

(1 mark)

3 (d) (ii) Explain why the free-energy change for this reaction is negative.

(2 marks)

4 Aluminium hydroxide is amphoteric.

4 (a) Define the term amphoteric.

(1 mark)

4 (b) Describe the appearance of aluminium hydroxide ($Al(H_2O)_3(OH)_{3(aq)}$).

(1 mark)

4 (c) Write an equation for the reaction of aluminium hydroxide ($Al(H_2O)_3(OH)_{3(aq)}$) with OH^- ions.

(2 marks)

4 (d) What type of acid is aluminium hydroxide acting as in this reaction? Explain your answer.

(2 marks)

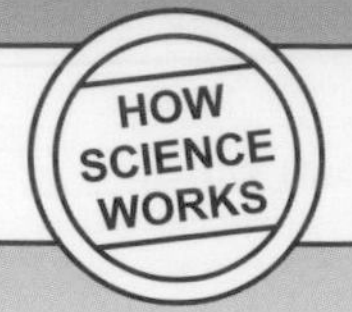

1. Variables and Data

When you're planning an experiment you need to think carefully about what things you're going to change, what things you're going to measure and how you're going to record your results.

Variables

You probably know this all off by heart but it's easy to get mixed up sometimes. So here's a quick recap. A **variable** is a quantity that has the potential to change, e.g. mass. There are two types of variable commonly referred to in experiments:

Tip: When you're drawing a graph, the dependent variable always goes on the y-axis and the independent variable on the x-axis.

Independent variable — the thing that you change in an experiment.

Dependent variable — the thing that you measure in an experiment.

Example

You could investigate the effect of temperature on rate of reaction using the apparatus in Figure 1:

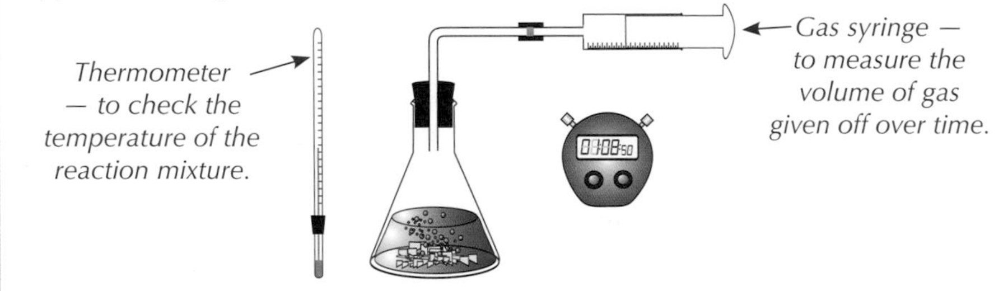

Figure 1: *Apparatus for measuring the rate of a reaction.*

- The independent variable will be temperature.
- The dependent variable will be the volume of gas produced.
- All the other variables must be kept the same. These include the concentration and volume of solutions, mass of solids, pressure, the presence of a catalyst and the surface area of any solid reactants.

Figure 2: *An acid-carbonate reaction. The number of bubbles produced is discrete data, but the volume of gas produced is continuous data.*

Types of data

Experiments always involve some sort of measurement to provide data. There are different types of data — and you need to know what they are.

1. Discrete data

You get discrete data by counting. E.g. the number of bubbles produced in a reaction would be discrete (see Figure 2). You can't have 1.25 bubbles. That'd be daft. Shoe size is another good example of a discrete variable.

2. Continuous data

A continuous variable can have any value on a scale. For example, the volume of gas produced or the mass of products from a reaction. You can never measure the exact value of a continuous variable.

3. Categoric data

A categoric variable has values that can be sorted into categories. For example, the colours of solutions might be blue, red and green (see Figure 3). Or types of material might be wood, steel, glass.

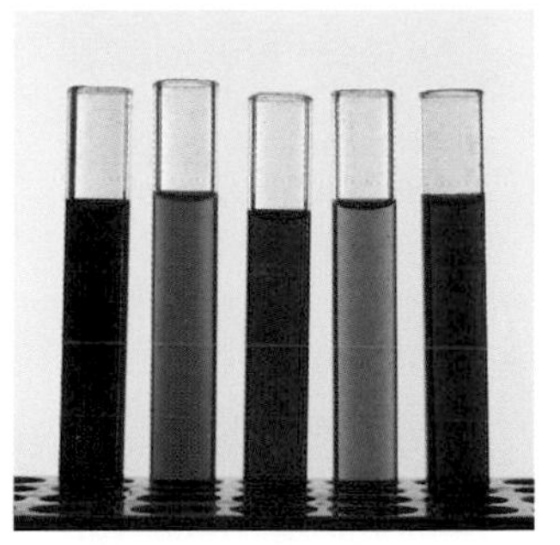

***Figure 3:** Different coloured solutions. Colour is a type of categoric data.*

4. Ordered (ordinal) data

Ordered data is similar to categoric, but the categories can be put in order. For example, if you classify reactions as 'slow', 'fairly fast' and 'very fast' you'd have ordered data.

Tables of data

Before you start your experiment, make a table to write your results in. You'll need to **repeat** each test at least three times to check your results are reliable (see p. 236 for more on reliable results). Figure 4 (below) is the sort of table you might end up with when you investigate the effect of temperature on reaction rate. (You'd then have to do the same for different temperatures.)

Temperature	Time (s)	Volume of gas evolved (cm^3) Run 1	Volume of gas evolved (cm^3) Run 2	Volume of gas evolved (cm^3) Run 3	Average volume of gas evolved (cm^3)
20 °C	10	8	7	8	**7.7**
	20	17	19	20	**18.7**
	30	28	20	30	**29**

***Figure 4:** Table of results showing the effect of temperature on the rate of reaction.*

Tip: To find the average of each set of repeated measurements you need to add them all up and divide by how many there are.

For example, for the average volume of gas evolved after 10 s, it's:

$8 + 7 + 8 \div 3 = 7.7$ cm^3

Watch out for **anomalous results**. These are ones that don't fit in with the other values and are likely to be wrong. They're usually due to random errors, such as making a mistake when measuring. You should ignore anomalous results when you calculate averages.

Example

Look at the table in Figure 4 again — the volume of gas evolved after 30 s in Run 2 looks like it might be an anomalous result. It's much lower than the values in the other two runs. It could have been caused by the syringe plunger getting stuck.

The anomalous result has been ignored when the average was calculated — that's why the average volume of gas evolved after 30 s is 29 cm^3 ($(28 + 30) \div 2 = 29$), rather than 26 cm^3 ($(28 + 20 + 30) \div 3 = 26$).

Tip: Just because you ignore anomalous results in your calculations you shouldn't ignore them in your write-up. Try to find an explanation for what went wrong so that it can be avoided in future experiments.

2. Graphs and Charts

You'll usually be expected to make a graph of your results. Graphs make your data easier to understand — so long as you choose the right type.

Types of graphs and charts

Tip: Use simple scales when you draw graphs — this'll make it easier to plot points.

Tip: Whatever type of graph you make, you'll only get full marks if you:

1. Choose a sensible scale — don't do a tiny graph in the corner of the paper.
2. Label both axes — including units.
3. Plot your points accurately — using a sharp pencil.

Bar charts

You should use a bar chart when one of your data sets is categoric or ordered data, like in Figure 1.

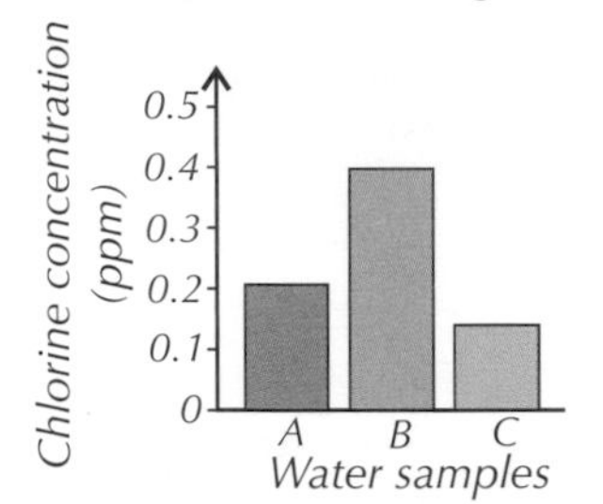

Figure 1: *Bar chart to show chlorine concentration in water samples.*

Pie charts

Pie charts are normally used to display categoric data, like in Figure 2.

transportation 4%
other 1%
industrial sources 10%
electric power stations 60%
fuel combustion 25%

Figure 2: *Pie chart to show sources of a country's sulfur dioxide emissions.*

Line Graphs

Line graphs are best when you have two sets of continuous data, like in Figure 3. Volume of gas and time are both continuous variables — you could get any value on the x or y-axis.

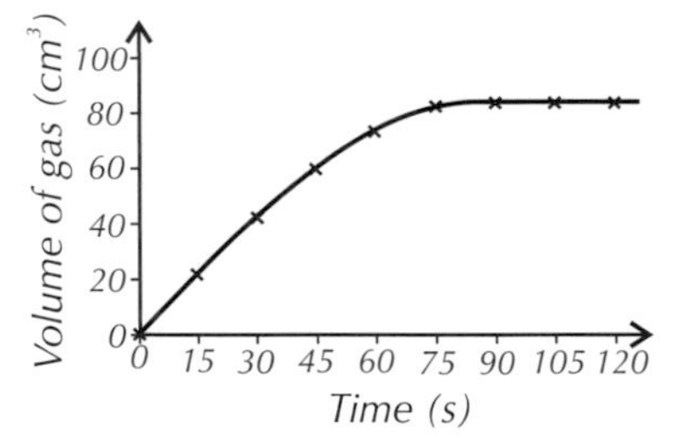

Figure 3: *Line graph to show volume of gas evolved against time.*

Scatter graphs

Scatter graphs, like Figure 4, are great for showing how two sets of data are related (or correlated — see below for more on correlation). Don't try to join all the points — draw a line of best fit to show the trend.

Tip: A line of best fit should have about half of the points above it and half of the points below. You can ignore any anomalous points like the one circled in Figure 4.

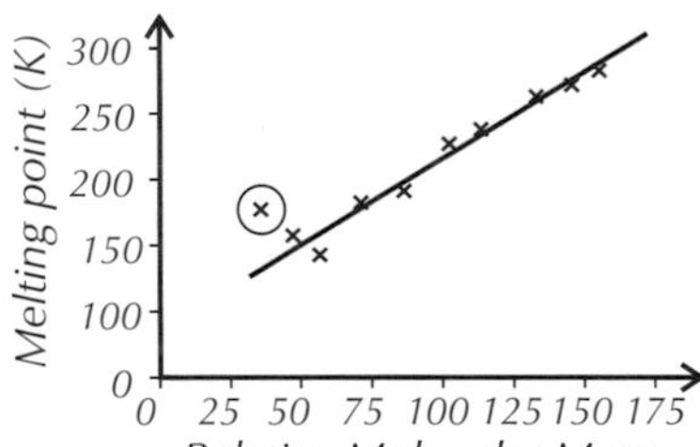

Figure 4: *Scatter graph showing the relationship between M_r and the melting point of alcohols.*

Scatter graphs and correlation

Correlation describes the relationship between two variables — usually the independent one and the dependent one. Data can show positive correlation, negative correlation or no correlation (see Figure 5).

Tip: Computers can make it a lot quicker to collect, record and analyse big sets of data from experiments — but you've still got to understand what all the numbers and graphs they churn out mean.

Positive correlation
As one variable increases the other also increases.

Negative correlation
As one variable increases the other decreases.

No correlation
There is no relationship between the variables.

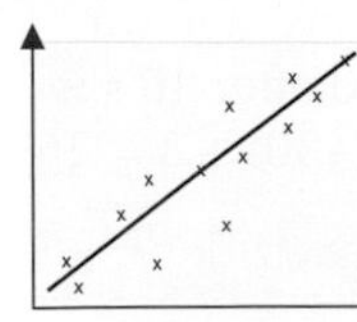

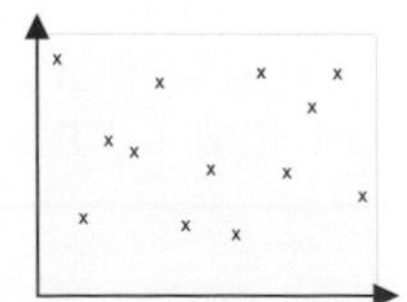

Figure 5: *Scatter graphs showing positive, negative and no correlation.*

3. Conclusions and Evaluations

Once you've got your results nicely presented in graphical form you can start to draw a conclusion. But be careful — you may have a graph showing a lovely correlation, but that doesn't always tell you as much as you might think.

Correlation and cause

Ideally, only two quantities would ever change in any experiment — everything else would remain constant. But in experiments or studies outside the lab, you can't usually control all the variables. So even if two variables are correlated, the change in one may not be causing the change in the other. Both changes might be caused by a third variable.

Tip: If an experiment really does confirm that changing one variable causes another to change, we say there's a causal link between them.

Example

Some studies have found a correlation between drinking chlorinated tap water and the risk of developing certain cancers. So some people argue that this means water shouldn't have chlorine added. But it's hard to control all the variables between people who drink tap water and people who don't. It could be many lifestyle factors. Or, the cancer risk could be affected by something else in tap water — or by whatever the non-tap water drinkers drink instead.

Tip: Watch out for bias too — for instance, a bottled water company might point these studies out to people without mentioning any of the doubts.

Drawing conclusions

The data should always support the conclusion. This may sound obvious but it's easy to jump to conclusions. Conclusions have to be specific — not make sweeping generalisations.

Example

The rate of an enzyme-controlled reaction was measured at 10 °C, 20 °C, 30 °C, 40 °C, 50 °C and 60 °C. All other variables were kept constant, and the results are shown in Figure 1.

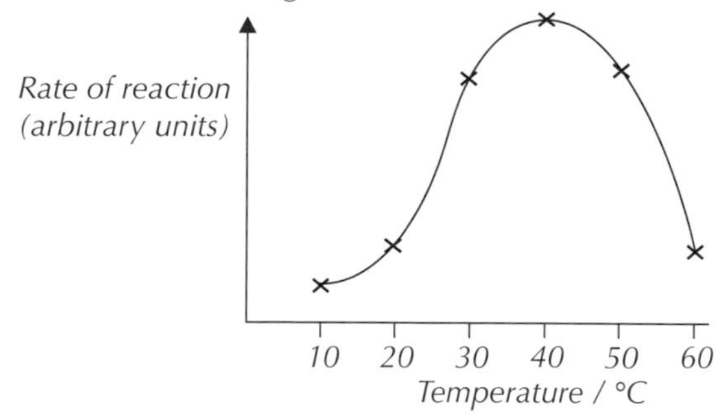

Figure 1: *Graph to show the effect of temperature on the rate of an enzyme-controlled reaction.*

A science magazine concluded from this data that enzyme X works best at 40 °C. The data doesn't support this. The enzyme could work best at 42 °C or 47 °C but you can't tell from the data because increases of 10 °C at a time were used. The rate of reaction at in-between temperatures wasn't measured. All you know is that it's faster at 40 °C than at any of the other temperatures tested.

Also, the experiment only gives information about this particular enzyme-controlled reaction. You can't conclude that all enzyme-controlled reactions happen faster at a particular temperature — only this one. And you can't say for sure that doing the experiment at, say, a different constant pressure, wouldn't give a different optimum temperature.

Tip: Whoever funded the research (e.g. a chemical manufacturer) may have some influence on what conclusions are drawn from the results, but scientists have a responsibility to make sure that the conclusions they draw are supported by the data.

Evaluations

There are a few terms that you need to understand. They'll be useful when you're evaluating how convincing your results are.

1. Valid results

Valid results answer the original question, using reliable data. For example, if you haven't controlled all the variables your results won't be valid, because you won't be testing just the thing you wanted to.

2. Accurate results

Accurate results are those that are really close to the true answer.

Tip: It's possible for results to be precise but not accurate, e.g. a balance that weighs to 1/1000th of a gram will give precise results, but if it's not calibrated properly the results won't be accurate.

3. Precise results

These are results taken using sensitive instruments that measure in small increments.

Example

A pH measured with a meter (e.g. pH 7.692) will be more precise than a pH measured with paper (e.g. pH 7).

4. Reliable results

Reliable means the results can be consistently reproduced in independent experiments. And if the results are reproducible they're more likely to be true. If the data isn't reliable, for whatever reason, you can't draw a valid conclusion. For experiments, the more repeats you do, the more reliable the data. If you get the same result twice, it could be the correct answer. But if you get the same result 20 times, it'd be much more reliable. And it'd be even more reliable if everyone in the class got about the same results using different apparatus.

Tip: Part of the scientific process (see pages 1-4) involves other scientists repeating your experiment too — then if they get the same results you can be more certain they're reliable.

5. Percentage error

You may have to calculate the percentage error of a measurement. If you know the precision that the measuring equipment is calibrated to, just divide this by the measurement taken and multiply by 100, as shown below.

Example

A balance is calibrated to within 0.1 g, and you measure a mass as 4.0 g.

The percentage error is: $(0.1 \div 4.0) \times 100 = 2.5\%$.

Using a larger quantity reduces the percentage error — a mass of 40.0 g has a percentage error of: $(0.1 \div 40.0) \times 100 = 0.25\%$.

Tip: You should always choose appropriate measuring equipment for the precision you need to work with.

Most measuring equipment has the precision it's calibrated to written on it. Where it doesn't, you can usually use the scale as a guide (e.g. if a measuring cylinder has a 1 ml scale, it is probably calibrated to within 0.5 ml).

Risks, hazards and ethical considerations

In any experiment you'll be expected to show that you've thought about the risks and hazards. It's generally a good thing to wear an apron and goggles, but you may need to take additional safety measures, depending on the experiment. For example, anything involving nasty gases will need to be done in a fume cupboard.

You need to make sure you're working ethically too. This is most important if there are other people or animals involved. You have to put their welfare first.

Figure 2: A scientist wearing protective clothing to handle hazardous chemicals.

Exam Help

1. Exam Structure and Technique

Revision is really, really important when it comes to exams, but it's not the only thing that'll help. Good exam technique and knowing the exam structure can help you pick up marks and make sure you do as well as you possibly can.

Exam structure

For AQA A2-Level Chemistry you're gonna have to sit through two exams (Unit 4 and Unit 5) and complete an internal assessment (Unit 6).

The exams

The two exams that you'll have to sit for A2 chemistry are:

- Unit 4 — Kinetics, Equilibria and Organic Chemistry
- Unit 5 — Energetics, Redox and Inorganic Chemistry

Both of these exams will be 1 hour 45 minutes long and there are 100 marks up for grabs in each. Each paper is worth 20% of your total A-level marks. Like your AS exams, the A2 exams are split up into two sections:

- Section A — contains 6-8 short answer questions.
- Section B — contains 2-3 longer structured questions.

The amount of time you should spend on each section can vary — it's usually about 70 minutes for section A and 35 minutes for section B. The time recommended for each section will be written on the front of the exam paper.

Unit 6 — Investigative and practical skills in A2 Chemistry

You'll do this unit in school with your teacher. It'll test your understanding of chemistry and your ability to plan, carry out, analyse and evaluate experiments in the lab. It's worth 10% of your total A-Level marks.

The assessments in Unit 6 test that you can use standard laboratory equipment, demonstrate safe and skilful practical techniques, plan a suitable experiment, take measurements with precision and accuracy, correctly record data and analyse and evaluate your experiment. This may sound a bit menacing but there's some stuff on pages 232-236 to help you out.

Synoptic assessment

At A2-level, some of the questions will have synoptic elements. This basically means that the examiner could ask you about things that you learnt at AS-level. So, you can't just forget all of the stuff you learnt at AS-level once you've finished your AS exams — you might need it for your A2 exams too. You could also be given a question where you have to use knowledge from lots of different areas of chemistry. But don't worry — as long as you know your stuff you'll be just fine.

Although you might be asked questions on AS material in the A2 exams, you won't be asked about stuff from Unit 4 in the Unit 5 exam, or about anything from Unit 5 in the Unit 4 exam. So that's good.

Exam Tip
Make sure you give this section on exam structure a good read. It might not seem important now but you don't want to get any nasty surprises just before an exam.

Exam Tip
Short answer questions are questions that are broken down into lots of different parts. They can still be worth lots of marks overall, it's just that you don't have to write that much for each individual part.

Tip: You might have noticed that the percentages on this page only add up to 50%. The other 50% comes from your AS-level exams.

Figure 1: *Fun times in a Chemistry lesson.*

Tip: This book covers everything on the A2 course and recaps some bits from AS, but you'll need to have a look back over your AS notes as well.

Quality of written communication (QWC)

All of the units you take for A2-Level Chemistry will have a quality of written communication element — this just means that the examiner will assess your ability to write properly. This may seem like a bit of a drag but you will lose marks if you don't do it. You need to make sure that:

- your scribble, sorry, writing is legible,
- your spelling, punctuation and grammar are accurate,
- your writing style is appropriate,
- you organise your answer clearly and coherently,
- you use specialist scientific vocabulary where it's appropriate.

In Section A of your Unit 4 and Unit 5 exam papers you're not specifically told that your quality of written communication will be assessed — but QWC will probably be tested here anyway. So... you must make sure you always write properly because you can never tell when those sneaky examiners are going to pop in some QWC marks. Section B of the exam papers require you to write in continuous prose when there's a long answer question — you will lose marks if you don't write in full sentences.

Exam Tip
You'll need to use a black pen in the exam, so make sure that you've got a few ready — you can never have too many spare pens (that's what I always say).

Exam Tip
You can use the number of marks available as a guide for how much you need to write for a question. For example, if it's a six-mark question, a one-sentence answer isn't going to be enough.

Time management

This is one of the most important exam skills to have. How long you spend on each question is really important in an exam — it could make all the difference to your grade. Check out the exam timings suggested by AQA. These timings give you about 1 minute per mark — try to stick to this to give yourself the best chance to pick up as many marks as possible.

Some questions will require lots of work for only a few marks but other questions will be much quicker. Don't spend ages struggling with questions that are only worth a couple of marks — move on. You can come back to them later when you've bagged loads of other marks elsewhere.

Examples

The questions below are both worth the same number of marks but require different amounts of work.

1 (a) Describe the bonding in and between molecules of SO_2.

(2 marks)

2 (a) Compounds A and B are hydrocarbons with relative molecular masses of 78 and 58 respectively. In their ^1H n.m.r. spectra, A has only one peak and B has two peaks.
Draw a possible structure for each compound.

(2 marks)

Question 1 (a) is just a fact recall question — if you can remember the facts, this shouldn't take you too long.

Question 2 (a) requires you to apply your knowledge of n.m.r. spectra and draw the structure of two compounds — this may take you a lot longer, especially if you have to draw out a few structures before getting it right.

So, if you're running out of time it makes sense to do questions like 1(a) first and come back to 2 (a) if you've got time at the end.

Exam Tip
Everyone has their own method of getting through the exam. Some people find it easier to go through the paper question by question and some people like to do the questions they find easiest first. The most important thing is to find out the way that suits you best before the exam — that means doing all the practice exams you can before the big day.

Exam Tip
Don't forget to go back and do any questions that you left the first time round — you don't want to miss out on marks because you forgot to do the question. Fold over the corner of the page or put a big star next to the questions to remind yourself to go back.

Calculations

There's no getting away from calculation questions — they come up a lot in A2 Chemistry. It's really important to remember to show your working — then even if your answer is wrong you could get marks for the method.

Units

Make sure you always give the correct units for your answer (see pages 244 and 245 for more on units).

Example

Here's an example of a question where you need to change the units so they match the answer the examiner wants.

1 Calculate the free energy change for the following reaction at 298 K, giving your answer in $kJmol^{-1}$:

$MgCO_3 \rightarrow MgO + CO_2$ $\Delta H^{\circ} = 1.17 \times 10^5$ $Jmol^{-1}$
$\Delta S^{\circ} = 175$ $JK^{-1}mol^{-1}$

(2 marks)

Here you use the equation: $\Delta G = \Delta H - T\Delta S$. Plugging the numbers in gives you an answer of +64850 $Jmol^{-1}$. But the question asks for the answer in $kJmol^{-1}$, so you have to divide by 1000, giving an answer of 64.85 $kJmol^{-1}$. If you left your answer as +64850 $Jmol^{-1}$ you'd lose a mark.

Significant figures

Use the number of significant figures given in the question as a guide for how many to give in the answer. You should always give your answer to the lowest number of significant figures (s.f.) given in the question — if you're really unsure, write down the full answer and then round it to 3 s.f. It always helps to write down the number of significant figures you've rounded to after your answer — it shows the examiner you really know what you're talking about.

Examples

In this question the data given to you is a good indication of how many significant figures you should give your answer to.

1 (b) Calculate the pH of 0.410 $moldm^{-3}$ ethanoic acid at 298 K.

(2 marks)

The concentration in the question is given to 3 s.f. so it makes sense to give your answer to 3 s.f. too. But sometimes it isn't as clear as that.

3 (b) 18.5 cm^3 of a 0.65 $moldm^{-3}$ solution of potassium hydroxide reacts with 1.5 $moldm^{-3}$ sulfuric acid. Calculate the volume of sulfuric acid needed to neutralise the potassium hydroxide.

(2 marks)

There are two types of data in this question, volume data and concentration data. The volume data is given to 3 s.f. and the concentration data is given to 2 s.f. You should always give your answer to the lowest number of significant figures given — in this case that's to 2 s.f. The answer in full is 4.00833... cm^3 so the answer rounded correctly would be 4.0 cm^3 (2 s.f.).

Exam Tip
It's really easy to accidentally mistype numbers into a calculator when you're under pressure in an exam. To make sure you don't lose marks, double-check your calculations (if you've got time) and always make sure the answer looks sensible.

Exam Tip
You'll need to know what units your figures need to be in for different formulas — see pages 242-243 for the units used in different formulas and pages 244-245 for how to convert between units.

Tip: The first significant figure of a number is the first digit that isn't a zero. The second, third and fourth significant figures follow on immediately after the first (even if they're zeros).

Exam Tip
Sometimes the question might say how many significant figures or decimal places you should give your answer to. If you are told, make sure that you follow the instructions or you'll lose valuable marks.

Standard form

You might be asked to give your answer in standard form. Standard form is used for writing very big or very small numbers in a more convenient way. Standard form must always look like this:

This number must always be between 1 and 10. → $A \times 10^n$ ← *This number is the number of places the decimal point moves.*

> **Tip:** Standard form is really useful once you get used to using it. Writing out the whole number takes longer and you'll be more likely to accidentally slip in an extra zero or two if you write out the full thing.

Examples

Here's how to write 480 000 in standard form.

- First write the non-zero digits with a decimal point after the first number and a '× 10' after it:

$$4.8 \times 10$$

- Then count how many places the decimal point has moved to the left. This number sits to the top right of the 10.

$$4\overset{5}{8}\overset{4}{0}\overset{3}{0}\overset{2}{0}\overset{1}{0} = 4.8 \times 10^5$$

- Et voilà... that's 480 000 written in standard form.

Here are some more examples.

- You can write 3 200 000 as 3.2×10^6.
- The number 0.00073 is 7.3×10^{-4} in standard form — the n is negative because the decimal point has moved to the right instead of the left.
- You can write 0.008294 as 8.294×10^{-3}.

> **Tip:** Your calculator might give you your answer in standard form automatically — result.

Diagrams

When you're asked to draw diagrams or mechanisms in an exam it's important that you draw everything correctly.

> **Tip:** Curly arrows show the movement of electrons. So it's important that the curly arrows come from a lone pair or a bond — that's where the electrons are found.

Examples

Drawing organic reaction mechanisms

When you're drawing organic reaction mechanisms the curly arrows must come from either a lone pair of electrons or from a bond, like this:

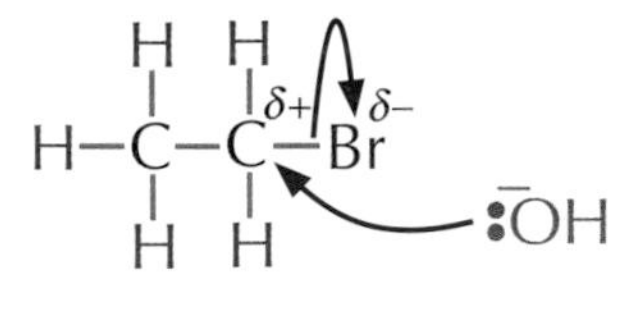

The mechanisms below are all incorrect — you wouldn't get marks for them:

You won't get marks for showing a bond as a line with dots on either side like this...

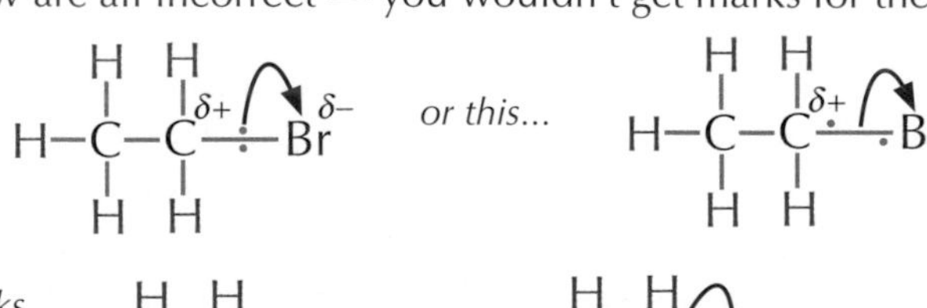

And you won't get marks if the curly arrows come from atoms, like this...

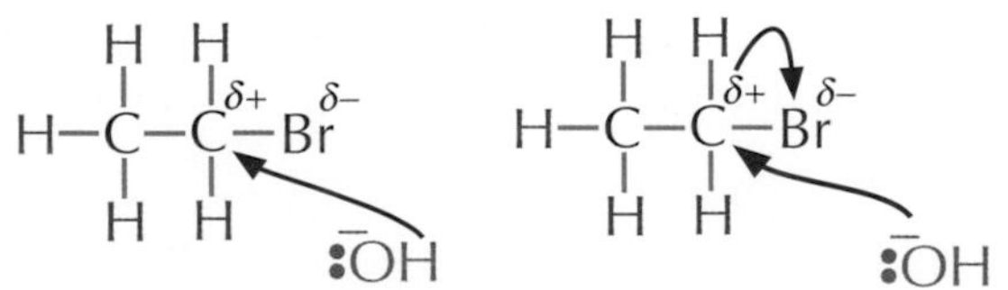

Drawing displayed formulas

If a question asks you for a displayed formula you have to show all of the bonds and all of the atoms in the molecule. That means you have to draw displayed formulas like this:

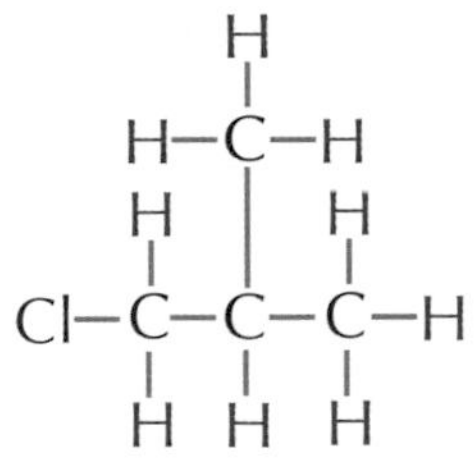

And not like this:

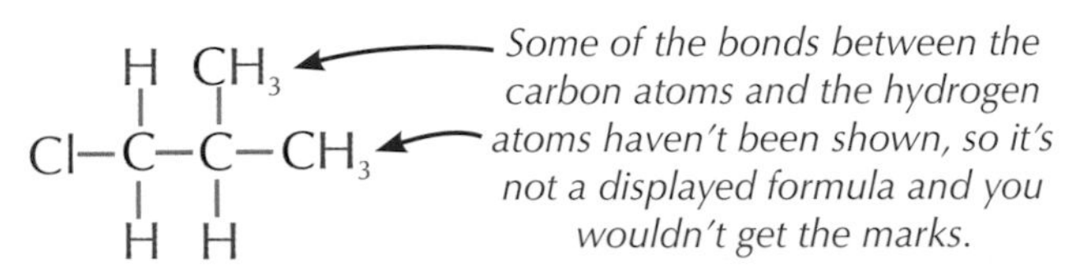

Some of the bonds between the carbon atoms and the hydrogen atoms haven't been shown, so it's not a displayed formula and you wouldn't get the marks.

If you're not asked specifically for a displayed formula then either of the diagrams above will do. Just make sure that the bonds are always drawn between the right atoms. For example, ethanol should be drawn like this:

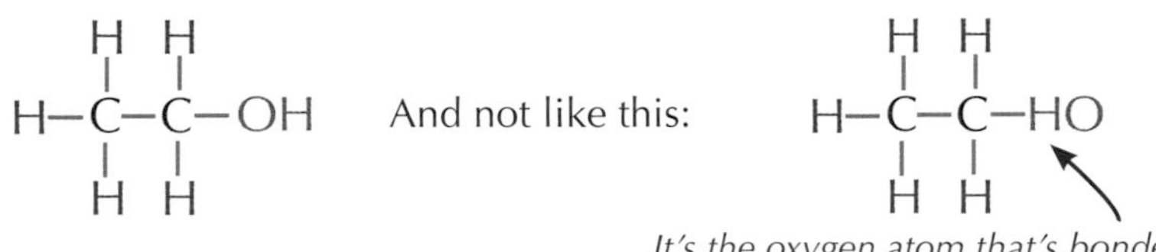

It's the oxygen atom that's bonded to carbon, not the hydrogen atom, so drawing it like this is just plain wrong.

Drawing the shapes of molecules

You're probably going to have to draw diagrams to show the shapes of molecules. Make sure that you show all of the atoms and draw on all of the lone pairs. For example, this would be a good drawing of ammonia:

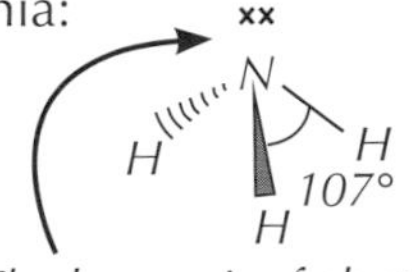

The lone pair of electrons is shown and all of the atoms and bonds are included.

This would not:

N

107°

The lone pair of electrons is missing and the hydrogen atoms have not been included.

When you're drawing any diagram make sure it's really clear what you're drawing. A small scribble in the bottom corner of a page isn't going to show enough detail to get you the marks. Draw the diagrams nice and big, but make sure that you stay within the space given for that answer — you won't get marks for anything that's drawn in the margin.

Exam Tip
If you've made a mistake when drawing a diagram, don't scribble part of it out and try to fix it — just cross the whole thing out and start again. Otherwise it'll look messy and be really hard for the examiner to figure out what you're trying to show.

Tip: A displayed formula shows how all the atoms are arranged, and all the bonds between them. See page 50 for more on displayed formulas.

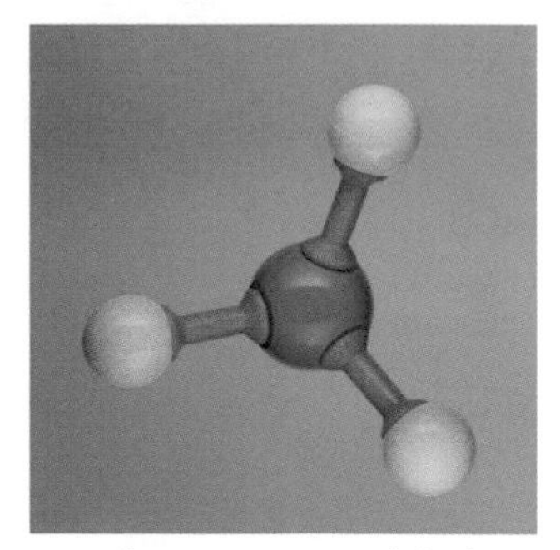

Figure 2: *A model of an NH_3 molecule.*

2. Formulas and Equations

You need to do a lot of calculations at A2-level, so there are loads of formulas you need to know. Here's a quick summary of the main formulas you'll need.

Tip: If something in an equation is in [square brackets] it means it's a concentration.

Unit 4 formulas

First up, it's the rate equation. You'll need this when looking at rates of reaction...

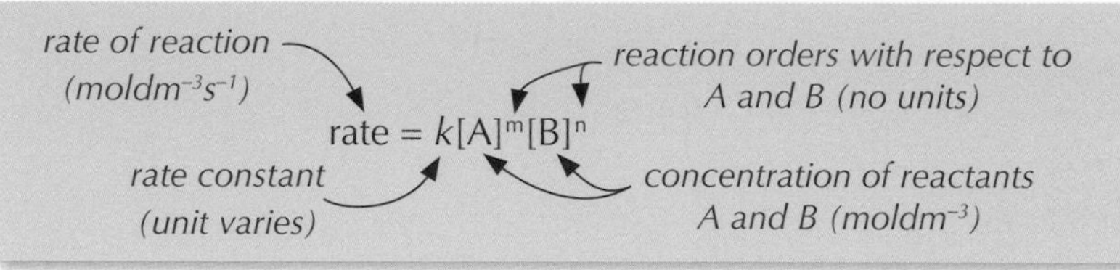

Tip: In this equation there are only two reactants (A and B), but you can have more. Here's the equation if you have three reactants: rate = $k[A]^m[B]^n[C]^x$

This is the equation for calculating the equilibrium constant (K_c)...

For the reaction $aA + bB \rightarrow dD + eE$: $K_c = \dfrac{[D]^d[E]^e}{[A]^a[B]^b}$

lower case letters are the number of moles

Tip: You have to calculate the unit of K_c. It's not always the same.

These are the equations for the ionic product of water (K_w) and the acid dissociation constant (K_a)...

$K_w = [H^+][OH^-]$ *in mol²dm⁻⁶*

$K_a = \dfrac{[H^+][A^-]}{[HA]}$ *in moldm⁻³*

Tip: In pure water, $[H^+] = [OH^-]$ so $K_w = [H^+]^2$.

And here are the equations for calculating pH and pK_a...

$pH = -\log_{10}[H^+]$

$pK_a = -\log_{10}[K_a]$

...which rearrange to ...

$[H^+] = 10^{-pH}$

$K_a = 10^{-pKa}$

Tip: Make sure you know how to use the log button on your calculator.

Finally, here's an equation for calculating the number of carbon atoms in a compound from a mass spectrum...

$$\text{No. of carbon atoms} = \frac{\text{height of M + 1 peak}}{\text{height of M peak}} \times 100$$

Exam Tip
Make sure you learn all of these formulas. You could need any one of them in the exam and you'll be gutted if you can't remember them.

Unit 5 formulas

In Unit 5 you need a few formulas to help you calculate free energy changes. To calculate the entropy change of a system you use:

$\Delta S_{system} = S_{products} - S_{reactants}$ where ΔS is the entropy change in $JK^{-1}mol^{-1}$

To calculate the entropy change of the surroundings you need:

$\Delta S_{surroundings} = -\dfrac{\Delta H}{T}$ where ΔH is the enthalpy change ($Jmol^{-1}$) of the reaction and T is the temperature (K)

Once you know the entropy change of the system and the entropy change of the surroundings you can calculate the total entropy change using:

$\Delta S_{total} = \Delta S_{system} + \Delta S_{surroundings}$

If you know the enthalpy change, the entropy change and temperature of a reaction, you can calculate the free energy change (ΔG) using:

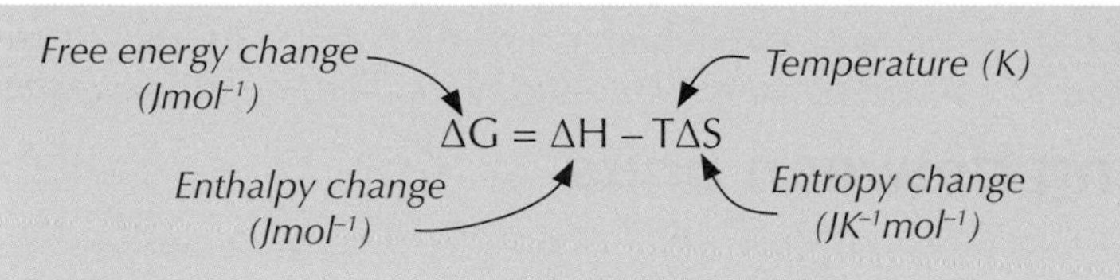

Exam Tip
Make sure you can rearrange all these formulas and give the units of each quantity as well.

You also might need this little equation — it's for calculating the energy absorbed when an electron moves between orbitals:

$$\Delta E = h\nu$$

Energy absorbed (J) — ΔE; *Frequency of light absorbed (hertz/Hz)* — ν; *Planck's constant (6.63×10^{-34} Js)* — h

And here's an equation for calculating standard cell potentials:

$$E^{\ominus}_{cell} = E^{\ominus}_{\text{right-hand side}} - E^{\ominus}_{\text{(left-hand side)}}$$

Tip: Electrode potentials are always measured in volts (V).

Formulas you might need from AS

There are some synoptic elements in the A2 exam so you might need some of these equations which you learnt at AS level. First up...

Tip: See page 237 for more on synoptic assessment.

$$\text{Number of moles} = \frac{\text{Mass of substance}}{\text{Molar mass}} \quad \text{also written as...} \quad n = \frac{m}{M_r}$$

You'll also need this one when you're dealing with solutions...

$$\text{Number of moles} = \text{Concentration} \times \text{Volume (in dm}^3\text{)}$$

Divide by 1000 if your volume's in cm³

And these when you've got gases at room temperature and pressure...

$$\text{Number of moles} = \frac{\text{Volume (in dm}^3\text{)}}{24} \qquad \text{Number of moles} = \frac{\text{Volume (in cm}^3\text{)}}{24\,000}$$

Here's the ideal gas equation...

$$pV = nRT$$

p (Pa), V (m³), n (moles), R (8.31 JK⁻¹mol⁻¹), T (K)

Tip: If you forget an equation in an exam, thinking about the units could help you out. For example, if you know concentration is in moldm⁻³, it tells you that to calculate a concentration you have to divide a number of moles by a volume in dm³. So the equation is concentration = moles ÷ volume.

Here are the equations for percentage yield and percentage atom economy...

$$\%\text{ atom economy} = \frac{\text{Mass of desired product}}{\text{Total mass of reactants}} \times 100$$

$$\%\text{ yield} = \frac{\text{Actual yield}}{\text{Theoretical yield}} \times 100$$

3. Units

Units aren't the most exciting bit of chemistry but you need to be able to use them. Here's how to convert between units and work them out from scratch.

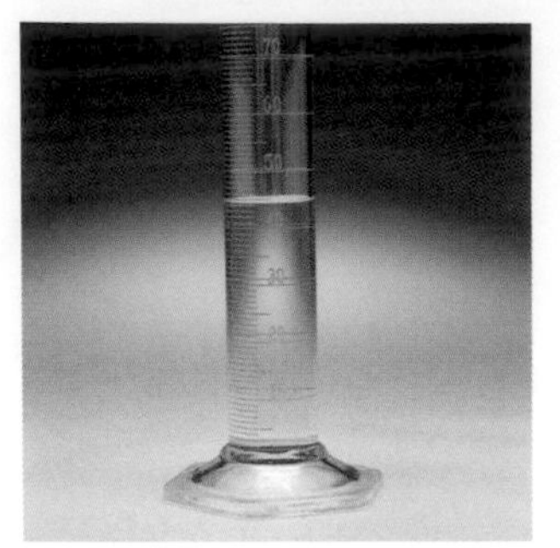

Figure 1: Measuring cylinders like this one measure volumes in cm³.

Tip: Standard form (that's showing numbers as, for example, 3×10^{-7}) is covered on page 240.

Converting between units

Volume

Volume can be measured in m^3, dm^3 and cm^3.

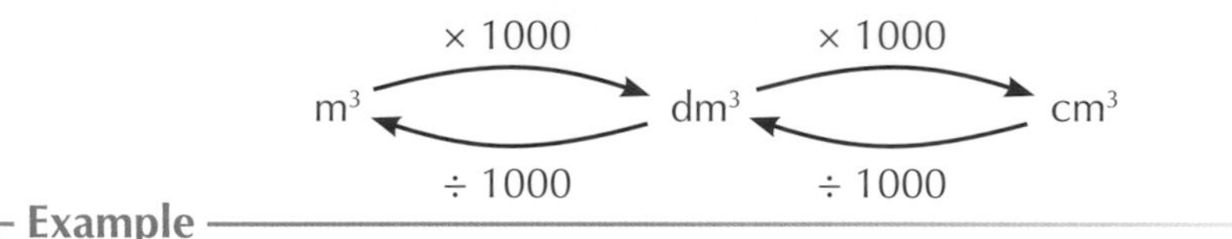

Example

Write 0.3 cm³ in dm³ and m³.

First, to convert 0.3 cm³ into dm³ you need to divide by 1000.

$$0.3 \text{ cm}^3 \div 1000 = 0.0003 \text{ dm}^3 = 3 \times 10^{-4} \text{ dm}^3$$

Then, to convert 0.0003 dm³ into m³ you need to divide by 1000.

$$0.0003 \text{ dm}^3 \div 1000 = 0.0000003 \text{ m}^3 = 3 \times 10^{-7} \text{ m}^3$$

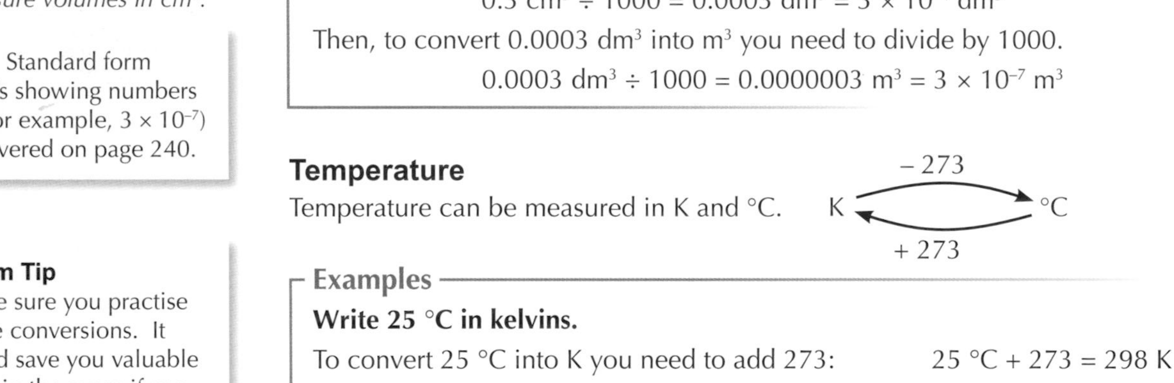

Temperature

Temperature can be measured in K and °C.

K → °C: − 273; °C → K: + 273

Examples

Write 25 °C in kelvins.

To convert 25 °C into K you need to add 273: 25 °C + 273 = 298 K

Exam Tip

Make sure you practise these conversions. It could save you valuable time in the exam if you can change between units confidently.

Pressure

Pressure can be measured in Pa and kPa.

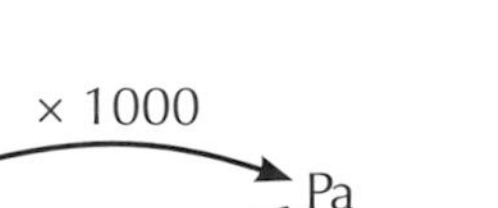

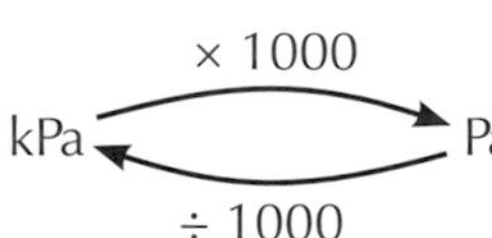

Example

Write 3200 Pa in kPa.

To convert 3200 Pa into kPa you need to divide by 1000.

$$3200 \text{ Pa} \div 1000 = 3.2 \text{ kPa}$$

Tip: A kPa is bigger than a Pa, so you'd expect the number to get smaller when you convert from Pa to kPa — each unit is worth more so you'll have fewer of them.

Mass

Mass can be measured in kg and g.

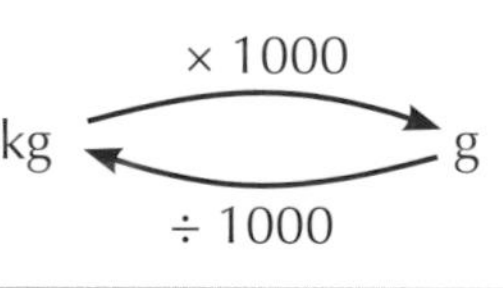

Example

Write 5.2 kg in g.

To convert 5.2 kg into g you need to multiply by 1000.

$$5.2 \text{ kg} \times 1000 = 5200 \text{ g}$$

Figure 2: This balance measures mass in g.

Energy

Energy can be measured in kJ and J.

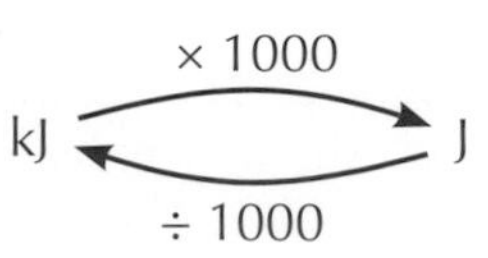

Example

Write 78 kJ in J.

To convert 78 kJ into J you need to multiply by 1000.

$$78 \text{ kJ} \times 1000 = 78\,000 \text{ J} = 7.8 \times 10^4 \text{ J}$$

Tip: If you get a bit confused converting between units, thinking about a conversion you are confident with might help. For example, if you know that 1 kJ is 1000 J, you know that to get from kJ to J you must have to multiply by 1000 — simple.

Concentration

Concentration can be measured in moldm^{-3} (M) and molcm^{-3}.

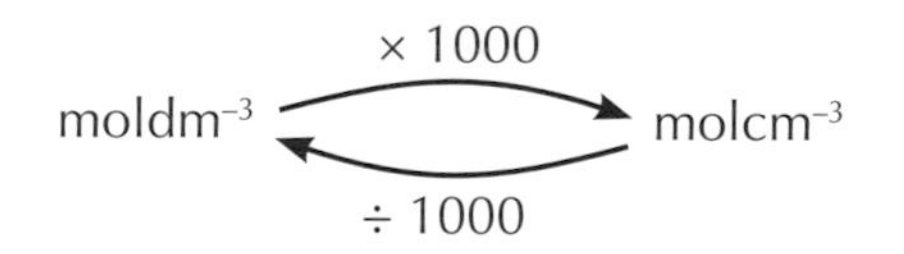

Example

Write 0.5 moldm^{-3} in molcm^{-3}.

To convert 0.5 moldm^{-3} into molcm^{-3} you need to multiply by 1000.

$$0.5 \text{ moldm}^{-3} \times 1000 = 500 \text{ molcm}^{-3}$$

Figure 3: When you're under pressure in an exam it's really easy to make mistakes. So don't be afraid to use your calculator, even for really simple calculations.

Life gets a bit confusing if you have to do lots of calculations one after the other — sometimes it can be difficult to keep track of your units.
To avoid this, always write down the units you're using with each line of the calculation. Then when you get to the end you know what units to give with your answer.

Calculating units

Some things, like the equilibrium constant (K_c) and the rate constant (k), have variable units. This means you'll need to work the units out — you can't just learn them. To work out the units, you just follow these steps:

- Substitute the units that you know into the equation you're using.
- Cancel out units wherever possible — if the same unit is present on the top and the bottom of a fraction, you can cancel them out.
- Get rid of any fractions by inversing the powers of the units on the bottom of the fraction — any positive powers become negative and any negative powers become positive.

Exam Tip

Always, always, always give units with your answers. It's really important that the examiner knows what units you're working in — 10 g is very different from 10 kg.

Examples

The rate equation for the reaction $CH_3COCH_3 + I_2 \rightarrow CH_3COCH_2I + H^+ + I^-$ is Rate = $k[CH_3COCH_3][H^+]$. The rate of reaction is in $\text{moldm}^{-3}\text{s}^{-1}$ and the concentrations are in moldm^{-3}. Find the units of *k*.

$$\text{Rate} = k[CH_3COCH_3][H^+] \quad \text{so} \quad k = \frac{\text{Rate}}{[CH_3COCH_3]\,[H^+]}$$

First substitute in the units you know:

$$k = \frac{\text{moldm}^{-3}\text{s}^{-1}}{(\text{moldm}^{-3})(\text{moldm}^{-3})}$$

Cancel out units where you can. In this case you can cancel a moldm^{-3} from the top and the bottom of the fraction:

$$k = \frac{\cancel{\text{moldm}^{-3}}\text{s}^{-1}}{\cancel{(\text{moldm}^{-3})}(\text{moldm}^{-3})} = \frac{\text{s}^{-1}}{\text{moldm}^{-3}}$$

Then get rid of the fraction by inversing the powers:

$$k = \text{s}^{-1}\text{mol}^{-1}\text{dm}^{3}$$

Tip: If you have more than one of a particular unit multiplied together, you add the powers together — e.g. $(\text{moldm}^{-3})(\text{moldm}^{-3})$ is $\text{mol}^2\text{dm}^{-6}$).

Tip: Just writing mol is the same as writing mol^1, so when you inverse the power, mol becomes mol^{-1}.

4. The Periodic Table — Facts and Trends

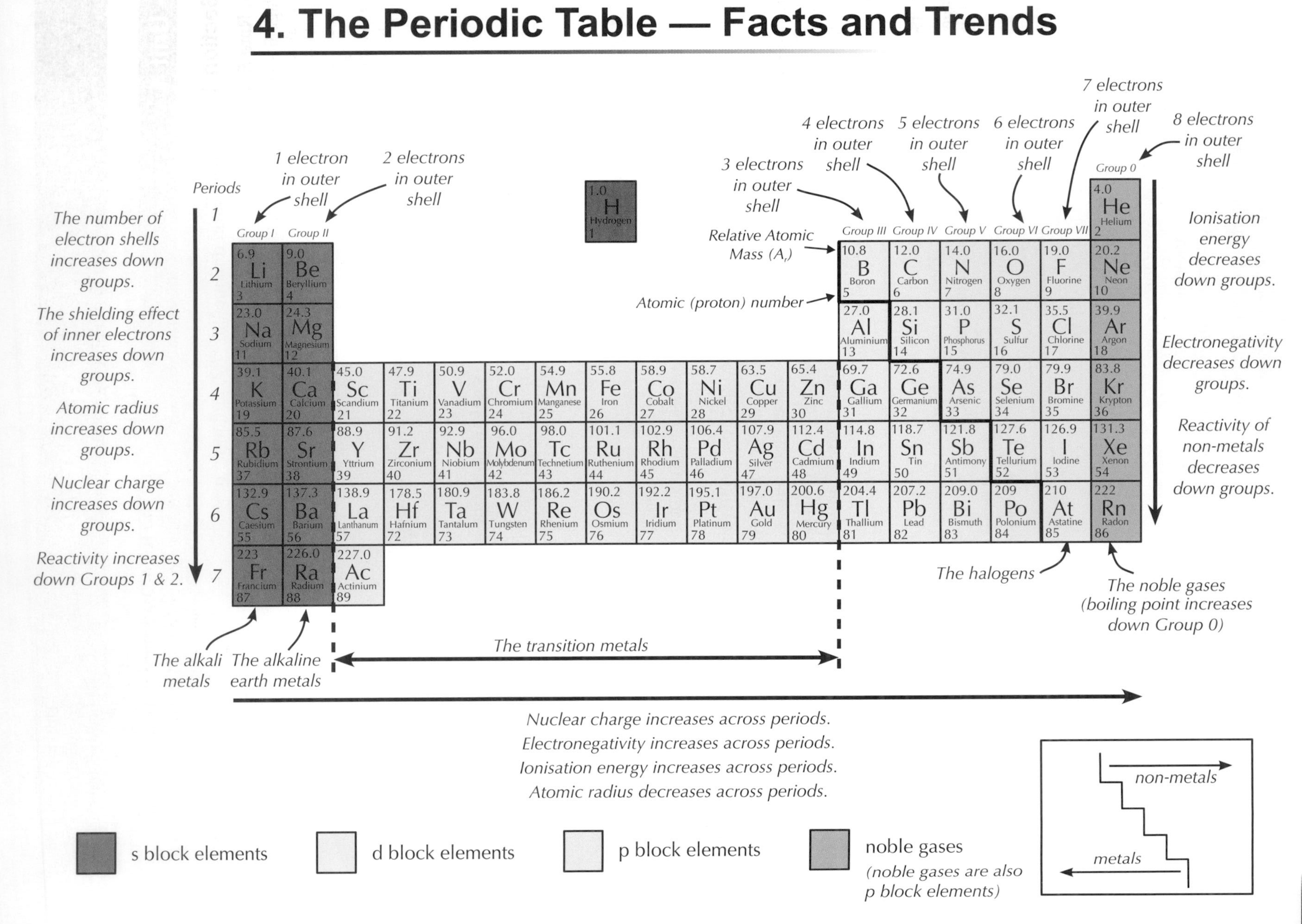

Answers

Unit 4

Section 1 — Kinetics and Equilibria

1. Rate Equations

Page 8 — Application Questions

Q1 a) Rate = $k[H_2][NO]^2$
b) 3
c) If the concentration of NO were doubled the rate of the reaction would be four times faster.

Q2 a) Rate = $k[NO]^2[Cl_2]$
b) $5.85 \times 10^{-6} = k(0.4)^2(0.4)$ so

$$k = \frac{5.85 \times 10^{-6}}{[0.4]^2[0.4]} = 9.14 \times 10^{-5}$$

$$k = \frac{\text{moldm}^{-3}\text{s}^{-1}}{(\text{moldm}^{-3})^2(\text{moldm}^{-3})} = \text{mol}^{-2}\text{dm}^6\text{s}^{-1}$$

$k =$ **9.14×10^{-5} mol^{-2}dm^{6}s^{-1}**

When calculating k in exams, don't forget to work out the units as well.

c) If the temperature was increased the value of k would increase.
d) Rate = $k[NO]^2[Cl_2]$
Rate = $(9.14 \times 10^{-5}) \times 0.5^2 \times 0.2$
= **4.57×10^{-6} moldm^{-3}s^{-1}**

These answers are all rounded to 3 significant figures. In your exam, round your answer to the same number of significant figures as is given in the question. If in doubt, go for 3.

Page 8 — Fact Recall Questions

Q1 A reaction rate is the change in the amount of reactants or products per unit time.

Q2 The rate equation tells you how the rate of a reaction is affected by the concentration of the reactants.

Q3 a) The rate constant.
b) The concentration of reactant A.
c) The order of the reaction with respect to A.

Q4 moldm^{-3}s^{-1}

2. The Initial Rates Method

Page 10 — Application Question

Q1 a) Looking at experiments 1 and 2: doubling [B] quadruples the rate so the reaction is order 2 with respect to [B]. Looking at experiments 2 and 3: tripling [C] triples the rate so the reaction is order 1 with respect to [C]. Looking at experiments 2 and 4: halving [A] halves the rate so the reaction is order 1 with respect to [A].
So, Rate = $k[A][B]^2[C]$
b) Rate = $k[A][B]^2[C]$ so k = rate ÷ $[A][B]^2[C]$
For experiment 1:
$k = 0.25 \div [(1.2) \times (1.2)^2 \times (1.2)] = 0.12$
k = moldm^{-3}s^{-1} ÷ [(moldm^{-3}) × (moldm^{-3})^2 × (moldm^{-3})]
= **0.12 mol^{-3}dm^{9}s^{-1}**

3. The Rate-Determining Step

Page 12 — Application Questions

Q1 a) Step 1. The rate equation shows that the rate-determining step involves two molecules of NO_2, and there are two NO_2 molecules in step 1.
Don't forget — if it's in the rate equation it must be involved in the rate-determining step.
b) If the reaction had a one-step mechanism, that step would have to involve CO. CO is not in the rate equation so can't be involved in the rate-determining step. So a one-step mechanism isn't possible.

Q2 Rate = $k[A]^2[B][C]$

Page 12 — Fact Recall Questions

Q1 The rate-determining step is the slowest step in a reaction mechanism, so it's the step which determines the overall rate of the reaction.

Q2 2

4. The Equilibrium Constant

Page 16 — Application Questions

Q1 a) $K_c = \frac{[C_2H_5OH]}{[C_2H_4][H_2O]}$

b) The equation tells you that if 1 mole of C_2H_5OH decomposes, 1 mole of C_2H_4 and 1 mole of H_2O are formed. So if 1.85 moles of C_2H_4 are produced at equilibrium, there will also be **1.85** moles of H_2O. 1.85 moles of C_2H_5OH has decomposed so there must be 5 – 1.85 = **3.15** moles of C_2H_5OH remaining.
c) The volume of the reaction is 15 dm^3. So the molar concentrations are:
For H_2O and C_2H_4: 1.85 ÷ 15 = **0.123 moldm^{-3}**.
For C_2H_5OH: 3.15 ÷ 15 = **0.210 moldm^{-3}**.

d) $$K_c = \frac{[C_2H_5OH]}{[C_2H_4][H_2O]} = \frac{0.210}{(0.123)(0.123)} = 13.9$$

$$K_c = \frac{\text{moldm}^{-3}}{(\text{moldm}^{-3})(\text{moldm}^{-3})} = \frac{1}{(\text{moldm}^{-3})}$$

K_c = **13.9 mol^{-1}dm^3**

Setting your answer out like this makes it clear to the examiner what you've done and will mean you're more likely to pick up some method marks.

e) $$K_c = \frac{[C_2H_5OH]}{[C_2H_4][H_2O]} \text{ so } 3.8 = \frac{0.8}{[C_2H_4][H_2O]}$$

$[C_2H_4][H_2O] = 0.8 \div 3.8 = 0.21$
$[C_2H_4]$ and $[H_2O] = \sqrt{0.21}$ = **0.46 moldm^{-3}**

Q2 a) $K_c = \frac{[SO_3]^2}{[SO_2]^2[O_2]}$

b) $K_c = \frac{[SO_3]^2}{[SO_2]^2[O_2]} = \frac{0.36^2}{(0.25)^2(0.18)} = 11.5$

$K_c = \frac{(moldm^{-3})^2}{(moldm^{-3})^2(moldm^{-3})} = \frac{1}{(moldm^{-3})}$

K_c = **11.5 mol⁻¹dm³**

c) $[SO_2]^2 = \frac{[SO_3]^2}{K_c \times [O_2]} = \frac{0.36^2}{15 \times 0.18} = 0.048$

$[SO_2] = \sqrt{0.048}$ = **0.22 moldm⁻³**

Page 16 — Fact Recall Questions

Q1 A dynamic equilibrium occurs when the reaction is still happening but the forward and backward reaction are going at exactly the same rate so there is no net change in the concentrations of the reagents.

Q2 For a dynamic equilibrium to be established it must be a closed system and the temperature must be constant.

Q3 $K_c = \frac{[D]^d[E]^e}{[A]^a[B]^b}$

Q4 The units of K_c change depending on the concentration terms in the reaction.

5. Changing the Equilibrium

Page 18 — Application Questions

Q1 a) No effect — if the concentration of C_2F_4 increases the equilibrium will shift to counteract the change and K_c will stay the same.

b) The reaction is endothermic in the forward direction so increasing the temperature will shift the equilibrium to the right. As a result more product will be produced, so K_c will increase.

c) No effect — catalysts only affect the time taken to reach equilibrium and not the position of the equilibrium itself.

Remember — only changing the temperature changes the value of K_c.

Q2 Exothermic. If decreasing the temperature increases K_c then it must increase the amount of product formed. The equilibrium must have shifted to the right, so the forward reaction must be exothermic.

Page 18 — Fact Recall Questions

Q1 If there's a change in concentration, pressure or temperature then an equilibrium will move to help counteract the change.

Q2 a) It will increase K_c.

b) It will decrease K_c.

Q3 If the concentration of a reagent is changed the equilibrium will shift and the concentrations of other reagents will also change. So K_c will stay the same.

Q4 Adding a catalyst doesn't change the position of the equilibrium or K_c, but it decreases the time taken to reach equilibrium.

6. Acids and Bases

Page 20 — Fact Recall Questions

Q1 a) Brønsted-Lowry acids are proton donors.

b) Brønsted-Lowry bases are proton acceptors.

Q2 a) $HA_{(aq)} \rightleftharpoons H^+_{(aq)} + A^-_{(aq)}$

b) $B_{(aq)} + H_2O_{(l)} \rightleftharpoons BH^+_{(aq)} + OH^-_{(aq)}$

c) $HA_{(aq)} + B_{(aq)} \rightleftharpoons BH^+_{(aq)} + A^-_{(aq)}$

When you're writing equations for reversible reactions don't forget to use the funky double arrows. If you just draw a normal arrow it won't be correct.

Q3 a) A strong acid

b) A weak base

Q4 $H_2O_{(l)} \rightleftharpoons H^+_{(aq)} + OH^-_{(aq)}$

Q5 a) K_w is a constant called the ionic product of water.

b) $K_w = [H^+][OH^-]$

c) mol^2dm^{-6}

Q6 In pure water there is always one H^+ ion per OH^- ion so $[H^+]=[OH^-]$ and $[H^+][OH^-]$ is the same as $[H^+]^2$.

7. pH Calculations

Page 21 — Application Questions

Q1 pH = –log[H⁺] = –log[0.05] = **1.30**

Q2 $[H^+] = 10^{-pH} = 10^{-2.86}$ = **1.38×10^{-3} moldm⁻³**

Q3 pH = –log[H⁺] = –log[0.02] = **1.70**

Page 23 — Application Questions

Q1 HCl is monoprotic so [H⁺] = [HCl] = 0.08 moldm⁻³

pH = –log[H⁺] = –log[0.08] = **1.10**

Q2 H_2SO_4 is diprotic so $[H^+] = 2[H_2SO_4] = 2 \times 0.025$ = 0.05 moldm⁻³

pH= –log[H⁺] = –log[0.05] = **1.30**

Q3 KOH is a strong base so [OH⁻] = [KOH] = 0.2 moldm⁻³

$K_w = [H^+][OH^-]$ so $[H^+] = K_w \div [OH^-]$

$= (5.48 \times 10^{-14}) \div 0.2 = 2.74 \times 10^{-13}$

pH = –log[H⁺] = $-\log[2.74 \times 10^{-13}]$ = **12.56**

Page 23 — Fact Recall Questions

Q1 pH = –log[H⁺]

Q2 Monoprotic means that each molecule of acid releases one proton. Diprotic means that each molecule of acid releases two protons.

Q3 $K_w = [H^+][OH^-]$

8. The Acid Dissociation Constant

Page 27 — Application Questions

Q1 a) $K_a = [H^+][CN^-] \div [HCN]$ or $K_a = [H^+]^2 \div [HCN]$

b) $K_a = [H^+]^2 \div [HCN]$ so $[H^+]^2 = K_a \times [HCN]$

$= (4.9 \times 10^{-10}) \times 2.0 = 9.8 \times 10^{-10}$

$[H^+] = \sqrt{9.8 \times 10^{-10}} = 3.13 \times 10^{-5}$ moldm⁻³

pH = $-\log[H^+] = -\log[3.13 \times 10^{-5}]$ = **4.50**

Q2 $[H^+] = 10^{-pH} = 10^{-3.8} = 1.58 \times 10^{-4}$ moldm⁻³

$K_a = [H^+]^2 \div [HNO_2]$ so $[HNO_2] = [H^+]^2 \div K_a$

$= (1.58 \times 10^{-4})^2 \div 4.0 \times 10^{-4}$ = **6.24×10^{-5} moldm⁻³**

Q3 $K_a = [H^+]^2 \div [HA]$ so $[H^+]^2 = K_a \times [HA]$

$= (1.38 \times 10^{-4}) \times 0.48 = 6.62 \times 10^{-5}$

$[H^+] = \sqrt{6.62 \times 10^{-5}} = 8.14 \times 10^{-3}$ moldm⁻³

pH = $-\log[8.14 \times 10^{-3}]$ = **2.09**

Q4 $[H^+] = 10^{-pH} = 10^{-4.11} = 7.76 \times 10^{-5}$ moldm⁻³

$K_a = [H^+]^2 \div [HA] = (7.76 \times 10^{-5})^2 \div 0.28$

= **2.15×10^{-8} moldm⁻³**

Q5 $[H^+] = 10^{-pH} = 10^{-3.67} = 2.14 \times 10^{-4}$ moldm⁻³

$K_a = [H^+]^2 \div [HCOOH]$ so $[HCOOH] = [H^+]^2 \div K_a$

$= (2.14 \times 10^{-4})^2 \div (1.8 \times 10^{-4})$ = **2.54×10^{-4} moldm⁻³**

Q6 a) $K_a = 10^{-pKa} = 10^{-4.78} =$ **1.66×10^{-5} moldm^{-3}**

b) $K_a = [H^+]^2 \div [CH_3COOH]$ so

$[H^+]^2 = K_a \times [CH_3COOH] = (1.66 \times 10^{-5}) \times 0.25$

$= 4.15 \times 10^{-6}$ mol^{2}dm^{-6}

$[H^+] = \sqrt{4.15 \times 10^{-6}} = 2.04 \times 10^{-3}$ moldm^{-3}

pH $= -\log[H^+] = -\log[2.04 \times 10^{-3}] =$ **2.69**

Q7 $[H^+] = 10^{-pH} = 10^{-4.5} = 3.16 \times 10^{-5}$ moldm^{-3}

$K_a = [H^+]^2 \div [HA] = (3.16 \times 10^{-5})^2 \div 0.154$

$= 6.49 \times 10^{-9}$ moldm^{-3}

$pK_a = -\log(K_a) = -\log(6.49 \times 10^{-9}) =$ **8.19**

Q8 $K_a = 10^{-pKa} = 10^{-3.14} = 7.24 \times 10^{-4}$ moldm^{-3}

$[H^+] = 10^{-pH} = 10^{-3.2} = 6.31 \times 10^{-4}$ moldm^{-3}

$K_a = [H^+]^2 \div [HF]$ so $[HF] = [H^+]^2 \div K_a$

$= (6.31 \times 10^{-4})^2 \div 7.24 \times 10^{-4} =$ **5.50×10^{-4} moldm^{-3}**

Q9 $K_a = 10^{-pKa} = 10^{-4.5} = 3.16 \times 10^{-5}$ moldm^{-3}

$K_a = [H^+]^2 \div [HX]$ so $[H^+]^2 = K_a \times [HX]$

$= (3.16 \times 10^{-5}) \times 0.6 = 1.90 \times 10^{-5}$ mol^{2}dm^{-6}

so $[H^+] = \sqrt{1.9 \times 10^{-5}} = 4.36 \times 10^{-3}$ moldm^{-3}

pH $= -\log[H^+] = -\log[4.36 \times 10^{-3}] =$ **2.36**

Page 27 — Fact Recall Questions

Q1 moldm^{-3}

Q2 a) $K_a = [H^+][A^-] \div [HA]$ or $K_a = [H^+]^2 \div [HA]$

b) $[HA] = [H^+][A^-] \div K_a$ or $[HA] = [H^+]^2 \div K_a$

Q3 E.g. Calculating the pH of a weak acid and calculating the concentration of a weak acid.

Q4 a) $pK_a = -\log_{10}(K_a)$

b) $K_a = 10^{-pKa}$

9. Titrations and pH Curves

Page 31 — Application Questions

Q1 a) Strong base/weak acid, phenolphthalein

b) Strong acid/weak base, methyl orange

c) Strong acid/strong base, phenolphthalein/cresol purple/litmus

d) Weak base/strong acid, methyl orange

Q2 Any curve with the vertical section covering pH 6.8 and pH 8.0. E.g.

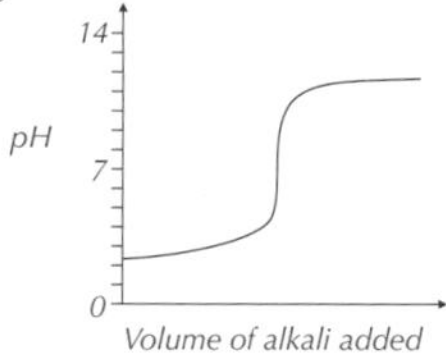

You could also have drawn a curve showing an acid being added to an alkali.

Page 31 — Fact Recall Questions

Q1 a) b)

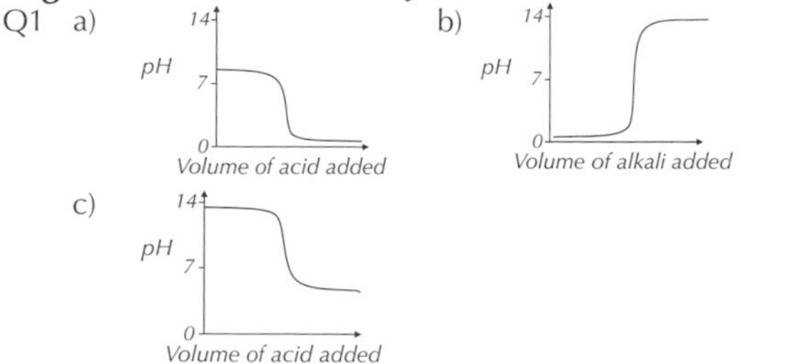

c)

14

pH 7

0

Volume of acid added

If the question says that a strong acid neutralises a strong base, the base is being neutralised so it's the acid that's added.

Q2 a) At the end point of a titration a tiny amount of acid/base causes a sudden big change in pH and the base/acid is just neutralised.

b) The pH indicator changes colour/the pH meter shows a sudden big change.

c) The pH curve becomes close to vertical.

Q3 For an indicator to be suitable it must change colour over a narrow pH range that lies entirely within the vertical part of the pH curve for the titration.

10. Titration Calculations

Pages 34-35 — Application Questions

Q1 Moles HCl = (conc. × volume) ÷ 1000

$= (1.5 \times 13.8) \div 1000 = 0.0207$ moles.

$HCl + NaOH \rightarrow NaCl + H_2O$ so 1 mole of HCl neutralises 1 mole of NaOH and 0.0207 moles of HCl must neutralise 0.0207 moles of NaOH.

Conc. NaOH = (moles × 1000) ÷ volume

$= (0.0207 \times 1000) \div 20 =$ **1.04 moldm^{-3}**

Q2 Moles NaOH = (conc. × volume) ÷ 1000

$= (0.25 \times 30) \div 1000 = 7.5 \times 10^{-3}$ moles.

$HNO_3 + NaOH \rightarrow NaNO_3 + H_2O$ so 1 mole of NaOH neutralises 1 mole of HCl and 7.5×10^{-3} moles of NaOH must neutralise 7.5×10^{-3} moles of HCl.

Conc. HNO_3 = (moles × 1000) ÷ volume

$= (7.5 \times 10^{-3} \times 1000) \div 17.8 =$ **0.42 moldm^{-3}**

Q3 a) average $= (22.38 + 22.45 + 22.42) \div 3$

$= 67.25 \div 3 =$ **22.42 cm^3**

b) Moles NaOH = (conc. × volume) ÷ 1000

$= (0.25 \times 22.42) \div 1000 = 5.6 \times 10^{-3}$ moles.

$HCl + NaOH \rightarrow NaCl + H_2O$ so 1 mole of NaOH neutralises 1 mole of HCl and 5.6×10^{-3} moles of NaOH must neutralise 5.6×10^{-3} moles of HCl.

Conc. HCl = (moles × 1000) ÷ volume

$= (5.6 \times 10^{-3} \times 1000) \div 24 =$ **0.23 moldm^{-3}**

Q4 From the graph, the volume of HCl required to neutralise the NaOH solution was 27.5 cm^3

This is the volume of HCl at the equivalence point.

Moles HCl = (conc. × volume) ÷ 1000

$= (0.85 \times 27.5) \div 1000 = 0.0234$ moles.

$HCl + NaOH \rightarrow NaCl + H_2O$ so 1 mole of HCl neutralises 1 mole of NaOH and 0.0234 moles of HCl must neutralise 0.0234 moles of NaOH.

Conc. NaOH = (moles × 1000) ÷ volume

$= (0.0234 \times 1000) \div 30 =$ **0.78 moldm^{-3}**

Q5 Moles H_2SO_4 = (conc. × volume) ÷ 1000

$= (0.4 \times 18) \div 1000 = 7.2 \times 10^{-3}$ moles.

$H_2SO_4 + 2NaOH \rightarrow Na_2SO_4 + 2H_2O$ so 1 mole of H_2SO_4 neutralises 2 moles of NaOH and 7.2×10^{-3} moles of H_2SO_4 must neutralise $(7.2 \times 10^{-3}) \times 2 = 0.0144$ moles of NaOH.

Conc. NaOH = (moles × 1000) ÷ volume

$= (0.0144 \times 1000) \div 32 =$ **0.45 moldm^{-3}**

Q6 Moles NaOH = (conc. × volume) ÷ 1000

$= (1.2 \times 26.2) \div 1000 = 0.0314$ moles.

$H_2CO_3 + 2NaOH \rightarrow Na_2CO_3 + 2H_2O$ so 2 moles of NaOH neutralises 1 mole of H_2CO_3 and 0.0314 moles of NaOH must neutralise $0.0314 \div 2 = 0.0157$ moles of H_2CO_3.

Conc. H_2CO_3 = (moles × 1000) ÷ volume

$= (0.0157 \times 1000) \div 20 =$ **0.79 moldm^{-3}**

Page 35 — Fact Recall Questions

Q1 moles = (concentration × volume) ÷ 1000 if the units are cm^3 or moles = concentration × volume if the units are dm^3.

Q2

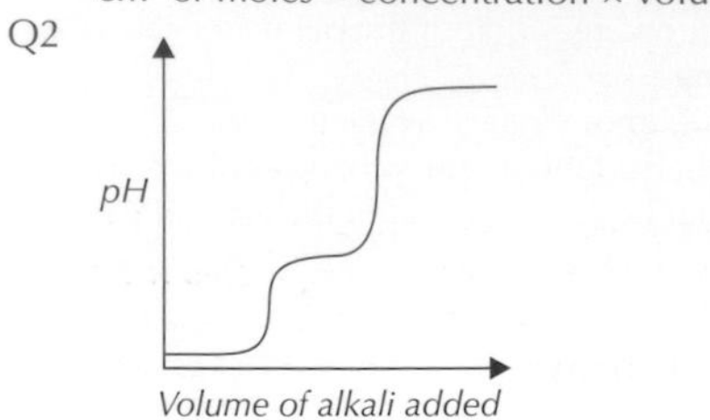

Q3 Diprotic acids release two protons when they react with a base. So, the pH curve for a diprotic acid has two equivalence points (one corresponding to the loss of the first proton and one corresponding to the loss of the second proton). Monoprotic acids only release one proton so pH curves for monoprotic acids only have one equivalence point.

Q4 0.5 mole

11. Buffer Action

Page 38 — Fact Recall Questions

Q1 A buffer is a solution that resists changes in pH when small amounts of acid or alkali are added.

Q2 Acidic buffers are made by mixing a weak acid with one of its salts.

Q3 a) When acid is added $[H^+]$ increases. Most of the extra H^+ ions combine with A^- ions to form HA. This shifts the equilibrium to the left so $[H^+]$ is reduced to close to its original value and the pH doesn't change much.

b) When a base is added $[OH^-]$ increases. Most of the extra OH^- ions react with H^+ ions to form water. This removes H^+ ions from the solution so the equilibrium shifts to the right to compensate by more HA dissociating. So more H^+ ions are formed and the pH doesn't change much.

Q4 Basic buffers are made by mixing a weak base with one of its salts.

Q5 a) When acid is added the H^+ concentration increases. These H^+ ions react with OH^- ions so $[OH^-]$ goes down. The equilibrium then shifts to the right to replace the lost OH^- ions, so the pH doesn't change much.

b) When a base is added, the OH^- concentration increases. These OH^- ions react with the salt to form more base and H_2O. So, the equilibrium shifts to the left to remove the excess OH^- ions in the solution and the pH doesn't change much.

Q6 Any two from, e.g. in shampoo/in biological washing powders/in biological systems (such as blood).

12. Calculating the pH of Buffers

Page 41 — Application Questions

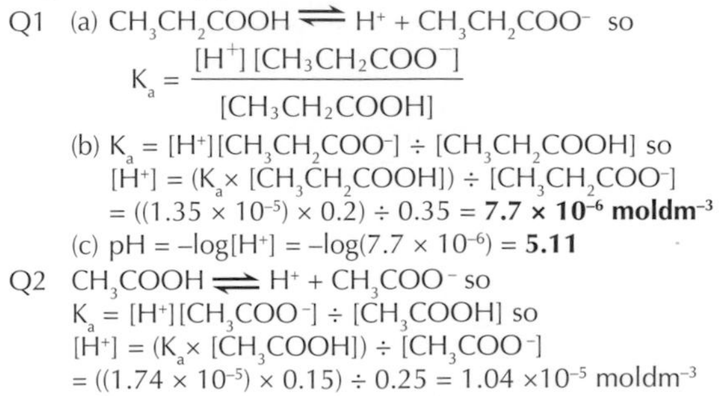

Q1 (a) $CH_3CH_2COOH \rightleftharpoons H^+ + CH_3CH_2COO^-$ so

$$K_a = \frac{[H^+][CH_3CH_2COO^-]}{[CH_3CH_2COOH]}$$

(b) $K_a = [H^+][CH_3CH_2COO^-] \div [CH_3CH_2COOH]$ so
$[H^+] = (K_a \times [CH_3CH_2COOH]) \div [CH_3CH_2COO^-]$
$= ((1.35 \times 10^{-5}) \times 0.2) \div 0.35 =$ **7.7×10^{-6} moldm^{-3}**

(c) $pH = -\log[H^+] = -\log(7.7 \times 10^{-6}) =$ **5.11**

Q2 $CH_3COOH \rightleftharpoons H^+ + CH_3COO^-$ so
$K_a = [H^+][CH_3COO^-] \div [CH_3COOH]$ so
$[H^+] = (K_a \times [CH_3COOH]) \div [CH_3COO^-]$
$= ((1.74 \times 10^{-5}) \times 0.15) \div 0.25 = 1.04 \times 10^{-5}$ moldm^{-3}
$pH = -\log[H^+] = -\log(1.04 \times 10^{-5}) =$ **4.98**

Q3 a) $CH_3CH_2COOH + KOH \rightarrow CH_3CH_2COO^-K^+ + H_2O$

b) initial moles CH_3CH_2COOH = (conc. × vol.) ÷ 1000
= (0.5 × 30) ÷ 1000 = **0.015 moles**.
initial moles KOH = (conc. × vol.) ÷ 1000
= (0.25 × 20) ÷ 1000 = **5×10^{-3} moles**.

c) From the equation, moles salt = moles base = 5×10^{-3} moles. Also, 1 mole of base neutralises 1 mole of acid so 5×10^{-3} moles of base neutralises 5×10^{-3} moles of acid. So $0.015 - (1.5 \times 10^{-3}) = 0.0135$ moles of acid remain.
Total volume = 30 + 20 = 50 cm^3
conc. acid in buffer = (moles × 1000) ÷ vol.
= (0.0135 × 1000) ÷ 50 = **0.27 moldm^{-3}**
conc. salt in buffer = (moles × 1000) ÷ vol.
= $((5 \times 10^{-3}) \times 1000) \div 50 =$ **0.1 moldm^{-3}**

d) $K_a = [H^+][CH_3CH_2COO^-] \div [CH_3CH_2COOH]$ so
$[H^+] = (K_a \times [CH_3CH_2COOH]) \div [CH_3CH_2COO^-]$
$= ((1.35 \times 10^{-5}) \times 0.27) \div 0.1$
= 3.65×10^{-5} moldm^{-3}

e) $pH = -\log[H^+] = -\log(3.65 \times 10^{-5}) =$ **4.44**

Q4 initial moles HCOOH = (conc. × vol.) ÷ 1000
= (0.2 × 25) ÷ 1000 = 5×10^{-3} moles.
initial moles NaOH = (conc. × vol.) ÷ 1000
= (0.1 × 15) ÷ 1000 = 1.5×10^{-3} moles.
$HCOOH + NaOH \rightarrow HCOO^-Na^+ + H_2O$ so moles salt = moles base = 1.5×10^{-3} moles. Also, 1 mole of base neutralises 1 mole of acid and 1.5×10^{-3} moles of base neutralises 1.5×10^{-3} moles of acid.
So $(5 \times 10^{-3}) - (1.5 \times 10^{-3}) = 3.5 \times 10^{-3}$ moles of acid remain.
Total volume = 15 + 25 = 40 cm^3
final conc. acid = (moles × 1000) ÷ vol.
$= ((3.5 \times 10^{-3}) \times 1000) \div 40 = 0.0875$ moldm^{-3}
final conc. salt = (moles × 1000) ÷ vol.
$= ((1.5 \times 10^{-3}) \times 1000) \div 40 = 0.0375$ moldm^{-3}
$K_a = [H^+][HCOO^-] \div [HCOOH]$ so
$[H^+] = (K_a \times [HCOOH]) \div [HCOO^-]$
$= ((1.6 \times 10^{-4}) \times 0.0875) \div 0.0375$
$= 3.73 \times 10^{-4}$ moldm^{-3}
$pH = -\log[H^+] = -\log(3.73 \times 10^{-4}) =$ **3.43**

Pages 43-45 — Exam-style Questions

1 (a) The reaction is first order with respect to H_2 ***(1 mark)*** and second order with respect to NO ***(1 mark)***.

Finding the reaction order with respect to NO is tricky. You know the reaction is first order with respect to H_2 from experiments 1 and 2, so if only $[H_2]$ changed from experiment 2 to 3 you would expect the rate of reaction to halve. But the rate of reaction is four times greater than this, so the reaction must be second order with respect to NO.

(b) rate = $k[H_2][NO]^2$ ***(1 mark)***

(c) rate = $k[H_2][NO]^2$ so k = rate ÷ $[H_2][NO]^2$
E.g. Using experiment 1:
$k = (4.5 \times 10^{-3}) \div (6 \times 10^{-3})(3 \times 10^{-3})^2 = 8.3 \times 10^4$
k = moldm^{-3}s^{-1} ÷ (moldm^{-3})(moldm^{-3})^2 = mol^{-2}dm^{6}s^{-1}
k = **8.3×10^4 mol^{-2}dm^{6}s^{-1}** ***(3 marks for correct answer, otherwise 1 mark for correct method and 1 mark for correct units.)***

(d) rate = $k[H_2][NO]^2$
$= (8.3 \times 10^4) \times (2.5 \times 10^{-3}) \times (4.5 \times 10^{-3})^2$
= 4.2×10^{-3} moldm^{-3}s^{-1} ***(1 mark for correct value, 1 mark for correct units — full marks if the method is correct but error carried forward from (c).)***

If you used 6.5×10^5 as your value for k, an answer of rate = 0.0329 moldm^{-3}s^{-1} will get you full marks.

(e) The rate equation shows that the rate-determining step involves 2 molecules of NO and 1 molecule of H_2 ***(1 mark)***. There are 2 molecules of H_2 in the overall equation so there must be another step involving another molecule of H_2 ***(1 mark)***.

2 (a) (i) $K_c = \frac{[CO_2][H_2]^4}{[CH_4][H_2O]^2}$ ***(1 mark)***.

(ii) $K_c = (0.2 \times (0.28)^4) \div (0.08 \times (0.32)^2) = 0.150$
$K_c = (moldm^{-3} \times (moldm^{-3})^4) \div (moldm^{-3} \times (moldm^{-3})^2)$
$= mol^2dm^{-6}$ so K_c = **0.150 mol²dm⁻⁶** ***(3 marks for correct answer, otherwise 1 mark for correct method and 1 mark for correct units.)***

(b) (i) $[CH_4] = \frac{[CO_2][H_2]^4}{K_c \times [H_2O]^2}$
$= (0.42 \times 0.48^4) \div (0.08 \times 0.56^2)$
= **0.889 moldm⁻³** ***(2 marks for correct answer, otherwise 1 mark for correct equation.)***

(ii) Lower ***(1 mark)***. K_c is lower at temperature Z than at temperature Y. This means temperature Z has caused the equilibrium to shift to the left ***(1 mark)***. As the reaction is endothermic in the forward direction, the temperature must be lowered to make it shift in the exothermic direction ***(1 mark)***.

(c) The value of K_c would not change ***(1 mark)***. Catalysts do not affect the position of the equilibrium, only the time taken to reach equilibrium ***(1 mark)***.

3 (a) (i) $K_w = [H^+][OH^-]$ ***(1 mark)***
(ii) $pH = -\log[H^+]$ ***(1 mark)***

(b) NaOH is a strong base so
$[OH^-] = [NaOH] = 0.15\ moldm^{-3}$
$K_w = [H^+][OH^-]$ so $[H^+] = K_w \div [OH^-]$
$= 1 \times 10^{-14} \div 0.15 = 6.67 \times 10^{-14}\ moldm^{-3}$
$pH = -\log[H^+] = -\log[6.67 \times 10^{-14}] = $ **13.18**
(3 marks for correct answer, otherwise 1 mark for [OH⁻] = 0.15 and 1 mark for [H⁺] = 6.67 × 10⁻⁴.)

(c) (i) B ***(1 mark)***

This titration was a strong acid against a strong base so the curve should start at around pH 14 and fall to around pH 1.

(ii) Moles NaOH = (conc. × volume) ÷ 1000
$= (0.15 \times 25) \div 1000 = 3.75 \times 10^{-3}$ moles.
$HCl + NaOH \rightarrow NaCl + H_2O$ so 1 mole of NaOH neutralises 1 mole of HCl and
3.75×10^{-3} moles of NaOH must neutralise
3.75×10^{-3} moles of HCl.
Conc. HCl = (moles × 1000) ÷ volume
$= ((3.75 \times 10^{-3}) \times 1000) \div 18.5 =$ **0.20 moldm⁻³**
(3 marks for correct answer, otherwise 1 mark for moles NaOH = 3.75 × 10⁻³ and 1 mark for moles HCl = 3.75 × 10⁻³.)

(iii) HCl is a strong acid and fully dissociates so
$[H^+] = [HCl] = 0.20\ moldm^{-3}$
$pH = -\log[H^+] = -\log(0.2) =$ **0.70**
(2 marks for correct answer, otherwise 1 mark for [H⁺] = 0.20 moldm⁻³.)

(d) (i) Any weak acid (e.g. methanoic acid/ethanoic acid/hydrogen cyanide) ***(1 mark)***. Any strong base (e.g. potassium hydroxide/sodium hydroxide) ***(1 mark)***.
(ii) Phenolphthalein ***(1 mark)***

4 (a) (i) $HCOOH \rightleftharpoons H^+ + HCOO^-$ ***(1 mark)***
(ii) $K_a = [H^+][HCOO^-] \div [HCOOH]$ or
$K_a = [H^+]^2 \div [HCOOH]$ ***(1 mark)***
(iii) $[H^+] = 10^{-pH} = 10^{-2.2} = 6.31 \times 10^{-3}$
$K_a = [H^+]^2 \div [HCOOH] = (6.31 \times 10^{-3})^2 \div 0.24$
$= 1.66 \times 10^{-4}\ moldm^{-3}$
$pK_a = -\log(K_a) = -\log(1.66 \times 10^{-4}) =$ **3.78**
(3 marks for correct answer, otherwise 1 mark for [H⁺] = 6.31 × 10⁻³ and 1 mark for Kₐ = 1.66 × 10⁻⁴.)

(b) (i) initial moles HCOOH = (conc. × vol.) ÷ 1000
$= (0.24 \times 30) \div 1000 = 7.2 \times 10^{-3}$ moles ***(1 mark)***
initial moles NaOH = (conc. × vol.) ÷ 1000
$= (0.15 \times 20) \div 1000 = 3.0 \times 10^{-3}$ moles ***(1 mark)***
moles salt = moles base = 3.0×10^{-3} moles ***(1 mark)***
$HCOOH + NaOH \rightarrow HCOO^-Na^+ + H_2O$ so 1 mole of base neutralises 1 mole of acid and 3.0×10^{-3} moles of base neutralise 3.0×10^{-3} moles of acid. So $(7.2 \times 10^{-3}) - (3.0 \times 10^{-3}) = 4.2 \times 10^{-3}$ moles of acid remain ***(1 mark)***.
Total volume = 20 + 30 = 50
final conc. acid = (moles × 1000) ÷ vol.
$= ((4.2 \times 10^{-3}) \times 1000) \div 50 = 0.084\ moldm^{-3}$
final conc. salt = (moles × 1000) ÷ vol.
$= ((3.0 \times 10^{-3}) \times 1000) \div 50 = 0.06\ moldm^{-3}$
$HCOOH \rightleftharpoons H^+ + HCOO^-$ so
$K_a = [H^+][HCOO^-] \div [HCOOH]$ so
$[H^+] = (K_a \times [HCOOH]) \div [HCOO^-]$
$= ((1.66 \times 10^{-4}) \times 0.084) \div (0.06)$
$= 2.32 \times 10^{-4}\ moldm^{-3}$ ***(1 mark)***
$pH = -\log[H^+] = -\log(2.32 \times 10^{-4}) =$ **3.63**
(1 mark) (Maximum of 6 marks for correct answer.)

You calculated K_a for this acid in the previous part of the question.

(ii) $HCOOH \rightleftharpoons H^+ + HCOO^-$. Adding an acid increases $[H^+]$ ***(1 mark)*** so the equilibrium shifts to the left to remove the excess H^+ ***(1 mark)***. The excess H^+ combines with $HCOO^-$ to form HCOOH ***(1 mark)***.

Section 2 — Basic Organic Chemistry & Isomerism

1. Nomenclature

Page 49 — Application Question

Q1 a) 3-bromo-3-ethylpentane
b) 2-chloro-5-fluoro-3-methylhex-1-ene
c) 3-methylpentan-1-ol
d) 1,2-dichloro-3,4-dimethylpent-2-ene

Page 49 — Fact Recall Questions

Q1 -ane
Q2 chloro-
Q3 -ol
Q4 Primary alcohols are alcohols that have their –OH group attached to a carbon with one alkyl group attached.

2. Formulas

Page 52 — Application Questions

Q1 a) $C_4H_{10}O$
b) $C_5H_9Cl_3$
c) $C_6H_{12}O$
d) $C_6H_{13}Cl$

Q2 a) $CH_3CH(CH_3)CH_2OH$
b) $CH_2ClCHClCHClCH_2CH_3$
c) $CH_3CH_2CH_2COCH_2CH_3$
d) $CH_3CCl(CH_3)CH(CH_3)CH_3$

Q3

```
   H  Br H  H
   |  |  |  |
H—C—C—C—C—H
   |  |  |  |
   H  H  O  H
         |
         H
```

Q4 a)

Skeletal formulas have a carbon atom at each end and at each junction.

b)

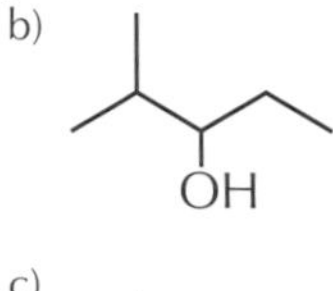

c)

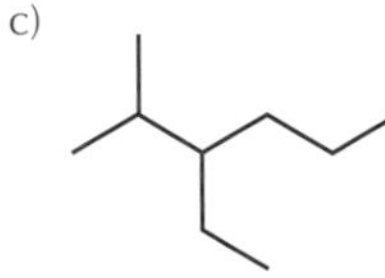

d)

Cl

Q5 a) 2,3-dimethylhexane
b) 2-ethylpent-1-ene
c) 3-chlorohex-3-ene
d) hexa-1,3-diene

Q6 a) C_4H_8O
b) CH_2F
c) $C_9H_{17}Cl_3$

Page 52 — Fact Recall Questions

Q1 A structural formula shows the atoms carbon by carbon, with the attached hydrogens and functional groups.

Q2 A displayed formula shows how all the atoms are arranged, and all the bonds between them.

Q3 A diagram of a molecule which shows the bonds of the carbon skeleton only, with any functional groups.

Q4 A general formula is an algebraic formula that can describe any member of a family of compounds.

3. Isomers

Page 55 — Application Questions

Q1 E.g.

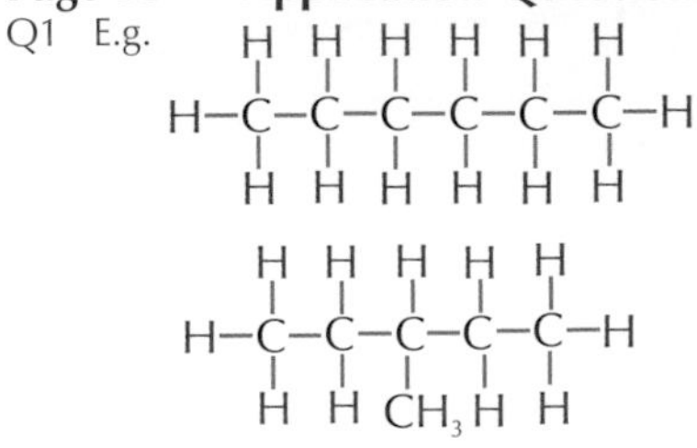

```
   H  CH3 H  H
   |  |   |  |
H—C—C—C—C—H
   |  |   |  |
   H  H  CH3 H
```

When you're asked to draw chain isomers start with the straight chain isomer. Then remove one methyl group at a time and add it as a branch to find the isomers.

Q2 a) structural isomerism/positional isomerism
b) structural isomerism/chain isomerism
c) stereoisomerism/E-Z isomerism

Q3 E.g.

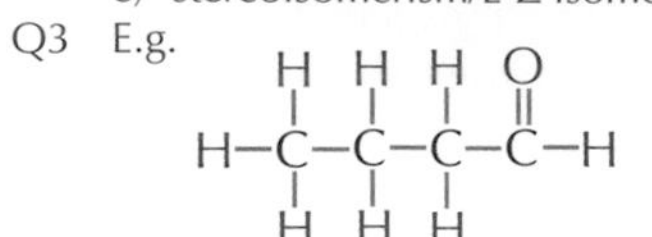

Q4 a) Z-isomer
b) E-isomer

Q5 E-isomer:

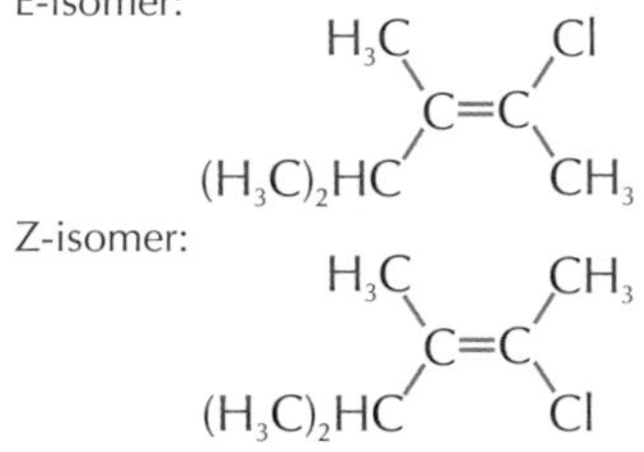

Page 55 — Fact Recall Questions

Q1 A molecule that contains the same atoms as another molecule but has a different arrangement of the carbon skeleton.

Q2 A molecule that has the same structural formula as another molecule but a different arrangement of the atoms in space.

Q3 You get E/Z-isomerism when a molecule has a carbon-carbon double bond and there are different groups attached to the carbons either side of the double bond. The restricted rotation of the carbon-carbon double bond means that the atoms can be arranged differently in space.

4. Optical Isomerism

Page 60 — Application Questions

Q1 a)

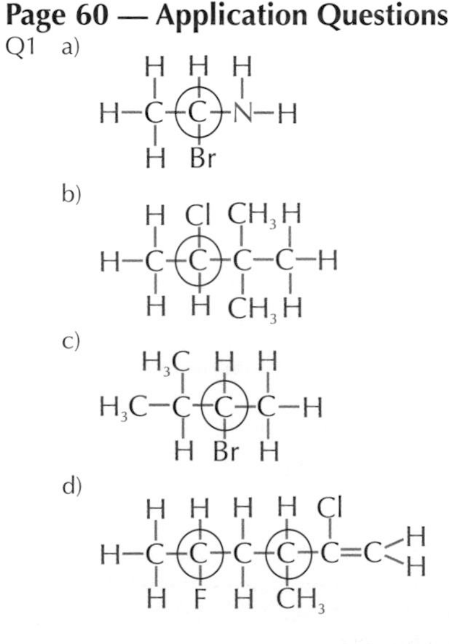

Q2 a) b) c) d)

Q3

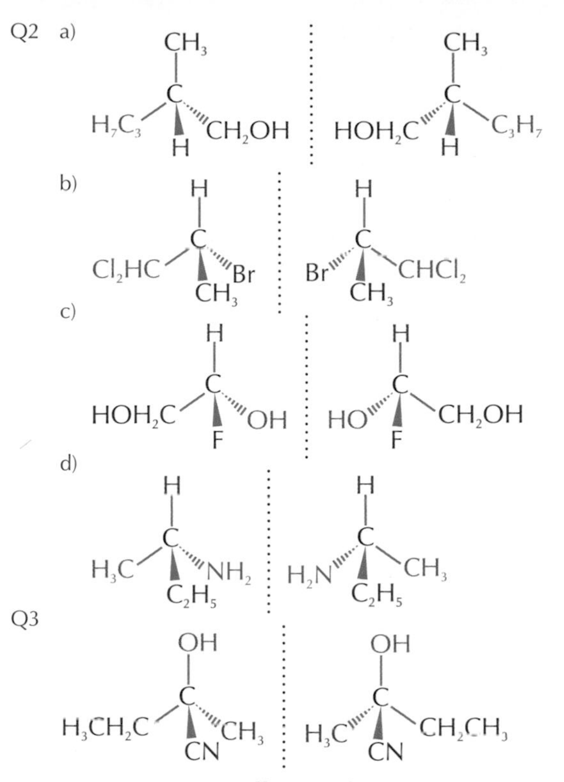

Page 60 — Fact Recall Questions

Q1 Optical isomerism is a type of stereoisomerism. In optical isomers four groups are arranged in two different ways around a central carbon atom so that two different molecules are made — these molecules are non-superimposable mirror images of each other and are called enantiomers or optical isomers.

Q2 A chiral carbon atom is one that has four different groups attached to it.

Q3 Optically active molecules will rotate plane-polarised light.

Q4 Racemic mixtures contain equal quantities of two enantiomers. The two enantiomers cancel each other's light-rotating effect so the mixture doesn't show any optical activity.

Q5 The other enantiomer could cause harmful side-effects or have no effect at all.

Q6 E.g. thalidomide.

Exam-style Questions — pages 62-64

1 a) (i) but-2-ene ***(1 mark)***

(ii) 2,3-dibromobutane ***(1 mark)***

b) $CH_3CHCHCH_3$ ***(1 mark)***

c) (i) E-isomer:

Z-isomer:

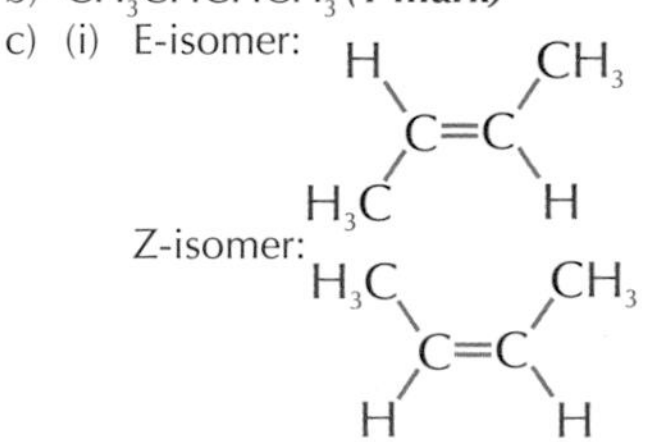

(1 mark for the correctly drawn E-isomer, 1 mark for the correctly drawn Z-isomer, 1 mark for correctly naming both isomers)

You could also draw both of the CH_3 groups below the bond for the Z-isomer.

(ii) stereoisomerism ***(1 mark)***

d) (i)

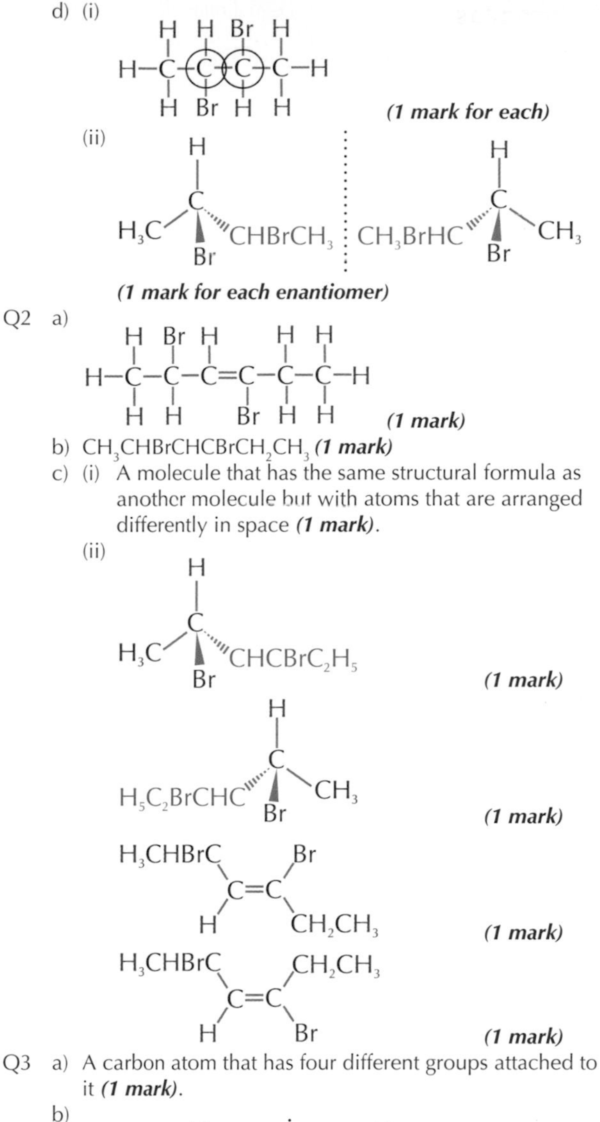

(1 mark for each)

(ii)

(1 mark for each enantiomer)

Q2 a) ***(1 mark)***

b) $CH_3CHBrCHCBrCH_2CH_3$ ***(1 mark)***

c) (i) A molecule that has the same structural formula as another molecule but with atoms that are arranged differently in space ***(1 mark)***.

(ii) ***(1 mark)***

(1 mark)

(1 mark)

(1 mark)

Q3 a) A carbon atom that has four different groups attached to it ***(1 mark)***.

b)

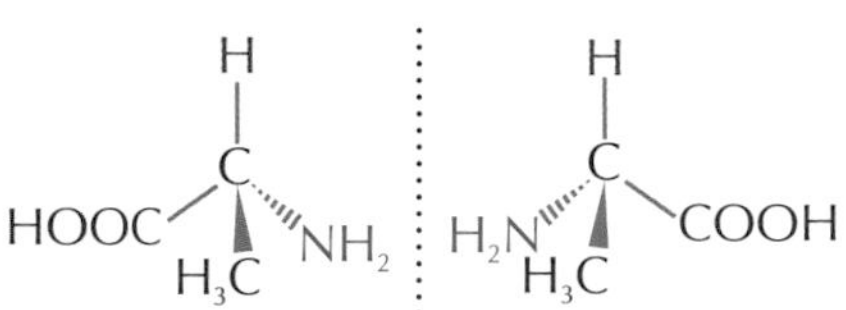

(1 mark for each enantiomer)

c) (i) Optically active means that the molecule will rotate plane-polarised light ***(1 mark)***.

(ii) If the reaction produces a 50:50 mixture of the enantiomers ***(1 mark)*** then one enantiomer will rotate the light in a clockwise direction, and the other will rotate it in an anticlockwise direction ***(1 mark)***. The two enantiomers will cancel out each other's light-rotating effect ***(1 mark)***.

d) Molecules A and C would have optical isomers ***(1 mark for each)***.

Q4 a) Racemic mixtures contain equal quantities of each enantiomer of an optically active compound ***(1 mark)***. An enantiomer is a molecule that has the same structural formula as another molecule but is arranged differently in space so that it is a non-superimposable mirror image of the other molecule ***(1 mark)***.

b) E.g. the other enantiomer might cause harmful side-effects ***(1 mark)*** or have no effect at all ***(1 mark)***.

c) Pass plane-polarised light through the samples ***(1 mark)***. Escitalopram would rotate plane-polarised light, citalopram would not — it's optically inactive ***(1 mark)***.

d) The starred molecule is chiral because it has four different groups attached to it ***(1 mark)***.

Section 3 — Carbonyl Compounds

1. Aldehydes and Ketones

Page 68 — Application Questions

Q1 a) butanal
b) hexan-2-one
c) pentan-3-one
d) 2-ethyl-3-methylbutanal

Q2 a)

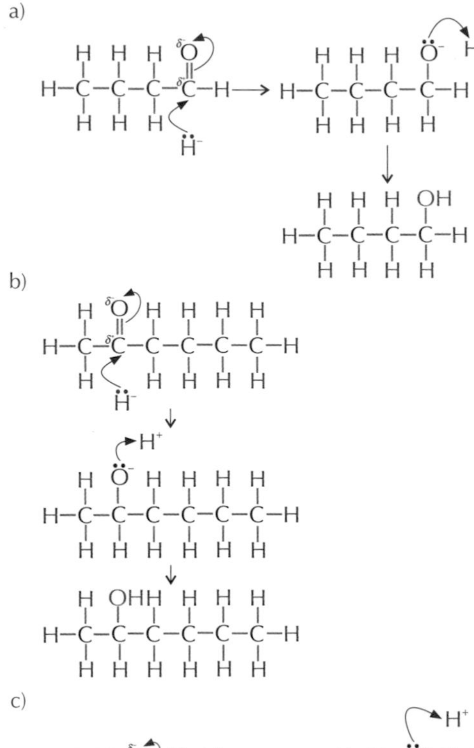

b)

c)

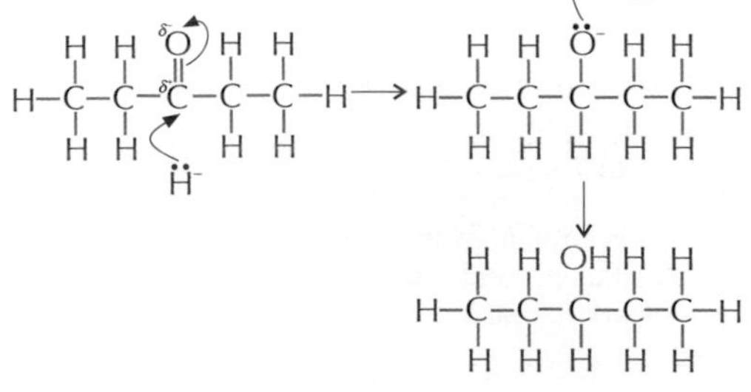

d)

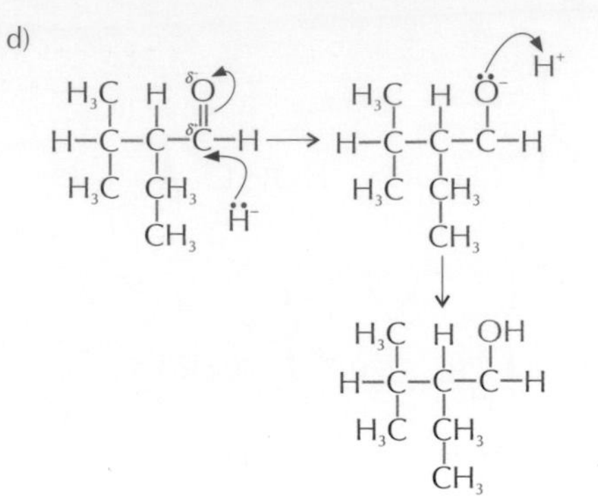

Q3 $CH_3COCH_2CH_2CH_3 + 2[H] \rightarrow CH_3CHOHCH_2CH_2CH_3$

Page 68 — Fact Recall Questions

Q1 Aldehydes have the carbonyl group at the end of the carbon chain, ketones have the carbonyl group in the middle of the carbon chain.

Q2 A carboxylic acid.

Q3 The carbonyl group is in the middle of the carbon chain so to oxidise it a carbon-carbon bond would have to be broken.

Q4 a) In the presence of an aldehyde a silver mirror is produced. In the presence of a ketone there is no change.
b) In the presence of an aldehyde a brick red precipitate is formed. In the presence of a ketone there is no change.

Q5 e.g. $NaBH_4$

2. Hydroxynitriles

Page 70 — Application Questions

Q1 a)

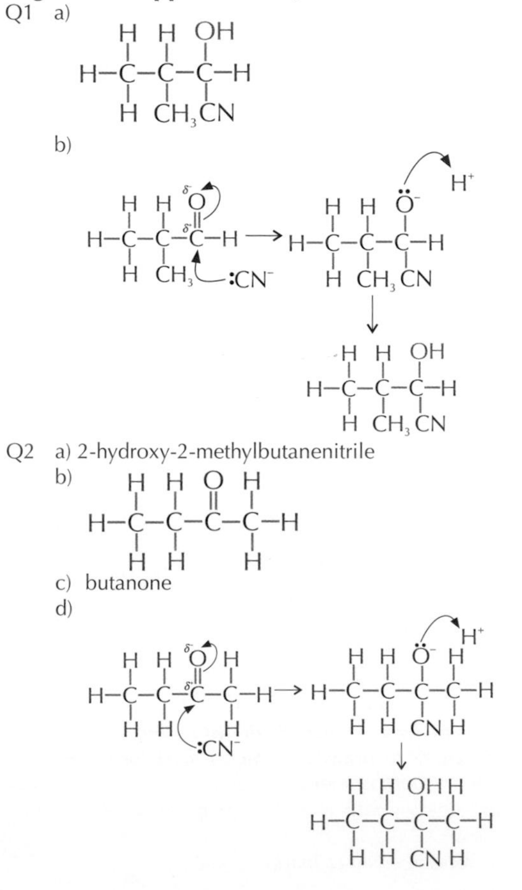

b)

Q2 a) 2-hydroxy-2-methylbutanenitrile
b)
c) butanone
d)

Page 70 — Fact Recall Questions

Q1 A hydroxynitrile is a molecule with a nitrile (CN) group and a hydroxy (OH) group.

Q2 nucleophilic addition

Q3 a) A risk assessment is a review of the hazards of the reacting chemicals, the products and any conditions needed, such as heat used in a chemical reaction.

b) So you can take all reasonable precautions to reduce the risk of an accident.

Q4 HCN is a highly toxic gas so acidified KCN is used instead because it can be stored more safely.

3. Carboxylic Acids and Esters

Page 73 — Application Questions

Q1 a) (i) methanoic acid

(ii) 2-ethyl-4-hydroxypentanoic acid

b) $2HCOOH_{(aq)} + Na_2CO_{3(s)} \rightarrow 2HCOONa_{(aq)} + H_2O_{(l)} + CO_{2(g)}$

Q2 a) (i) propyl methanoate

(ii) ethyl benzoate

b) (i) propan-1-ol and methanoic acid

(ii) ethanol and benzoic acid

Q3 a)

```
     O
    //   H  H
H–C      |  |
    \ O–C––C–H
         |  |
       H3C  H
```

b) $HCOOH + CH_3CH(OH)CH_3 \rightarrow$
$HCOOCH(CH_3)CH_3 + H_2O$

Page 73 — Fact Recall Questions

Q1 A salt, water and carbon dioxide.

Q2 a) Esterification reaction.

b) A strong acid catalyst.
E.g. H_2SO_4/HCl/H_3PO_4.

4. Reactions and Uses of Esters

Page 77 — Application Questions

Q1 a) $CH_3CH_2COOCH_3 + H_2O \rightarrow CH_3CH_2COOH + CH_3OH$

b) $CH_3CH_2COOCH_3 + OH^- \rightarrow CH_3CH_2COO^- + CH_3OH$

Q2 a)

```
   H     O
   |     ||
H–C–O–C– (CH2)16CH3
   |
   |     O
   |     ||
H–C–O–C– (CH2)16CH3
   |
   |     O
   |     ||
H–C–O–C– (CH2)16CH3
   |
   H
```

b)

```
   H     O
   |     ||
H–C–O–C– (CH2)16CH3
   |
   |     O
   |     ||
H–C–O–C– (CH2)16CH3   + 3NaOH
   |
   |     O
   |     ||
H–C–O–C– (CH2)16CH3
   |
   H
          ↓
   H
   |
H–C–OH
   |
H–C–OH      + 3CH3(CH2)16COO–Na+
   |
H–C–OH
   |
   H
```

We've had to write the equation vertically here so it'll fit on the page. In the exam, write the equation horizontally like normal.

c) Mix the sodium salt produced above with a strong acid such as HCl.

Q3 a)

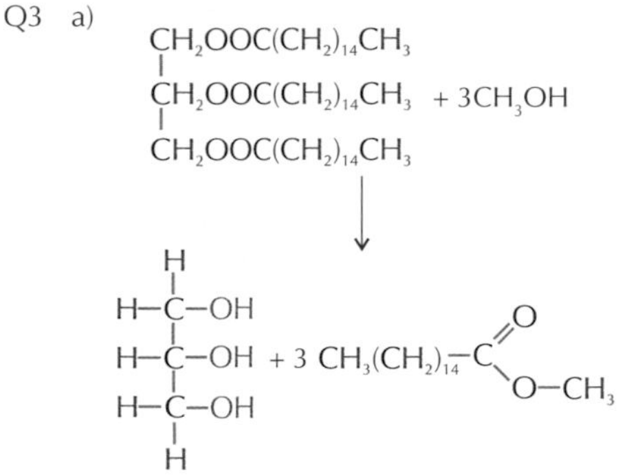

b) E.g. KOH/potassium hydroxide or NaOH/sodium hydroxide.

Page 77 — Fact Recall Questions

Q1 Any three from: e.g. in perfumes / as food flavourings / as solvents (e.g. in glue/printing ink) / as plasticisers / to produce methyl esters for biofuels.

Q2 a) A carboxylic acid and an alcohol.

b) A carboxylate ion/carboxylate salt and an alcohol.

Q3 Glycerol (propane-1,2,3-triol) and long chain carboxylic acids (fatty acids).

Q4 Fats contain mostly saturated hydrocarbon chains which pack together tightly with strong van der Waals forces. As a result a higher temperature is needed to melt them and they are solid at room temperature.
Oils contain mostly unsaturated hydrocarbon chains which pack together loosely with weak van der Waals forces. As a result a lower temperature is needed to melt them and they are liquid at room temperature.

Q5 Glycerol and a sodium salt of a fatty acid (soap).

Q6 By reacting rapeseed/vegetable oils with methanol in the presence of a KOH catalyst to form methyl esters. Biodiesel is a mixture of methyl esters.

Q7 Biodiesel isn't always 100% carbon neutral because energy is used to make the fertilizer to grow the crop and is used in planting, harvesting and converting the plants to oil. This energy often comes from burning fossil fuels, which produces CO_2, so the process isn't carbon neutral overall.

5. Acyl Chlorides

Page 80 — Application Questions

Q1 a) methanoyl chloride
b) propanoyl chloride
c) 2-methylpropanoyl chloride
d) 4-hydroxy-2-methylbutanoyl chloride

Q2 a)

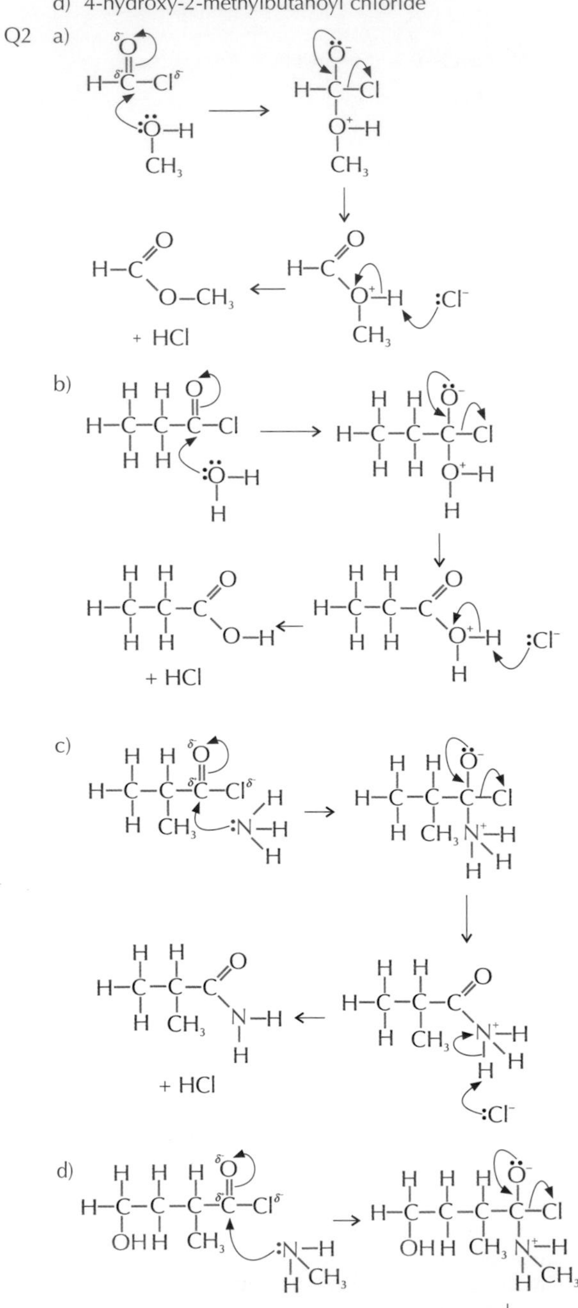

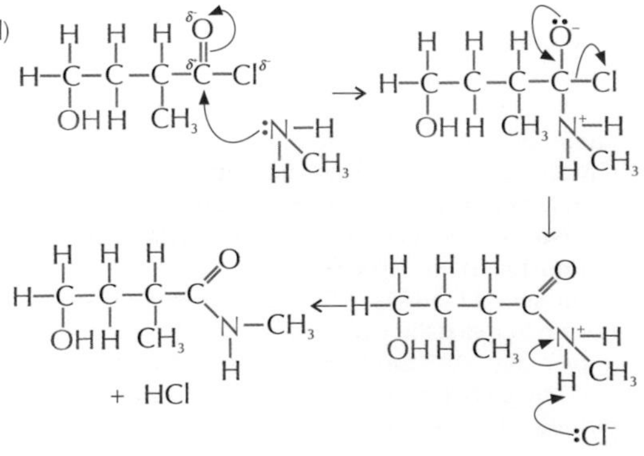

Page 80 — Fact Recall Questions

Q1 $C_nH_{2n-1}OCl$

Q2 a) A carboxylic acid and HCl.
b) An ester and HCl.
c) An amide and HCl.
d) An N-substituted amide and HCl.

Q3 nucleophilic addition-elimination

6. Acid Anhydrides

Page 82 — Application Questions

Q1 a) b) 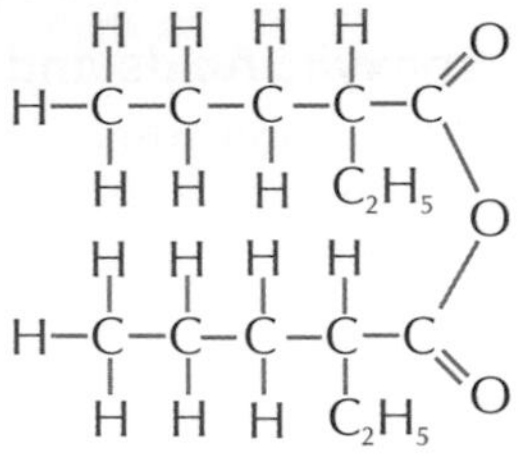 c)

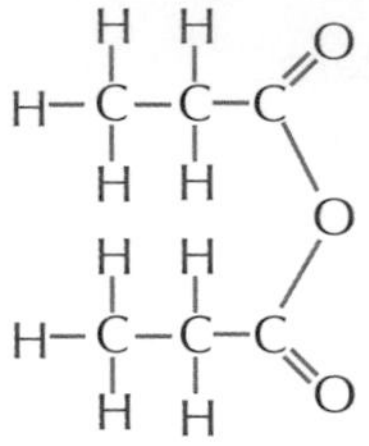

Q2 a)

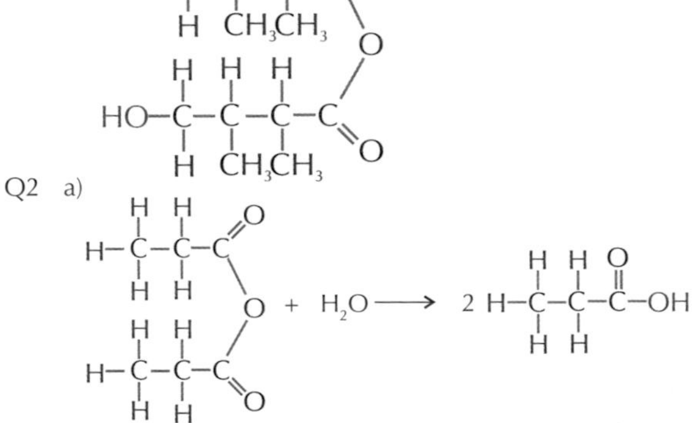

In the exam you don't have to draw out the full display formula for the molecule. You could just have written this equation as $CH_3CH_2COOCOCH_2CH_3 + H_2O \rightarrow 2CH_3CH_2COOH$. Either way of writing the equation will get you the marks.

b)

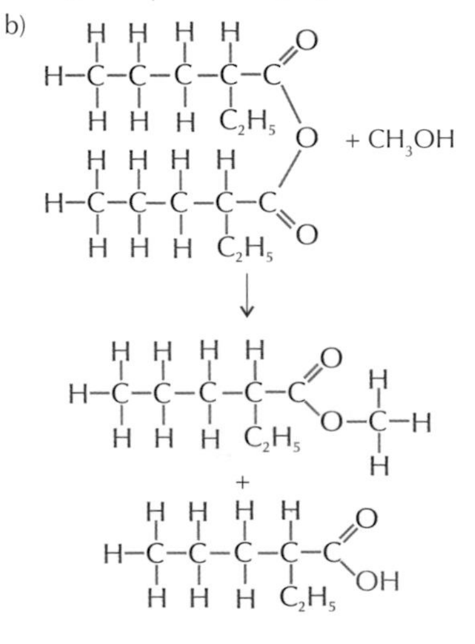

c)

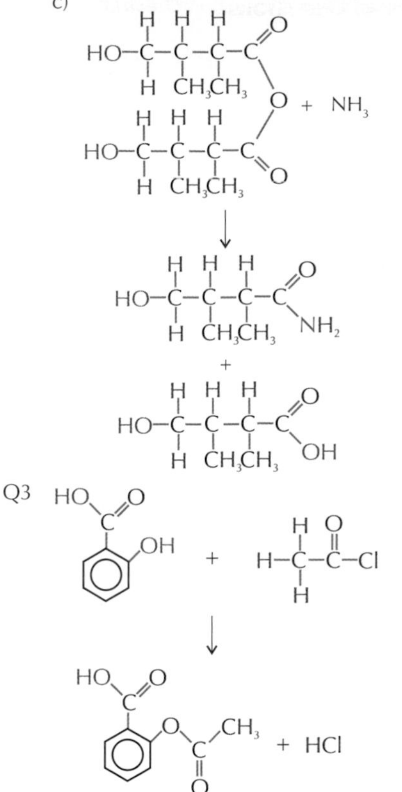

Q3

These equations are written vertically for space.
In the exam, write them horizontally.

Page 82 — Fact Recall Questions

Q1 water

Q2 Ethanoic anhydride is cheaper than ethanoyl chloride. Ethanoic anhydride is safer than ethanoyl chloride because it's less corrosive, reacts more slowly with water and doesn't produce dangerous HCl fumes.

Exam-style Questions — pages 84-86

1 a) A — propanal ***(1 mark)***
B — propanone ***(1 mark)***

b) E.g. Tollens' reagent ***(1 mark)*** produces a silver mirror with A but not with B ***(1 mark)***/Fehling's solution or Benedict's solution ***(1 mark)*** produces a brick red precipitate with A but not B ***(1 mark)***.

c) (i) $NaBH_4$/sodium borohydride/sodium tetrahydridoborate(III) ***(1 mark)***.

(ii)

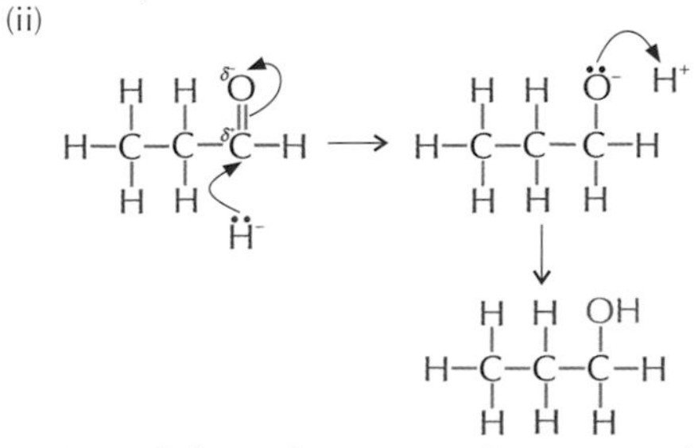

(1 mark for each correct curly arrow, maximum 3 marks).

To get a mark for your curly arrow the end of the arrow must start at a lone pair of electrons or a bond and the point of the arrow must point to wherever the electrons are heading.

d) (i) nucleophilic addition ***(1 mark)***

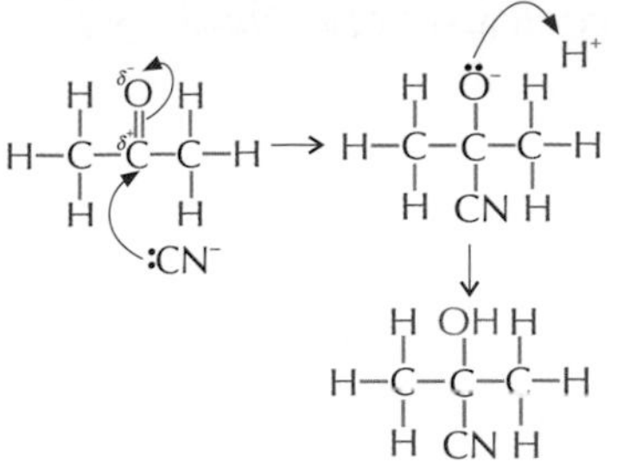

(1 mark for each correct curly arrow, maximum 3 marks).

(ii) 2-hydroxy-2-methylpropanenitrile ***(1 mark)***

(iii) E.g. acidified KCN ***(1 mark)***.

2 a)

```
    H  H  O
    |  |  ||
 H—C—C—C—OH
    |  |
    H  CH3
```

(1 mark)

b) $2CH_3CH(CH_3)COOH + Na_2CO_3 \rightarrow$
$2CH_3CH(CH_3)COONa + H_2O + CO_2$
(1 mark for correct products, 1 mark for balancing the equation).

c) (i)

```
    H  H     O
    |  |    //     H
 H—C—C—C          |
    |  |    \O—C—H
    H  CH3         |
                   H
```

(1 mark)

(ii) methyl 2-methylpropanoate ***(1 mark)***

(iii) Any strong acid (e.g. $HCl/H_2SO_4/H_3PO_4$) ***(1 mark)***.

(iv)

```
    H  H     O
    |  |    //     H
 H—C—C—C          |
    |  |    \O—C—H   +  OH⁻
    H  CH3         |
                   H

          ⇌ reflux

    H  H  O               H
    |  |  ||              |
 H—C—C—C—O⁻   +   H—C—OH
    |  |                  |
    H  CH3                H
```

(1 mark for correct equation, 1 mark for correct structure of products).

d) E.g. food flavouring / perfume / plasticisers / solvent / biodiesel production / soap production ***(1 mark)***.

3 a) Fats contain mainly saturated hydrocarbon chains/ oils contain mainly unsaturated hydrocarbon chains ***(1 mark)***. Saturated hydrocarbon chains fit neatly together increasing the van der Waals forces between them/ unsaturated hydrocarbon chains are bent and don't pack well decreasing the van der Waals forces between them ***(1 mark)***. Stronger van der Waals forces mean a higher melting temperature so fats are solid at room temperature/ weaker van der Waals forces mean a lower melting temperature so oils are liquid at room temperature ***(1 mark)***.

b) (i)

$$\begin{array}{l} CH_2OOC(CH_2)_{16}CH_3 \\ CH_2OOC(CH_2)_{16}CH_3 \quad + 3NaOH \\ CH_2OOC(CH_2)_{16}CH_3 \end{array}$$

$$\downarrow$$

$$\begin{array}{l} H{-}C(H_2){-}OH \\ H{-}C(H){-}OH \quad + 3CH_3(CH_2)_{16}COO^-Na^+ \\ H{-}C(H_2){-}OH \end{array}$$

(1 mark for glycerol, 1 mark for correct sodium salt, 1 mark for balancing the equation).

(ii) soap ***(1 mark)***

c) (i) Biodiesel is a mixture of methyl esters that can be used as a fuel ***(1 mark)***.

(ii)

$$\begin{array}{l} CH_2OOC(CH_2)_{16}CH_3 \\ CH_2OOC(CH_2)_{16}CH_3 \quad + 3CH_3OH \\ CH_2OOC(CH_2)_{16}CH_3 \end{array}$$

$$\downarrow$$

$$\begin{array}{l} H{-}C(H_2){-}OH \\ H{-}C(H){-}OH \quad + 3CH_3(CH_2)_{16}COOCH_3 \\ H{-}C(H_2){-}OH \end{array}$$

(1 mark for methanol, 1 mark for correct methyl ester, 1 mark for balancing the equation).

These equations are written vertically for space. In the exam, write them horizontally.

(iii) KOH acts as a catalyst ***(1 mark)***.

4 a) (i)

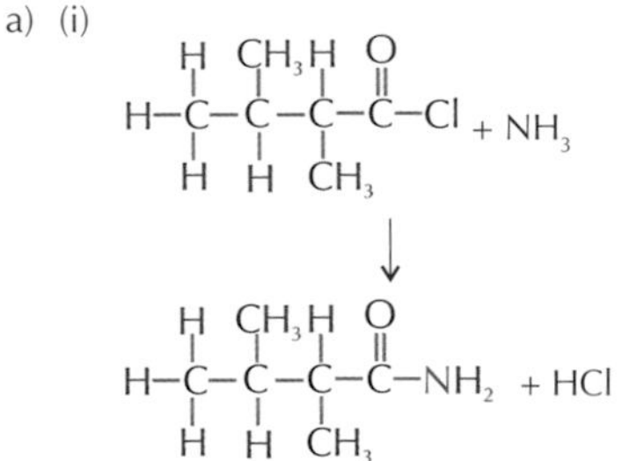

(1 mark for each correct product, maximum 2 marks).

This equation could also have been written as:
$CH_3CH(CH_3)CH(CH_3)COCl + NH_3 \rightarrow$
$CH_3CH(CH_3)CH(CH_3)CONH_2 + HCl$

(ii) nucleophilic addition elimination ***(1 mark)***

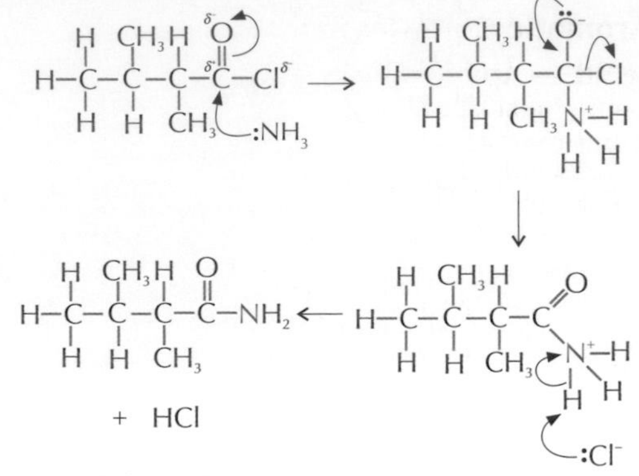

(1 mark for each correct curly arrow, maximum 5 marks)

Examiners often ask you to name and outline mechanisms. Don't forget to name it — it's easy to get carried away with the mechanism and lose a mark just for forgetting to put the name of the mechanism.

b) (i)

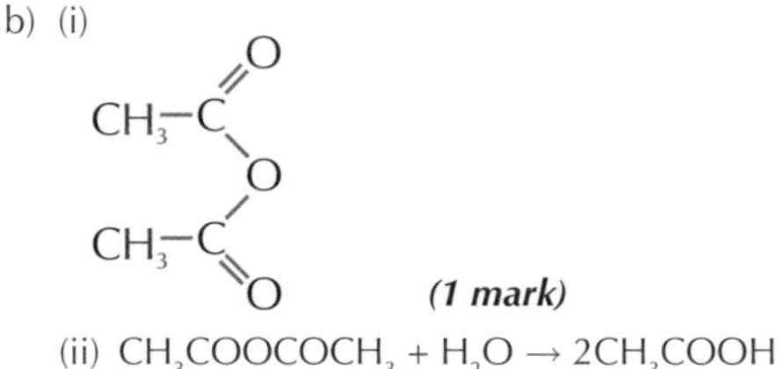

(1 mark)

(ii) $CH_3COOCOCH_3 + H_2O \rightarrow 2CH_3COOH$
(1 mark for correct product, 1 mark for balancing the equation).

c) (i)

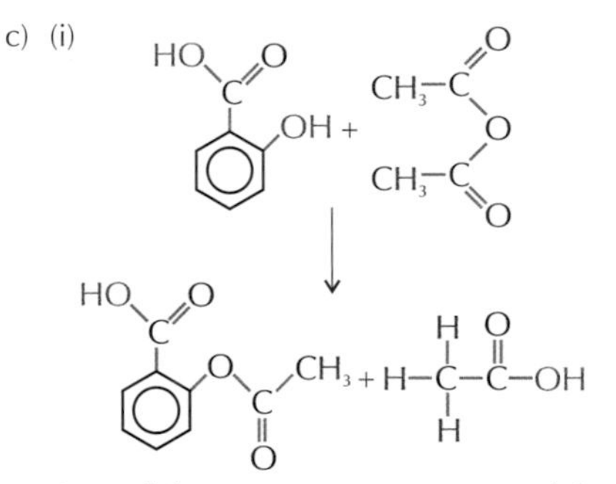

(1 mark for correct reactants, 1 mark for correct products).

(ii) Ethanoic acid ***(1 mark)***. Any two from e.g. ethanoic anhydride is cheaper / less corrosive / reacts less vigorously / doesn't produce toxic HCl fumes ***(1 mark for each)***.

Section 4 — More Organic Chemistry

1. Aromatic Compounds

Page 90 — Application Questions

Q1 a) 1,2-dinitrobenzene
b) 4-methylphenol
c) 2,4,6-trichlorophenylamine

Q2 a) Kekulé proposed that the structure of benzene was a ring of six carbons joined together by alternating double and single bonds. He later adapted this model to say that the benzene molecule was constantly flipping between two isomers.
b) The $\Delta H_{hydrogenation}$ for cyclohexene is –120 kJmol^{-1}. So if benzene had three double bonds you would expect it to have a $\Delta H_{hydrogenation}$ of –360 kJmol^{-1}. But, $\Delta H_{hydrogenation}$ for benzene is only –208 kJmol^{-1}. This is far less exothermic than expected so benzene must be more stable than the proposed Kekulé structure and the Kekulé model cannot be correct.

Page 90 — Fact Recall Questions

Q1 Aromatic compounds are compounds that contain a benzene ring.

Q2 According to the delocalisation model, each of the six carbons in benzene donates an electron from its p-orbital. These electrons combine to form a ring of delocalised electrons. All the carbon-carbon bonds in the ring are the same and so are the same length.

Q3 If the Kekulé model were correct, half of the bonds in benzene would be the length of C=C double bonds (135 pm) and the other half would be the length of C–C single bonds (147 pm). But X-ray diffraction studies have shown that all the bonds in benzene are the same length (140 pm — between that of single and double bonds). So this is evidence for the delocalisation model.

2. Reactions of Aromatics

Page 93 — Application Questions

Q1 a)

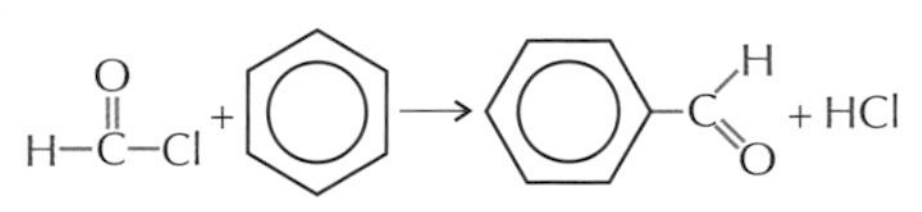

b) $AlCl_3$
c) Electrophilic substitution.
$CHOCl + AlCl_3 \rightarrow CHO^+ + AlCl_4^-$

You could draw the mechanism out with arrows or just show the equation (like above) for the first part of the mechanism.

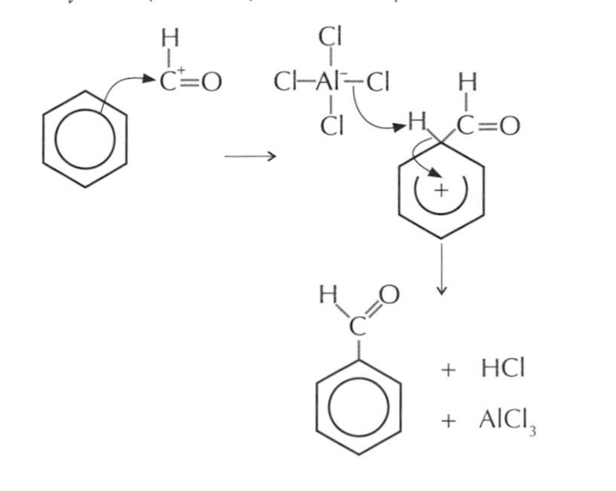

Q2 a) $HNO_3 + H_2SO_4 \rightarrow HSO_4^- + NO_2^+ + H_2O$

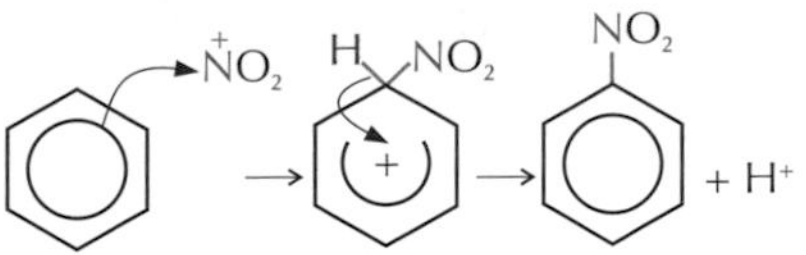

Don't forget that the formation of the nitronium ion is part of the mechanism too.

b) A concentrated H_2SO_4 catalyst and a temperature below 55 °C.

Page 93 — Fact Recall Questions

Q1 Aromatic compounds contain a benzene ring, which is a region of high electron density. Electrophiles are electron deficient so are attracted to the regions of high electron density found in aromatic compounds.

Q2 E.g. nitro compounds can be reduced to form aromatic amines which are used to manufacture dyes and pharmaceuticals / nitro compounds decompose violently when heated so can be used as explosives (e.g. TNT).

Q3 $AlCl_3$ is a halogen carrier. It accepts a lone pair of electrons from the acyl chloride, forming a carbocation. This carbocation is a much stronger electrophile than the acyl chloride and is strong enough to react with the benzene ring.

3. Amines and Amides

Page 97 — Application Questions

Q1 a) ethylamine
b) dipropylamine
c) ethyldimethylamine

Q2 a) Ethylamine is the strongest base. The alkyl group on this amine pushes electrons away from itself so the electron density on the nitrogen atom increases. This makes the lone pair more available to form a dative bond with a hydrogen ion.
b) Phenylamine is the weakest base. The benzene ring draws electrons towards itself so the lone pair of electrons is partially delocalised onto the ring and the electron density on the nitrogen decreases. This makes the lone pair less available to bond with a hydrogen ion.

Q3 a) propanamide
b) N-propylmethanamide

Page 97 — Fact Recall Questions

Q1 A quaternary ammonium ion is a positively charged ion that consists of a nitrogen atom with four alkyl groups attached.

Q2 a) A quaternary ammonium salt with at least one long hydrocarbon chain.
b) E.g. in fabric softener / in hair conditioner.

Q3 The availability of the lone pair of electrons on the nitrogen/ the electron density around the nitrogen.

4. Reactions of Amines

Page 100 — Application Questions

Q1 a) $CH_3Cl + 2NH_3 \rightarrow CH_3NH_2 + NH_4Cl$
b) nucleophilic substitution

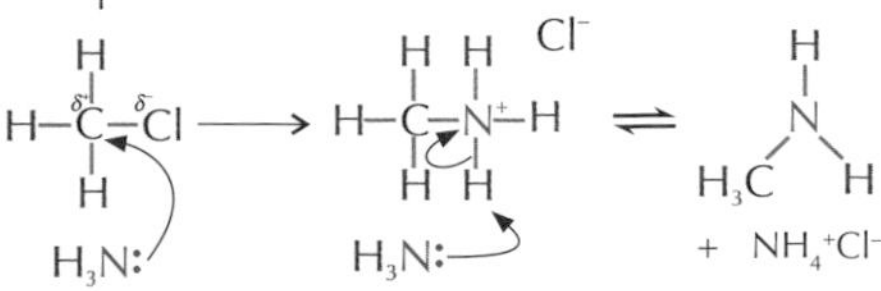

Q2 a) $CH_3CH_2CN + 2H_2 \rightarrow CH_3CH_2CH_2NH_2$
b) A platinum/nickel catalyst and high temperature and pressure.

Q3

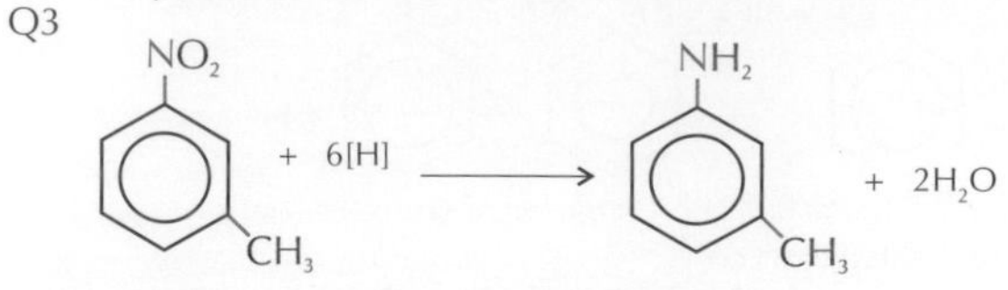

Page 100 — Fact Recall Questions

Q1 a) Heat the haloalkane with an excess of ammonia.
b) The amine that is formed still has a lone pair of electrons on the nitrogen so it can still act as a nucleophile. This means that further substitutions can take place, and a mixture of primary, secondary and tertiary amines and quaternary ammonium salts can be produced.
c) By fractional distillation.

Q2 a) E.g. by reducing the nitrile with $LiAlH_4$ and adding dilute acid. By refluxing the nitrile with sodium metal and ethanol. By catalytic hydrogenation (using a platinum/nickel catalyst and high temperatures and pressures).
b) Catalytic hydrogenation. $LiAlH_4$ and sodium are too expensive for industrial use.

Q3 Take a nitro compound (e.g. nitrobenzene). Heat the nitro compound with tin metal and concentrated HCl under reflux to form a salt. Mix the salt with an alkali (e.g. NaOH) to produce an aromatic amine.

5. Amino Acids and Proteins

Page 104 — Application Question

Q1 a) A — 2-aminopropanoic acid
B — 2-amino-3-hydroxypropanoic acid
b) (i) (ii) (iii)
c)

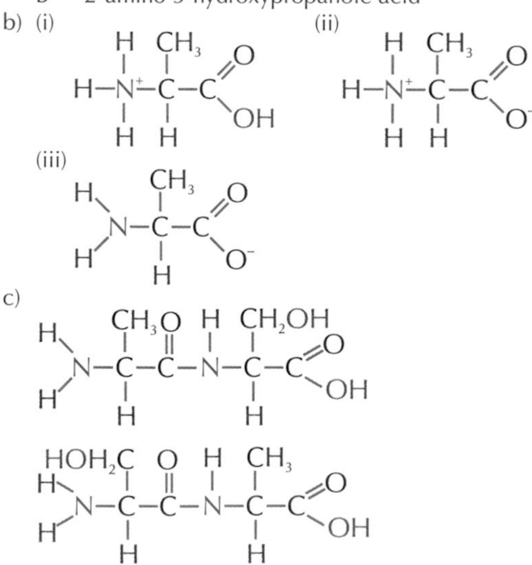

Page 104 — Fact Recall Questions

Q1 Amino acids are amphoteric because they have a basic amino group and an acidic carboxyl group and so have both acidic and basic properties.

Q2 a) A zwitterion is a dipolar ion that has both a positive and a negative charge in different parts of the molecule.
b) At the isoelectric point — the pH where the average overall charge is zero for that amino acid.

Q3 Put a concentrated spot of amino acid mixture onto a piece of chromatography paper. Dip the bottom of the paper in solvent. As the solvent spreads up the paper the amino acids move with it. Different amino acids move at different rates so they are separated.

Q4 a) condensation
b) hydrolysis

Q5 Add aqueous 6 M hydrochloric acid and heat under reflux for 24 hours.

Q6 a) peptide links
b) hydrogen bonds

6. Polymers

Page 107 — Application Questions

Q1 a) An addition polymer.
b)

Q2

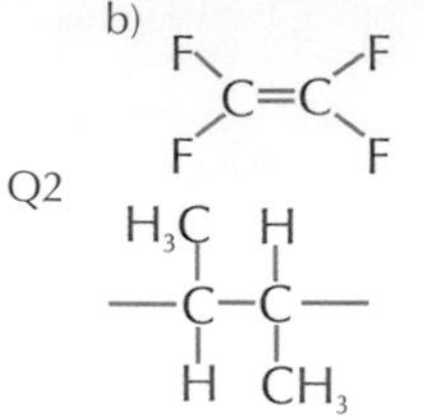

When you're drawing the repeating unit of a polymer you don't have to include the square brackets. You only have to draw the square brackets if you're writing an equation for the formation of a polymer.

Page 107 — Fact Recall Questions

Q1 Individual small molecules which can join together to make polymers.

Q2 a) dicarboxylic acids and diamines
b) dicarboxylic acids and diols

Q3 condensation reactions

Q4 a)

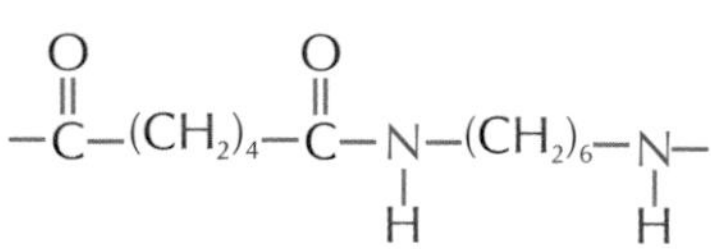

b)

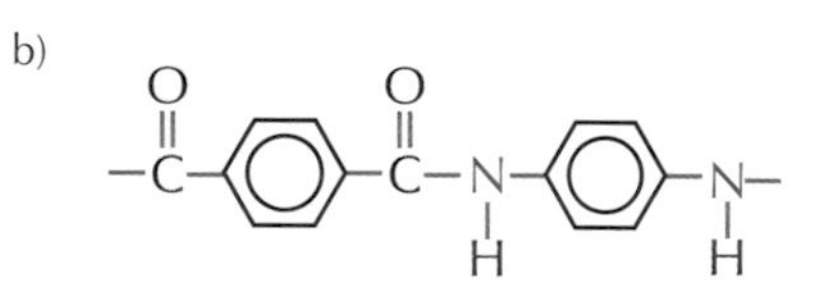

c)

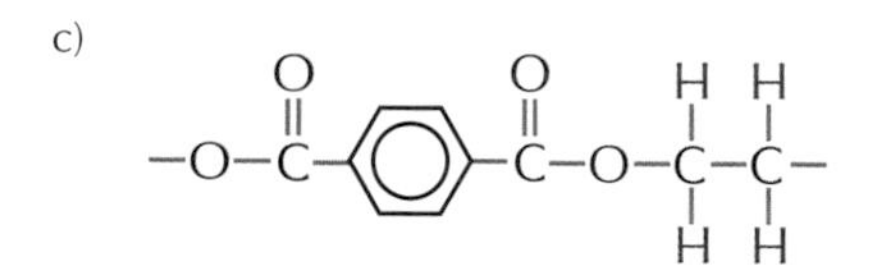

7. Disposing of Polymers

Page 110 — Application Question

Q1 Polymer A is biodegradable.

Page 110 — Fact Recall Questions

Q1 a) The bonds in addition polymers are non-polar so they are not susceptible to attack by nucleophiles and won't react easily.
b) It means they don't react with things and degrade when they are being used.
c) It means that addition polymers are non-biodegradable.

Q2 a) biodegradable
b) The bonds in condensation polymers are polar.
This means they are susceptible to attack by nucleophiles and can be broken by hydrolysis. This means the polymer will break down naturally. Addition polymers have non-polar bonds which can't be hydrolysed so won't break down naturally.

Q3 E.g. it requires areas of land / as the waste decomposes it releases methane (a greenhouse gas) / leaks from landfill sites can contaminate water supplies.

Q4 By passing the waste gases through scrubbers which can neutralise toxic gases by allowing them to react with a base.

Q5 a) E.g. by melting and remoulding / by cracking into monomers which can be used to make more plastic or other chemicals.

b) Plastic products are marked with numbers which show what type of plastic they are made from.

c) Advantages: any two from: e.g. it reduces the amount of waste going into landfill / it saves raw materials / the cost is lower than making plastics from scratch / it produces less CO_2 emissions than burning plastic.
Disadvantages: any two from: e.g. it is technically difficult / it is more expensive than burning/landfill / the product isn't usually suitable for its original purpose / the plastic can be easily contaminated.

Exam-style Questions — pages 112-114

1 a) E.g. bond length: If Kekulé was correct you would expect benzene to have 3 bonds with the length of a C–C single bond and 3 bonds with the length of a C=C double bond ***(1 mark)***. X-ray diffraction studies show that the carbon-carbon bonds in benzene are all the same length ***(1 mark)*** intermediate between that of double and single bonds ***(1 mark)***. / Enthalpy data: Cyclohexene (which has 1 double bond) has an enthalpy of hydrogenation of $-120\ kJmol^{-1}$ ***(1 mark)***. So if Kekulé was correct benzene would have an enthalpy of hydrogenation of $-360\ kJmol^{-1}$ ***(1 mark)***. The actual enthalpy of hydrogenation for benzene is $-208\ kJmol^{-1}$ — much less exothermic than Kekulé's structure suggests ***(1 mark)***.

b) (i)

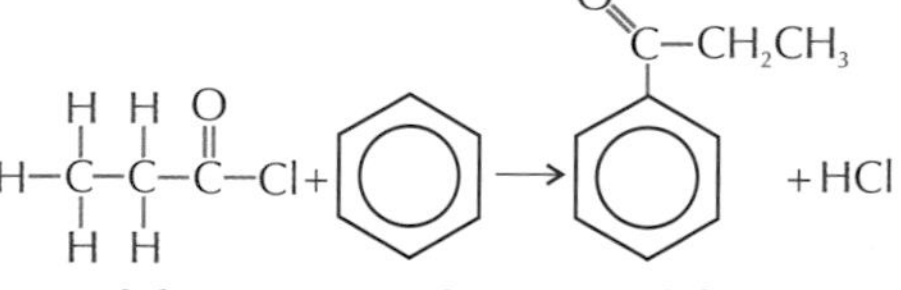

(1 mark for correct products, 1 mark for correct structure of phenylpropanone).

(ii) $AlCl_3$ accepts a lone pair of electrons from the propanoyl chloride ***(1 mark)***. The resulting carbocation is a much stronger nucleophile ***(1 mark)***.

(iii) $CH_3CH_2COCl + AlCl_3 \rightarrow CH_3CH_2CO^+ + AlCl_4^-$
(1 mark, this mark is also awarded if the mechanism for this part of the reaction is correctly shown with curly arrows).

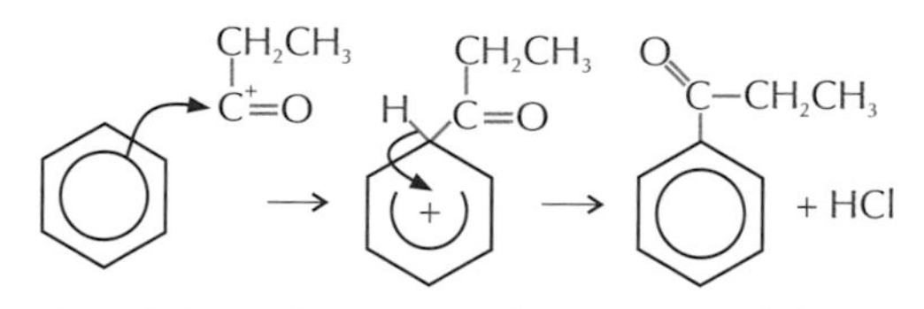

(1 mark for each correct curly arrow, 1 mark for correct structure of intermediate, maximum 3 marks).

Examiners are quite picky about their structures. To get the marks for the structure of the intermediate the semicircle can't extend beyond carbon-2 or carbon-6, but it can be smaller — and you must put the + in the middle.

c) (i) $HNO_3 + H_2SO_4 \rightarrow HSO_4^- + NO_2^+ + H_2O$ ***(1 mark)***

(ii)

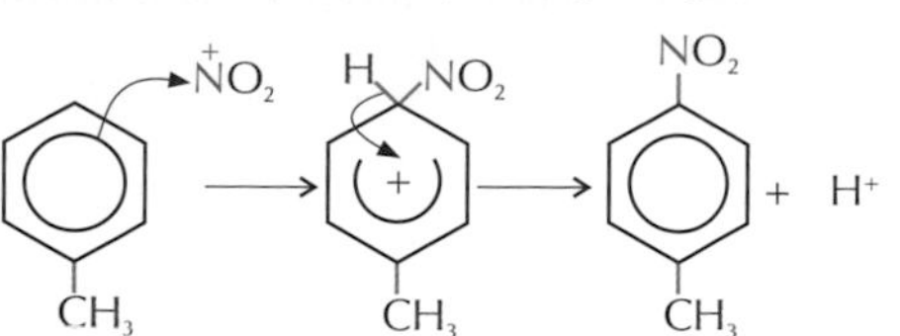

(1 mark for each correct curly arrow, 1 mark for correct structure of intermediate, maximum 3 marks).

d) (i)

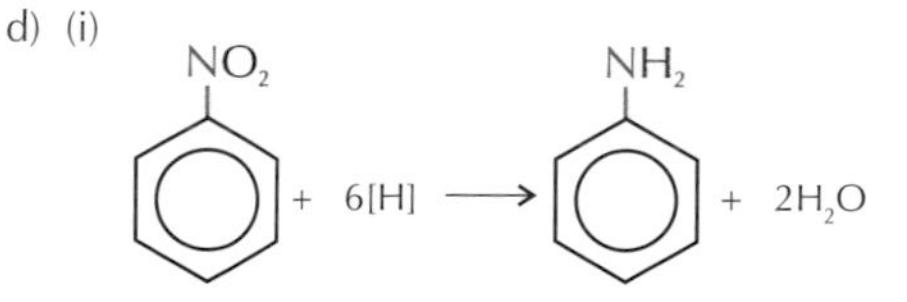

(1 mark for correct reactants and products, 1 mark for balanced equation, maximum 2 marks).

(ii) Reflux ***(1 mark)*** with tin (Sn) ***(1 mark)*** and concentrated HCl ***(1 mark)***.

2 a) X is 2-methylpropylamine ***(1 mark)***.
Y is 2,3-dimethylphenylamine ***(1 mark)***.

b) (i) $2NH_3 + CH_3CH(CH_3)CH_2Br \rightarrow CH_3CH(CH_3)CH_2NH_2 + NH_4^+Br^-$
(1 mark for correct reactants and products, 1 mark for balanced equation, maximum 2 marks).

(ii) Nucleophilic substitution ***(1 mark)***.

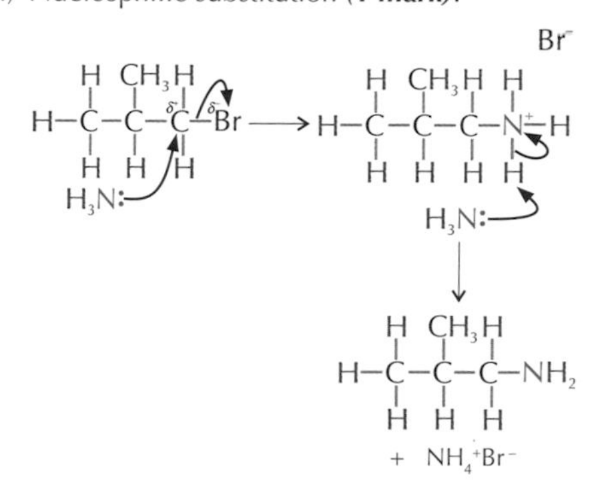

(1 mark for each correct curly arrow, 1 mark for correct structure of intermediate, maximum 4 marks).

c) (i) More than one of the hydrogens attached to the nitrogen may be substituted ***(1 mark)***.

(ii) E.g.

$CH_2CH(CH_3)CH_3$
|
N
H $CH_2CH(CH_3)CH_3$

Triamine and quaternary ammonium salt also acceptable ***(1 mark)***.

If you're asked to draw a structure like this and you're given a choice, always just draw the easiest one. You won't get any extra marks for giving harder answers and you're more likely to get it wrong. For example, if you drew the quaternary ammonium salt for this answer and forgot to give it a positive charge you wouldn't get the mark.

(iii) E.g. increase the concentration of ammonia ***(1 mark)***.

d) (i) E.g. $CH_3CH(CH_3)CN + 4[H] \rightarrow CH_3CH(CH_3)CH_2NH_2$ ***(1 mark)***.

(ii) Further substitutions aren't possible ***(1 mark)***.
So amine X is the only possible product ***(1 mark)***.

e) (i) There is a lone pair of electrons on the nitrogen which can be donated to form a dative bond with an H^+ ion ***(1 mark)***.

(ii) Amine X is the stronger base ***(1 mark)***. In amine X the alkyl group pushes electrons away from itself/in amine Y the benzene ring draws electrons towards itself ***(1 mark)***. This increases electron density on the nitrogen in amine X/this decreases electron density on the nitrogen in amine Y ***(1 mark)***. So the lone pair of electrons is more available to form a bond with hydrogen in amine X/so the lone pair of electrons is less available to form a bond with hydrogen in amine Y ***(1 mark)***.

3 a) 2-amino-4-methylpentanoic acid ***(1 mark)***.

b) (i) Species B ***(1 mark)***.

(ii) A zwitterion ***(1 mark)***.

c) (i)

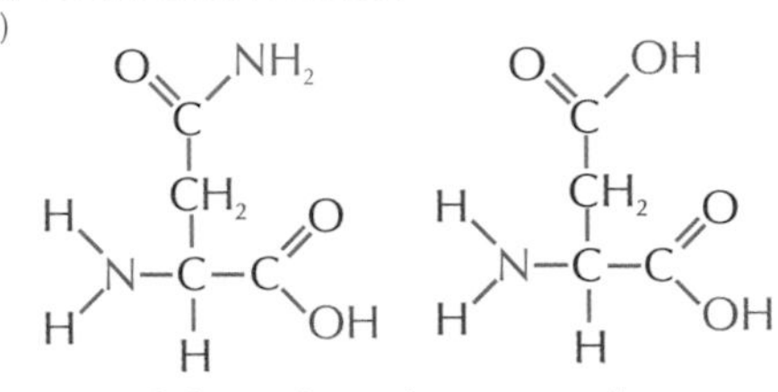

(1 mark for each, maximum 2 marks).

(ii) Aqueous 6M HCl ***(1 mark)***. Heat under reflux for 24 hours ***(1 mark)***.

4 a) A condensation polymer / polyamide ***(1 mark)***.

b)

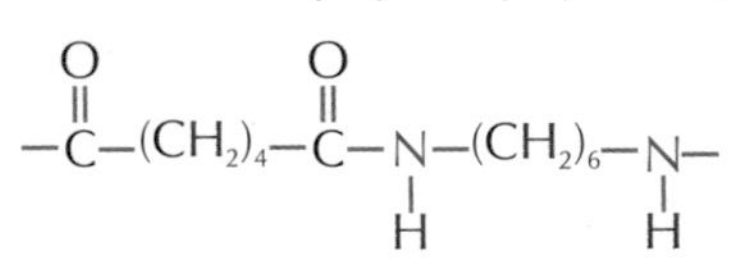

(1 mark).

When drawing repeating units make sure you include the trailing bonds which join the repeating units together. You'll lose a mark if you don't.

c) Biodegradable ***(1 mark)***. The amide bonds in nylon 6,6 are polar ***(1 mark)***, so they are susceptible to attack by nucleophiles ***(1 mark)*** and can be hydrolysed ***(1 mark)***.

d) Advantages: e.g. it reduces the amount of waste going into landfill / it saves raw materials / the cost is lower than making plastics from scratch / it produces less CO_2 emissions than burning the nylon ***(1 mark for each, maximum 2 marks)***.

Disadvantages: e.g. it is technically difficult / it is more expensive than burning/landfill / the recycled nylon may not be suitable for its original purpose / the nylon can easily be contaminated during recycling ***(1 mark for each, maximum 2 marks)***.

If you get an "advantages/disadvantages" question, make sure you discuss both. If you only give advantages or only give disadvantages you'll only get half marks, no matter how many correct points you've made.

Section 5 — Synthesis and Analysis

1. Organic Synthesis

Page 120 — Application Questions

Q1 a) H_3PO_4 catalyst, steam, 300 °C, 60 atm

b) Cl_2, U.V. light

c) CH_3COCl, $AlCl_3$ catalyst, reflux, non-aqueous environment

d) ammonia, heat

Q2 a) step 1: conc. H_2SO_4, conc. HNO_3, below 55 °C

step 2: tin, conc. HCl, reflux, $NaOH_{(aq)}$

b) step 1: warm $NaOH_{(aq)}$, reflux

step 2: $K_2Cr_2O_7$, H_2SO_4, heat in distillation apparatus

You have to do this reaction in distillation apparatus so that you don't form the carboxylic acid.

c) step 1: Cl_2, U.V. light

step 2: $KCN_{(aq)}$, ethanol, reflux

d) step 1: $K_2Cr_2O_7$, H_2SO_4, reflux

step 2: methanol, conc. H_2SO_4 catalyst, heat

Q3 step 1: conc. H_2SO_4, conc. HNO_3, below 55 °C

step 2: tin, concentrated HCl, reflux, $NaOH_{(aq)}$

step 3: CH_3COCl

Q4 step 1: warm $NaOH_{(aq)}$, reflux

step 2: $K_2Cr_2O_7$, H_2SO_4, heat, reflux

step 3: ethanol, conc. H_2SO_4 catalyst, heat

Page 120 — Fact Recall Questions

Q1 acidified potassium dichromate(VI)

Q2 orange bromine solution/bromine water

Q3 A cream precipitate would form.

Q4 $$\% \text{ yield} = \frac{\text{actual yield}}{\text{theoretical yield}} \times 100$$

Q5 $$\% \text{ atom economy} = \frac{\text{mass of desired product}}{\text{total mass of reactants}} \times 100$$

Q6 –CHO

Q7 (primary) amines

2. Mass Spectrometry

Page 123 — Application Questions

Q1 $CH_3COCH_3 \rightarrow [CH_3COCH_3]^+ + e^-$

Q2 (height of M+1 peak ÷ height of M peak) × 100

= (3.16 ÷ 53.04) × 100 = 5.96

So the molecule contains **6** carbon atoms.

Q3 There are four possible combinations of Cl-35 and Cl-37 isotopes when you have three chlorine atoms:

1: ^{35}Cl, ^{35}Cl, ^{35}Cl

2: ^{35}Cl, ^{35}Cl, ^{37}Cl

3: ^{35}Cl, ^{37}Cl, ^{37}Cl

4: ^{37}Cl, ^{37}Cl, ^{37}Cl

So, there will be **4** molecular ion peaks in a molecule with three chlorine atoms.

Page 123 — Fact Recall Questions

Q1 The mass/charge value of the molecular ion. This tells you the molecular mass of the molecule/compound (assuming the ion has 1+ charge, which it normally will have).

Q2 If a molecule contains chlorine, it will give an M peak and an M+2 peak with heights in the ratio 3:1.

Q3 The presence of an M+4 peak on a mass spectrum indicates that there are two halogen atoms in the molecule.

3. More Mass Spectrometry

Page 127 — Application Questions

Q1 $CH_3CH_2CO^+$

Q2 The molecule is propanal.

```
   H  H  O
   |  |  ||
H—C—C—C—H
   |  |
   H  H
```

This table shows all the m/z peaks from the mass spectrum and some of the fragment ions they can be assigned to:

m/z	fragment ion
15	CH_3^+
28	$C{=}O^+$
29	$CH_3CH_2^+$ / CHO^+
42	CH_2CO^+
57	$C_3H_5O^+$
58	M ($C_3H_6O^+$)
59	M+1

Don't forget that you don't have to assign all of these peaks — just as long as you've done enough to be able to prove that it's propanal...

Page 127 — Fact Recall Questions

Q1 CH_3^+

Q2 Tertiary carbocations are more stable than primary or secondary carbocations because they have more alkyl groups which donate more electron density to stabilise the carbocation.

Q3 The acylium ion has two different resonance forms. Resonance in an ion helps to stabilise what would otherwise be an unstable structure.

4. NMR Spectroscopy

Page 131 — Application Questions

Q1 Carbon 2 will have the highest chemical shift.
That's because it is next to 2 electronegative O atoms.

Q2 Butanone has four different carbon environments so there will be four different peaks on a ^{13}C NMR spectrum of butanone.

Q3 You would see four peaks as there are four different carbon environments in the molecule.
When you're looking for carbon environments on cyclic rings sometimes it helps to look at the symmetry of the molecule.

Page 131 — Fact Recall Questions

Q1 Carbon atoms in different environments will have different amounts of shielding from the magnetic field used in ^{13}C NMR. This means they will absorb different frequencies of energy and therefore have different chemical shifts on a ^{13}C NMR spectrum.

Q2 parts per million/ppm

Q3 a) tetramethylsilane/TMS/$Si(CH_3)_4$
b) E.g. TMS produces a single absorption peak. / It's absorption peak is well away from most other absorption peaks. / TMS is inert (so it doesn't react with the sample). / TMS is volatile (so it's easy to remove from the sample).

5. More About NMR

Page 136 — Application Questions

Q1 These hydrogen atoms correspond to peak **B**.

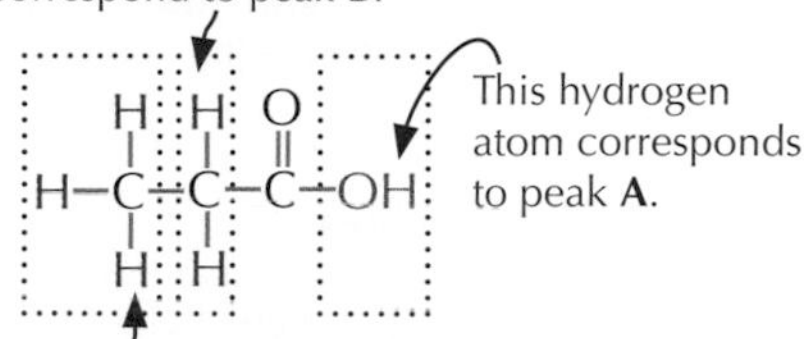

These hydrogen atoms correspond to peak **C**.

Q2 There are three peaks, so there must be three hydrogen environments in molecule **X**.
The peak at δ ~ 2.5 ppm is likely to be formed by hydrogens in a RCOCH environment and from the area ratio this peak has been caused by two protons (a $COCH_2$ group).
The peak at δ ~ 2 ppm is likely to be formed by hydrogens in a RCOCH environment and from the area ratio this peak has been caused by three protons (a $COCH_3$ group).
The peak at δ ~ 1 ppm is likely to be formed by hydrogens in a R–CH_3 environment and from the area ratio this peak has been caused by three protons.
So the groups contained in molecule **X** are $COCH_2$, $COCH_3$ and CH_3. We know that the molecular formula is C_4H_8O and that the CH_3 group must be next to the $COCH_2$ (because their peaks are split into a triplet and a quartet). So, the molecule must be butan-2-one:

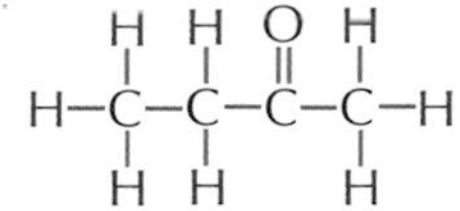

Page 136 — Fact Recall Questions

Q1 The number of peaks corresponds to the number of hydrogen (proton) environments in a compound.

Q2 The area under the peaks corresponds to the relative number of hydrogen atoms in each environment.

Q3 The chemical shift.

Q4 E.g. CCl_4 / D_2O / $CDCl_3$.

6. Infrared Spectroscopy

Page 138 — Application Questions

Q1 The peak at ~1680 cm^{-1} could be the amide carbonyl group and the peak at 3350 cm^{-1} could be due to the amide N–H bond.

Q2 The strong, sharp peak at 1680 cm^{-1} is probably a C=O bond in an aldehyde, ketone, carboxylic acid or ester. The broad peak at 2800 cm^{-1} could be a carboxylic acid OH bond. The medium peak at 3300 cm^{-1} is caused by a primary amine bond. So the compound must contain an NH_2 group and a COOH group. Since the molecular formula is $C_3H_7NO_2$, it must also contain two other carbon atoms and four other hydrogen atoms. Putting all those groups together the compound could either be:

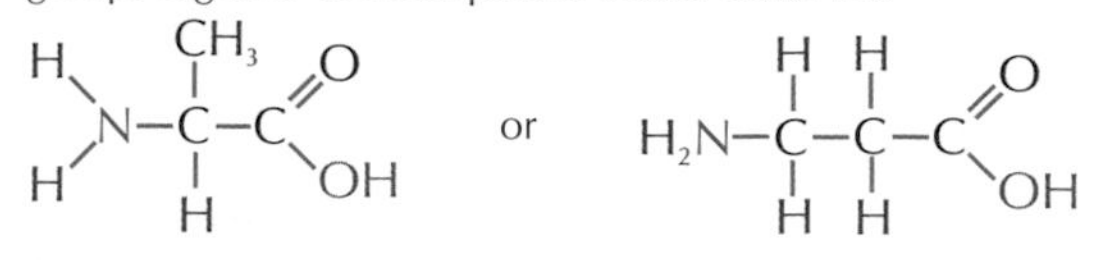

7. Chromatography

Page 141 — Application Questions

Q1 Components that are more strongly adsorbed to the stationary phase take longer to pass down the column so the pure product will leave the column after the impurities.

Q2 a) peak A
b) component B

Page 141 — Fact Recall Questions

Q1 Chromatography is used to separate stuff in a mixture.

Q2 E.g. aluminium oxide (coated with water).

Q3 A chromatography column has a liquid mobile phase, and a solid stationary phase. When a mixture of components is added to the column, some will be more soluble in the mobile phase and some will be more strongly adsorbed to the stationary phase. This means that the components will spend different amounts of time adsorbed onto the stationary phase and dissolved in the mobile phase. So the different components will take different amounts of time to pass through the column and will be separated out.

Q4 E.g. nitrogen.

Q5 The time taken for a component of a mixture to pass through the tube/column to the detector at the other end.

Q6 E.g. GLC can be used to find the level of alcohol in blood or urine. / GLC can be used to find the proportions of various esters in oils used in paints — this lets picture restorers know exactly what paint was originally used.

Pages 143-145 — Exam-style Questions

1 a) CH_3COCl ***(1 mark)***, reflux in a non-aqueous environment ***(1 mark)***. with an $AlCl_3$ catalyst ***(1 mark)***.

b) E.g. Tollens' reagent — with an aldehyde a silver mirror is formed with a ketone there's no reaction. / Fehling's solution — an aldehyde gives a brick red precipitate, there's no reaction with a ketone. / Benedict's solution — an aldehyde gives a brick red precipitate, there's no reaction with a ketone. ***(1 mark for correct reagent name, 1 mark for correct description of observation)***.

c) Spectrum C ***(1 mark)***. Phenylethanone has six different carbon environments ***(1 mark)*** and so will have six peaks on its ^{13}C NMR spectrum ***(1 mark)***.

d) Some components of the mixture will be more soluble in the mobile phase and some will be more strongly adsorbed to the stationary phase ***(1 mark)***. this means that the phenylethanone will take a different amount of time passing through the column to the impurities ***(1 mark)*** so they can be collected separately ***(1 mark)***. A stationary phase that could be used is aluminium oxide (coated with water) ***(1 mark)***.

2 a) A medium strength absorption peak at 3350 cm^{-1} on an IR spectrum corresponds to a primary amine ***(1 mark)***.
Number of carbons atoms in compound X
= (height of M+1 peak ÷ height of M peak) × 100
= (6 ÷ 100) × 100 = 6 ***(1 mark)***.
These six carbon atoms must be in the aromatic ring, so there are no other carbon atoms in the molecule ***(1 mark)***. The M_r of compound X is 93 (from the M peak on the mass spectrum). The mass of an aromatic ring with an amine group attached is:
((12 × 6) + 5) + (14 + (2 × 1)) = 93 ***(1 mark)***.
So the structure of compound X must be:

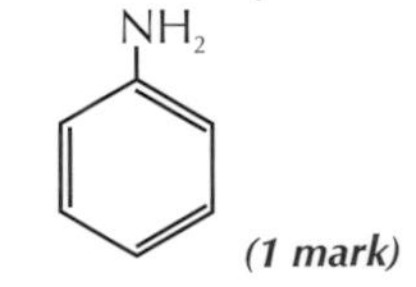

(1 mark)

b) Compound Y has two hydrogen environments ***(1 mark)***. The one at ~5.8 ppm is a quartet so must be attached to a carbon that is attached to three protons ***(1 mark)***. The environment at ~2.4 ppm is a doublet so must be attached to a carbon that is attached to one proton ***(1 mark)***. There are only two carbon atoms in the molecule, so one must have three hydrogen atoms attached and one must have one hydrogen attached ***(1 mark)***. Compound Y must be 1,1-dibromoethane:

```
  H  Br
  |  |
H-C--C-H
  |  |
  H  Br
```

(1 mark)

c) The ^{13}C NMR has three peaks which must correspond to three different carbon environments ***(1 mark)***. The peak at 172 ppm on the ^{13}C spectrum is most likely caused by a carbonyl group ***(1 mark)***. The peak at 52 ppm on the ^{13}C spectrum is most likely cause by a carbon-oxygen single bond ***(1 mark)***. The ^1H NMR spectrum has two peaks, so there are two hydrogen environments ***(1 mark)***. The peaks are both singlets, so the hydrogens are attached to a carbons with no hydrogens on adjacent carbons ***(1 mark)***. The ratio of areas under the peaks in the ^1H NMR is 1 : 1 which means that the environments each have the same number of hydrogen atoms in them ***(1 mark)***. The M_r = 74 so the carbonyl group, two other carbons and a singly bonded oxygen only leaves space for six hydrogen atoms (74 – (12 + 16 + 12 + 12 + 16) = 6) ***(1 mark)***. So, the structure of compound Z must be:

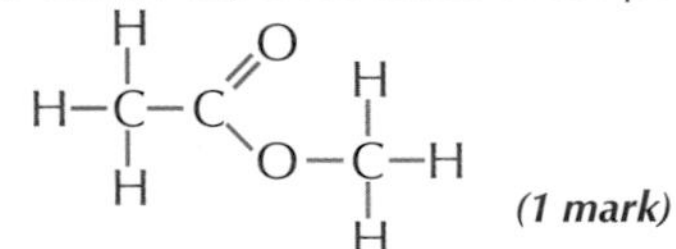

(1 mark)

3 a) compound J — pent-1-ene ***(1 mark)***
compound K — pentan-2-ol ***(1 mark)***
compound L — pentan-2-one ***(1 mark)***

b) (i) heat under reflux/in distillation apparatus ***(1 mark)***
(ii) $K_2Cr_2O_7$ acts as an oxidising agent in the reaction ***(1 mark)***.

c) The secondary alcohol is formed via a secondary carbocation, which is more stable than the primary carbocation that would form a primary alcohol ***(1 mark)***. As more stable carbocations are more likely to form the secondary alcohol is much more likely to form than the primary alcohol ***(1 mark)***.

d)

```
  H H H          H O
  | | |          | ||
H-C-C-C+       H-C-C+
  | | |          |
  H H H          H
```

(1 mark for each)

e) Compound J corresponds to spectrum A ***(1 mark)***.
Compound K corresponds to spectrum C ***(1 mark)***.
Compound L corresponds to spectrum B ***(1 mark)***.

You can see the broad OH peak in spectrum C so that's obviously compound K. The other ones are a bit more tricky but the peak at ~1700 cm^{-1} is much sharper and stronger in spectrum B than spectrum A so spectrum B is more likely to be the ketone and spectrum A the alkene.

Unit 5

Section 1 — Thermodynamics

1. Lattice Enthalpies

Page 148 — Fact Recall Questions

Q1 Enthalpy change is the heat energy transferred in a reaction at constant pressure.

Q2 ΔH

Q3 Lattice formation enthalpy is the enthalpy change when 1 mole of a solid ionic compound is formed from its gaseous ions under standard conditions.
Lattice dissociation enthalpy is the enthalpy change when 1 mole of a solid ionic compound is completely dissociated into its gaseous ions under standard conditions.

Q4 a) Enthalpy change of formation is the enthalpy change when 1 mole of a compound is formed from its elements in their standard states under standard conditions.
b) Second electron affinity is the enthalpy change when 1 mole of gaseous 2– ions is made from 1 mole of gaseous 1– ions.
c) The enthalpy change of solution is the enthalpy change when 1 mole of solute is dissolved in sufficient solvent that no further enthalpy change occurs on further dilution.

Q5 a) Enthalpy change of atomisation of an element.
b) The first ionisation enthalpy.

Q6 a) ΔH°_{hyd}
b) ΔH°_{diss}

2. Calculating Lattice Enthalpies

Page 152 — Application Questions

Q1 $\Delta H6 = -\Delta H5 - \Delta H4 - \Delta H3 - \Delta H2 + \Delta H1$
$= -(-349) - (+520) - (+159) - (+122) + (-409)$
$= \mathbf{-861\ kJmol^{-1}}$

Q2

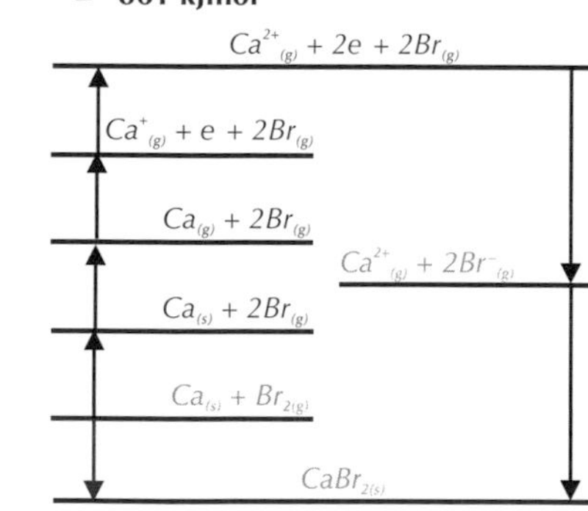

Q3 a)

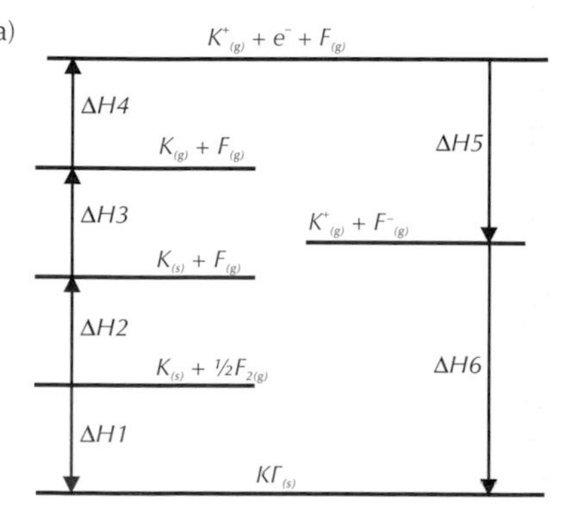

b) $\Delta H6 = -\Delta H5 - \Delta H4 - \Delta H3 - \Delta H2 + \Delta H1$
$= -(-328) - (+419) - (+89) - (+79) + (-563)$
$= \mathbf{-822\ kJmol^{-1}}$

Page 152 — Fact Recall Questions

Q1 The total enthalpy change of a reaction is always the same, no matter which route is taken.

Q2 The purely ionic model of a lattice, which theoretical lattice enthalpies are based on, assumes that all the ions are spherical, and have their charge evenly distributed around them. But the experimental lattice enthalpy from the Born-Haber cycle is usually different. This is because ionic compounds usually have some covalent character. The positive and negative ions in a lattice aren't usually exactly spherical. Positive ions polarise neighbouring negative ions to different extents, and the more polarisation there is, the more covalent the bonding will be.

3. Enthalpies of Solution

Page 155 — Application Questions

Q1 $\Delta H3 = \Delta H1 + \Delta H2 = +826 + (-520 + -364) = \mathbf{-58\ kJmol^{-1}}$

Q2 Bonds broken = 12 × C–H + 7 × O=O + 2 × C–C
$= (12 \times 413) + (7 \times 498) + (2 \times 347) = 9136\ kJmol^{-1}$
Bonds formed = 8 × C=O + 12 × O–H
$= (8 \times 805) + (12 \times 460) = 11960\ kJmol^{-1}$
Enthalpy change of reaction = 9136 – 11960

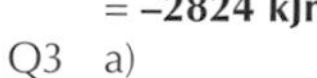

$= \mathbf{-2824\ kJmol^{-1}}$

Q3 a)

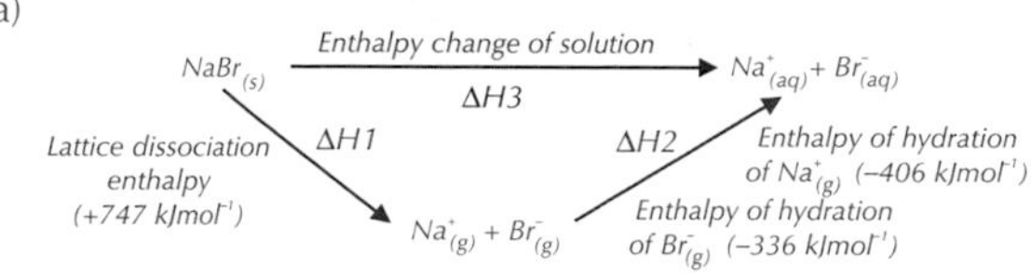

b) $\Delta H3 = \Delta H1 + \Delta H2 = +747 + (-406 + -336)$
$= \mathbf{+5\ kJmol^{-1}}$

Q4 a) $\Delta H3 = \Delta H1 + \Delta H2 = +807 + (-520 + -336)$
$= \mathbf{-49\ kJmol^{-1}}$
b) $\Delta H3 = \Delta H1 + \Delta H2 = +701 + (-322 + -364)$
$= \mathbf{+15\ kJmol^{-1}}$
c) $\Delta H3 = \Delta H1 + \Delta H2 = +2440 + (-1921 + (-336 \times 2))$
$= \mathbf{-153\ kJmol^{-1}}$

Page 155 — Fact Recall Questions

Q1 a) The bonds between the ions break, and bonds between the ions and water are made.
b) Bonds breaking is endothermic, and bonds being made is exothermic.

Q2 The lattice enthalpy of dissociation and enthalpy change of hydration.

Q3 enthalpy change of reaction = total energy absorbed – total energy released
or enthalpy change of reaction = sum of enthalpies of bonds broken – sum of enthalpies of bonds formed

Q4 A given type of bond will vary in strength from compound to compound and can even vary within a compound. Mean bond enthalpies are the averages of these bond enthalpies. So calculations done using mean bond enthalpies will never be perfectly accurate. You get much more exact results from experimental data obtained from the specific compounds.

4. Entropy

Page 158 — Application Questions

Q1 The entropy will increase when the solid sodium hydroxide dissolves in the aqueous hydrogen chloride. The entropy of the water will increase when it turns to a gas and the entropy of the sodium chloride will decrease when it turns to a solid.

Q2 a) $\Delta S_{system} = S_{products} - S_{reactants}$
$= (214 + (2 \times 69.9)) - (186 + (2 \times 205))$
$= \mathbf{-242\ JK^{-1}mol^{-1}}$

b) $\Delta H^{\circ} = -730\ kJmol^{-1} = -730 \times 10^3\ Jmol^{-1}$
$\Delta S_{surroundings} = -\Delta H \div T = -(-730 \times 10^3) \div 298$
$= \mathbf{-2450\ JK^{-1}mol^{-1}}$

c) $\Delta S^{\circ}_{total} = \Delta S^{\circ}_{system} + \Delta S^{\circ}_{surroundings}$
$= -242 + (-2450) = \mathbf{-2692\ JK^{-1}mol^{-1}}$

d) The reaction won't happen spontaneously because ΔS°_{total} is negative.

Q3 $\Delta S_{system} = S_{products} - S_{reactants}$
$= ((3 \times 31.6) + (2 \times 69.9)) - (248 + (2 \times 206))$
$= -425\ JK^{-1}mol^{-1}$
$\Delta H^{\circ} = -235\ kJmol^{-1} = -235 \times 10^3\ Jmol^{-1}$
$\Delta S_{surroundings} = -\Delta H \div T = -(-235 \times 10^3) \div 298$
$= +789\ JK^{-1}mol^{-1}$
$\Delta S^{\circ}_{total} = \Delta S^{\circ}_{system} + \Delta S^{\circ}_{surroundings}$
$= -425.4 + (+789) = \mathbf{+364\ JK^{-1}mol^{-1}}$

Page 158 — Fact Recall Questions

Q1 a) It is a measure of the amount of disorder in a system (e.g. the number of ways that particles can be arranged and the number of ways that the energy can be shared out between particles).

b) ΔS

Q2 a) The entropy increases because particles move around more in gases than in liquids and their arrangement is more random.

b) The entropy increases because particles move around more in liquids than in solids and their arrangement is more random.

c) The entropy increases because the more particles you've got, the more ways they and their energy can be arranged.

Q3 Enthalpy is not the only factor to affect entropy. Things like changing states and changing the number of molecules can also affect entropy. If the increase in entropy due to other factors is greater than the decrease in entropy due to the reaction being endothermic, then the overall entropy change will be positive and the reaction will happen spontaneously.

Q4 a) $\Delta S_{total} = \Delta S_{system} + \Delta S_{surroundings}$

b) $\Delta S_{system} = S_{products} - S_{reactants}$

c) $\Delta S_{surroundings} = -\Delta H \div T$

5. Free-Energy Change

Pages 160-161 — Application Questions

Q1 a) $\Delta S_{system} = S_{products} - S_{reactants}$
$= ((2 \times 28.3) + (3 \times 27.0)) - (51.0 + (3 \times 32.5))$
$= \mathbf{-10.9\ JK^{-1}mol^{-1}}$

b) $\Delta H^{\circ} = -130\ kJmol^{-1} = -130 \times 10^3\ Jmol^{-1}$
$\Delta G = \Delta H - T\Delta S_{system}$
$= -130 \times 10^3 - (298 \times -10.9)$
$= \mathbf{-126\ 752\ Jmol^{-1}}$

c) The reaction is feasible at 298 K because ΔG is negative.

Q2 $\Delta H^{\circ} = 178\ kJmol^{-1} = 178 \times 10^3\ Jmol^{-1}$
$T = \Delta H \div \Delta S_{system} = 178 \times 10^3 \div 165 = \mathbf{1079\ K}$

Page 161 — Fact Recall Questions

Q1 a) Free energy change is a measure used to predict whether a reaction is feasible. It is 0 or negative for a feasible reaction and positive for a non-feasible reaction.

b) ΔG

c) $Jmol^{-1}$

Q2 $\Delta G = \Delta H - T\Delta S_{system}$

Q3 no

Q4 $T = \Delta H \div \Delta S_{system}$

Exam-style Questions — pages 162-164

1 a) It is the enthalpy change when 1 mole of gaseous atoms is formed ***(1 mark)*** from an element in its standard state ***(1 mark)***.

b)

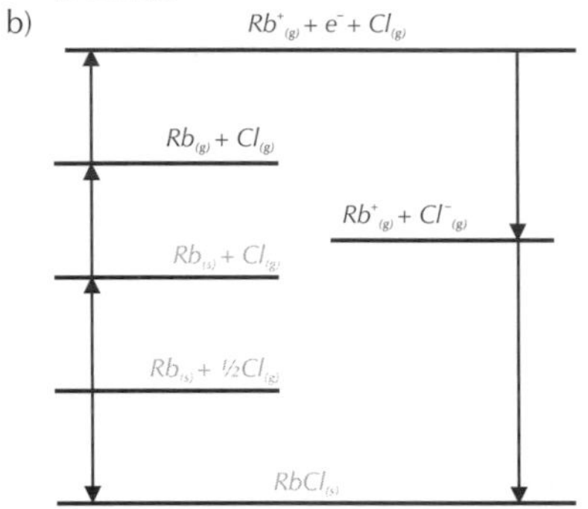

(1 mark for each correct label).

c) $\Delta H6 = -\Delta H5 - \Delta H4 - \Delta H3 - \Delta H2 + \Delta H1$
$= -(-349) - (+403) - (+81) - (+122) + (-435)$
$= \mathbf{-692\ kJmol^{-1}}$
(3 marks for correct answer, otherwise 1 mark for correct equation, 1 mark for correct substitution)

d) When experimental and theoretical lattice enthalpies are very similar, it shows that a compound has very little covalent character ***(1 mark)***. This means that rubidium chloride fits the purely ionic model very well and so the ions are close to spherical and unpolarised ***(1 mark)***.

e) (i) $+ 692\ kJmol^{-1}$ ***(1 mark)***
(ii) Enthalpy change of solution ***(1 mark)***.
(iii) $\Delta H3 = \Delta H1 + \Delta H2 = +692 + (-296 + -364)$
$= \mathbf{+32\ kJmol^{-1}}$ ***(1 mark)***

If you used the value of +300 kJmol⁻¹ for the enthalpy change of dissociation you'll get an answer of −360 kJmol⁻¹. If you got this answer, give yourself full marks.

2 a) (i) Increase. 5 molecules of reactant is going to 6 molecules of product ***(1 mark)*** so the products will have higher entropy because there are more ways of arranging 6 molecules than 5 ***(1 mark)***.

You generally don't get marks for 50:50 guesses at A2 — so you won't get any marks just for saying it increases. The marks come for the explanation.

(ii) It would decrease ***(1 mark)***. Particles move around less in liquids than in gases and their arrangement is less random, so liquids have lower entropy ***(1 mark)***.

b) $\Delta H_r = \Delta H_f(\text{products}) - \Delta H_f(\text{reactants})$
$= ((2 \times -111) + (4 \times -242)) - ((2 \times -78) + (3 \times 0))$
$= \mathbf{-1034\ kJmol^{-1}}$
(3 marks for correct answer, otherwise 1 mark for correct equation, 1 mark for correct substitution).

You learnt how to do this type of question at AS level and you may need to do it in your A2 exam as well.

c) $\Delta S_{system} = S_{products} - S_{reactants}$
$= ((2 \times 198) + (4 \times 189)) - ((2 \times 186) + (3 \times 205))$
$= \mathbf{+165\ JK^{-1}mol^{-1}}$
(3 marks for correct answer, otherwise 1 mark for correct equation, 1 mark for correct substitution).

d) (i) $\Delta G = \Delta H - T\Delta S_{system}$ ***(1 mark).***
(ii) ΔH is negative and ΔS_{system} is positive ***(1 mark).*** This means that the value of ΔG will always be negative irrespective of the temperature ***(1 mark).***

3 a) (i) $\Delta S_{system} = S_{products} - S_{reactants}$
$= (32 + 214) - (53 + 5.7)$
$= +187.3\ JK^{-1}mol^{-1}$ ***(1 mark).***
$\Delta H^{\circ} = +127\ kJmol^{-1} = +127 \times 10^3\ Jmol^{-1}$
$\Delta G = \Delta H - T\Delta S_{system}$ ***(1 mark).***
$= (+127 \times 10^3) - (1473 \times +187.3)$ ***(1 mark).***
$= \mathbf{-148893\ Jmol^{-1}}$ or $\mathbf{-148.9\ kJmol^{-1}}$ ***(1 mark).***
(ii) If the free energy change is negative or equal to zero the reaction is feasible ***(1 mark).*** If the free energy change is positive, the reaction is not feasible ***(1 mark).***

b) (i) $T = \Delta H \div \Delta S_{system}$ ***(1 mark).***
(ii) $T = (+127 \times 10^3) \div 187.3$
$= \mathbf{678\ K}$
(1 mark for correct substitution, 1 mark for correct answer).

Don't forget, reactions become feasible when ΔG is 0.

c) (i) The standard enthalpy change of formation is the enthalpy change when 1 mole of a compound is formed from its elements ***(1 mark)*** in their standard states and under standard conditions ***(1 mark).***
(ii) The formation of manganese(IV) oxide would be exothermic ***(1 mark).***

It's an exothermic reaction because ΔH is negative.

(iii) In MnO_2 two Mn-O bonds are formed whereas in MnO only one Mn-O bond is formed ***(1 mark).*** So less energy is released when MnO forms and it's standard enthalpy of formation is higher (less negative) ***(1 mark).***

Section 2 — Period 3 and Redox Equilibria

1. Period 3 Elements

Page 166 — Application Question

Q1 a) A is sodium, B is magnesium, C is sulfur.
b) A: $2Na_{(s)} + \frac{1}{2}O_{2(g)} \rightarrow Na_2O_{(s)}$
B: $Mg_{(s)} + \frac{1}{2}O_{2(g)} \rightarrow MgO_{(s)}$
C: $S_{(s)} + O_{2(g)} \rightarrow SO_{2(g)}$

Page 166 — Fact Recall Questions

Q1 a) (i) $2Na_{(s)} + 2H_2O_{(l)} \rightarrow 2NaOH_{(aq)} + H_{2(g)}$
(ii) $Mg_{(s)} + 2H_2O_{(l)} \rightarrow Mg(OH)_{2(aq)} + H_{2(g)}$
b) Sodium reacts more vigorously. Sodium is in Group 1 and magnesium is in Group 2. So when they react sodium loses one electron and magnesium loses two. It takes less energy to lose one electron than it does to lose two, so sodium is more reactive.

Q2 a) $2Al_{(s)} + 1\frac{1}{2}O_{2(g)} \rightarrow Al_2O_{3(s)}$
b) $P_{4(s)} + 5O_{2(g)} \rightarrow P_4O_{10(s)}$

2. Period 3 Oxides

Page 168 — Application Question

Q1 a) A is magnesium oxide (MgO), B is aluminium oxide (Al_2O_3), C is silicon dioxide (SiO_2).
b) Magnesium oxide has a higher melting point than aluminium oxide because the Al^{3+} ions in aluminium oxide distort the oxygen's electron cloud, making the bonds partially covalent. This makes them weaker than the ionic bonds in magnesium oxide. So more heat energy is required to break the bonds in magnesium oxide and melt it.

Page 168 — Fact Recall Questions

Q1 a) (i) MgO forms a giant ionic lattice with strong ionic bonds between the ions.
(ii) Al_2O_3 forms a giant ionic lattice. Bonding is ionic with partial covalent character because the Al^{3+} ions distort the oxygen electron clouds.
(iii) SiO_2 has a giant macromolecular structure with strong covalent bonds between the atoms.
(iv) P_4O_{10} has a simple molecular structure with weak intermolecular forces (e.g. dipole-dipole/van der Waals) between the molecules.
b) $MgO_{(s)} + H_2O_{(l)} \rightarrow Mg(OH)_{2(aq)}$
$P_4O_{10(s)} + 6H_2O_{(l)} \rightarrow 4H_3PO_{4(aq)}$
c) (i) Basic
(ii) Amphoteric
(iii) Acidic
(iv) Acidic

Q2 a) $MgO_{(s)} + 2HCl_{(aq)} \rightarrow MgCl_{2(aq)} + H_2O_{(l)}$
b) $SO_{2(g)} + 2NaOH_{(aq)} \rightarrow Na_2SO_{3(aq)} + H_2O_{(l)}$

3. Redox Equations

Page 171 — Application Questions

Q1 a) +1
b) +7
c) −1

Q2 a) Oxidation: $Cu_{(s)} \rightarrow Cu^{2+}_{(aq)} + 2e^-$
Reduction: $Ag^+_{(aq)} + e^- \rightarrow Ag_{(s)}$

If you're asked for the half-equations for a reaction, make sure you label which one is oxidation and which one is reduction.

b) $Cu_{(s)} + 2Ag^+_{(aq)} \rightarrow Cu^{2+}_{(aq)} + 2Ag_{(s)}$

Q3 Oxidation: $Fe^{2+}_{(aq)} \rightarrow Fe^{3+}_{(aq)} + e^-$
Reduction: $Cl_{2(g)} + 2e^- \rightarrow 2Cl^-_{(aq)}$
Full equation: $Cl_{2(g)} + 2Fe^{2+}_{(aq)} \rightarrow 2Cl^-_{(aq)} + 2Fe^{3+}_{(aq)}$

Q4 a) $H_2O_2 \rightarrow O_2 + 2H^+ + 2e^-$
b) $MnO_4^- + 8H^+ + 5e^- \rightarrow Mn^{2+} + 4H_2O$
c) $5H_2O_2 + 2MnO_4^- + 6H^+ \rightarrow 5O_2 + 2Mn^{2+} + 8H_2O$

Don't forget to double-check that the charges on each side of the equation balance, as well as the atoms.

Page 171 — Fact Recall Questions

Q1 a) The loss of electrons.
b) Something which can accept electrons and therefore oxidise other reactants.

Q2 a) 0
b) The same as the charge on that ion.
c) +1

Q3 It decreases by one.

Q4 Ionic half-equations show oxidation or reduction.

4. Electrode Potentials

Page 176 — Application Questions

Q1 a) $Ca_{(s)}\ |\ Ca^{2+}_{(aq)}\ ||\ Ag^+_{(aq)}\ |\ Ag_{(s)}$
b) (i) $Ag^+_{(aq)} + e^- \rightarrow Ag_{(s)}$
(ii) $Ca_{(s)} \rightarrow Ca^{2+}_{(aq)} + 2e^-$
c) $E_{cell} = E_{RHS} - E_{LHS} = 0.80 - (-2.87) = 3.67\ V$

Q2 a) At the positive electrode: $Tl^{3+}_{(aq)} + 2e^- \rightarrow Tl^+_{(aq)}$

At the negative electrode: $Fe^{2+}_{(aq)} \rightarrow Fe^{3+}_{(aq)} + e^-$

b) $E_{RHS} = E_{cell} + E_{LHS} = 0.48 + 0.77 = 1.25$ V

Q3 a) The Mg^{2+}/Mg half-cell.

b) $Mg_{(s)} \mid Mg^{2+}_{(aq)} \parallel Fe^{3+}_{(aq)}, Fe^{2+}_{(aq)} \mid Pt$

Page 176 — Fact Recall Questions

Q1 a) A platinum electrode

b) Platinum is inert, so it won't react with the solution, but it is a solid that conducts electricity.

Q2 Reduction

Q3 Any two from, e.g. the half-cell with the more negative potential goes on the left / the oxidised species go in the centre of the cell diagram / the reduced species go at the edge of the cell diagram / double vertical lines are used to show a salt bridge / things in different phases are separate by a vertical line / things in the same phase are separated by a comma.

Any two facts about how to draw a cell diagram will do here — just flick back to the page if you need a quick reminder.

5. Standard Electrode Potentials

Page 178 — Application Question

Q1 a) $Pt \mid H_{2(g)} \mid H^+_{(aq)} \parallel Pb^{2+}_{(aq)} \mid Pb_{(s)}$

b) –0.13 V

c) Oxidation

The electrode potential of the standard hydrogen electrode is 0.00 V so the Pb^{2+}/Pb half-cell has the more negative electrode potential and oxidation occurs in this half-cell.

Page 178 — Fact Recall Questions

Q1 Temperature, pressure and concentration of reactants.

Q2 Hydrogen gas is bubbled into a solution of aqueous H^+ ions. The electrode is made of platinum. The standard conditions used are a temperature of 298 K (25 °C), a pressure of 100 kPa and all solutions of ions having a concentration of 1.00 moldm^{-3}.

Q3 a) 0.00 V

b) It is zero by definition (scientists decided it would have that value).

Q4 The voltage measured under standard conditions when the half-cell is connected to a standard hydrogen electrode

6. Electrochemical Series

Page 182 — Application Questions

Q1 a) Aluminium — they are both metals and aluminium has the more negative standard electrode potential.

b) Chlorine — they are both non-metals and chlorine has the more positive standard electrode potential.

c) Copper — they are both metals and copper has the more negative (least positive) standard electrode potential.

Although the electrode potential for copper is positive, it is still more negative than that for silver, so copper is more reactive.

Q2 Magnesium and zinc are both metals. Magnesium has the more negative standard electrode potential, so it can lose electrons more easily and is more reactive.

Q3 a)

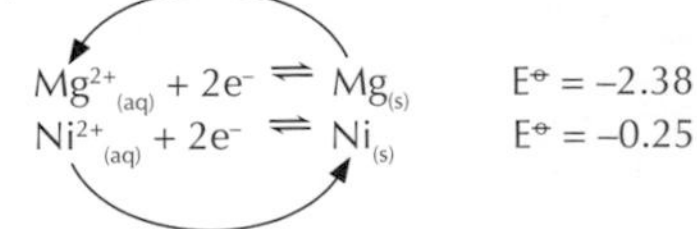

Yes, the reaction will occur.

b)

$Fe^{3+}_{(aq)} + e^- \rightleftharpoons Fe^{2+}_{(aq)}$ $E^\ominus = +0.77$

$Br_{2(aq)} + 2e^- \rightleftharpoons 2Br^-_{(aq)}$ $E^\ominus = +1.09$

No, the reaction will not occur.

c)

$Sn^{4+}_{(aq)} + 2e^- \rightleftharpoons Sn^{2+}_{(aq)}$ $E^\ominus = +0.15$

$Cu^{2+}_{(aq)} + 2e^- \rightleftharpoons Cu_{(s)}$ $E^\ominus = +0.34$

Yes, the reaction will occur.

Q4 a) $E^\ominus_{cell} = (E^\ominus_{bottom} - E^\ominus_{top}) = 0.80 - (-1.66) = +2.46$ V

b) $E^\ominus_{cell} = (E^\ominus_{bottom} - E^\ominus_{top}) = 1.36 - 0.34 = +1.02$ V

c) $E^\ominus_{cell} = (E^\ominus_{bottom} - E^\ominus_{top}) = 0.77 - 0.15 = +0.62$ V

Your values for the e.m.f. should always be positive. If you get a negative answer, go back and check your calculation because you must have gone wrong somewhere.

Q5 $E^\ominus$ for Sn^{4+}/Sn^{2+} is more negative than $E^\ominus$ for Ag^+/Ag, so Sn^{2+} ions will react with Ag^+ ions in solution.

Page 182 — Fact Recall Questions

Q1 A list of electrode potentials for different electrochemical half-cells, written in order from the most negative to the most positive.

Q2 In the direction of reduction.

Q3 Reduction.

Q4 a) Very negative.

b) Very positive.

Q5 a) The anticlockwise rule.

b) $E^\ominus_{cell} = (E^\ominus_{bottom} - E^\ominus_{top})$

7. Electrochemical Cells

Page 185 — Application Questions

Q1 a) $E^\ominus_{cell} = (E^\ominus_{R.H.S.} - E^\ominus_{L.H.S}) = 0.52 - (-0.88) = \mathbf{+1.4\ V}$

b) $2NiO(OH)_{(s)} + Cd_{(s)} + 2H_2O_{(l)} \rightarrow 2Ni(OH)_{2(s)} + Cd(OH)_{2(s)}$

Q2 a) $2H_2 + O_2 \rightarrow 2H_2O$

b) $Pt \mid H_{2(g)} \mid H^+_{(aq)} \parallel O_{2(g)} \mid H^+_{(aq)}, H_2O_{(l)} \mid Pt$

Page 185 — Fact Recall Questions

Q1 You can recharge a rechargeable battery because the reaction that occurs within it can be reversed if a current is supplied to force the electrons to flow in the opposite direction around the circuit.

Q2 Advantages: they are cheaper to buy/they will work for longer/they are less toxic.

Disadvantages: they need to be replaced more often so are more expensive in the long run/they can't be reused/they can't supply as much power/they create more waste/they use more resources.

Q3 There are two platinum electrodes separated by ion exchange membranes. Hydrogen is fed into the negative electrode where it is oxidised to H^+ ions and electrons. The electrons can't cross the ion exchange membranes so travel round the external circuit, generating electricity. The H^+ ions travel across the ion exchange membrane to the positive electrode where they combine with oxygen to form water.

Q4 You need energy to produce the supply of hydrogen and oxygen. This is normally generated by burning fossil fuels.

Q5 Advantages: they don't need electrically recharging/the only waste product is water/they don't produce CO_2 emissions.

Disadvantages: they are not usually carbon neutral/hydrogen is highly flammable so needs to be handled carefully.

Exam-style Questions — page 187-189

1 (a) (i) $Mg_{(s)} + 2H_2O_{(l)} \rightarrow Mg(OH)_{2(aq)} + H_{2(g)}$ ***(1 mark).***

(ii) Magnesium loses two electrons to form an Mg^{2+} ion but sodium only loses one electron to form an Na^+ ion ***(1 mark).*** It takes less energy for sodium to lose one electron than it does for magnesium to lose two ***(1 mark).*** So more energy is needed for magnesium to react ***(1 mark).***

(b) (i) $2Na_{(s)} + ½O_{2(g)} \rightarrow Na_2O_{(s)}$ ***(1 mark)***

(ii) Yellow ***(1 mark)***

(iii) Both form giant ionic lattices ***(1 mark),*** with strong ionic bonds between each ion ***(1 mark).***

(iv) MgO has the higher melting temperature ***(1 mark).*** Magnesium forms Mg^{2+} ions, which attract O^{2-} ions more strongly than the Na^+ ions in Na_2O, so the ionic bonds in MgO are stronger ***(1 mark)*** and more heat energy is required to break the bonds ***(1 mark).***

(c) (i) Sulfur dioxide has a simple molecular structure ***(1 mark).*** Only weak intermolecular forces (e.g. dipole-dipole/van der Waals) hold the molecules together ***(1 mark).*** Little heat energy is needed to overcome these forces ***(1 mark).***

(ii) Silicon dioxide has a giant macromolecular structure ***(1 mark),*** with strong covalent bonds holding the molecules together ***(1 mark).*** Lots of energy is required to break these bonds ***(1 mark).***

(d) (i) $MgO_{(s)} + H_2O_{(l)} \rightarrow Mg(OH)_{2(aq)}$ ***(1 mark)***

pH 9-10 ***(1 mark)***

$SO_{2(g)} + H_2O_{(l)} \rightarrow H_2SO_{3(aq)}$ ***(1 mark)***

pH 0-2 ***(1 mark)***

(ii) Aluminium oxide/silicon dioxide ***(1 mark).***

(e) (i) Aluminium oxide ***(1 mark).***

(ii) $Al_2O_{3(s)} + 3H_2SO_{4(aq)} \rightarrow Al_2(SO_4)_{3(aq)} + 3H_2O_{(l)}$ ***(1 mark)***

$Al_2O_{3(s)} + 2NaOH_{(aq)} + 3H_2O_{(l)} \rightarrow 2NaAl(OH)_{4(aq)}$ ***(1 mark)***

2 (a) $E^{\ominus}$ for Sn^{4+}/Sn^{2+} is more negative than $E^{\ominus}$ for VO_2^+/VO^{2+}, so Sn^{2+} ions will react with VO_2^+ ions ***(1 mark).***

$2VO_2^+{}_{(aq)} + Sn^{2+}{}_{(aq)} + 4H^+{}_{(aq)} \rightarrow 2VO^{2+}{}_{(aq)} + Sn^{4+}{}_{(aq)} + 2H_2O_{(l)}$ ***(1 mark).***

$E^{\ominus}$ for Sn^{4+}/Sn^{2+} is more negative than $E^{\ominus}$ for VO^{2+}/V^{3+}, so Sn^{2+} ions will react with VO^{2+} ions created in the previous reaction ***(1 mark).***

$2VO^{2+}{}_{(aq)} + Sn^{2+}{}_{(aq)} + 4H^+{}_{(aq)} \rightarrow 2V^{3+} + Sn^{4+} + 2H_2O$ ***(1 mark).***

The V^{3+} ions made in this reaction don't react with the Sn^{2+} ions because the electrode potential for V^{3+}/V^{2+} is more negative than that for Sn^{4+}/Sn^{2+}.

(b) (i) $Mg_{(s)} \mid Mg^{2+}{}_{(aq)} \parallel Fe^{3+}{}_{(aq)} \mid Fe^{2+}{}_{(aq)} \mid Pt$

(1 mark for left-hand side correct, 1 mark for right-hand side correct)

Don't forget to include the platinum electrode...

(ii) $E_{cell} = E_{RHS} - E_{LHS} = 0.77 - (-2.38) =$ **3.15 V** ***(1 mark).***

(iii) Oxidation: $Mg_{(s)} \rightarrow Mg^{2+}{}_{(aq)} + 2e^-$ ***(1 mark).***

Reduction: $Fe^{3+}{}_{(aq)} + e^- \rightarrow Fe^{2+}{}_{(aq)}$ ***(1 mark).***

(c) (i) A temperature of 298 K ***(1 mark).*** A pressure of 100 kPa ***(1 mark).*** Any solutions of ions have a concentration of 1.00 $moldm^{-3}$ ***(1 mark).***

(ii) It is zero by definition/scientists decided it would be that value ***(1 mark).***

(iii) Platinum is inert ***(1 mark).***

(d) (i) +0.80 V ***(1 mark).***

(ii) Silver is less reactive than vanadium ***(1 mark)*** because it has a less negative electrode potential ***(1 mark).***

3 (a) The reactions that occur within them can be reversed if a current is supplied to force the electrons to flow in the opposite direction around the circuit ***(1 mark).***

(b) $PbO_{2(s)} + 2SO_4^{2-}{}_{(aq)} + 4H^+ + Pb_{(s)} \rightarrow 2PbSO_{4(s)} + 2H_2O_{(l)}$ ***(1 mark).***

(c) Advantages: they don't have to be replaced when they run out so are cheaper in the long run/they can supply more power than non-rechargeables/they result in less waste because they can be reused.

Disadvantages: they are more expensive to buy/they don't work for as long/they often contain toxic metals/they are more hazardous if put into landfill ***(1 mark for each, maximum 4 marks).***

To get full marks on a question like this you have to include at least one advantage and one disadvantage. Just talking about one or the other won't get full marks.

(d) (i) It is cheaper ***(1 mark)*** and it provides a larger surface area so the reaction goes faster ***(1 mark).***

(ii) Any two from, e.g. they don't need electrically recharging/the only waste product is water/they don't produce CO_2 emissions ***(1 mark for each).***

4 (a) $Cr_2O_7^{2-}{}_{(aq)} + 14H^+{}_{(aq)} + 6e^- \rightarrow 2Cr^{3+}{}_{(aq)} + 7H_2O_{(l)}$

(1 mark for correct reactants and products, 1 mark for balancing the equation).

(b) $E_{RHS} = E_{LHS} + E_{cell} = 0.17 + 1.16 =$ **+1.33 V** ***(1 mark).***

(c) $Pt \mid H_{2(g)} \mid H^+{}_{(aq)} \parallel Cr_2O_7^{2-}{}_{(aq)}, Cr^{3+}{}_{(aq)} \mid Pt$ ***(1 mark).***

Section 3 — Transition metals

1. Transition Metals — The Basics

Page 193 — Application Questions

Q1 a) $[Ar]3d^34s^2$

b) $[Ar]3d^74s^2$

c) $[Ar]3d^{10}4s^1$

d) $[Ar]3d^84s^2$

For these questions you don't have to write [Ar]. If you've written out the whole electron configuration starting from $1s^2$ that's fine too — but in the exam it'll save you lots of time if you can use the shorthand.

Q2 a) $[Ar]3d^2$

b) $[Ar]3d^7$

c) $[Ar]3d^9$

d) $[Ar]3d^8$

Don't forget, the s electrons are always removed first, then the d electrons.

Q3 Zinc has the electron configuration $[Ar]3d^{10}4s^2$. It can only form Zn^{2+} ions which have an electron configuration of $[Ar]3d^{10}$. This ion has a full d-subshell, so zinc cannot form a stable ion with a partially filled d-subshell and it therefore can't be a transition metal.

Page 193 — Fact Recall Questions

Q1 In the d-block.

Q2 A transition metal is a metal that can form one or more stable ions with a partially filled d-subshell.

Q3 10

Q4 Electrons fill up the lowest energy subshells first and electrons fill orbitals singly before they start sharing.

Q5 a) Chromium prefers to have one electron in each orbital of the 3d subshell and just one in the 4s subshell because this gives it more stability.

b) Copper prefers to have a full 3d subshell and just one electron in the 4s subshell because it's more stable that way.

Q6 Even though they are in the d-block, they can't form any stable ions with a partially filled d-subshell and so are not transition metals.

Q7 a) Any three from: e.g. they all have a high density / they all have high melting points / they all have high boiling points / they all have similar ionic radii.

b) They can form complex ions, form coloured ions, act as catalysts and exist in variable oxidation states.

Q8 Their incomplete d-subshell.

2. Complex Ions

Page 197 — Application Questions

Q1 a) Octahedral:

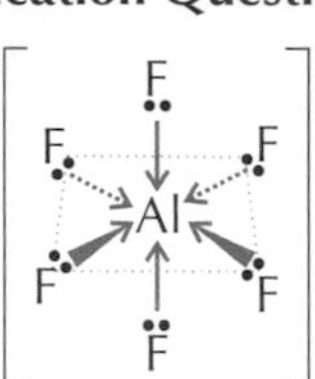

When you're drawing the shapes of ions and molecules make sure you include the dashed arrows and the chunky arrows to show that it's 3D.

b) Linear:

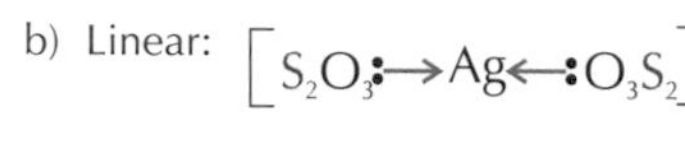

c) Tetrahedral:

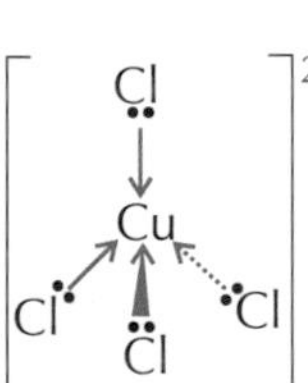

Q2 a) Overall oxidation state of $[AlF_6]^{3-}$ is −3. Each F^- ion has an oxidation state of −1 so the oxidation state of aluminium must be −3 − (6 × −1) = **+3**.

b) Overall oxidation state of $[Ag(S_2O_3)_2]^{3-}$ is −3. Each $S_2O_3^{2-}$ ion has an oxidation state of −2 so the oxidation state of silver must be −3 − (2 × −2) = **+1**.

c) Overall oxidation state of $[CuCl_4]^{2-}$ is −2. Each Cl^- ion has an oxidation state of −1 so the oxidation state of copper must be −2 − (4 × −1) = **+2**

Q3 a) 6

b) 2

c) 4

Q4 a)

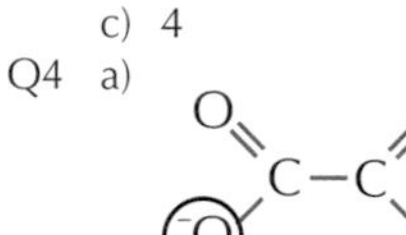
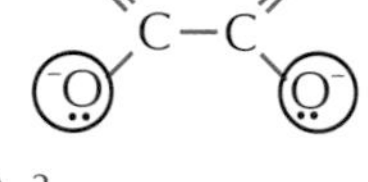
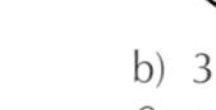

b) 3

Oxygen atoms are small so six of them will fit around a central metal ion and form coordinate bonds with it. This means that three molecules of $C_2O_4^{2-}$ will each form two coordinate bonds with the ion.

Q5 Square planar:

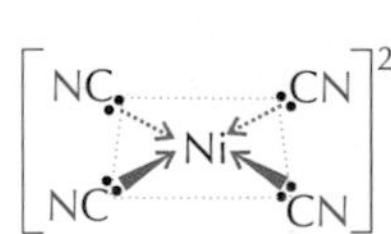

Page 197 — Fact Recall Questions

Q1 a) An atom, ion or molecule that donates a pair of electrons to a central metal ion.

b) A covalent bond where both of the electrons in the shared pair come from the same atom.

c) A metal ion surrounded by coordinately bonded ligands.

Q2 a) Unidentate means that a ligand can form one coordinate bond, bidentate means that a ligand can form two coordinate bonds and multidentate means that a ligand can form two or more coordinate bonds.

b) unidentate: e.g. $H_2O/NH_3/Cl^-$
bidentate: e.g. $NH_2CH_2CH_2NH_2$
multidentate: e.g. $EDTA^{4-}$

Q3 The number of coordinate bonds that are formed with the central metal ion in a complex ion.

Q4 a) It helps transport oxygen around the body.

b) Four come from nitrogen atoms in the porphyrin ring, one comes from a nitrogen atom in a globin protein and one comes from either water or oxygen.

3. Formation of Coloured Ions

Page 201 — Application Questions

Q1 The change in the ligand.

Q2 The change in the oxidation state of iron.

Page 201 — Fact Recall Questions

Q1 They split into two different energy levels.

Q2 a) Light energy.

b) $\Delta E = h\nu$

Q3 Transition metal ions have incomplete 3d subshells. When visible light hits transition metal ions, some of the frequencies are absorbed by electrons which jump up to the higher energy orbitals. The frequencies that remain are reflected and these make up the colour you see.

Q4 A change in oxidation state, a change in coordination number and a change in ligand.

Q5 a) Blue to yellow.

b) Pink to straw coloured.

Q6 a) White light is shone through a filter, which is chosen to only let the colour of light through that is absorbed by the sample. The light then passes through the sample to a colorimeter, which measures how much light is absorbed by the sample.

b) Measure the absorbances of known concentrations of solutions and plot the results on a graph with absorbance on the *y*-axis and concentration on the *x*-axis.

4. Variable Oxidation States

Page 204 — Application Questions

Q1 a) $2Cr^{3+}_{(aq)} + 10OH^-_{(aq)} + 3H_2O_{2(aq)} \rightarrow 2CrO_4^{2-}{}_{(aq)} + 8H_2O_{(l)}$

b) Green to yellow.

c) By reducing the $Cr_2O_7^{2-}$ ions with a good reducing agent e.g. zinc and dilute acid.

Q2 a) $[Co(H_2O)_4(OH)_2]_{(s)}$

b) By adding an excess of aqueous ammonia to generate a solution of $[Co(NH_3)_6]^{2+}{}_{(aq)}$ ions.

c) Dark brown.

d) Because $[Co(NH_3)_6]^{2+}{}_{(aq)}$ is much easier to oxidise than $[Co(H_2O)_6]^{2+}{}_{(aq)}$.

Page 204 — Fact Recall Questions

Q1 a) +2, +3 and +6.

b) Chromium has an oxidation state of +2 in Cr^{2+}, of +3 in Cr^{3+} and of +6 in $CrO_4^{2-}/Cr_2O_7^{2-}$.

c) Cr^{2+} is blue, Cr^{3+} is green/violet, CrO_4^{2-} is yellow/$Cr_2O_7^{2-}$ is orange.

Q2 a) $Cr_2O_7^{2-}{}_{(aq)} + H_2O_{(l)} \rightleftharpoons 2CrO_4^{2-}{}_{(aq)} + 2H^+_{(aq)}$
b) By adding in extra OH^- ions.

Q3 a) Zinc and dilute acid.
b) Without an inert atmosphere any Cr^{2+} produced will be oxidised straight back to Cr^{3+}.

Q4 a) $2Co^{2+}_{(aq)} + H_2O_{2(aq)} \rightarrow 2Co^{3+}_{(aq)} + 2OH^-_{(aq)}$
b) Add ammonia solution and expose to air.

5. Transition Metal Titrations

Page 207 — Application Questions

Q1 Moles Fe^{2+} = (conc. × volume) ÷ 1000
= (0.05 × 28.3) ÷ 1000 = 1.415×10^{-3} moles.
$MnO_4^-{}_{(aq)} + 8H^+_{(aq)} + 5Fe^{2+}_{(aq)} \rightarrow Mn^{2+}_{(aq)} + 4H_2O_{(l)} + 5Fe^{3+}_{(aq)}$
so 5 moles of Fe^{2+} reacts with 1 mole of MnO_4^- and 1.415×10^{-3} moles of Fe^{2+} must react with $(1.415 \times 10^{-3}) \div 5 = 2.83 \times 10^{-4}$ moles of MnO_4^-.
Conc. MnO_4^- = (moles × 1000) ÷ volume
= $((2.83 \times 10^{-4}) \times 1000) \div 30$ = **0.0094 moldm^{-3}**

Q2 Moles $Cr_2O_7^{2-}$ = (conc. × volume) ÷ 1000
= (0.15 × 22.5) ÷ 1000 = 3.38×10^{-3} moles.
$Cr_2O_7^{2-}{}_{(aq)} + 14H^+_{(aq)} + 6Fe^{2+}_{(aq)} \rightarrow 2Cr^{3+}_{(aq)} + 7H_2O_{(l)} + 6Fe^{3+}_{(aq)}$
so 1 mole of $Cr_2O_7^{2-}$ reacts with 6 moles of Fe^{2+} and 3.38×10^{-3} moles of $Cr_2O_7^{2-}$ must react with $(3.38 \times 10^{-3}) \times 6 = 0.020$ moles of Fe^{2+}.
Conc. Fe^{2+} = (moles × 1000) ÷ volume
= (0.020 × 1000) ÷ 20 = **1.0 moldm^{-3}**

Q3 Moles Fe^{2+} = (conc. × volume) ÷ 1000
= (0.60 × 28) ÷ 1000 = 0.0168 moles.
$MnO_4^-{}_{(aq)} + 8H^+_{(aq)} + 5Fe^{2+}_{(aq)} \rightarrow Mn^{2+}_{(aq)} + 4H_2O_{(l)} + 5Fe^{3+}_{(aq)}$
so 5 moles of Fe^{2+} reacts with 1 mole of MnO_4^- and 0.0168 moles of Fe^{2+} must react with $(0.0168) \div 5 = 3.36 \times 10^{-3}$ moles of MnO_4^-.
Volume MnO_4^- = (moles × 1000) ÷ conc.
= $((3.36 \times 10^{-3}) \times 1000) \div 0.075$ = **44.8 cm^3**

Q4 Moles $Cr_2O_7^{2-}$ = (conc. × volume) ÷ 1000
= (0.055 × 24) ÷ 1000 = 1.32×10^{-3} moles.
$Cr_2O_7^{2-}{}_{(aq)} + 14H^+_{(aq)} + 6Fe^{2+}_{(aq)} \rightarrow 2Cr^{3+}_{(aq)} + 7H_2O_{(l)} + 6Fe^{3+}_{(aq)}$
so 1 mole of $Cr_2O_7^{2-}$ reacts with 6 moles of Fe^{2+} and 1.32×10^{-3} moles of $Cr_2O_7^{2-}$ must react with $(1.32 \times 10^{-3}) \times 6 = 7.92 \times 10^{-3}$ moles of Fe^{2+}.
Volume Fe^{2+} = (moles × 1000) ÷ conc.
= $((7.92 \times 10^{-3}) \times 1000) \div 0.45$ = **17.6 cm^3**

Page 207 — Fact Recall Questions

Q1 Acid is added to make sure there are plenty of H^+ ions to allow all the oxidising agent to be reduced.

Q2 a) Manganate(VII) ions (MnO_4^-) and dichromate(VI) ions ($Cr_2O_7^{2-}$).
b) MnO_4^- = purple, $Cr_2O_7^{2-}$ = orange.

6. Transition Metals as Catalysts

Page 211 — Application Question

Q1 a) A heterogenous catalyst.
b) Mn is a transition metal. Transition metals have incomplete d-subshells so can have multiple oxidation states. This means they can transfer electrons to speed up reactions.

Page 211 — Fact Recall Questions

Q1 Transition metals make good catalysts because they can change oxidation states by gaining or losing electrons within their d orbitals. This means they can transfer electrons to speed up reactions.

Q2 A heterogenous catalyst is a catalyst in a different phase from the reactants and a homogenous catalyst is a catalyst in the same phase as the reactants.

Q3 The Haber Process. Iron is the catalyst. It catalyses the reaction $N_{2(g)} + 3H_{2(g)} \rightarrow 2NH_{3(g)}$.
The Contact Process. Vanadium(V) oxide (V_2O_5) is the catalyst. It catalyses the reaction $SO_{2(g)} + ½O_{2(g)} \rightarrow SO_{3(g)}$.
The manufacture of methanol. Chromium(III) oxide (Cr_2O_3) is the catalyst. It catalyses the reaction $CO_{(g)} + 2H_{2(g)} \rightarrow CH_3OH_{(g)}$.

Q4 The reaction happens on the surface of the heterogenous catalyst. So increasing the surface area of the catalyst increases the rate of reaction. Using support mediums maximises the surface area for minimal extra cost.

Q5 a) Catalytic poisoning is when impurities bind to the surface of the catalyst and block reactants from being adsorbed. It can be reduced by purifying the reactants to remove as many impurities as possible.
b) Lead poisons the rhodium catalyst in catalytic converters. Sulfur poisons the iron catalyst in the Haber process.

Q6 The reaction between $S_2O_8^{2-}$ and I^- is very slow because both ions are negatively charged and repel each other. When Fe^{2+} ions are added, the reaction can proceed in two stages, both involving a positive and a negative ion, so there's no repulsion and the reaction happens a lot faster.

Q7 Autocatalysis is when one of the products of a reaction also catalyses it. E.g. the catalysis of the reaction between $C_2O_4^{2-}$ and MnO_4^- by Mn^{2+}.

7. Other Uses of Transition Metals

Page 213 — Fact Recall Questions

Q1 a) In the lungs, the concentration of oxygen is high. So water ligands that were bound to the haemoglobin are substituted for oxygen ligands, forming oxyhaemoglobin.
b) At sites where oxygen is needed the concentration of oxygen is low. So oxygen ligands are substituted for water ligands, forming deoxyhaemoglobin.

Q2 Carbon monoxide is a very strong ligand for haemoglobin. When it is inhaled, it binds to haemoglobin and prevents it from binding to oxygen. As a result, oxygen can no longer be transported around the body.

Q3 a) Cisplatin binds to DNA and prevents cancer cells from replicating.
b) E.g. it prevents hair cells from replicating, leading to hair loss/it prevents blood cells from replicating, leading to immunosuppression/it can cause kidney damage.

Q4 a) Tollens' reagent is used to distinguish between aldehydes and ketones.
b) Aldehydes react with Tollens' reagent, forming a silver mirror. Ketones do not react with Tollens' reagent

Exam-style Questions — pages 215-217

1 a) A transition metal is a metal that can form one or more stable ions with a partially filled d-subshell ***(1 mark)***.
b) The energy levels of the 4s and 3d subshells are very close to one another ***(1 mark)***. So different numbers of electrons can be gained or lost using fairly similar amounts of energy ***(1 mark)***.
c) (i) X = $Cr_2O_7^{2-}$ ***(1 mark)***. It is orange in colour ***(1 mark)***.
$Cr_2O_7^{2-}{}_{(aq)} + 14H^+_{(aq)} + 3Zn_{(s)} \rightarrow 3Zn^{2+}_{(aq)} + 2Cr^{3+}_{(aq)} + 7H_2O_{(l)}$ ***(1 mark)***.
(ii) +6 ***(1 mark)***
(iii) Zn is a reducing agent ***(1 mark)***. Dilute acid is added to make sure there are enough H^+ ions in the solution for all the $Cr_2O_7^{2-}$ ions to be reduced ***(1 mark)***.

d) Q = Cr^{2+} ***(1 mark)***. An inert atmosphere is needed to prevent the Cr^{2+} being oxidised back to Cr^{3+} in air ***(1 mark)***.

e) (i) H_2O_2 ***(1 mark)*** in an alkaline solution ***(1 mark)***.

(ii) $2Cr^{3+}_{(aq)} + 10OH^-_{(aq)} + 3H_2O_{2(aq)}$
$\rightarrow 2CrO_4^{2-}{}_{(aq)} + 8H_2O_{(l)}$ ***(1 mark)***.
Colour change would be green to yellow ***(1 mark)***.

2 a) A complex ion is a metal ion surrounded by ligands ***(1 mark)*** which bind to the metal ion using coordinate bonds ***(1 mark)***.

b) (i) When visible light hits the complex ion, some frequencies are absorbed ***(1 mark)*** by electrons jumping up to higher energy orbitals ***(1 mark)***. The frequencies of light not absorbed are reflected and this makes up the colour we see ***(1 mark)***.

(ii) Any two from: e.g. oxidation state / coordination number / ligand ***(1 mark for each, maximum 2 marks)***.

c) (i) Multidentate means the ligand can form more than one coordinate bond ***(1 mark)***.

(ii)

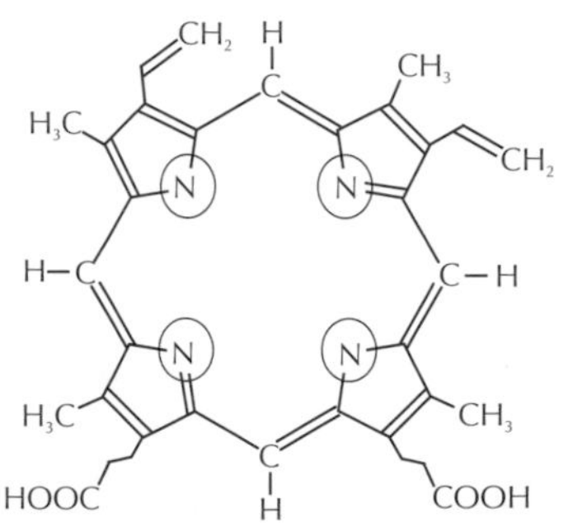

For an atom to form a coordinate bond it must have a lone pair of electrons. The only atoms with lone pairs of electrons in porphyrin are the nitrogens in the middle.

(iii) The coordination number is the number of coordinate bonds that are formed by the central metal ion ***(1 mark)***. The coordination number of the Fe^{2+} ions in haemoglobin is 6 ***(1 mark)***.

d) (i) Haemoglobin transports oxygen around the body ***(1 mark)***.

(ii) Carbon monoxide displaces oxygen/water, forming a strong coordinate bond with haemoglobin ***(1 mark)***, so haemoglobin can no longer carry oxygen ***(1 mark)***.

3 a) (i) Transition metals exist in variable oxidation states ***(1 mark)*** so they can transfer electrons to speed up reactions ***(1 mark)***.

(ii) A heterogenous catalyst ***(1 mark)***.

It's a heterogenous catalyst because it's in a different physical state than the reactants.

b) The reaction happens on the surface of the heterogenous catalyst ***(1 mark)***. Using a ceramic lattice increases the surface area, making it more effective ***(1 mark)*** and reduces the cost because only a thin layer of catalyst is needed ***(1 mark)***.

c) Catalytic poisoning is when impurities bind to the surface of a catalyst ***(1 mark)*** and block reactants from being adsorbed ***(1 mark)***. This reduces the surface area of the catalyst available to the reactants, slowing down the reaction ***(1 mark)***. Rhodium is poisoned by lead, so using unleaded petrol prevents poisoning in catalytic converters ***(1 mark)***.

d) (i) The reacting ions are both negatively charged ***(1 mark)*** so they will repel each other and are unlikely to collide ***(1 mark)***.

(ii) $S_2O_8^{2-}{}_{(aq)} + 2Fe^{2+}_{(aq)} \rightarrow 2Fe^{3+}_{(aq)} + 2SO_4^{2-}{}_{(aq)}$ ***(1 mark)***.
$2Fe^{3+}_{(aq)} + 2I^-_{(aq)} \rightarrow I_{2(aq)} + 2Fe^{2+}_{(aq)}$ ***(1 mark)***.

(iii) Add starch solution ***(1 mark)***.
The solution will turn blue-black if iodine is present ***(1 mark)***.

4 a) Cisplatin binds to DNA and prevents it from being replicated ***(1 mark)***. As a result, cancer cells cannot replicate ***(1 mark)***. But, normal cells are also prevented from replicating ***(1 mark)***. This means side effects can include hair loss/immunosupression/kidney damage ***(1 mark)***.

With big questions like this, make sure you answer all of the parts of the question. If you miss one out you'll lose marks for sure.

b) The complex ion present is $[Ag(NH_3)_2]^+$ ***(1 mark)***.

$[H_3N\!:\!\rightarrow Ag \leftarrow\!:\!NH_3]^+$ ***(1 mark)***.

The shape of the molecule is linear ***(1 mark)***.
Tollens' reagent is used to distinguish between aldehydes and ketones ***(1 mark)***. It reacts with aldehydes to form a silver mirror ***(1 mark)***. It does not react with ketones ***(1 mark)***.

c) Moles Fe^{2+} = (conc. × volume) ÷ 1000
= (0.15 × 30) ÷ 1000 = 4.5×10^{-3} moles ***(1 mark)***.
$MnO_4^-{}_{(aq)} + 8H^+_{(aq)} + 5Fe^{2+}_{(aq)}$
$\rightarrow Mn^{2+}_{(aq)} + 4H_2O_{(l)} + 5Fe^{3+}_{(aq)}$ ***(1 mark)***
so 5 moles of Fe^{2+} reacts with 1 mole of MnO_4^-
and 4.5×10^{-3} moles of Fe^{2+} must react with
$(4.5 \times 10^{-3}) \div 5 = 9.0 \times 10^{-4}$ moles of MnO_4^- ***(1 mark)***.
Conc. MnO_4^- = (moles × 1000) ÷ volume
= $((9.0 \times 10^{-4}) \times 1000) \div 15.8$ = **0.057 moldm^{-3}** ***(1 mark)***.
The solution will be purple at the end point ***(1 mark)***

Section 4 — Inorganic Reactions

1. Lewis Acids and Bases

Page 219 — Application Questions

Q1 a) both
b) Lewis acid
c) Lewis acid

Q2 a) both
b) both
c) Lewis base

Q3 a) The H^+ ion is the acid and the NH_3 molecule is the base.
b) The H^+ ion (the acid) is acting as a Lewis acid because it is accepting a pair of electrons from the NH_3 molecule. It is also acting as a Brønsted-Lowry acid because it is donating a proton to the NH_3 molecule.

Page 219 — Fact Recall Questions

Q1 A proton donor.
Q2 A Brønsted-Lowry base is a proton acceptor.
Q3 An electron pair acceptor.
Q4 A Lewis base is an electron pair donor.

2. Metal-Aqua Ions

Page 223 — Application Questions

Q1 cobalt 2+/Co^{2+}

Q2 $Cr(H_2O)_6{}^{3+}{}_{(aq)} + H_2O_{(l)} \rightleftharpoons [Cr(H_2O)_5(OH)]^{2+}{}_{(aq)} + H_3O^+{}_{(aq)}$
$[Cr(H_2O)_5(OH)]^{2+}{}_{(aq)} + H_2O_{(l)} \rightleftharpoons [Cr(H_2O)_4(OH)_2]^+{}_{(aq)} + H_3O^+{}_{(aq)}$
$[Cr(H_2O)_4(OH)_2]^+{}_{(aq)} + H_2O_{(l)} \rightleftharpoons Cr(H_2O)_3(OH)_{3(s)} + H_3O^+{}_{(aq)}$

You could also write these equations using $OH^-{}_{(aq)}$ instead of $H_2O_{(l)}$ and replacing $H_3O^+{}_{(aq)}$ with $H_2O_{(l)}$. For example:
$Cr(H_2O)_6{}^{3+}{}_{(aq)} + OH^-{}_{(aq)} \rightleftharpoons [Cr(H_2O)_5(OH)]^{2+}{}_{(aq)} + H_2O_{(l)}$

Page 223 — Fact Recall Questions

Q1 coordinate/dative covalent bonds

Q2 Metal 3+ ions have a high charge density (charge/size ratio). The metal 2+ ions have a much lower charge density. This makes the 3+ ions much more polarising than the 2+ ions. More polarising power means that they attract electrons from the oxygen atoms of the coordinated water molecules more strongly, weakening the O–H bond. So it's more likely that a hydrogen ion will be released. And more hydrogen ions means a more acidic solution. This means that metal-aqua 3+ ions are more acidic than metal-aqua 2+ ions.

Q3 A white precipitate would form in the colourless solution.

Q4 The solution would turn from pink to straw coloured/pale brown.

3. Ligand Substitution

Page 228 — Application Questions

Q1 a) octahedral
b) tetrahedral

Q2 a) $[Cu(H_2O)_6]^{2+}{}_{(aq)} + 4NH_{3(aq)}$
$\rightarrow [Cu(NH_3)_4(H_2O)_2]^{2+}{}_{(aq)} + 4H_2O_{(l)}$
b) elongated octahedral
c) The strength of the bonds being broken is about the same as the strength of the bonds being made. The enthalpy change of the reaction is the enthalpy of the bonds broken minus the enthalpy of the bonds formed and so the enthalpy change for the reaction is small.

Q3 a) $[Cr(NH_3)_6]^{3+} + 3NH_2CH_2CH_2NH_2 \rightarrow$
$[Cr(NH_2CH_2CH_2NH_2)_3]^{3+} + 6NH_3$
b) The enthalpy change (ΔH) for this reaction will be very small because six Cr–N bonds are broken and six Cr–N bonds are formed. The entropy change (ΔS) will be positive because the number of particles increases during the reaction. $\Delta G = \Delta H - T\Delta S$, so ΔG will be negative.

Page 228 — Fact Recall Questions

Q1 a) There will be no change in coordination number or shape but the colour may change.
b) There will be a change in coordination number and shape and the colour may change.

Q2 A bidentate ligand is a ligand that has two lone pairs of electrons to donate so it can form two coordinate bonds with a central metal ion.

Q3 A ligand that donates more than one lone pair of electrons to form more than one coordinate bond with a metal ion.

Q4 When unidentate ligands are substituted with bidentate or multidentate ligands, the number of particles and the entropy increases. Reactions that result in an increase in entropy are more likely to occur and so multidentate ligands form much more stable complexes than unidentate ligands. This is the chelate effect.

Exam-style Questions — pages 230-231

Q1 a) The crystals will dissolve to form a violet solution ***(1 mark)***.
$Cr^{3+}{}_{(s)} + 6H_2O_{(l)} \rightarrow [Cr(H_2O)_6]^{3+}{}_{(aq)}$ ***(1 mark)***
$[Cr(H_2O)_6]^{3+}{}_{(aq)} + H_2O_{(l)} \rightleftharpoons [Cr(H_2O)_5(OH)]^{2+}{}_{(aq)} + H_3O^+{}_{(aq)}$ ***(1 mark)***
octahedral ***(1 mark)***
b) A green precipitate will form ***(1 mark)***.
$[Cr(H_2O)_5(OH)]^{2+}{}_{(aq)} + H_2O_{(l)}$
$\rightleftharpoons [Cr(H_2O)_4(OH)_2]^+{}_{(aq)} + H_3O^+{}_{(aq)}$ ***(1 mark)***
$[Cr(H_2O)_4(OH)_2]^+{}_{(aq)} + H_2O_{(l)}$
$\rightleftharpoons Cr(H_2O)_3(OH)_{3(aq)} + H_3O^+{}_{(aq)}$ ***(1 mark)***
octahedral ***(1 mark)***
c) A purple solution will form ***(1 mark)***
$Cr(H_2O)_3(OH)_{3(aq)} + 6NH_{3(aq)}$
$\rightarrow [Cr(NH_3)_6]^{3+}{}_{(aq)} + 3H_2O_{(l)} + 3OH^-{}_{(aq)}$ ***(1 mark)***
octahedral ***(1 mark)***

Q2 a) A ligand with more than one lone pair of electrons to donate ***(1 mark)*** to form a dative covalent/coordinate bond with a metal ion ***(1 mark)***.
b) When the six H_2O molecules are substituted by one $EDTA^{4-}$ ion the enthalpy of the system stays roughly the same (as similar bonds are broken and made) ***(1 mark)***. The entropy of the system greatly increases when $EDTA^{4-}$ is added ***(1 mark)*** because there are more particles than before present in the solution ***(1 mark)***.
You can think about this in terms of free energy too. Because $\Delta H \approx 0$ and ΔS is positive, ΔG for the reaction will be negative. That means the complex ion with the $EDTA^{4-}$ is more stable.

Q3 a) Water molecules form coordinate/dative covalent bonds with the central metal ion ***(1 mark)***. Each water molecule acts as a Lewis base and donates a pair of electrons to the central metal ion ***(1 mark)***.
b) (i) $[Co(H_2O)_6]^{2+}{}_{(aq)}$ ***(1 mark)***
(ii) $[Co(H_2O)_6]^{2+}{}_{(aq)} + H_2O_{(l)}$
$\rightleftharpoons [Co(H_2O)_5(OH)]^+{}_{(aq)} + H_3O^+{}_{(aq)}$ ***(1 mark)***
(iii) Al^{3+} has a higher charge density (charge/size ratio) than Co^{2+} ***(1 mark)***. This makes the Al^{3+} ions much more polarising than the Co^{2+} ions ***(1 mark)***. More polarising power means that they attract electrons from the oxygen atoms of the coordinated water molecules more strongly, weakening the O–H bond ***(1 mark)***. So it's more likely that a hydrogen ion will be released. And more hydrogen ions means a more acidic solution ***(1 mark)***.
(iv) The solution will remain pink ***(1 mark)*** but a blue-green precipitate will form ***(1 mark)***.
c) (i) $[Fe(H_2O)_6]^{3+}{}_{(aq)}$ ***(1 mark)***
(ii) $2[Fe(H_2O)_6]^{3+}{}_{(aq)} + 3CO_3{}^{2-}{}_{(aq)}$
$\rightleftharpoons 2Fe(H_2O)_3(OH)_{3(s)} + 3CO_{2(g)} + 3H_2O_{(l)}$ ***(1 mark)***
(iii) A brown precipitate would form ***(1 mark)*** and bubbles of CO_2 gas would be given off ***(1 mark)***.
d) (i) $[Al(H_2O)_6]^{3+}{}_{(aq)} + 3NH_2CH_2CH_2NH_{2(aq)} \rightarrow$
$[Al(NH_2CH_2CH_2NH_2)_3]^{3+}{}_{(aq)} + 6H_2O_{(l)}$ ***(1 mark)***
(ii) The entropy change (ΔS) will be positive because the number of particles increases during the reaction ***(1 mark)***. So because $\Delta G = \Delta H - T\Delta S$, ΔG will be negative ***(1 mark)***.

Q4 a) An amphoteric species can act as both a base and an acid ***(1 mark)***.
b) white precipitate ***(1 mark)***
c) $Al(H_2O)_3(OH)_{3(s)} + OH^-{}_{(aq)} \rightleftharpoons [Al(H_2O)_2(OH)_4]^-{}_{(aq)} + H_2O_{(l)}$
(2 marks, 1 mark for correct products, 1 mark for correct charge on product ion)
d) It is acting as a Brønsted-Lowry acid ***(1 mark)*** because it's donating H^+ ions in the reaction ***(1 mark)***.

Glossary

Achiral molecule
A molecule that can be superimposed on its mirror image.

Acid anhydride
A molecule formed from two identical carboxylic acid molecules joined via an oxygen atom.

Acid dissociation constant, K_a
An equilibrium constant specific to weak acids that relates the acid concentration to the concentration of $[H^+]$ ions. $K_a = [H^+][A^-] \div [HA]$.

Acidic buffer
A buffer with a pH of less than 7 made by mixing a weak acid with one of its salts.

Acyl chloride
A molecule which contains the functional group COCl.

Acylation
When an acyl group (–COR) is added to a molecule.

Addition polymer
A type of polymer formed by joining small alkenes (monomers) together.

Alcohol
A substance with the general formula $C_nH_{2n+1}OH$.

Aldehyde
A substance with the general formula $C_nH_{2n}O$ which has a hydrogen and one alkyl group attached to a carbonyl carbon atom.

Aliphatic compound
An organic compound that does not contain a benzene ring.

Alkane
A hydrocarbon with the general formula C_nH_{2n+2}.

Alkene
A hydrocarbon with the general formula C_nH_{2n} and containing at least one carbon-carbon double bond.

Amide
A carboxylic acid derivative which contains the functional group $CONH_2$.

Amine
A molecule where one or more of the hydrogen atoms in ammonia have been replaced with an organic functional group.

Amino acid
A molecule with an amino group (NH_2) and a carboxyl group (COOH).

Ammoniacal solution
A solution that contains ammonia.

Amphoteric
Having both acidic and basic properties.

Aromatic compound
A compound that contains a benzene ring.

Atom economy
A measure of the proportion of reactant atoms that become part of the desired product in a chemical reaction.

Autocatalysis
When a reaction is catalysed by one of its products.

Basic buffer
A buffer with a pH of more than 7 made by mixing a weak base with one of its salts.

Benedict's solution
A blue solution of complexed copper(II) ions dissolved in sodium carbonate which can be used to distinguish between aldehydes and ketones.

Bidentate
When a ligand can form two coordinate bonds in a complex ion.

Biodegradable
Will break down naturally.

Biodiesel
A mixture of methyl esters of fatty acids which can be used as a carbon neutral fuel.

Bond dissociation enthalpy (ΔH°_{diss})
The enthalpy change when all the bonds of the same type in 1 mole of gaseous molecules are broken.

Born-Haber cycle
An enthalpy cycle that allows you to calculate the lattice enthalpy change of formation for a system.

Brønsted-Lowry acid
A proton donor.

Brønsted-Lowry base
A proton acceptor.

Buffer
A solution that resists changes in pH when small amounts of acid or alkali are added.

Calibration graph
A graph which shows the relationship between a measurement taken in an experiment and a property of a substance. It can be used to determine an unknown value.

Carbocation
An ion containing a positively charged carbon atom.

Carbonyl compound
An organic compound which contains a carbonyl group (C=O) as its only functional group.

Carboxylic acid
A molecule which contains a carboxyl group (COOH).

Catalyst
A substance that increases the rate of a reaction by providing an alternative reaction pathway with a lower activation energy. The catalyst is chemically unchanged at the end of the reaction.

Catalyst poisoning
When impurities in a reaction mixture bind to a catalyst's surface, blocking reactants from being adsorbed and reducing the effectiveness of the catalyst.

Catalytic hydrogenation
A chemical reaction between molecular hydrogen (H_2) and another compound/element in the presence of a catalyst.

Cationic surfactant
A surfactant which is positively charged.

Cell potential
The voltage between two half-cells in an electrochemical cell.

Chain isomer
A molecule that contains the same atoms as another molecule but has a different arrangement of the carbon skeleton.

Chelate effect
When unidentate ligands are substituted with multidentate ligands, the number of particles and the entropy of the system increases. Reactions that result in an increase in entropy are more likely to occur, so multidentate ligands form much more stable complexes than unidentate ligands.

Chemical shift
Nuclei in different environments absorb energy of different frequencies. NMR spectroscopy measures these differences relative to a standard substance — the difference is called the chemical shift (δ).

Chiral carbon
A carbon atom that has four different groups attached to it.

Chromatography
An analytical technique which uses a mobile phase and a stationary phase to separate out mixtures.

Cisplatin
A platinum containing complex ion with a square planar shape that can be used as an anti-cancer drug.

Colorimeter
An instrument for measuring how much light is absorbed by a sample.

Complex ion
A metal ion surrounded by coordinately bonded ligands.

Condensation polymer
A type of polymer formed through a series of condensation reactions.

Condensation reaction
A chemical reaction in which two molecules are joined together and a small molecule is eliminated.

Contact Process
An industrially used method of producing sulfuric acid.

Coordinate bond
A covalent bond in which both electrons in the shared pair come from the same atom (also called a dative covalent bond).

Coordination number
The number of coordinate bonds that are formed with the central metal ion in a complex ion.

d-block
The block of elements in the middle of the periodic table.

d-subshell
A type of subshell. Each can hold ten electrons.

Dative covalent bond
A covalent bond in which both electrons in the shared pair come from the same atom (also called a coordinate bond).

Delocalisation
When an electron is no longer associated with a single atom or one covalent bond.

Deuterated solvent
A solvent which has had all of its hydrogen atoms exchanged for deuterium atoms.

Deuterium
An isotope of hydrogen. It contains one neutron, one proton and one electron.

Diprotic acid
An acid that releases two H^+ ions per molecule.

Displayed formula
A way of representing a molecule that shows how all the atoms are arranged, and all the bonds between them.

Dynamic equilibrium
When the forward and backward reactions of a reversible reaction are happening at exactly the same rate, so the concentration of reactants and products doesn't change.

E/Z-isomerism
A type of stereoisomerism that is caused by the restricted rotation about a carbon-carbon double bond. Each of the carbon atoms must have two different groups attached.

Electrochemical cell
An electrical circuit made from two metal electrodes dipped in salt solutions and connected by a wire.

Electrochemical series
A list of electrode potentials written in order from most negative to most positive.

Electrode potential
The voltage measured when a half-cell is connected to a standard hydrogen electrode.

Electromotive force (e.m.f.)
Another name for the cell potential.

Electrophile
An electron deficient (and usually positively charged) species which is attracted to regions of high electron density.

Electrophilic substitution
A reaction mechanism where an electrophile substitutes for a hydrogen atom in a molecule.

Empirical formula
The simplest whole number ratio of atoms of each element in a compound.

Enantiomer
A molecule that has the same structural formula as another molecule but with four groups arranged around a chiral carbon atom so that it is a non-superimposable mirror image of the other molecule.

End point
The point in a titration at which all the acid is just neutralised and the pH curve becomes vertical.

Endothermic reaction
A reaction that absorbs energy (ΔH is positive).

Energy gap, ΔE
The amount of energy needed for an electron to transfer to a higher orbital.

Enthalpy change of atomisation of a compound (ΔH°_{at})
The enthalpy change when 1 mole of a compound in its standard state is converted to gaseous atoms.

Enthalpy change of atomisation of an element (ΔH°_{at})
The enthalpy change when 1 mole of gaseous atoms is formed from an element in its standard state.

Enthalpy change of formation (ΔH°_{f})
The enthalpy change when 1 mole of a compound is formed from its elements in their standard states under standard conditions.

Enthalpy change of hydration (ΔH°_{hyd})
The enthalpy change when 1 mole of aqueous ions is formed from gaseous ions.

Enthalpy change of solution ($\Delta H^{\circ}_{solution}$)
The enthalpy change when 1 mole of solute is dissolved in sufficient solvent that no further enthalpy change occurs on further dilution.

Entropy (S)
A measure of the amount of disorder in a system (e.g. the number of ways that particles can be arranged and the number of ways that the energy can be shared out between the particles).

Ester
A molecule that contains the functional group RCOOR.

Esterification
Forming an ester by heating a carboxylic acid and an alcohol in the presence of a strong acid catalyst.

Equilibrium constant, K_c
A ratio worked out from the concentration of the products and reactants once a reversible reaction has reached equilibrium.

Exothermic reaction
A reaction that gives out energy (ΔH is negative).

Fatty acid
A long chain carboxylic acid which can combine with glycerol to form a fat or an oil.

Feasible reaction
A reaction which has a free energy change that is less than or equal to zero and will happen spontaneously.

Fehling's solution
A blue solution of complexed copper(II) ions dissolved in sodium hydroxide which can be used to distinguish between aldehydes and ketones.

First electron affinity (ΔH°_{ea1})
The enthalpy change when 1 mole of gaseous 1– ions is made from 1 mole of gaseous atoms.

First ionisation enthalpy (ΔH°_{ie1})
The enthalpy change when 1 mole of gaseous 1+ ions is formed from 1 mole of gaseous atoms.

Fragment ion
A charged fragment produced when a molecular ion breaks up inside a mass spectrometer.

Free energy change (ΔG)
A measure which links enthalpy and entropy changes to predict whether a reaction is feasible.
$\Delta G = \Delta H - T\Delta S_{system}$

Fuel cell
A device that converts the energy of a fuel into electricity through an oxidation reaction.

Functional group isomer
A molecule that has the same molecular formula as another molecule, but with the atoms arranged into different functional groups.

General formula
An algebraic formula that can describe any member of a family of compounds.

H

Haber Process
An industrially used method of producing ammonia.

Haemoglobin
A protein found in blood that helps to transport oxygen around the body.

Half-cell
One half of an electrochemical cell.

Half-equation
An ionic equation that shows oxidation or reduction — one half of a full redox equation.

Haloalkane
An alkane with at least one halogen atom in place of a hydrogen atom.

Hess's law
The total enthalpy change of a reaction is always the same, no matter which route is taken.

Heterogeneous catalyst
A catalyst which is in a different physical state to the reactants.

Homogeneous catalyst
A catalyst which is in the same physical state as the reactants.

Homologous series
A group of organic compounds that have the same general formula and similar chemical properties.

Hydrogen bonding
A type of weak bonding which occurs between hydrogen atoms and electronegative atoms in polar groups (e.g. $-NH_2$ and $-OH$).

Hydrolysis
A reaction where molecules are split apart by water molecules.

Hydroxynitrile
A molecule which contains a hydroxyl group (OH) and a nitrile group (CN).

Indicator
A substance that changes colour over a particular pH range.

Inert atmosphere
An atmosphere made out of a non-reactive gas like nitrogen or helium.

Infrared (IR) spectroscopy
An analytical technique used to identify the functional groups present in a molecule by measuring the frequency of energy absorbed by its bonds.

Initial rates method
An experimental technique that can be used to work out the orders of a reaction.

Integration trace
A line on an ^1H NMR spectrum that has a change in height that is proportional to the area of the peak it's next to.

Ionic product of water, K_w
A constant generated by multiplying the K_c for the dissociation of water by $[H_2O]$. $K_w = [H^+][OH^-]$.

Isoelectric point
The pH at which the average overall charge on a molecule is zero.

Ketone
A substance with the general formula $C_nH_{2n}O$ which has two alkyl groups attached to a carbonyl carbon atom.

L

Lattice dissociation enthalpy
The enthalpy change when 1 mole of a solid ionic compound is completely dissociated into its gaseous ions under standard conditions.

Lattice formation enthalpy
The enthalpy change when 1 mole of a solid ionic compound is formed from its gaseous ions under standard conditions.

Le Chatelier's Principle
If there's a change in concentration, pressure or temperature, an equilibrium will move to help counteract the change.

Lewis acid
An electron pair acceptor.

Lewis base
An electron pair donor.

Ligand
An atom, ion or molecule that donates a pair of electrons to a central metal ion in a complex ion.

Ligand substitution/exchange reaction
A reaction where one or more ligands are changed for one or more other ligands in a metal complex ion.

M peak
The peak on a mass spectrum caused by the molecular ion.

Mass spectrometry
An analytical technique used to find the structure of a molecule by looking at the pattern of ions it produces when it is bombarded with electrons.

Mass spectrum
A chart produced by a mass spectrometer giving information on relative isotopic mass and relative abundance of isotopes.

Mean bond enthalpy
An average value for the bond dissociation enthalpy of a particular bond over the range of compounds it is found in.

Metal-aqua complex ion
A species formed when transition metal ions dissolve in water. The water molecules form coordinate bonds with the metal ions.

Methyl orange
A pH indicator that changes colour between pH 3.1 and 4.4.

Mobile phase
A liquid or a gas used in chromatography which contains molecules that can move.

Molecular formula
A way of representing molecules that shows the actual number of atoms of each element in a molecule.

Monomer
A small molecule which can join together with other monomers to form a polymer.

Monoprotic acid
An acid that releases one H^+ ion per molecule.

Multidentate
When a ligand can form two or more coordinate bonds in a complex ion.

n+1 rule
Peaks on a ^1H NMR spectrum always split into the number of hydrogens on the neighbouring carbon, plus one.

N-substituted amides
An amide where one of the hydrogens attached to the nitrogen has been substituted with another functional group.

Nitration
A reaction in which a nitro group (NO_2) is added to a molecule

Nuclear magnetic resonance (NMR) spectroscopy
An analytical technique which uses the nuclear spin of a nucleus to determine the relative environment of that nucleus in a compound.

Nuclear spin
Any nucleus that contains an odd number of protons and neutrons will spin on its axis creating a weak magnetic field. This is called nuclear spin.

Nucleophile
A species that forms a bond with an electrophile by donating a pair of electrons.

Nucleophilic addition
A reaction mechanism where a nucleophile adds on to the δ^+ carbon atom of a carbonyl group.

Nucleophilic addition-elimination
A reaction mechanism where a nucleophile adds on to the δ^+ carbon atom of a carbonyl group and another molecule is eliminated.

Nucleophilic substitution
A reaction mechanism where a nucleophile substitutes for an atom (or group of atoms) in a molecule.

O

Optical isomer
A molecule that has the same structural formula as another molecule but with four groups arranged around a chiral carbon atom so that it is a non-superimposable mirror image of the other molecule.

Orbital
A region of a subshell that contains a maximum of 2 electrons.

Oxidation
The loss of electrons.

Oxidation state
The total number of electrons an element has donated or accepted. Also called an oxidation number.

Oxidising agent
Something that accepts electrons and gets reduced.

Paper chromatography
A technique which can be used to separate out mixtures of different compounds.

Peptide link (bond)
The bonds which hold amino acids together in a protein.

Percentage yield
A comparison between the amount of product that should theoretically form during a reaction and the amount that actually forms.

Period
A row in the periodic table.

Periodicity
The trends that occur across a period of the Periodic Table.

pH
A measure of the hydrogen ion concentration in a solution.
$pH = -\log_{10}[H^+]$

pH curve
A graph of pH against volume of acid/alkali added.

Phenolphthalein
A pH indicator that changes colour between pH 8.3 and 10.

Plane-polarised light
Light in which all the waves are vibrating in the same plane.

Polyamide
A polymer formed from reactions between dicarboxylic acids and diamines.

Polyester
A polymer formed from reactions between dicarboxylic acids and diols.

Polymer
A long molecule formed from lots of repeating units (called monomers).

Polypeptide
A polymer formed from reactions between amino acids.

Porphyrin
A multidentate ligand found in a number of biological molecules including haemoglobin.

Positional isomer
A molecule with the same molecular formula as another molecule but with the functional group in a different position.

Primary alcohol
An alcohol that has the –OH group attached to a carbon with one alkyl group attached.

Protein
One or more polypeptides folded into a structure which has a biological function.

Purely ionic model of a lattice
A model which assumes that all the ions in a lattice are spherical and have their charge evenly distributed around them. This model is also known as the perfect ionic model.

R

Racemate (or racemic mixture)
A mixture that contains equal quantities of each enantiomer of an optically active compound.

Rate constant, k
A constant in the rate equation. The larger it is the faster the rate of reaction.

Rate-determining step
The slowest step in a reaction mechanism which determines the overall rate of a reaction.

Rate equation
An equation of the form $rate = k[A]^m[B]^n$ which tells you how the rate of a reaction is affected by the concentration of reactants.

Reaction order
A number that tells you how the concentration of a particular reactant affects the reaction rate.

Reaction rate
The change in the amount of reactants or products over time.

Redox reaction
A reaction where reduction and oxidation happen simultaneously.

Redox titration
A titration which can be performed to determine how much reducing agent is needed to exactly react with a quantity of oxidising agent, or vice versa.

Reducing agent
Something that donates electrons and gets oxidised.

Reduction
The gain of electrons.

Resonance forms
A molecule has resonance forms when it cannot be described by one structural representation. Instead a number of different structures must be combined to give a good description of the molecule. These different structures are called resonance forms.

Retention
The process of being adsorbed onto the stationary phase in chromatography.

Retention time
The time taken for a component of a mixture to pass through a chromatography column to the detector at the other end.

Risk assessment
A review of the hazards of the reacting chemicals, the products and any conditions needed for a reaction.

Salt bridge
A connection between two half-cells that ions can flow through, used to complete the circuit. Usually a piece of filter paper soaked in a salt solution or a glass tube filled with a salt solution.

Saturated fatty acid
A fatty acid that contains no double bonds — found in fats.

Second electron affinity (ΔH°_{ea2})
The enthalpy change when 1 mole of gaseous 2– ions is made from 1 mole of gaseous 1– ions.

Second ionisation enthalpy (ΔH°_{ie2})
The enthalpy change when 1 mole of gaseous 2+ ions is formed from 1 mole of gaseous 1+ ions.

Secondary alcohol
An alcohol that has the –OH group attached to a carbon with two alkyl groups attached.

Skeletal formula
A way of representing molecules that shows the bonds of the carbon skeleton only, with any functional groups.

Spectrometry
The study of what happens when radiation interacts with matter.

Splitting pattern
Peaks in ^{1}H NMR spectra may be split into further peaks. The resultant group of peaks is called a splitting pattern.

Spontaneous reaction
A reaction that occurs by itself.

Standard conditions
A temperature of 298 K (25 °C), a pressure of 100 kPa and all ion solutions having a concentration of 1.00 moldm^{-3}.

Standard electrode potential
The voltage measured under standard conditions when a half-cell is connected to a standard hydrogen electrode.

Standard hydrogen electrode
An electrode where hydrogen gas is bubbled through a solution of aqueous H^{+} ions under standard conditions.

Stationary phase
A solid, or a liquid held in a solid, used in chromatography which contains molecules that can't move.

Stereoisomer
A molecule that has the same structural formula as another molecule but with the atoms arranged differently in space.

Strong acid/base
An acid or base that fully dissociates in water.

Structural formula
A way of representing molecules that shows the atoms carbon by carbon, with the attached hydrogens and functional groups.

Structural isomer
A molecule with the same molecular formula as another molecule, but with the atoms connected in a different way.

Subshell
A subdivision of an energy level (shell). Subshells may be s, p, d or f subshells.

Surfactant
A compound which is partly soluble and partly insoluble in water.

Synthesis
A method detailing how to create a chemical.

Tertiary alcohol
An alcohol that has the –OH group attached to a carbon with three alkyl groups attached.

Titration
An experimental technique that lets you work out exactly how much alkali is needed to neutralise a quantity of acid.

Tollens' reagent
A colourless solution of silver nitrate dissolved in aqueous ammonia which can be used to distinguish between aldehydes and ketones.

Transition element
A metal that can form one or more stable ions with a partially filled d-subshell.

Unidentate
When a ligand can only form one coordinate bond in a complex ion.

Unsaturated fatty acid
A fatty acid that contains double bonds — found in oils.

Weak acid/base
An acid or base that only partially dissociates in water.

Z/E-isomerism
A type of stereoisomerism that is caused by the restricted rotation about a carbon-carbon double bond. Each of the carbon atoms must have two different groups attached.

Zwitterion
A dipolar ion which has both a negative and a positive charge in different parts of the molecule.

Acknowledgements

Photograph acknowledgements
Cover Photo Science Photo Library, p 1 **Charles D. Winters**/Science Photo Library, p 2 Science Photo Library, p 3 **NASA**/Science Photo Library, p 4 (top) **David R. Frazier**/Science Photo Library, p 4 (bottom) **Robert Brook**/Science Photo Library, p 6 **Andrew Lambert Photography**/Science Photo Library, p 9 (top) **Andrew Lambert Photography**/Science Photo Library, p 9 (bottom) **Andrew Lambert Photography**/Science Photo Library, p 13 **Charles D. Winters**/Science Photo Library, p 17 Science Photo Library, p 18 (top) **Martyn F. Chillmaid**/Science Photo Library, p 18 (bottom) **Martyn F. Chillmaid**/Science Photo Library, p 19 Science Photo Library, p 21 **Charles D. Winters**/Science Photo Library, p 22 (top) **Richard J. Green**/Science Photo Library, p 22 (bottom) **Martyn F. Chillmaid**/Science Photo Library, p 23 (top) **Martyn F. Chillmaid**/Science Photo Library, p 23 (bottom) **Martyn F. Chillmaid**/Science Photo Library, p 24 **Martyn F. Chillmaid**/Science Photo Library, p 25 **Andrew Lambert Photography**/Science Photo Library, p 28 **Martyn F. Chillmaid**/Science Photo Library, p 29 Science Photo Library, p 30 (top) **Andrew Lambert Photography**/Science Photo Library, p 30 (bottom) **Andrew Lambert Photography**/Science Photo Library, p 32 **Andrew Lambert Photography**/Science Photo Library, p 36 **Charles D. Winters**/Science Photo Library, p 37 (top) **Charles D. Winters**/Science Photo Library, p 37 (bottom) **Andrew Brookes, National Physical Laboratory**/Science Photo Library, p 38 **Paul Whitehill**/Science Photo Library, p 54 (top) **Dr Tim Evans**/Science Photo Library, p 54 (bottom) **Dr Tim Evans**/Science Photo Library, p 56 **Klaus Guldbrandsen**/Science Photo Library, p 58 **Sheila Terry**/Science Photo Library, p 59 (top) **Pasieka**/Science Photo Library, p 59 (bottom) **National Cancer Institute**/Science Photo Library, p 66 (top) **Andrew Lambert Photography**/Science Photo Library, p 66 (bottom) **Andrew Lambert Photography**/Science Photo Library, p 67 **Andrew Lambert Photography**/Science Photo Library, p 70 **Tek Image**/Science Photo Library, p 72 **Cristina Pedrazzini**/Science Photo Library, p 75 **Maximilian Stock Ltd.**/Science Photo Library, p 76 **Andrew Lambert Photography**/Science Photo Library, p 77 **Ria Novosti**/Science Photo Library, p 78 **Andrew Lambert Photography**/Science Photo Library, p 82 **Cordelia Molloy**/Science Photo Library, p 88 **Clive Freeman, The Royal Institution**/Science Photo Library, p 92 (top) **Ria Novosti**/Science Photo Library, p 92 (bottom) Science Photo Library, p 95 **Hande Guleryuz Yuce**/iStockphoto, p 100 **Andrew Lambert Photography**/Science Photo Library, p 103 **Andrew Lambert Photography**/Science Photo Library, p 105 **AJ Photo**/Science Photo Library, p 106 **Cordelia Molloy**/Science Photo Library, p 107 **Cordelia Molloy**/Science Photo Library, p 109 **Andrew Lambert Photography**/Science Photo Library, p 110 **Maria Platt-Evans**/Science Photo Library, p 115 **Andrew Lambert Photography**/Science Photo Library, p 116 (top) **Andrew Lambert Photography**/Science Photo Library, p 116 (bottom) **Andrew Lambert Photography**/Science Photo Library, p 119 **Martyn F. Chillmaid**/Science Photo Library, p 121 **Pascal Goetgheluck**/Science Photo Library, p 129 **Hank Morgan**/Science Photo Library, p 134 **Hank Morgan**/Science Photo Library, p 135 **Friedrich Saurer**/Science Photo Library, p 138 Science Photo Library, p 139 **Sinclair Stammers**/Science Photo Library, p 140 **Pasieka**/Science Photo Library, p 141 **Chagnon**/Science Photo Library, p 147 **David Taylor**/Science Photo Library, p 149 Science Photo Library, p 150 **Andrew Lambert Photography**/Science Photo Library, p 153 **Andrew Lambert Photography**/Science Photo Library, p 156 **Adam Hart-Davis**/Science Photo Library, p 157 **Peter Menzel**/Science Photo Library, p 159 Science Photo Library, p 165 **Charles D. Winters**/Science Photo Library, p 166 (top) **Jerry Mason**/Science Photo Library, p 166 (bottom) **Andrew Lambert Photography**/Science Photo Library, p 167 **Martyn F. Chillmaid**/Science Photo Library, p 172 **Charles D. Winters**/Science Photo Library, p 173 **Martyn F. Chillmaid**/Science Photo Library, p 177 **E.R.Degginger**/Science Photo Library, p 180 **Andrew Lambert Photography**/Science Photo Library, p 183 **Martyn F. Chillmaid**/Science Photo Library, p 184 (top) **Cordelia Molloy**/Science Photo Library, p 184 (bottom) **Martin Bond**/Science Photo Library, p 185 **Charles D. Winters**/Science Photo Library, p 190 **Klaus Guldbrandsen**/Science Photo Library, p 192 **Andrew Lambert Photography**/Science Photo Library, p 195 **Dr Mark J. Winter**/Science Photo Library, p 196 **Andrew Lambert Photography**/Science Photo Library, p 197 **Susumu Nishinaga**/Science Photo Library, p 199 (left) **Andrew Lambert Photography**/Science Photo Library, p 199 (right) **Andrew Lambert Photography**/Science Photo Library, p 200 **Andrew Lambert Photography**/Science Photo Library, p 202 **Andrew Lambert Photography**/Science Photo Library, p 203 **Martyn F. Chillmaid**/Science Photo Library, p 204 **Andrew Lambert Photography**/Science Photo Library, p 205 **Martyn F. Chillmaid**/Science Photo Library, p 206 (top) **Andrew Lambert Photography**/Science Photo Library, p 206 (bottom) **Andrew Lambert Photography**/Science Photo Library, p 209 **Sheila Terry**/Science Photo Library, p 210 **Andrew Lambert Photography**/Science Photo Library, p 212 **Martyn F. Chillmaid**/Science Photo Library, p 218 **Emilio Segre Visual Archives/American Institute of Physics**/Science Photo Library, p 221 **Andrew Lambert Photography**/Science Photo Library, p 222 (top) **Charles D. Winters**/Science Photo Library, p 222 (bottom) **Chris Hellier**/Science Photo Library, p 223 **Andrew Lambert Photography**/Science Photo Library, p 225 **Andrew Lambert Photography**/Science Photo Library, p 226 **Dr Tim Evans**/Science Photo Library, p 232 **Martyn F. Chillmaid**/Science Photo Library, p 233 **Garry Watson**/Science Photo Library, p 236 **Monty Rakusen**/Science Photo Library, p 237 Science Photo Library, p 241 **Adam Hart-Davis**/Science Photo Library, p 244 (top) **Charles D. Winters**/Science Photo Library, p 244 (bottom) **Martyn F. Chillmaid**/Science Photo Library, p 245 **Photostock-Israel**/Science Photo Library.

Index

The Periodic Table

Relative Atomic Mass (A_r)

Atomic (proton) number

Periods	Group 1	Group 2											Group 3	Group 4	Group 5	Group 6	Group 7	Group 0
1								1.0 H Hydrogen 1										4.0 He Helium 2
2	6.9 Li Lithium 3	9.0 Be Beryllium 4											10.8 B Boron 5	12.0 C Carbon 6	14.0 N Nitrogen 7	16.0 O Oxygen 8	19.0 F Fluorine 9	20.2 Ne Neon 10
3	23.0 Na Sodium 11	24.3 Mg Magnesium 12											27.0 Al Aluminium 13	28.1 Si Silicon 14	31.0 P Phosphorus 15	32.1 S Sulfur 16	35.5 Cl Chlorine 17	39.9 Ar Argon 18
4	39.1 K Potassium 19	40.1 Ca Calcium 20	45.0 Sc Scandium 21	47.9 Ti Titanium 22	50.9 V Vanadium 23	52.0 Cr Chromium 24	54.9 Mn Manganese 25	55.8 Fe Iron 26	58.9 Co Cobalt 27	58.7 Ni Nickel 28	63.5 Cu Copper 29	65.4 Zn Zinc 30	69.7 Ga Gallium 31	72.6 Ge Germanium 32	74.9 As Arsenic 33	79.0 Se Selenium 34	79.9 Br Bromine 35	83.8 Kr Krypton 36
5	85.5 Rb Rubidium 37	87.6 Sr Strontium 38	88.9 Y Yttrium 39	91.2 Zr Zirconium 40	92.9 Nb Niobium 41	96.0 Mo Molybdenum 42	98 Tc Technetium 43	101.1 Ru Ruthenium 44	102.9 Rh Rhodium 45	106.4 Pd Palladium 46	107.9 Ag Silver 47	112.4 Cd Cadmium 48	114.8 In Indium 49	118.7 Sn Tin 50	121.8 Sb Antimony 51	127.6 Te Tellurium 52	126.9 I Iodine 53	131.3 Xe Xenon 54
6	132.9 Cs Caesium 55	137.3 Ba Barium 56	138.9 La Lanthanum 57	178.5 Hf Hafnium 72	180.9 Ta Tantalum 73	183.8 W Tungsten 74	186.2 Re Rhenium 75	190.2 Os Osmium 76	192.2 Ir Iridium 77	195.1 Pt Platinum 78	197.0 Au Gold 79	200.6 Hg Mercury 80	204.4 Tl Thallium 81	207.2 Pb Lead 82	209.0 Bi Bismuth 83	209 Po Polonium 84	210 At Astatine 85	222 Rn Radon 86
7	223 Fr Francium 87	226.0 Ra Radium 88	227.0 Ac Actinium 89	267 Rf Rutherfordium 104	268 Db Dubnium 105	271 Sg Seaborgium 106	272 Bh Bohrium 107	270 Hs Hassium 108	276 Mt Meitnerium 109	281 Ds Darmstadium 110	280 Rg Roentgenium 111							

The Lanthanides	140.1 Ce Cerium 58	140.9 Pr Praseodymium 59	144.2 Nd Neodymium 60	145 Pm Promethium 61	150.4 Sm Samarium 62	152.0 Eu Europium 63	157.3 Gd Gadolinium 64	158.9 Tb Terbium 65	162.5 Dy Dysprosium 66	164.9 Ho Holmium 67	167.3 Er Erbium 68	168.9 Tm Thulium 69	173.1 Yb Ytterbium 70	175.0 Lu Lutetium 71
The Actinides	232.0 Th Thorium 90	231.0 Pa Protactinium 91	238.0 U Uranium 92	237.0 Np Neptunium 93	244 Pu Plutonium 94	243 Am Americium 95	247 Cm Curium 96	247 Bk Berkelium 97	251 Cf Californium 98	252 Es Einsteinium 99	257 Fm Fermium 100	258 Md Mendelevium 101	259 No Nobelium 102	262 Lr Lawrencium 103